BUDDHIST LOGIC

BUDDHIST LOGIC

Volume II

Containing a Translation of the Short Treatise of Logic by Dharmakīrti, and of its commentary by Dharmottara, with Notes, Appendices and Indices

TH. STCHERBATSKY

MOTILAL BANARSIDASS
INTERNATIONAL
DELHI

Reprint Edition: Delhi, 2024
First Indian Edition: Delhi, 1993

ISBN : 978-81-19196-02-9 (Vol.-I)
ISBN : 978-81-19196-26-5 (Vol.-II)
ISBN : 978-81-19196-08-1 (Set)

<u>*Also available at*</u>

MOTILAL BANARSIDASS INTERNATIONAL

H. O. : 41 U.A. Bungalow Road, (Back Lane) Jawahar Nagar, Delhi - 110 007
4261/3 (basement), Ansari Road, Darya Ganj, New Delhi - 110 002
203 Royapettah High Road, Mylapore, Chennai - 600 004
12/1A, 2nd Floor, Bankim Chatterjee Street, Kolkata - 700 073
Stockist : Motilal Books, Ashok Rajpath, Near Kali Mandir, Patna - 800 004

Printed in India
MOTILAL BANARSIDASS INTERNATIONAL

TABLE OF CONTENTS

PREFACE

More than twenty years have elapsed since we have first treated the subject of Buddhist logic and epistemology as they were taught in the schools of Mahāyāna Buddhism. Our nearly unique source at that time was the Nyāya-bindu and ṭīkā, this solitary sanscrit remnant of what has been a vast field of literary production. Since that time our knowledge of the subject has been considerably enlarged. Important sanscrit texts have been discovered and published in India. The interconnection and mutual influences of Indian systems are better known. The Tibetan literature reveals itself as an almost illimited source of information. Prof. H. Jacobi has contributed a series of articles on the early history of Indian systems. Prof. J. Tucci has recently elucidated the problem of Buddhist logic before Dignāga. Prof. de la Vallée Poussin has brought to a successful end his monumental translation of the Abhidharma-Koša. Prof. Sylvani Lévi has enriched our knowledge by important discoveries in Nepal. Prof. M. Walleser has founded in Heidelberg an active society for the study of Mahāyāna. A great deal of work has been done by Indian and Japanese scholars. The Nyāya-bindu is no more a solitary rock in an unknown sea. Buddhist logic reveals itself as the culminating point of a long course of Indian philosophic history. Its birth, its growth and its decline run parallel with the birth, the growth and the decline of Indian civilisation. The time has come to reconsider the subject of Buddhist logic in its historical connections. This is done in these two volumes of which the second apears before the first. It contains translations which aim at being intelligible, a reservation not unnecessary in Indian matters, since we have witnessed translations by authoritative pens which read like an absolutely unintelligible rigmarole. In the copious notes the literary renderings are given where needed. This will enable the reader fully to appreciate the sometimes enormous distance which lies between the words of the sanscrit phrasing and their philosophic meaning rendered according to our habits of thought. The notes contain also a philosophic comment of the translated texts. The reader who would like to have a *vue d'ensemble* of Buddhist philosophy as it is represented in its logical part will have to go through the labyrinth of these notes and texts and make for himself a statement as well as an estimate of that doctrine. This task is facilitated in the first volume which will contain a historical sketch as well as a synthetical reconstruction of the whole edifice of the final shape of Buddhist philosophy, as far as it can be achieved at present. The second volume thus contains the material as well as the justification for this reconstruction. The first volume is in the press and we hope that it will appear before long.

A SHORT TREATISE OF LOGIC,

NYĀYA-BINDU

BY

DHARMAKĪRTI

WITH

A COMMENTARY (ṬĪKĀ) BY DHARMOTTARA

CHAPTER I.

PERCEPTION.

§ 1. Subject Matter and Purpose of this Work.

1. **All successful human action is preceded by right knowledge. Therefore this (knowledge will be here) investigated.**

(1.6). In this sentence the importance of the subject of the present work is pointed to. The body of a literary work, indeed, has a double aspect, it consists of words and subject matter. The words, in the present case, have no other purpose than to convey their meaning; they will not be analysed. But if the subject matter were of no use, no work could be devoted to an enquiry[1] into it, just as no reasonable man would ever undertake an enquiry about the teeth of the crow, because this would serve no purpose.[2] Wishing to show that this treatise deserves to be written, the author points to the importance of its subject matter (1.10). Because (says he) all successful human action is preceded by right knowledge, therefore this (phenomenon) must be investigated, and with this aim the present treatise is undertaken. Such is the meauing of the (prefatory) sentence.[3] (2.2). (By making this statement, viz.) by stating that right knowledge — the

---

[1] *pratipatti* = *bstan-pa.*

[2] We would expect *kāka-danta-parīkṣā-prayojana-abhāvāt*, since the meaning is not that the teeth are useless, but that an *investigation* about unexisting teeth is useless, cp. Tātp., p. 1. 17, and *infra*, p. 2. 22. (text). This would agree with Vinītadeva's interpretation according to whom the *vyutpatti* (= *parīkṣā*) must have a *prayojana*. Since *vyutpatti* is already the *prayojana* of the treatise itself (*prakaraṇa-śarīra*), its importance will then be *prayojanasya prayojanam*. To this double *prayojana* Dharmottara takes exception, he is thus obliged to give a somewhat awkward turn to his example. But cp. Tātp., p. 28. 12, *niṣprayojane* (*-ām?*) *parīkṣām.*

[3] Vinītadeva, p. 31. 10, has interpreted the first sentence as containing an indication 1) of the subject-matter (*abhidheya* = *samyag-jñāna*), 2) of its aim (*prayojana* = *vyutpatti*), 3) their connection (*sambandha*) and 4) the aim of the aim (*prayojanasya api prayojanam*), the latter referring to the real importance of the study of the theory of cognition, since cognition is involved in every purposive action. Dharmottara objects to the unusual *prayojanasya prayojanam*. He takes the first sentence as a whole, indicating the importance of a study of the theory of

subject matter of this treatise — is the cause[1] of all successful human action, the importance (of a theory of cognition is alone) stated (directly). (2.3) But by making such a statement the subject-matter (of the work), its aim and its fitness[2] (for that aim) are (indirectly) indicated. Indeed when it is being stated that right knowledge, the source of all (successful) human action,[3] will be analysed in the present work, it is also implied that right knowledge is the subject-matter of this literary composition, its aim is an analysis of (the phenomenon) of knowledge, and the work itself represents the means through which the analysis (is achieved). (2.5). Directly stated is thus only (one) point, the importance of the subject matter, (the other points), its fitness etc., are then implicitly understood.[4] The (prefatory) sentence alone is not adequate to give a direct statement of the subject matter, the purpose and the connection between them (separately). By naming directly only one point, it indirectly alludes to all three. (2. 7). The word «this» (knowledge) points here to the subject matter. The words «will be investigated» — to the purpose. The purpose here meant (is double). For the author it is the task of composing the work, whilst for the student it is the task of studying it. (2.9). Indeed, all reasonable men set themselves to work when they have some useful aim in view. To the questions[5] as to why has the Master written this treatise and why should it be studied by the pupils, it is answered that its purpose is an analysis (of knowledge). It is written by the author in order that he may himself become the teacher for those

---

cognition, and then the three usual preliminaries as implicitly contained in it. He thinks that a distinction between *prakaraṇasya śarīra-prayojanam* and *abhidheya-prayojanam* is useless, since *śarīra* is first of all *śabda* which is not investigated.

1 *uktvā* must be inserted before *prayojana*, p. 2.2, cp. Tib. *rgyu-ñid-du bstan-pas.*

2 *sambandha.*

3 *puruṣa-artha-upayogi* = *puruṣa-artha-siddhi-hetu.*

4 Lit., p. 2.5. «Therefore by the force of direct statement (*abhidhāna*) of the importance (*prayojana*) of the part (which is) the subject, connection etc. are expressed». Dh. thus insists that the first sūtra, as a whole (*samudāyārtha*), refers directly to *abhidheya-prayojana*, i. e. to the importance of a theory of cognition, the three usual preliminaries are then to be understood implicitly. Vinītadeva thinks that *abhidheya* and *prayojana* are expressed directly (read *mṅon-du* instead of *sṅon-du*, p. 32. 2 of M. de la Vallée-Poussin's edition in B. I.) and *sambandha* indirectly. The importance of a theory of cognition is then conceived by him as a *prayojanasya api prayojanam* (p. 33. 8).

5 *iti saṃśaye.*

who are being instructed in (the theory of) cognition, and it is studied by the pupils desirous of acquiring for themselves the instruction delivered by the Master. An analysis of knowledge is thus the purpose of both the composition and the study of the work. (2.13). No word (in the prefatory sentence) indicates the connection between the subject matter and the purpose. It must be supplied from the context.[1] Indeed when a reasonable man is working at this treatise for the sake of an analysis of right knowledge, this treatise is just the means of attaining his purpose and there is no other. Thus it is clear that the relation between this treatise and its aim is that of an expedient and the thing to be expedited.

(2.16). However, (the advisability of stating these topics at the beginning can be questioned), since, even if they are stated, no reasonable man will accept them without further evidence, before having looked into the book. This is true! Without a foregoing study of the book these topics, although stated, cannot be appreciated. But when stated, even without being authenticated, they provoke the spirit of inquisitiveness[2] by which people are incited to work (2.18). Indeed, when reasonable men presume that a thing may be of some use to them,[3] they (immediately) set to work; whereas when they suspect that it is of no use,[4] they give it up. (2. 19). Therefore the author of a scientific work is especially expected to make at the beginning a statement about the connection (between his aim and the subject matter). For it is all very well for writers of romance to make false statements in order to amuse,[5] but we cannot imagine what would be the aim of a scientific author if he went (the length of) misstating his subject-matter. Neither (do we see that this actually) occurs. Therefore it is natural to expect inquisitiveness concerning such (works). (2.22). If it were not stated, the student might possibly think that the subject matter served no purpose at all as, e. g., an enquiry about the teeth of a crow; or that (the aim) was irrealizable as, e. g., the instruction to adorn oneself with the demon Takṣaka's crest jewel which releases from fever[6]; or that its aim was undesirable, like the instruc-

---

1 *sāmarthyāt.*

2 *saṃśaya.*

3 *artha-saṃśaya.*

4 *anartha-saṃśaya.*

5 Lit., 2.20. «Indeed the words of story-tellers may be imagined in a different way for the sake of sport etc. (Tib. = *krīḍādi*)».

6 Cp. the same simile Tātp., p. 3. 6.

tion about the ritual to be followed at the (re-)marriage ceremony of one's own mother[1]; or that the aim could possibly be attained in an easier way than through this book; or again that it was altogether useless. If any such presentiment of uselessness arises, reasonable men will not apply themselves to the study of the book. By stating the subject matter etc. some useful purpose is (always) suggested, and this checks the suspicion of uselessness. Reasonable men are thus incited to take action. Thus it is clear that the connection (between the subject matter and the purpose) is stated in order that the book may be credited with efficiency, since such consideration incites human activity.

§ 2. Right knowledge defined.

(3. 5). Right knowledge is knowledge not contradicted (by experience).[2] In common life we likewise say that (a man) has spoken truth when he makes us reach the object he has first pointed out. Similarly (we can also say) that knowledge is right when it makes us reach an object it did point to. But by «making us reach an object» nothing else is meant than the fact of turning (our attention) straight to the object. Indeed knowledge does not create an object and does not offer it to us, but in turning (our attention) straight to the object it (*eo ipso*) makes us reach it. Again «to turn a man straight to the object» is nothing else than to point it out as an aim of a (possible) purposive action. Indeed, (one should not imagine) that knowledge has the power forcibly to incite a man (against his will).[3]

---

[1] This is an indication that Buddhists had in India the same aversion to the remarriage of widows as the brahminical Hindus.

[2] This is the Buddhist definition of empirical knowledge (*samyag-jñāna* = *pramāṇa*). It is opposed to the definitions of the Mīmāṃsakas (*artha-avabodha*), of the Cārvākas (*artha-darśana*), the Naiyāyikas (*pramā-karaṇa*). Mādhyamikas and Yogācāras held that this knowledge is a transcendental illusion (*ālambane bhrāntam*). With this reservation the first accepted the realistic Logic of the Naiyāyiks, the second adhered to the reform of Dignāga, cp. my Nirvāṇa, p. 156 n. For Vinītadeva, p. 34. 1, 40. 13, and Kamalaśīla, Tattvasg., p. 392 .6, the definition refers to the field of experience only (*prāpaka-viṣaye*) and thus agrees both with the Yogācāra and Sautrāntika views (*ubhaya-naya-samāśrayeṇa*). But the Ṭipp., p. 18—19, thinks that the Yogācāra idealism is here forsaken and the Sautrāntika realism adhered to. As to Jinendrabuddhi's view cp. Appendix.

[3] Thus *jñānam* is a *jñāpaka-hetu*, not a *kāraka-hetu*. These remarks are probably directed against Vinītadeva who explains *puruṣārtha* = *prayojana*, *siddhi* = *sādhaka* (*grub-par-byed-pa*) and *pūrvaka* as *hetu*. He thus converts *jñāna* into a *kāraka-hetu*. Kamalaśīla, just as Dh., defines *avisaṃvāditva* as

(3. 9). For this very reason (as will be stated later on)[1] the only ultimate result of an act of cognizing is (simply) a distinct cognition. When an object has been cognized, man has been (*eo ipso*) turned towards it and the object reached.[2] The (proper) function of cognition is thus at an end just after the object has been cognized. (3. 10). For this very reason cognition is concerned with an object not yet cognized. But when it has been first cognized, the same act of cognition has also drawn (the attention) of man and has made him reach the object, (i. e., reach it by his cognition). Any further act concerning that very object cannot be regarded as its cognition.[3] Consequently (a purposive action directed towards) an object already cognized will not be an act of cognizing it.[4]

(3. 12). (Turning now to the different modes of cognition we see that) when an object has been apprehended by direct experience,[5] it has been converted into an object of (possible) purposive action through sense-perception. Because (we say) that sense-perception has pointed out an object, when the function of that knowledge which consists in making us feel its presence in our ken is followed by a construction (of its image).[6] Therefore (we say) that an object has been pointed out by sense-perception, when it is cognized as something directly perceived. (3. 15). Inference (or indirect cognition, differs) in that it points out the mark of the object, and by thus (indirectly) making sure (its existence) submits it as an object of possible purpo-

referring to a possible, not to an actual successful action (=*abhimata-artha-kriyā-samartha- artha-prāpaṇa-śaktimattvam, na tu prāpanam eva., op. cit* p. 392. 7).

[1] About *pramāṇa-phala* cp. *infra*, text, p. 14. 16 and 18.8 cp. transl. and notes.

[2] The Mīmāṃsaka assumes three stages in the development of every cognitive act, the first apprehension (*darśana*), man's purposive action (*pravartana*) and the successful reaching of the object (*prāpaṇa* or *hāna-upādāna*), every following stage being the result (*phala*) of the preceding one. According to Dh., the first stage alone belongs to the domain of cognition proper, the subsequent idea of a purposive action is not an act of cognizing the same thing. cp. Tipp., p. 8. 5, and Šlokav., pratyakṣa 60—70.

[3] Lit., p. 3. 12. «Regarding that very object what can another cognition make additionally?»

[4] «Reaching» (*prāpaṇa*) as understood by the Mīmāṃsaka and Naiyāyika means actual successful action; as understood by Dh., it here means possible purposive action, *prāpaṇa-yogyī-karaṇa*, cp. Ṭipp., p. 8. 6. Cp. Tātparyaṭ., p. 15. 5.

[5] *dṛṣṭa* refers to all sense-faculties, not vision alone.

[6] This is the real definition of sense perception, it is conceived as a moment of indefinite sensation (*vijñāna*) which is followed by a construction (*kalpanā* = *vikalpa*) of a definite image. The definition as given on p. 6. 15 is made *vipratipatti-nirākaraṇārtham*, cp. the same definition *infra*. text, p. 11. 12.

sive action. Thus it is that sense-perception points out a definite[1] object, (i. e., an object localized in time and space) which appears before us directly,[2] and inference likewise points out a definite object by way of the mark it is connected with. These two (methods of cognizing) point out definite objects, therefore they are right knowledge. (3. 17). What differs from them is not (right) knowledge. Knowledge is right when it makes us reach the object, and it makes us reach it when it has pointed to an attainable object.[3] But an object pointed out in some different way, not according to the above mentioned two (methods of right knowlegde), is either absolutely unreal as, e. g., water seen as a vision in a desert — it does not exist, it cannot be reached — or it is uncertain as to whether it exists or not as, e. g., every problematic object. Since there is no such object in the world, which at the same time would be existent and non-existent, therefore such (a problematic object) can never be attained. (3. 21). And all imagination[4] which is not produced by the (real) mark of the

---

[1] *niyata* is here contrasted with *saṃśaya* and *viparyaya*, it is the same as *niścita*. Cp. *niyata-pratibhāsa* on p. 8. 10, and *niyata-ākāra* on p. 70. 11, where the meaning of *niyata* varies.

[2] *pratibhāsa* = *nirbhāsa* = *ābhāsa* = *pratibimbana*, cp. Ṭipp., p. 12. 12.

[3] Lit., p. 3. 17. «There is no other *vijñāna*. What points to an object, which it is possible to attain, fetches, and by fetching it is right knowledge». We would have a better meaning if this first sentence were united with the following two. «No other sensation (*vijñāna*) indicating (*ādarśayat* = *upadarśayat*) an object capable of being reached is such as «makes reach» (*prāpaka*) and through making us reach (the object) is right knowledge». But the Tibetan translation does not support this interpretation. *Vijñāna* in logic loses its meaning of an indefinite pure sensation (= *nirvikalpaka-jñāna*) which it had in Abhidharma where it was contrasted with *saṃjñā* as a definite idea. With the Yogācāras and Mādhyamikas it is often contrasted with *jñāna* which has then the sense of transcendental knowledge (= Tib. *ye-śes*). Here it has the general sense of knowledge, idea, or representation, just as in the term *vijñāna-vādin*; *jñāna* and *vijñāna* are here used indiscriminately, as the next following *jñānena* proves, *anyaj jñānam* is then = *mithyā jñānam* as p. 3. 23, cp. my Nirvāṇa, Index. However there are some contexts where, as will be seen below, we must take into account the original meaning of *vijñāna* or *vijñāna-skandha* as pure sensation. Cp. Vācaspati's remark that when *jñāna* stands instead of *vijñāna* = *vistṣṭa-jñāna* it excludes every element of *smṛti* or *saṃskāra*, cp. N. vārt., p. 48. 5—6 and Tātp., p. 114. 1. But the relation may be reversed, cp. Jinendrabuddhi, f. 40. a. 7.

[4] *kalpanā* meaning primarily «arrangement» (*yojanā*) and *vikalpa* meaning choice, dichotomy (*dvaidhī-karaṇa*), are both used in the sense of imagination, but pure imagination (*utprekṣaṇa-vyāpāra*) is distingnished from constructive imagination (*liṅgaja-vikalpa*). A doubt appertains always to the imaginative part of knowledge, not to sensation, *yas tu saṃśayaḥ, (sa) vikalpakasya jñānasya*, Tipp., p. 10. 11.

object, which operates (freely) without taking notice of limitation (by reality) can but refer to a problematic fact (about which we neither know) that it exists nor that it does not exist. Such an object can never be reached. Therefore every cognition other (than perception or inference) is not a source of right knowledge, since it presents an object which cannot be reached, an object which is (either) absolutely unreal (or) uncertain as to whether it exists or not.[1]

(3.23). (Sentient beings) strive for desired ends. They want that knowledge which leads them to the attainment of objects fitted for successful action. The knowledge that is investigated by the theory (of cognition) is just the knowledge they want. Therefore right knowledge is knowledge which points to reality, (a reality which) is capable of experiencing purposive action.[2] (4.1). And that object alone which has been pointed out by such right knowledge can be «reached», (i. e., clearly and distinctly cognized), because, as we have stated above (p. 4), we understand by «reaching» an object its definite cognition. (4.2). Now, if there is a divergence between what is pointed out (by our cognition) and the real object, the latter has either a different

---

[1] The realistic systems as well as, in a limited sense, the Mādhyamikas and Vedāntins admit additional sources of knowledge, besides perception and inference, e. g., testimony, analogy, negation, similarity. Buddhist logic includes them all in inference, or indirect knowledge. Therefore whatsoever is neither perception nor inference is wrong knowledge. In realistic systems there is also a difference between *pramāṇa* (=*pramā-karaṇa*) and *pramā* (=*pramāṇa-phala*). In Buddhist logic this difference is denied and *pramāṇa*=*samyag-jñāna*; the «reaching of the object (*prāpaṇa*)» which was interpreted above, p. 4, as «reaching by definite cognition» is here taken in the sense of an actual successive action.

[2] Although the school of Dignāga (they are called the later Yogācāras, or the Vijñānavādi logicians, or the Sautrāntika-Yogācāras) deny the reality of an external world corresponding to our ideas, they in their logic and epistemology investigate cognition from the empirical point of view, cp. Candrakīrti, Mādhy. vṛtti, p. 58. 14. transl. in my Nirvāṇa, p. 140 ff. Therefore their definition of reality as efficiency (*artha-kriyā-kāritva*) and of knowledge as *artha-kriyā-samartha-artha-pradarśana* are purely empirical. But they contend that their analysis of empirical cognition leads to the establishment of an uncognizable transcendental substratum, the *sva-lakṣaṇa-paramārtha-sat*, the «thing in itself». The validity (*prāmāṇyam*) of empirical knowledge is thus established by a subsequent step (*parataḥ*). The question whether the act of cognizing carries in itself (*svataḥ*) the feeling of its validity, or whether this is due to a further cognition (*parataḥ*) is very much debated in Indian philosophy. The school of Dignāga has thus established the validity of cognition in opposition to the condemnation of all logic by the Mādhyamikas. This *pramāṇa-viniścaya-vāda* is represented by Vācaspati, Tātparyaṭ., p. 7. 28.

quality or a different place or a different time.[1] Indeed every variation in its characteristics (makes the characterized object) «another» object. (When we say that) the real object is «other», (we mean) that it either has another quality or another place or another time (than what is contained in our cognition).[2] Thus cognition representing one form of the object, is not to be considered as a right cognition when the real object has a different form, e.g., the yellow conch-shell seen (by the daltonist) is not a right cognition of this conch-shell, since it is really white. Neither is cognition right when it wrongly represents the place of the object, e. g., the radiance of a jewel seen through the chink in a door, when mistaken for the jewel itself which is in the room (behind the door), is not a right cognition of this jewel.[4] (4. 6.). Nor is our cognition right when it represents the object as

---

[1] The proper place for these remarks would have been, as stated by the Ṭipp., p. 11. 8, later on, p. 16, when discussing the non-illusiveness of sense-perception. They are directed against Vinītadeva's theory that the image may be wrong while sensation is right, since the real object is nevertheless reached by subsequent purposive action (*artha-mātrasya prāpteḥ*, Ṭipp., p. 11. 4).

[2] The law of «otherness», as understood by the Buddhists, is here alluded to. Concepts, ideas, objects are artificial cuts in an uninterrupted flow of moments. Every variation in time, space and quality (*svabhāva*) is an indication of something «other» (*yad viruddha-dharma-saṃsṛṣṭam tan nānā*). The identity of an idea or an object thus reduces to a single moment which has neither duration in time (*kāla-ananugata*), nor extension in space (*deśa-ananugata*), nor any quality, *kṣaṇabhedena vastuno bhedaḥ, deśa-kāla-vyatirikta-avayavy-abhāvāt* (read thus Ṭipp., p. 11. 7). From this point of view every definite cognition, since it corresponds to a subsequent moment, when the sensation is over, will be a cognition of an «other» object, strictly speaking it will be wrong. But empirical cognition refers to series of moments (*santāna*), infinitesimal time (*sūkṣma-kāla-bheda*) is not taken into account. The definition of knowledge is framed so as to agree with realities having some stability, *santāna-apekṣayā prāmāṇya-lakṣaṇam ucyate*, Ṭipp., p. 11.16 About «otherness» cp. W. E. Johnson, Logic I, p. XXXI.

[3] Cp. Tātparyaṭ., p. 56. Some logicians have maintained that since the object reached in a subsequent action is the real white conch-shell, the cognition will be a right one. But Dharmottara thinks that the image of the yellow conch-shell is nevertheless a wrong cognition, the white conch-shell is «reached» on the basis of another cognition. He has enlarged upon this point in his ṭīkā upon Pramāṇa-viniścaya of Dharmakīrti.

[4] The shining of a jewel, as well as of light in general, is moving matter (*gati-dharman*) and spreads in light-waves (*taranga-nyāyena*). But this is only the empirical view. The transcendental reality of what appears as a motion is but a series of point-instants in contiguous places following one-another, each representing an «other» thing, cp. Tātparyaṭ., p. 394. 10. But this theory is here overlooked and empirical illusion alone referred to. cp. also N. b. t., p. 69. 2—*na kṣaṇayor virodhaḥ*.

existing at a time when we really do not perceive it. E.g., seeing in a dream at midnight an object which we really have seen at noon cannot be considered as a right cognition of an object really present at midnight.[1]

(4. 8.). (It can be objected) that a cognition of the object's own form or its own place can be admitted, but to cognize its own time, (the unique moment to which its real existence) is confined, is impossible. However we do not maintain that it should be reached by distinct cognition at that very moment to which its existence is confined. We have the moment of sensation and the different moment of distinct perception. We maintain that we can distinctly cognize that very object whose existence was confined to (a previous) moment. (The unity which thus appears to exist between different moments) is a unity produced by the synthesis of distinct apprehension, and represents (in reality) a chain of momentary existences.

(4. 12). (The prefatory sentence) mentions right knowledge which «precedes» successful human action, i.e., which is the cause of it. The cause exists previously to the result, therefore it is said that knowledge precedes (action). If the word «cause» had been used (instead of «precedes») we might have understood that right knowledge is the immediate cause producing successful human action. But by using the word «precedes» its mere antecedence (is elicited). (4. 13). Right knowledge is twofold, it either is (intuitive), directly presenting to the mind the right way of action,[2] or (discursive), di-

---

1 Lit., p. 4. 2—4. 7. «Here the real object which is different from what is pointed out has another form, another place and another time. Indeed by combining with incompatible qualities, the real object is other, and a difference of place, time and form is a combination with incompatible qualities. Therefore when apprehending a real object in another form cognition is not right in regard of the object having a different form, as apprehending a yellow conch-shell (is wrong) in regard of a white one. And apprehending what is situated in one place cognition is not right for what is situated in a different place, as cognition apprehending a jewel in the radiance in the chink of a door (is wrong) for the jewel in the room. And apprehending what is related to another time is not right cognition regarding a real object at a different time, as a dream at midnight about an object (seen) at noon is not a right cognition of a real object (existing) at midnight». About the Buddhist theory of dream and the celebrated identification of reality with a dream by the Vijñānavādins interesting remarks are to be found in Dharmakīrti's Santānāntara-siddhi. But here again this theory is overlooked and dream is taken as an illusion in the usual empirical sense.

2 *artha-kriyāyā nirbhāsaḥ = artha-kriyā-sādhana-nirbhāsaḥ*, cp Ṭipp., p. 12. 11.

recting our attention towards a possible object of successful action.[1] Of these two only (the last variety), that knowledge which stimulates purposive action, will be here examined. It merely precedes, but does not directly produce successful action. (4. 15). When we acquire right knowledge we must remember what we have seen before. Remembrance stimulates will,[2] will produces action and action reaches the object. Therefore such knowledge is not a direct cause. (4. 17). In cases when purposive action presents itself directly (the aim) is reached straight off and (the process) cannot be analysed. But in cases when reasonable men strive and doubt, it may be analysed. By intuitive knowledge[3] the aims of man are attained (directly), in such cases men have no doubt about their aims. This makes an analysis impossible. (4. 19). Thus it is that the word «cause»[4] has been omitted, and the word «precedes» used in order to suggest that right knowledge, when it is not immediately followed by action, is worthy of being analysed.

(4. 21). Human action has an aim. That which is aimed at is an object, i. e., that which is desired.[5] There are objects to be avoided and objects to be attained. An object to be avoided is an object which we wish to avoid. An object to be attained is an object which we wish to attain.[6] There is no other class of objects different from these two. The indifferent object, since it is not desired, belongs to the class of undesirable ones.[7]

(4. 23). Success is the (actual) attaining or avoiding of the object. When success is achieved by causes, it is called production. But when it is achieved by knowledge it is called behaviour.[8] It consists in

---

1 *artha-kriyā-samarthe* must be interpreted as *artha-kriyā-sādhana-samarthe* (Ṭipp, p. 12. 13, read *evam uttaratrāpi....*). But an alternative explanation is likewise suggested by the Ṭipp., p. 12. 13-15, according to which *artha-kriyā-jñānam* would be *anantara-kāraṇam* in the first case, and with respect to behaviour it would then be *vyavahitam sādhana-nirbhāsa-jñānam*.

2 *abhilāṣa*, desire.

3 *artha-kriyā-nirbhāse jñāne*, lit., «when there is knowledge (sc. consciousness) reflected in purposive action».

4 Vinītadeva has interpreted *pūrvaka* as meanig *hetu*.

5 *artha* is here derived from the root *arth*, the usual etymology is from the root *ṛ* with the *uṇādi* suffix *than*.

6 Vinītadeva has explained *artha-siddhi* as meaning *prayojana-niṣpatti*, but this is wrong. since *samyag-jñāna* is a *jñāpaka-hetu*, not a *kāraka-hetu*, cp. Ṭipp., p. 13. 3.

7 Indifferent objects are assumed by the Naiyāyiks, cp. Tātp., p. 65. 1 ff.

8 *anuṣṭhāna*.

avoiding the avoidable and attaining the attainable. Behaviour consisting in such activity is called succesful action.

(5.2.). When the (prefatory sentence) mentions «all successful human action» the word «all» is used to indicate the totality of the objects, but not the different ways of action. Therefore it is not meant that the (above stated) two varieties of purposive action depend upon right knowledge, but it is suggested that every successful action, whatsoever it may be, the totality of actions, depends upon right knowledge. Accidental success through false knowledge is impossible.[1]

(5.5). Indeed, successful action is possible when (knowledge) has rightly constructed[2] the object whose (existence) has been pointed out by sensation.[3] And this is done by right knowledge alone, not by wrong knowledge.[4] How could cognition which has not rightly constructed (its object) lead to successful action? Wrong knowledge indeed does not lead to it. That knowledge which alone leads to it is right knowledge. (5.8). For this very reason it must be carefully investigated. And since it is the only cause of every successful human action, therefore the author, when stating this, (has emphasized) that «all» (success) is preceded by right knowledge.[5] (5.10). Thus the meaning of the (prefatory) sentence runs as follows,—because every efficient action is preceded by right knowledge, therefore this knowledge is investigated in the present treatise.

(5.14). The word «investigated» refers (to the method adopted) which consists in expounding the subject (indirectly) by refuting all contrary opinions. They are fourfold, in so far as they concern the number of varieties, their definition, their object and their result.

---

1 Vinītadeva and Šāntirakṣita (?) think that a succesful action may happen accidentally when acting upon a supposition, as e. g., when you approach a well and reach water without knowing beforehand whether there really is water in the well. They thus interpret the word «all» as referring to both ways of behaviour, obtaining and abstaining. They maintain that success is mostly (*bāhulyena*) achieved when acting upon right knowledge, but may be accidentally produced by uncertain or wrong cognition. Dh. denies that, but he has a special theory about accidental successful action explained in his Prāmāṇa-viniščaya-ṭīkā, cp. Ṭipp., p. 10. 13, 13. 12 ff., and *infra* p. 17, 3. Cp. also Kamalašīla, p. 404. 2 and Dh.'s own words above, p. 3—4.

2 *prāpayati*, cp above, p. 4 n. 3.

3 *pradaršana* = *ādaršana* = *upadaršana* = *ālocana* = *nirvikalpaka-pratyakṣa*.

4 Lit., p. 5. 6. «What produces the reaching of the shown is right knowledge only, what does not produce the reaching of the shown is wrong knowledge».

5 Lit., p. 5. 10. «The word *iti* is used in the sense of «therefore», *yad* and *tad* are necessarily correlative».

§ 3. Varieties of right knowledge.

(5. 15). In order to reject misconception regarding the number of its varieties, it is said,—

2. Right knowledge is twofold.

(5. 17). It is twofold, it has two varieties. By stating the number, the division into two varieties is indicated. There are two varieties of right knowledge. When the division into two varieties has been stated, it becomes possible to make a definition of right knowledge which (will consist of definitions) confined to each variety separately. (5. 19). Otherwise it is impossible to indicate a unique essence which would embrace all varieties. Therefore the indication that there is a number of different (varieties) is nothing but an (indirect) way of stating that the essence (of knowledge) is double. Without mentioning the number, i. e., the different varieties, it is impossible to express this double essence. The number has thus been stated at the beginning, because this is the only way to specify the essence of knowledge.[1]

(5. 22). Now, what are these two varieties?

3. Direct and indirect (perceptive and inferential).

(6. 2). The word for direct knowledge (or perception) means knowledge dependent upon the senses.[2] (This meaning) of a knowledge dependent upon the senses is suggested by the etymo-

[1] This remark is a repetition of what later on, p. 17, text, is said in regard of the twofold division of inference. But there it is quite natural, since two absolutely different things are designated by the term «inference», a method of cognition and its expression in propositions. In this place the remark is strange, since the author has just been dealing at some length with a general definition of right knowledge. It may be Dharmottara had the feeling that his definition of right knowledge as uncontradicted by experience was, to a certain extent, merely verbal, meaningless without reference to its both varieties of direct and indirect cognition. Vinītadeva's comment contains the remark about the impossibility of a general definition only in the right place, i. e., with regard to the definition of inference.

[2] Lit., p. 6. 2. «*Pratyakṣa* means that the sense-organ is approached, reposed upon. The compound word is composed according to (the rule) that prepositions like *ati* etc. in the sense of (*ati*)-*krānta* etc. can enter into composition with (their complement) in the accusative case. In words compounded with *prāpta*, *āpanna*, *alam* and prepositions (the rule) according to which the gender of the componnd must be the same as the gender of its last member is not observed, (and therefore) it agrees in gender with the object to which it is referred, (and thus) the word *pratyakṣa* is established as (an adjective which can be used in any gender)», cp. Vārt ad Pāṇini, II, 4. 26.

logical analysis[1] of the word, not by its actual use[2] (in philosophy). The idea of being dependent upon the senses contains, as its implication,[3] the idea of direct knowledge[4] which is thus being suggested.[5] This alone is the real meaning[6] of the term perception. Therefore any knowledge that makes the object (appear) before us directly is called perceptive. (6. 6). If the proper use of the word involved nothing but dependence upon the senses, then sense-knowledge (or sensation) alone could be called direct knowledge, but not (the three remaining varieties of it), mental sensation etc. Thus it is, e. g., that the (sanscrit) word *go* «cow», although it is etymologically derived from the root *gam* «to move», is actually used to express the idea of a cow. This idea is incidentally suggested by the fact of motion when it is inherent in the same object. But then it comes to be generally accepted to denote a cow, whether she moves or not.[7]

(6. 10) (The word for inference means etymologically «subsequent measure»). The word «measure» suggests an instrument (by which an object is measured, i. e., cognized). A source of knowledge is thereby indicated, whose characteristic essence is coordination.[8] It is called «subsequent measure», because it appears after the logical mark (or middle term) has been apprehended, and its concomitance (or major premise) has been brought to memory. (6. 11). When the presence of the mark upon the subject (i. e., the minor premise) has been apprehended, and the concomitance between the minor and the major term, (i. e., the major premise) brought to memory, the inference (or conclusion) follows. Therefore it is called «subsequent».

---

1 *vyutpatti.*

2 *pravṛtti.*

3 *samāveta.*

4 *artha-sākṣāt-kāritva.*

5 *lakṣyate.*

6 *pravṛtti-nimitta.* The Tib. translation contains, p. 13. 5, a characteristic addition «*pratyakṣa* has not the meaning of being dependent upon the senses». This definition (*akṣam pratītya jñānam*) belongs to Praśastapāda, p. 186. 12.

7 The word *go* «cow» is explained as deriving from the verbal root *gam* «to go» in order to conform with the general conception of the Pāṇinean school of grammarians according to which every word must be necessarily explained as deriving from some verbal root. According to this interpretation of the term «perception» it will embrace also the supernatural mystic intuition of Saints, Bodhisattvas and Yogins.

8 Coordination (*sārūpya*) is a characteristic not only of inferential, but also of perceptive knowledge in its final stage (*pramāṇa-phala*), cp. *infra*, p. 15 (text). Pure sensation (*nirvikalpaka*) alone contains no coordination.

(6.12). The word «and» (connecting direct and indirect knowledge) coordinates perception and inference as having equal force.[1] Just as perception is a source of right knowledge, because being always connected with some (real) object it leads to successful purposive action, just the same is the case of inference. It likewise is a source of right knowledge always connected with some (real) object, in as much as it leads to the attainment of an object circumscribed by its mark.

§ 4. Perception defined.

4. **Direct knowledge means here neither construction (judgment) nor illusion.**

(6.16). The word «here» indicates localization,[2] but it is (moreover) used to indicate a selection. Thus the meaning of the sentence is the following one. «Here», i. e., among direct and indirect knowledge — this is a reference to the inclusive whole, «direct knowledge» — this refers to one part of it. A part is thus separated or selected from the whole, because the latter is the general term[3] (with reference to the former). (6.18). Direct knowledge is here taken as subject and the

[1] The tenet that there are only two sources of cognition, the senses and the intellect, has a capital importance for the whole Buddhist system. Cp. the discussions about *pramāṇa-samplava* and *pramāṇa-vyavasthā*, in Nyāyavārt., p.5. 1, and Tātparyaṭ., p. 12. 3 ff.; cp. Candrakīrti's polemic against it in my Nirvāṇa p. 141 ff. The realistic systems admit a greater number of *pramāṇas* and maintain at the same time that perception is the chief *pramāṇa*. In the Buddhist view both are mental constructions on the basis of pure sensation, in this they have equal force. Perceptive knowledge is directly produced by an object (*vastu*), inferential is indirectly produced through the medium of something identical with it or through its effect (*tādātmya-tadutpatti*), cp. Vinītadeva, p. 39. 1. The Buddhist division pretends to be exhaustive since it corresponds to the double essence in every object, the particular (conceived as the extreme concrete and particular, the uniqne, the *kṣaṇa*, the *sva-lakṣaṇa*) and the general, or the coordinated, the similar. The concrete individual object as far as it represents a complex of general features is not considered as a particular (*sva-lakṣaṇa*). All general charecteristics are universals even when included in a concrete object. Every cognition of a universal is not sense-cognition. The term inference thus has a much wider conuotation than our inference. When so understood perception and inference represent the passive and the active part in cognition, the senses and the intellect. They have thus an equal force, because they produce knowledge together, they can produce no real knowledge separately. Without any possible sensation it will be pure imagination, without any inferring or comparing (*sārūpya*) it will be pure indefinite sensation.

[2] *saptamī-arthe.*

[3] *pratyakṣatva-jātyā* = Tib. *mnon-sum-ñid-kyi rigs-kyis*, cp. Ṭipp., p. 17.2— *pratyakṣāṇām bahutvāt.*

characteristics of non-constructive and non-illusive (cognition) are predicated. (It is not a definition of its essence.[1] What its essence is) you and I very well know (in general). It is a kind of cognition which makes us (feel) that the objects are present to us directly. It is (now intimated) that it should be viewed as (something) non-constructive and (something) containing no illusion. (It may be objected, that since we do not very well know what these characteristics mean, we neither can know what direct knowledge is. But this is not so!) We must not imagine that if (the notions of) non-constructive and non-illusive are not familiar to us, we must refer them to some different special kind of direct knowledge which has been given this name and is here spoken of. The term «direct knowledge» (or perception) is familiar to everybody from its application (to that variety of direct cognition) which makes the object present to our sense-faculties and which is invariably connected with them.

(6. 22). This (perception) is referred to, and the characteristics of being neither a construction nor an illusion are predicated. Not[2] to

---

[1] As e. g., in the sentence «sound is impermanent» impermanence is a characteristic (*lakṣaṇa*) of the sound, but not its essence (*svarūpa*). These remarks are directed against Vinītadeva who has interpreted the sūtra as containing a definition and has even reversed the order of subject and predicate by stating that «whatsoever is non-constructive and non-illusive is direct knowledge» (p. 39. 12). The same is done by Kamalaśīla, *op. cit.* p. 366. 25, who maintains that, although *pratyakṣa* is here the *lakṣya*, it is also the predicate (*vidhīyate*). Cp. Tipp., p. 17—18. The term *pratyakṣa* is greater in extension than sense-perception (*indriya-jñāna*), cp. above, text p. 6. 6—7. But a thing must be known *in general* when its special characteristics are given and what «direct knowledge» is in general that everyone knows from the *example* of sense perception.

[2] Thus this celebrated definition (*kalpanāpoḍha*) of Dignāga which is discussed almost in every sanscrit work on philosophy or logic is not at all supposed to represent any exhaustive definition of perception, but only an indication of one of its characteristics. The feeling of the presence of the object in the range of our senses is its essential function (*sākṣāt-kāritva-vyāpāra*) and it is followed by a construction or judgment (*vikalpena anugamyate*). The Buddhists admit both pure sensation (*nirvikalpaka* = *kalpanāpoḍha*) and definite perception (*savikalpaka*), the latter under the names of *pramāṇa-phala*, *artha-pratīti*, *sārūpya-jñāna*. The same distinction is already contained in Nyāya-sūtra I. 4, where, according to the interpretations of Vātsyāyana, Uddyotakāra and Vācaspati, the word *avyapadeśya* refers to the *nirvikalpaka*, and the word *vyavasāyātmaka* — to the *savikalpaka pratyakṣa*. The difference between both conceptions consists in the prominence given by Dignāga to pure sensation (*nirvikalpaka*) as the only source of knowledge through which we come in touch with «absolute reality» (*paramārthasat*), with the «thing in itself» (*sva-lakṣaṇa*). In my «Logic and Epistemology» (German translation, p. 192) I ascribed the distinction of pure sensation and definite perception to Dignāga, and its introduction into brahmanic Nyāya to

be a construction means to be foreign to constrnction, not to have the nature of an arrangement (or judgment). «Not an illusion» means not contradicted by that (underlying) essence of reality which possesses efficiency. This essence consists of patches of colour which are the substratum underlying the arrangement (of parts in an object).[1] Non-illusive means knowledge which is not at variance with this (direct reality).

(7.3). (However, as they stand) these two characteristics are intended to clear away wrong conceptions, not (alone) to distinguish (direct from) indirect cognition. The characteristic of «not being a construction» would have been alone quite sufficient for that. (7.4). But if (the second characteristic) of «not being an illusion» were not added, (the following misconception would not have been guarded against. (There are some who maintain that) the vision of a moving tree (by an observer travelling by ship) and similar perceptions are right perceptions, because (there is in this case an underlying reality which) is not a construction. (7.5). Indeed a man acting upon such a perception reaches something which is a tree,[2] hence (it is supposed) that experience supports[3] his perception. It would thus be consistent knowledge and so far would be direct, as not being a (mere) construction. (7.7). In order to guard against this view the characteristic of «not being an illusion» has been inserted. It is an illusion. It is not a (right) perception. Neither is it an inference, since it is not derived from some mark in its threefold aspect.[4] No other way of cognition is possible. We maintain therefore that the vision of a moving tree is error. (7.8).

Vācaspati, but this is perhaps true, to a certain extent, only in respect of the formulation of the theory. I did not realize then that its essence is already perfectly well known to the earliest Buddhists, where it is contained under the names of *vijñāna-skandha* (= *nirvikalpaka-jñāna*) and *samjñā-skandha* (= *savikalpaka-jñāna*) respectively. Cp. my Central Conception, p. 18, and Udayana' Pariśuddhi, p. 214. 1.

[1] By pure sensation we may cognize the presence of an object which is a patch of blue colour, (we shall have *nīla-vijñānam* = *nīlasya vijñānam*), but we will not know that it is blue (we will not have the *nīlam iti vijñānam*), since this knowledge is arrived at by contrasting it with other objects and contrast (*vyāvṛtti*) is the work of intellect, not of pure sensation, cp. my Nirvāṇa, p. 162 n. 3. The reading *varṇātmaka* is supported by the Tib. transl. The alternative reading *dharmātmaka* conveys just the same idea since *varṇa* (or *rūpa*) is here a *dharma*, an ultimate element in the system of Hīnayāna, cp. Central Conception, p. 11.

[2] *vṛkṣa-mātram* = *vṛkṣa-svarūpa*, sc. *artha-kriyā-kṣamam vastu-rūpam*.

[3] *saṃvādakatvāt*. Dignāga assumed that such perceptions are right, cp. Tattvasg., p. 394. 20.

[4] About the three aspects of a logical mark cp. p. 18. 17 (text).

If it is error, how are we to explain that a tree is nevertheless reached (when acting upon such erroneous perception)? The tree is not (really) reached upon it, since a tree changing its position in space is the definite image[1] (corresponding to the visual sensation), and a tree fixed on one place is actually reached. (7.10). Therefore the object which has produced the sensation of a moving tree is not actually reached,[2] and (*vice versa*) the tree actually reached is not (the object which) has produced the visual sensation. Nothing at all is reached on the basis of this (wrong cognition). If a tree is actually reached, it depends upon an altogether different cognitive act. Thus it is that the characteristic of «non-illusion» has been introduced in order to clear away the theory (that illusion may lead to success).[3]

(7.12). However, the characteristic of «non-illusion» might also be taken as suggesting a difference between (direct cognition and) inference.[4] In that case the characteristic of «neither construction» would be directed against those contrary theories (which include some synthetic activity of the intellect into direct perception).[5] For, indeed, inference, (as indirect knowledge, is to a certain extent) an illusion. The course it takes consists in having to deal *prima facie* with mental contents of a (general), unreal character, and in ascertaining through them some real fact. On the other hand, what direct cognition *prima facie* apprehends is (pure reality), not unreality.[6]

---

[1] *paricchinna.*

[2] Lit., p. 7. 10. «Therefore where-placed the moving tree has been seen there-placed it is not reached».

[3] Dharmottara has discussed this question at length in his Pramāṇa-viniścaya-ṭīkā. Tattvasg., p. 394. 16 ff., ascribes the view that illusion may sometimes be right (*vibhrame'pi pramāṇatā*) to Dignāga, who therefore has omitted the word *abhrānta* in his definition. He also objects to the inclusion of the characteristic «non-illusive» (*avyabhicārin*) by the Naiyāyikas into their definition of sense-perception, N. S., I. 1. 4, because, says he, illusion is always mental (*yid-kyi yul ni ḥkhrul-pai yul yin*, cp. Pr. samucc., I. 19). Under kārikā I. 8 he states that *pratyakṣa-ābhāsa*, or illusions, are due to imagination (*brtags-nas ḥjug-pa=vikalpa-pravṛtta*). Cp. Ṭipp., p. 10. 11—*saṃśayo vikalpasya.*

[4] In the printed text of my edition (B. B. VIII) on p. 7. 12 the following passage, confirmed by the Tibetan translation, must be inserted after *nirāsārtham*—*tathābhrānta-grahaṇenāpy anumāne nivartite kalpanāpoḍha-grahaṇam vipratipatti-nirākāṇārtham, (bhrāntam hy. . . .).*

[5] According to the Abh. Kośa, I. 30, there is always included in every sensation a rudimentary synthesis called *svarūpa-vitarka* (*vitarka=vikalpa*).

[6] Lit., p. 7. 12—13 (with the sentence restored according to the Tib.) «Thus likewise by mentioning «non-illusive» inference being rejected, the mentioning of «non-constructive» is (then) in order to reject divergent views. Indeed in-

(7.13). (In any case) one should not take «non-illusive» to be here an equivalent of «consistent». Direct perception is nothing but (a variety) of consistent knowledge. This circumstance alone is sufficient for making it consistent. To repeat it would be useless. The meaning of the sentence would then be, — «that kind of consistent knowledge which is called direct perception is free from construction and is consistent». Perfectly useless repetition! Thus it is clear that non-illusive here means not contradicted by that (underlying) essence of reality which possesses efficiency.[1]

(7.19). What kind of «construction» is here alluded to?

ference is an illusion, since it operates through ascertaining an object in the non-object which represents (this inference's) own reflex. Perception, on the contrary, is not mistaken in regard of the essence (*rūpe* = *sva-rūpe*) grasped (immediately)». Perception, e. g., of fire proceeds from a momentary sensation to a constructed representation of the object fire. The first possesses more reality than the second. The first is a sense-datum, the second, the physical object « fire », a construction, a «non-object (*anartha*)». The first, as Bertrand Russel (Problems of Philosophy, ch. V.) puts it, is cognized «by acquaintance», the second «by description». When we infer the presence of fire from the presence of smoke the process of thought can be regarded as reversed. The cognized, or inferred, fire is a generality. The Buddhists do not distinguish here between concrete and abstract generality. Both for them are constructions (*kalpanā*). But the construction in order to be a real cognition must be referred to a possibility of sensation. Thus inference proceeds from the general to the particular, whereas perception takes the opposite course, from the particular sense-datum to some general construction. The term *pratibhāsa* is used to denote the *prima facie* mental content. Both perception and inference possess a *sva-pratibhāsa* (= *grāhya-svarūpa* as contrasted with their *adhyavaseya-svarūpa*). Thus *kalpanāpoḍha* refers to sensation, but *abhrānta*, according to sūtra I. 6, to Vinītadeva and Kamalaśīla, is the same as *avisaṃvādin*, it refers to false construction (*prāpya-viṣaye*); accoding to Dh. it differs from *avisamvādin*, and refers to sensation (*grāhya-viṣaye*). Cp. Anekāntaj., p. 203.

[1] In this alternative interpretation the term « non-illusive » (*abhrānta*) becomes almost a synonym of «non-constructive» (*kalpanāpoḍha*), since all construction, every judgment or inference, represents illusion when compared with pure sensation, the genuine source of real cognition. Inference is indirect knowledge, it is an illusion, because it is indirect. It is constructed, synthetical, subjective knowledge. It is nevertheless right knowledge, since it, although indirectly (*paramparayā*), also leads to successful purposive action (*bhrāntam apy anumānam artha-sambandhena pramāṇam,* Tātp. p. 262). Thus it is that inference (or judgment) is right knowledge empirically, but at the same time it is an illusion transcendentally. There are for Dignāga, just as in Kant's Transcendental Dialectic (M. Müller's transl., p. 238), two kinds of illusion, an empirical and a transcendental one. The moving tree is an empirical illusion, but the standing tree, although an empirical reality, is an illusive construction when compared with the underlying «thing in itself». All the fabric of the empirical world, this interconnected whole of substances and their qualities (*dharmi-dharma-bhāva*) and the inferential knowledge founded

5: Construction (or judgment) implies a distinct cognition[1] of a mental reflex[2] which is capable of coalescing with a verbal designation.

(7.21). A «verbal designation» is a word of speech through which something is denoted. To «coalesce» with a word means (such a condition when) the denoted aspect of the object and its verbal aspect[3] are mixed up in its apprehended aspect. Thus, when the denoted fact and the word denoting it have entered into one act of cognition, then the word and the object have «coalesced».[4]

(8.1). A distinct cognition of such a denoted reflex is thus mentioned which is *capable* of coalescing with a word. We may have,

upon it (*sarvo'yam anumāna-anumeya-bhāva*) is, according to Dignāga, a construction of our mind (*buddhy-ārūḍha* = *kalpita*), it does not adequately represent external reality (*na sad-asad apekṣate*), cp. Tātp., p. 39. 13, 127. 2, 252. 14 and H. N. Randle, Diṅnāga, p. 51. But «the senses (= *pratyakṣam*), says Kant, *loco cit.*, cannot err, because there is in them no judgment at all (= *kalpanāpoḍha*) whether true or false (= *abhrānta*)». The coincidence between Kant and Dharmakīrti in this point is remarkable. That kalpanā means judgment is proved below, p. 20 n. 6. Thus it is that Dh.'s alternative interpretation of the term *abhrānta* can be vindicated. The circumstance, however, that he is giving two somewhat different interpretations of the same term in the same context betrays a certain artificiality of his position. Vinītadeva, p. 40. 14, has interpreted *abhrānta* as meaning the same as *avisaṃvādin;* Kamalašīla, p. 392. 5, likewise. Dignāga's definition, both in Pr. samucc. and in Nyāya-dvāra, does not contain the word *abhrānta;* it is an innovation of Dharmakīrti, and Vācaspati informs us, Nyāya-Kaṇikā, p. 192, that he introduced it in order to exclude from the province of perception hallucinations, or objectless illusions (*niradhiṣṭhānam kešādi-jñānam apratyakṣatayā vyākhyātam*). This is also attested by Šāntarakṣita in Tattvas., p. 392. 3. But Pr. samucc. treats in kārikā I. 8 about *pratyakṣābhāsa*, and this corresponds to sūtra I. 6 of the Nyāyab. Both Dignāga and Dharmakīrti are perfectly aware that error is produced by a wrong interpretation of the sense-datum by the intellect, cp. above, p. 17. n. 3. If they nevertheless consider the characteristic of «non illusive», it is probably because they, like Kant (*loco cit.*) think that «sensibility...., is the source of real knowledge, but sensibility, if it influences the action of the understanding itself and leads ito n to a judgment, may become an (indirect) cause of error». A wrong construction is not a sensation, but it may be metaphorically called a wrong sense-perception (*pratyakṣābhāsa*) when a sensation is its *asādhāraṇa-kāraṇa*, cp. Pr. samucc., I. 4. Thus it is that sense-illusion (*indriya-bhrānti*) is also possible, cp. Tattvas., p. 392. 19.

1 *pratīti.* 2 *pratibhāsa.* 3 *ākāra* = *pratibhāsa.*

4 Vinītadeva, p. 51. 6, has explained *abhilāpa* as *vācyaḥ sāmānyādiḥ.* Dh. insists that it means (as *karaṇa-sādhana*) *vācakaḥ šabdaḥ*, since the word *yogya*, in his interpretation, proves that *abhilāpa* refers to the word and not to its meaning The latter (*jātyādi*) is of course also understood, but indirectly (*sāmarthyāt*), cp. Ṭipp., p. 21. 8 ff, and the controversy below, p. 23, cp. p. 23 n. 2.

indeed, a distinct cognition in which the mental reflex[1] has coalesced with its designation by speech[2] as, e. g., the constructed[3] (cognition) «jar» with a man to whom this word is familiar.[4] It contains such a mental reflex which is accompanied by the word «jar».

(8. 3). But we may also have (mental constructions) which, although not accompanied by corresponding words, are capable of being so accompanied as, e. g., the mental constructions of a baby not knowing the import of words. (8. 4). If constructions referring to mental reflexes accompanied by words were (alone) here mentioned, the constructions of those who do not speak would not have been included. But since it is said «*capable* of coalescing», they also are included. Although the mental constructions of a new born[5] babe are not accompanied by words, they certainly are suitable for such a connection. Those that are connected are (*eo ipso*) also suitable. Thus by inserting the word «capable» both (the primitive and developed constructions) are included.[6]

---

1 *ābhāsa* = *pratibhāsa*.

2 Lit., p. 8. 1–2. «Among them (*tatra*) some distinct cognition (*pratīti*) exists possessing a reflex (*ābhāsa* = *pratibhāsa* = *pratibimba*) united with a word».

3 *kalpanā* = *yojanā*, more lit. «the constructive judgment («this is a jar»)».

4 *vyutpanna-sanketa*.

5 *tadaharjāta*, cp. Tattvas., p. 367.12 ff.

6 This *kalpanā* (= *vikalpa*) must be distinguished from the *vikalpa* (= *vitarka*) of the Vaibhāṣikas. About the meaning of *vitarka* and *vicāra* in the Abhidharma, cp. my Central Conception, p. 104. They also assume a special kind of *vitarka* which they name *svabhāva-vitarka*, a rudimentary instinctive synthesis inherent in all sensation, cp. Abhidh. Koša ad I. 30. The Yogācāras understand by *vikalpa* (= *dvaidhī-karaṇa*) the bifurcation of consciousness into subject and object, *grāhya-grāhakatva-vikalpa*. Dignāga, Pramāṇa-samucc. I. 3 understands by this term *nāma-jāti-guṇa-kriyā-dravya-kalpanā*, i. e., a construction or an arrangement (*yojanā*) of a presentation which includes name, genus or species, quality, function and appurtenances, the whole complex being referred to a particular moment of efficient reality (*svalakṣaṇa*). The name, i. e., the proper name (*yadṛcchā šabda* = *ḥdod-rgyal-gyi sgra*, e. g., Ḍittha) is here by no means the designation of an extreme particular, as in European philosophy. Devadatta (or Socrates) would be for Dignāga only the designation of a series of occurrences *saṃskāra-samūha*). Thus we must consider here *abhilāpa-saṃsarga* as including all other syntheses, cp. Tattvas., 1226—8. The Ṭipp., p. 21. 8, remarks that if we understand the mental synthesis in the same way as it is done in other systems we will not get the meaning of pure sensation for perception — *teṣām grahaṇe sati indriya-vijñāna-pratyakṣatva-anupapattiḥ*. *Kalpanā* thus corresponds to our judgment and more specially to a judgment in which the subject represents *Hoc Aliquid*. i.e., something indefinite to be made definite by the predicate, a judgment of the

(8. 8) It may be questioned that if (mental constructions) are not accompanied by words, how can we have the certainty that they are capable of being accompanied? We answer — because they are mental reflexes not limited[1] (strictly to the actually perceived). They are not limited, inasmuch as the cause which would be a limit, (the fact which would exactly correspond to them) is absent. An object apprehended[2] (by acquaintance) can produce in the mind only something limited (to the actually present) as, e. g., a patch of colour producing a visual impression[3] can only produce a mental reflex limited to that very patch. But constructed knowledge[4] is not produced by the object (actually apprehended) and therefore it is not a (narrowly) restricted mental reflex, since the factor corresponding to it does not exist, (it is created by the synthesis of productive imagination). (8. 12) Why is it that such a construction (of productive imagination) is not produ-

---

form «this is that» *sa evāyam*, cp. Ṭipp., p. 23. 4; e. g., «this is Ḍittha» is *nāma-kalpanā*, «this is a patch of blue colour» is *guṇa-kalpanā*, «this is a cow» is *jāti-kalpanā* etc. This can be called the «epistemological» form of judgment and every judgment reduces to this form, since it is a known fact, admitted now in European Logic, that in every real judgment a reference to some reality is always understood, cp. Sigwart, Logik,[3] p. 67. It can be also viewed as a construction, a division, a bifurcation, an imagination *(vikapla)* etc., since every such judgment suggests in its predicate a division of the whole into the predicate and its counterpart, e. g., blue and not-blue, cow and not-cow etc. Cp. about *vikalpa* Mādhy. vṛtti, p. 350. 12. A detailed discussion of Dignāga's *kalpanā* is found in Tattvas., 1214—1311.

[1] The term *niyata* was used above, p. 3. 16, in the sense of *niścita*, it was then the contrary of doubt and error. Both *pratyakṣa* and *anumāna* have each their *niyata-pratibhāsa* = *sva-pratibhāsa*, cp. p. 7. 13 and 12. 19, this *pratibhāsa* is referred to *anartha* in the case of *anumāna*, hence it is *vikalpa-viṣaya* Infra, p. 70. 11 (*niyata-ākāraḥ kalpito draṣṭavyaḥ*) it likewise refers to the constructed, synthetic object, not to the momentary sensation (*kṣaṇa*), not to the absolutely particular (*svalakṣaṇa*). But here, in the sense of «limited», it is referred just to that momentary indefinite sensation. Even the representations of a new-born child are supposed to be synthetic images when compared with such sensation. The author assumes as quite evident that a mental construction is not something «limited», i. e., limited to a single indefinite momentary sensation, *vikalpa-jñānasya aniyata-pratibhasātvam eva*, cp. Ṭipp., p. 22. 13. Thus it is that what is called *aniyata-pratibhāsa* (= *aniyata-ākāra*) in the context of p. 8. 8, is called *niyata-ākāra* in the context of p. 70. 11.

[2] *grāhya* is contrasted with *adhyavaseya* = *prāpaṇīya*, cp. p. 12. 16—17.

[3] *cakṣur-vijñāna*. Here *vijñāna* is used as in Abhidharma, it is «pure sensation» *produced* by colour and the organ of sight, cp. my Central Conception, p. 16.

[4] *vikalpa-vijñānam*. In the Abhidharma this would not be termed *vijñāna*, but *saṃjñā* (= *nimitta-udgrahaṇa*), cp. Central Conception, p. 18.

ced by the object, (i. e., the particular moment which is being apprehended)? Because it does not (exclusively) depend upon what is present. A (new born) babe indeed does not stop crying and does not press his lips upon his mother's breast, so long as it has not produced a synthesis[1] of the breast it sees before him with the breast it has experienced in the foregoing (existence), by thinking (instinctively), «there it is». (8. 14) A cognition[2] which unites former experiences with later ones has not its object present to it, because the former experience is not present. Not having its object present it does not depend upon it. An independent cognition is not a reflex[3] (narrowly) restricted (to one momentary sensation), because the (assembled) factors which would (exactly) correspond (to the synthetic image) are absent.[4] Such (a synthetic image) is capable of coalescing with a word. (8. 16) Sense-knowledge is (strictly) dependent upon its object, since it is receptive only in regard to what is (really) present before it. And since the (real) object is a cause confining the reflex (to itself), (the corresponding cognition) refers to a (strictly) limited reflex, (to something unique) which therefore is not capable of coalescing with a word.

(8. 18) (This equally applies to every particular sound of the speech). Although we admit that a (particular sound) can have a meaning,[5] we nevertheless, just for the reasons (stated above), maintain such non-constructiveness[6] of the particular,[7] (the absolutely unique sound). Indeed although the strictly particular (sound) can be significative, nevertheless the cognition of an object associated with such verbal expression is a (synthetic) construction.

(8. 20) (Objection). Now, a sensation,[8] since it is a reflex strictly limited (to a unique particular) object, cannot produce a reflex capable

---

[1] *pratyavamṛśati* = *pratyabhijānāti* = *ekīkaroti.*

[2] Here again *vijñāna* is used contrary to its meaning in Abhidharma, it refers to a judgment, «*sa evāyam*» *ity anena vikalpasya avasthā ucyate*, cp. Ṭipp., 23. 4—5. The abhidharmic sense is then expressed by the compound *indriya-vijñāna*, cp. p. 8. 16 and 8. 20.

[3] *prātibhāsa* = *pratibimba* «reflex», «as in a mirror» (*ādarśavat*), as appears from this passage, can be either simple and direct (*niyata*) or indirect and conditioned (*aniyata*). Its counter part is *niścaya* = *adhyavasāya*. Dharmakīrti says — *pratyakṣam* — *gṛhṇāti na niścayena, kin tarhi tat-pratibhāsena*, cp. Anekāntaj., p. 177. Inference has also a *sva-pratibhāsa*, cp. text p. 7. 13 and *vikalpa* can be *avastu-nirbhāsa*, cp. N. kaṇikā, p. 124.

[4] Lit., p. 8. 15-16. «And the independent, since there is no cause limiting the reflex, possesses no limited reflex».

[5] *vācya-vācaka-bhāva.*

[6] *avikalpakatva.*

[7] *svalakṣaṇa.*

[8] *indriya-vijñāna.*

of being associated with a word, it is non-constructive. But an auditive sensation[1] apprehends a strictly particular sound. This strictly particular sound (has a double character), on the one side it is a sound, on the other it can have a meaning. It follows that the strictly particular (sensation of a) sound corresponds to a mental reflex which is capable of coalescing with a word, and (there you are!), it is a construction![2]

(8.23) (Answer). The objection is not founded! It is true that the strictly particular sound may have this (double character) of a sound and a meaning, (and that meaning involves synthesis), nevertheless it is really apprehended in this double aspect (not as a present fact, but) as something which was experienced at the time of the formation of language[3], (when sounds at first received their conventional meaning). (8.24) The fact that an entity has been experienced at that time (is bygone and) does not exist at present. And just as that experience[4] has now vanished, just so is it impossible for a present object to be apprehended by past experience.[5] Hence an auditive sensation cannot

---

1 We would expect, p. 8. 21, *śrotra-vijñāna*, cp. Tib., p. 20. 5, *rna-bai rnam-par-šes-pa.*

2 These remarks are directed against Vinītadeva. He has explained, p 41. 6, that the words «a mental reflex capable of coalescing with a word» refer to the fact that the general aspect of an object can coalesce with a general term, because there is between these two generalities an invariable connection (*anvaya-vyatireka*). There can be none between particulars. The particular must here be taken in the Buddhist sense as the absolute particular, the unique (*kṣaṇa-svalakṣaṇa*). The point-instant cannot coalesce with a word, cannot be named, (p. 41. 8) *arthasya viśeṣaḥ, svarūpasya (sva)-lakṣaṇasya rūpam, abhilāpayitum na śakyate* (read *mi-nus-te* instead of *bzhus te*). Neither can any particular sound or word have a meaning (ibid., p. 41. 15., = *śabda-viśeṣeṇa abhilāpayitum na śakyate*); cp. Tattvasg., p. 378. 7 *na hi svalakṣaṇe saṃketaḥ, nāpi śabda-sva-lakṣaṇe, ...* .... *aśakya-samayo nīlādīnām ātmā*. But the contention that «the *particular* word can have no meaning» has given Dharmottara an opportunity for criticism. He insists that a particular word can have a meaning, not the momentary sound by itself, but its traditional associations which may reach back to the time of the formation of language. No doubt Vinītadeva means the same and Dharmottara's criticism is unfair. The Ṭipp. remarks, p. 23. 15-16, *paramārthataḥ sāmānyayor eva vācya-vācakatvam, nārtha-śabda-viśeṣasya.* If such particulars would be named we would have a so called *atiprasanga*, an «over-absurdity», we could name the cow a horse and *vice versa*, because the underlying point-instants, the *svalakṣaṇas* are undistinguishable. Cp. also above p. 19 n. 4. In his introduction to Santānāntara-siddhi-ṭīkā Vinītadeva gives expression to similar ideas.

3 *saṃketa-kāla.*

4 *darśana.*

5 Lit., p. 9. 1. «Indeed just as perception existing at the time of name-giving is now extinct, just so there is to-day also no «its objectivity» of the thing».

directly grasp the sound and the meaning, because it cannot apprehend (now) what has been experienced a long time ago.

(9. 2) The same kind of argument must be applied to the (exceptional) sagacity of the Yogis. The meaning of all words is present to them, (they know it directly). It is not synthetic knowledge however, it does not grasp former experiences which happened at the time of the formation of language. (9. 4).

6. Knowledge exempt from such (construction), when it is not affected by an illusion produced by colour-blindness, rapid motion, travelling on board a ship, sickness or other causes, is perceptive (right) knowledge.

(9. 6). Knowledge which is free from constructiveness, i. e., contains (an element that is not) an arrangement (or judgment), if it is (at the same time not illusive, is perceptive knowledge—this is how the sentence should be connected with what follows, because absence of construction and absence of illusion constitute the definition of perception taken together and not separately. In order to point out this, it is said that knowledge which is free from construction, if at the same time it does not produce an illusion, is perceptive knowledge. Thus it is shown that both these characteristics combined with one another determine the essence of perception.

(9. 9). Colour-blindness is an eye-disease. This is a cause of illusion located in the organ of sense. Rapid movement (calls forth an illusion) as, e. g., when we rapidly swing a firebrand, (we have the illusion of a fiery circle). If we swing the firebrand slowly, we do not have it. Therefore the swinging is qualified by the word «rapid». This is a cause of delusion which is located in the object of perception. (9. 11). Travelling by ship (produces illusion as, e. g.), when the ship is moving, a person standing (on the deck) has the illusion of moving trees on the shore. The word «travelling» points to this circumstance. Here illusion depends on the place where one is situated. (9. 13). Disease is the disturbance (of one of the three humours of the body, i. e.,) the gaseous, the bilious and the phlegmy.[1] When the gaseous principle in the body is disturbed, deceitful images like that of a flaming post arise.[2] This is

[1] These three humours do not represent exactly air, bile and phlegm, but three very subtle principles conventionally so called, whose equipoise is equivalent to health, whose disturbed equipoise is equivalent to sickness.

[2] All psychical diseases are attributed to an abnormal condition of the gaseous principle.

an internal cause of illusion. (9.14). But each of these causes, whether they be located in the organ or in the object, whether external or internal, invariably affect the organ of sense, because when the organ of sense is normal[1] there can be no illusive sensation.[2] All these causes of disease, down to the internal one, are but an exemplification of the possible causes. (9.16). The words «and other causes» are added in order to include such organic diseases as the disturbance of vision by jaundice, such objective causes as a rapid movement to and frow. When, e. g., the firebrand is seen rapidly moving to and fro, we have the illusion of a fiery-coloured stick. Such external causes as riding on an elephant and such internal ones as the effect of strong blows on vulnerable parts of the body are also included. Cognition when it is free from illusion called forth by these causes is perceptive knowledge.[3]

§ 5. The varieties of direct knowledge.

(9.20). After having thus given the definition (of direct knowledge the author now) proceeds to point out its different varieties, in order to refute the divergent opinions of those who maintain that there is no other direct knowledge but sense-perception, of those who find fault with our definition of mental sensation, and of those who admit neither selfconsciousness nor the transcendental intuition of the Buddhist Saint. He says,

7. It is fourfold.

(10.2). There are four varieties of direct knowledge.

---

1 *avikṛta.*

2 *indriya-bhrānti.* It follows from this expression, if it is not a metaphorical one, that illusions are partly to be put on the account of the senses, and partly on the account of the interpretation of sense-data by the reason, cp. above, p. 19 n.

3 Vinītadeva, p. 43. 9, calls attention to the fact that the word «knowledge» (*jñāna*) is absent in sūtra I. 4, where the definition of perception is given, but it appears here, in sūtra I. 6. It seems as though some opponents had objected to an absolutely pure sense-perception without the slightest admixture of the combining intellect and maintained that it would not even represent knowledge, since the senses are by themselves unconscious, *ajñāna-svabhāvam... pratyakṣam*, cp. Tattvasg., p. 366. 21. Vinītadeva, p. 43. 10 ff., and Kamalašīla, p. 367. 1 ff., therefore maintain (in supporting their view by the same example) that *jñāna* must be understood in the definition implicitly. This apparently is approved by Dh., cp. Ṭipp., p. 26. 6 (read *bhrānter*). Dharmakīrti's addition of the word *abhrānta* has given rise to a great deal of disagreement among all commentators. He himself here explains it as including not only hallucinations, but every kind of illusive perception. Dignāga includes all empirical knowledge (*samvṛti*), as well as all inference into his *pratyakṣābhāsa*, cp. Pr. samucc, I. 8. The term *pramāṇa* is thus used either in a direct or in an indirect sense. Real *pramāṇa* is only the pure *pratyakṣa*.

8. Sense knowledge (sensation).

(10. 4). Cognition, as far as it depends (on the activity) of the senses (alone), is sensation.

(10. 5). In order to answer the criticism raised against the theory of mental sensation the author proceeds to give its definition.

9. Mental sensation follows (the first moment of every) sense-cognition (which is thus) its immediately preceding homogeneous cause. (The latter) is cooperating with (the corresponding moment of) the object, (i. e., with that momentary object) which immediately follows the proper (momentary) object (of sensation).

(10. 8). The proper object of sense-knowledge (is the object in the moment corresponding to sensation). The following object is the object which is not different, (is quite similar to it). Difference here means interval in time as well as difference in quality. (10. 9). Thus, (every) difference (between the two momentary objects) is denied. The quite similar second moment following upon the moment when the object has produced sensation and supported (by the preceding one) is here alluded to.[1] (10. 10). This being the case, (it is clear) that the next following moment of the object, after the moment corresponding to sensation, a member of the same compact series of moments, is here meant. This (second moment) is here said to cooperate with sensation. (10. 11). Cooperation (or causation) can have two different meanings. It can mean either a real mutual influence of (one fact upon the other), or (the compresence of two facts followed by another fact called their) one result. (10. 12). Since we are here (on Buddhist ground) all reality is reduced to momentary (sense-data). A momentary reality can not possibly have an increment (as a result), therefore cooperation (is to be taken in the second sense), as one resulting fact (following upon preceding two facts). (10. 13). Because the object and the sensation (first produced by it) are together producing (i. e., are only followed by) one mental sensation, therefore there is no mutual (real) influence between them.[2]

[1] Lit., p. 10. 9-10. «Therefore when difference is excluded, the supported (*upādeya*) moment of the object of sensation (*indriya-vijñāna*) which exists in the second moment (and) is homogeneous, is taken».

[2] Buddhist philosophy has gone deeper into the analysis of the idea of Causality than perhaps any other philosophy has done. The literature devoted to that subject is very extensive. Some details will be found in my Nirvāṇa, p. 39 ff. and

(10.14). A similar (correlation exists between the sensations of ordinary men and those of the Yogi who is supposed to be capable of apprehending them directly. But in that case a foreign) sensation is the objective fact followed by the Yogi's perception of it.[1] In order to distinguish this (analogous case of correlation between a sensation and the following moment of consciousness) the words «immediate» and «homogeneous» have been inserted. It is homogeneous as a mental content, and it is immediate, since there is no interval between them, and it is a cause, since it is followed by it. Thus it is an immediately preceding (moment in the same chain of momentary entities). Upon it (a mental sensation follows, i. e.), springs up. (10.16). Thus it is being expressed that the outer sense and the inner sense represent (two succeeding moments), two parts of the same compact series (of one stream of thought, and in this sense) mental (or internal) sensation is a species of direct knowledge. Thus the intuition of the Yogi is discriminated, since it is part of another stream (of thought, different from the stream to which the sensation he is able to divine belongs).

(10.18). (Two objections have been raised against this theory of a mental sensation, 1) it is a repeated cognition of the same object and is no new cognition at all, and 2) if it is a real cognition of an external object, then the blind and the deaf would be able to apprehend colour and sound through mental sensation). But since the object of the inner sense differs from the object of the outer sense, (the reproach of repetition, i. e.), of not being a cognition because of apprehending what has been already apprehended by the outer senses, is ill-founded. (10.19). On the other hand, since the moment of grasping by the outer sense is underlying the moment of grasping by the inner

---

164 ff. and Index 6, s. v. Causality. The main point is here very well expressed. There is no question, in the Buddhist outlook, of one entity really *producing* or *influencing* another out of itself or with the help of other forces, but there is a *coordination* between moments following one another in an uninterrupted flow of a stream of becoming events. There is no duration, no stabilized entities which could have the time to produce one another. This is the real general import of *pratītya-samutpāda* as contrasted with *adhītya-samutpāda* and other theories.

[1] Lit., p. 10.14. «By such sensation, when it becomes an objective condition, a direct perception of the Yogi (can) be produced», i. e., the Yogi owing to his extraordinary gift of divination may guess what the sensations of another man are, but the relation of the guessed sensations to his intuition will not be that of *samanantara-pratyaya* towards its *phala*, but that of an *ālambana-pratyaya*. In an irreproachable *(kṣoda-kṣama)* scientific definition even such subtle faults against precision must be foreseen in order to make it secure against all cavil.

sense (both are inseparable). The deduction *ad absurdum*, that namely the blind and the deaf would not exist, if the inner sense could apprehend a special object, (a moment of it) not apprehended by the outer sense — this deduction is thereby refuted.[1]

(10.21). Now we contend that such internal sensation is (a kind of) direct cognitive process (in the presumption that) the efficiency of the outer sense is extinct (in one moment). The (indefinite) sensation of colour which we have at (the moment) when the sense of vision is efficient is entirely and exclusively sense-cognition. (10. 22). Otherwise (if both these sensations, by the outer sense and by the inner sense, were simultaneous), we would have no (pure sensation at all), no sensation at all depending (e. g.) upon the organ of sight exclusively.[2]

(11. 1). This internal sensation is a postulate of our system. There are no facts to prove it (directly). But there is no contradiction in admitting it, if it were of the described kind. In this sense its definition has been given.[3]

(11. 3). Self-consciousness is next being defined.

---

1 Lit., p. 10. 18—21. «And since the object of mental sensation (*mano-vijñānasya*) is different from the object of sensation proper (*indriya-jñāna* corresponding to the abhidharmic *vijñāna*), therefore the fault of non-validity, imputed (*āsañjita*) because of cognizing the cognized, is discarded. And since the moment is taken which has a substratum in the object of sensation, therefore the deduction of the fault (*doṣa-prasanga*) of the absence of the blind and the deaf is discarded, because it cognizes another object which has not been cognized by sensation».

2 Since the second moment would be likewise *indriya-vijñāna* it will not be possible to distinguish between *indriya-vijñāna* and *mano-vijñāna*, cp. Ṭipp., p. 30. 3-5. «If the organ of sight will operate, why indeed should the (same) sensation not arise in the second moment, it is the same, provided it will make the object present (*yogya-karaṇe* = *sākṣātkāriṇi*). Therefore how is it that both will not be called sensations (of the outer sense)?» Cp. also Tātp., p. 111. 2.

3 The *siddhānta* mentioned p. 11. 1 can include the *āgama* quoted in the Ṭipp, p. 26. 10, where Buddha declares that colour is apprehended in two ways, by the sense of vision and by the internal sense evoked by the external one. Dh. deems it a sufficient proof and no other proofs are needed. The remark is directed against Jñānagarbha and his followers who devised a formal argument in favour of the existence of such a thing as mental sensation. Since sensation and mental construction are, in this system, two quite heterogeneous sources of knowledge, something intermediate must be found which would be sensuous on one side and mental on the other, in order to account for a knowledge which combines sense-data with mental constructions. Thus the existence of an internal sense is proved by the existence of a subsequent mental construction (*nīla-mano-vijñānāt samāna-jātīya-nīla-vikalpa-udayāt*). Dharmottara rejects the argument, as the Ṭipp., p. 30, assumes, because he admits the possibility of a result being pro-

10. Every consciousness and every mental phenomenon are self-conscious.

(11.5). Consciousness simply apprehends (the presence) of an object. Mental phenomena apprehend special states of consciousness, such as pleasure etc.[1] It is (emphasized) that every (flash of) consciousness and every special state of it are self-conscious. Indeed pleasure etc. are being clearly experienced and therefore are present to the mind. (Self-consciousness) is not itself a (special) mental phenomenon differing from all others. In order to remove this supposition the word «every» has been inserted into the definition.[2] (11.7). There is no mental phenomenon whatsoever it may be which could be unconscious of its own existence. (This feeling of its own existence, is) immediate (direct) cognition.[3] (11.8). For, indeed, (we feel our own existence in some way or other, and) this aspect of our knowledge, which represents a feeling of its own existence, is direct knowledge.[4] (11.9). According to our (system when an external) reality, such as (a patch) of colour, is apprehended, we at the same time feel some-

---

duced from a heterogeneous cause. But then the hypothesis becomes useless. Dharmottara seems to say «let it be useless, but it involves no contradiction». It is evidently not what was meant by Dignāga. Dh. is again misled by his polemical fervour. The position regarding *mano-vijñāna* or *mano-vijñāna-dhātu*, the *dhātu* № 18, is quite different, cp. my Central Conception, p. 17. After having established a radical distinction between the parts of the senses and of the intellect in cognition, Dignāga was evidently in want of something which would be partly sensuous and partly mental. He thus established his «mental sensation». A similar course, as is well known, has been taken in European philosophy. Some particulars about this exceedingly interesting theory of a mental sensation as well as translations from Vācaspati and the Ṭipp. will be given in an Appendix.

[1] Not aloue feelings are here meant, but all other mental phenomena, all *caitasika-dharmas*, ideas, volitions, passions, etc.

[2] According to the Abhidharma consciousness (*cittam* = *manaḥ* = *vijñāna* = *mana-āyatana* = *mano-dhātu*) is imagined as a separate element of pure consciousness which accompanies every cognition, cp. my Central Conception p. 16.

[3] Lit., p. 11.7—8. «There is whatsoever no condition of consciousness in which the cognition of its own self is not immediate».

[4] Lit., p. 11.8. «Indeed in what form the Self is felt in that form the feeling of the Self is immediate (*pratyakṣa*)». This remark is directed against the Indian realists, the Naiyāyikas and the Mīmāṃsakas who imagined in self-perception a real relation of cognizing mind towards a cognized Self. According to the Sautrāntikas and Yogācāras this relation does not exist in reality. Our knowledge is self-luminous (*svayam-prakāśa*) like the light of a lamp that does not want another light in order to be illuminated. The Vaibhāṣikas and Mādhyamikas did not agree in this doctrine.

thing (internally) in the shape of well-being or (some other emotion) which is a thing different (from the patch of colour). It is not possible to maintain that a patch of, e. g., blue colour is felt as being itself the pleasure (it affords us), because the verdict of our intellect does not support (the judgment) «this patch of blue colour has itself the form of pleasure.» (11. 11). If it were the case, if we were satisfied that blue and pleasure are felt as equivalents, then we could maintain such identity.[1] (11. 12). (We call) cognized directly that aspect of (the object) regarding which the function of direct perception, i. e., the mere pointing out of its presence, is followed by the construction (of the corresponding image). But (we cannot maintain that the sensation produced by a patch) of blue is followed by an image (not of blue, but of) pleasure. (11. 13). Therefore we really are experiencing pleasure as something quite different from the object blue, as something which is not equivalent to blue, and this is, no doubt, knowledge. Therefore we do experience our own knowledge. Selfconsiousness is essentially a case of knowledge, it makes present to us our own Self. It is not a construction, it is not an illusion, and therefore it is direct knowledge.

(11. 16). The intuition of (the Buddhist Saint), the Yogi, is next explained.

11. The (mystic) intuition of the Saint (the Yogi) is produced from the subculminational state of deep meditation on transcendental reality.[2]

---

1 These remarks are directed against the Sānkhya theory which assumes that pleasure and pain are something external, inherent in the objects which produce pleasure and pain. Cp. Ṭipp., p. 32. 10.

2 This is a kind of perception which is entirely mental, not at all sensuous. It can be, to a certain degree, assimilated to sense-perception because of the vividness with which the contemplated picture presents itself to the imagination. In a system which assimilates all representations, even the perceptive presentations, to dreams, the difference between a dream and a perception consists mainly in the vividness (*sphuṭābhatva*) of the latter. A new characteristic of perception is therefore introduced, the vividness of the mental image. The two former characteristics of «non-constructive» and «non-illusive», and the general characteristic of «not contradicted by experience» (*avisaṃvādi*) may be interpreted so as to cover this kind of perception, but not without some difficulty. Mystic intuition (*yogi-pratyakṣa*) is that faculty of the Buddhist Saint (*ārya*) by which he is capable completely to change all ordinary habits of thought and contemplate directly, in a vivid image, that condition of the Universe which has been established by the abstract constructions of the philosopher. The Buddhist Saint is a man who, in addition to his moral perfections, is capable of contemplating the Universe ***sub specie***

(11.18). Reality is something really existing, (i. e., transcendental reality). Such reality is elicited (by the philosopher) after logical criticism, e. g., the Four Truths of the Buddhist Saint.[1] The contemplation of transcendental reality means its repeated forcing into consciousness. The culminating point of such contemplation means the point when our mind, containing the image of the contemplated object, begins to reach a condition of clarity (as though the fact were present before the meditator). (11.20). The adjoining (stage is that stage) when the clarity is as yet not quite complete. Indeed, as long as the clarity of the image is not quite complete, progress is going on, when it is complete progress ceases. Thus, what is called a condition nearly culminational is that degree of clarity which precedes complete vividness. (11.23). (A state of mind) which is brought about by this underculminational point, a knowledge apprehending with absolute vividness the contemplated (image), as though it were actually present before the meditator, this is the Saint's direct perception.

(12.1). There are indeed here (three degrees of transic absorbtion, the first) is that when the image begins to be clear, contemplation is in progress; the (second) is the subculminational degree, when (the Saint) contemplates the (ideal) reality as though it were veiled by a thin cloud; in (the third) the object is perceived just as clearly as though it were a small grain on the palm of one's hand — this latter is the Saint's direct knowledge.[2] (12.3). It has indeed the

aeternitatis. Cp. my Nirvāṇa, p. 16 ff. The Mīmāṃsakas deny the existence of *yogis* and of mystic intuition altogether, cp Ṭipp., 25.5, where correct *na santi* instead of *na samprati*.

[1] About the Four Truths cp. my Nirvāṇa p. 16 and 55. Their Mahāyānistic interpretation is here alluded to. They then are the equivalent of the «two truths», the empirical and the absolute, the latter is the *bhūtārtha=yan-dag-pai don*, i. e., the real condition of things, or transcendental reality, so as it has been established by the philosopher (*pramāṇena viniścita*), it is *kṣaṇikatvādi-grāhi mano vijñānam* (Ṭipp., p. 33.9), *kṣaṇi katva* is contemplated also by the Hīnayānistic Saint, the Arhat. The Bodhisattva contemplates *śūnyatā* either in its idealistic (Yogācāra) or in its relativistic (Mādhyamika) interpretation. But the abstract form of these philosophic constructions (*alīkākāram vācya-vācaka-rūpam*) then vanishes and remains a kind of direct vivid consciousness (*niyam vitti-rūpam*), cp. Ṭipp., p. 34.7.

[2] According to Vinītadeva, p. 47, the *bhāvanā-prakarṣa* comprises 4 degrees, *smṛty-upasthāna, uṣmagata, mūrdhan* and *kṣānti*; the *prakarṣa-paryanta* is the same as *laukikāgradharma*. About these so called *nirvedha-bhagīya*-stages and the *smṛty-upasthānas* cp. Abhidh. Kośa, VI. 14 ff. and VI. 20 ff. After that comes the decisive moment, the meditating man suddenly acquires the faculty of transcendental intuition (*yogi-pratyakṣa*), he changes completely, it is another *pudgala*, a Saint, an *ārya*, a *bodhisattva*. All his habits of thought have changed, he has

vividness (of direct perception), and just for this reason it (ceases to be) a construction. (12.3). Constructed (synthetic) knowledge would apprehend the (same) reality in mental images capable of coalescing with words, (indirectly including) experiences (which go back to the time) of the formation of language. An experience (which reaches back to the time) of the formation of language means that its object has been apprehended by some knowledge produced at that time. (12.5). But just as a cognition that has happened a long time ago is gone and does not exist any more at present, just so is it impossible for an entity to be apprehended by past knowledge at the present moment. (12.6). This (synthetic knowledge) apprehends something that does not really exist, and since it does not apprehend its object as something present before the observer, it lacks the vividness (of direct perception) without which it remains a construction. But when this vividness is reached it becomes non-constructed (direct, non-synthetic knowledge). (12.8). Moreover it is not contradicted by experience, since (the object of meditation) which is being apprehended represents the «pure» object (the point-instants of efficiency that are elicited) by

---

acquired the habit of realizing the Relativity (*śūnyatā*) and unreality of the phenomenal veil (*saṃvṛti*) concealing absolute Reality (*paramārtha* = *bhūtārtha*). He enters the Mahāyānistic *dṛṣṭi-mārga* and the first of the ten Mahāyānistic stages (*bhūmi*), the stage called *pramuditā*. At the same time he becomes filled with overwhelming devotion to the Salvation of all living beings (*mahā-kāruṇā*). Cp. Mādhy. avatāra, I. 4 ff. He then understands the «Four Truths of the Saint» in their Mahāyānistic interpretation as a formula intended to suggest the equipollency of Saṃsāra and Nirvāṇa in a monistic Universe. This intuition is a transcendental (*lokottara*) capacity, it is not, like Spinoza's *intuitus*, supposed to be rational. *Yogi-pratyakṣa* is not a *pramāṇa* in the sense indicated above, p. 8 n. 2. It is an intuition of a condition uncognizable by logical methods (*aprameya-vastūnām aviparīta-dṛṣṭiḥ*) However, according to the school of Yogācāra Logicians, it is a *pramāṇa* indirectly, because the relativity of all our conceptions (*vikalpa*) or judgments (*kalpanā*), as well as the non-relative, absolute (*paramārtha*) character of the uncognizable «thing in itself» (*svalakṣaṇa*) is established by logical analysis. Logic destroys the naive realism of a pluralistic universe. The underlying Unity *sāṃvṛtā śūnyatā*) is uncharacterizable (*anirvacanīya*) according to the Relativists (*śūnya-vādin*), it is pure, undifferentiated consciousness (*śūnyatā* = *vijñāna-mātram grāhya-grāhaka-nirmuktam*) according to the Idealists (*vijñāna-vādin*). Cp. the controversy between the Logicians and the Relativists in my Nirvāṇa, p. 140 ff. Cp. also the masterly exposition of the *Naiyāyika-abhimata-yogi-pratyakṣa* in Tātp., p. 49. 17 ff. and N. Kaṇikā, p. 147. 4 ff. According to Santānāntaras. (concl.) the supreme Yogi, i. e., the Buddha alone possibly intuits the undifferentiated Absolute, the ordinary Yogins can intuit only its subject-object aspect, cp. *infra* p. 34 n. 4. Cp. analogous ideas of Kant on impossibity of «intellectuelle Anschauung», Kritik,[2] pp. 72, 149, 308.

logical (analysis).[1] Hence it is direct knowledge, just as (sensation) and other varieties of direct cognition are. Yoga is ecstatic (direct) contemplation. The man who possesses this faculty is a Saint.[2]

(12.9). So much is to be said about the different varieties of direct knowledge.

§ 6. The object of direct knowledge.

(12.11). Having done with the exposition of the varieties of direct knowledge which (includes) no construction and no illusion, (the author) proceeds to clear away the misconceptions concerning its object and says,

12. Its object is the (extreme) particular.

(12.14). Its object, i. e., the object of the fourfold direct knowledge, must be conceived as being the particular. The particular means an entity or an essence which is unique, which is shared by nothing else (which is the thing in itself).[3]

---

[1] *pramāṇa-šuddha-artha-grāhi* either means *pramāṇena šuddham artham gṛhṇāti* or *šuddhārtham pramāṇena gṛhṇāti*. The first would mean *pramāṇena šuddham* = *pramāṇena vinišcitam, artham* = *bhūtārtham, gṛhṇāti*. The second — *šuddhārtham* = *svalakṣaṇam* = *artha-kriyā-kāri-kṣaṇam pramāṇena gṛhṇāti*. The Ṭipp., p. 35.1, seems to favour the second interpretation, on p. 24.5 and 24.9 it uses the word *šuddha* in a similar way. The expressions *šuddhā kalpanā, šuddham pratyakṣam, šuddhārthaḥ* remind us of Kant's terminology of «reine Vernunft», «reine Sinnlichkeit», «reines Object». The definition of right knowledge as knowledge «not contradicted by experience» (*avisaṃvādı*), which sounds so empirical, is here, in mystic intuition, interpreted as referring to the transcendental object.

[2] Vinītadeva, p. 48—49, reckons likewise as *yogi-pratyakṣa* the various gifts of supernatural divination and prophesy with which the Yogis are credited. Dh.'s comment contains here not a single word about them.

[3] The peculiarity of Dignāga's doctrine about the particular and the general consists in its conception of the particular as the unique. The existence in every direct cognition of «something *unique* by being present to me in perception» is also pointed out by Bosanquet, Logic, I. 76. Here it assnmes the rôle of the «thing in itself», it is the absolute particular, the limit of all synthetic construction. It represents a single moment (*kṣaṇa*), it has no extension in space (*deša-ananugata*), no duration in time (*kāla-ananugata*), it is similar to nothing (*sarvato-vyāvṛtta*), it is unique (*trailokya-vyāvṛtta*), cp. Tātparyaṭ. p. 12. 20. It is a transcendental reality, since it cannot be realized in a definıte representation (*jñānena prāpayitum ašakyatvāt*). Cognized are only generalitieɾ or similarities, relations, coordinations, by a synthesis of moments (*pūrvāpara-kṣaṇānām abheda-adhyavasāyāt*). It is the absolute reality, the «thing in itself» which nnderlies every efficient empirical reality (*dāhādy-artha-kriyā*). Dignāga has established

(12. 15). (Every) reality, indeed, has its real essence which is the particular (the unique) and a general (imagined aspect). That which is apprehended in direct perception is the unique. The object of cognition is really double, the *prima facie* apprehended and the definitely realized. (The first is) that aspect which appears directly (in the first moment).[1] (The second is the form which is constructed in a perceptive) judgment.[2] (12. 17). The directly perceived and the distinctly conceived are indeed two different things. What is immediately apprehended in sensation[3] is only one moment. What is distinctly conceived is always a compact chain of moments cognized in a construction[4] on the basis of sensation, (e. g., «this is blue»). And just this constructed synthesis of a chain of moments is (finally) realized by direct perception, because a unique moment can never be realized in a definite cognition. (12. 19). (The opposite course is taken by) indirect knowledge (inference). An unreality appears in it to the mind, and its course consists in distinctly cognizing an unreality as (a kind of) reality.[5] It apprehends (*prima facie*) an unreality. But this imagined object, which is apprehended (by inference), is definitely referred to an (imagined) particular. (12. 21). Thus it is that constructed particulars are the proper province of inference, but its immediate object is an unreality. (12. 22). Consequently when the author makes the statement that the object of direct knowledge is the particular, he means the immediate (*prima facie*) object (i. e., one moment, the unique).[6]

(12. 23). Further, how can we recognize (the presence of such a momentary) object of knowledge which is the particular?

---

this point of absolute reality against the Mādhyamikas who maintained a Universal Relativity (*śūnyatā*) of knowledge, and tried to prove that even this «thing in itself» was relative, cp. the interesting controversy about the relativity of the «thing in itself» between Candrakīrti and Dignāga in the Mādhy. vṛtti, translated in my Nirvāṇa, p. 149 ff. Cp. Ṭipp., p. 35 and Bradley, Princ.,[2] p. 647 ff.

1 *yadākāram* is an *avyayībhāva* = *yasya ākāram anatikrāmya.*

2 *yam adhyavasyati.* 3 *pratyakṣasya.*

4 *niścayena* = *kalpanayā* = *vikalpena* = *adhyavasāyena*, cp. Tātp., p. 87. 25.

5 For the lit. rendering cp. p. 17 n. 6 (text, p. 7. 13).

6 Dharmakīrti evidently uses the term «thing in itself» (*svalakṣaṇa*) in more than one sense. The same, as is well known, has happened in European philosophy. It means, 1) existence absolutely indefinite, not even differentiated into subject and object, it is then *grāhya-grāhaka-kalpanā-apoḍha*—it is the Absolute of the Yogācāras, the *śūnyatā* in its idealistic conception (*buddhy-ātmā*), cp. my Nirvāṇa, p. 146 ff., the verses quoted in Sarvad., p. 16.7 ff. (B. I.) and the concluding passage of Sāntānāntara-siddhi; 2) the *extreme* concrete and parti-

13. When the mental image varies according as the object is near or remote, the object then is the particular.

(13.2). The term «object» means object of cognition, i. e., an object which is being cognized. «Near» means localized in a near place, «remote» — localized in a remote place.[1] (13.3). According as the object is near or remote, it produces a different mental image, a different form of the directly cognized (first moment), making it either vivid or dim.[2] (13.4). When an object of cognition produces a vivid (flash) of consciousness, if it is near, and a dim one, if it is, although remote, but still amenable to the senses, it is a particular. (13.6). Indeed, all (external) reality is vividly experienced when near, and dimly apprehended at a distance. This is (an indication of the presence of) a particular.

---

cular, the *Hoc Aliquid*=*kiṃcid idam*, the pure *ālambana*, existence localized in time-space (*kṣaṇa*), the limit of all mental constructions (*nāma-jātyādi-kalpanā-apoḍha*, but not *grāhya-grāhaka-kalpanā-apoḍha*), the point-instant of efficiency capable of affecting our sensibility (*artha-kriyā-samartha*); it then already contains what Kant would have called the *a priori* forms ot our sensibility, the possibility of coordination (*sārūpya*), if not already some rndimentary coordination; snch is the meaning here and on this score it is sometimes supposed (Ṭipp., p. 19.10) that Dignāga's school was partly Sautrāntika; 3) (metaphorically) every concrete and particular (= *vyakti*) object, since its substratum is the thing in itself.

[1] Vinītadeva has explained *sannidhāna* as presence in the ken and *asannidhana* as total absence, p. 50.1, *thams-cad-kyi thams-cad-du med-pa*, cp. Ṭipp., p. 36. 9—10. The sūtra would then refer to the presence or absence of an object in the ken. This interpretation seems much preferable.

[2] In order to understand this passage we must fully realize that, according to Dh.'s terminology, e. g., a fire, the physical object fire, is a construction, hence it is a generality or an assemblage of generalities. The strictly particular is its underlying substratum (*upādhi*), the efficient point-instant (*artha-kriyā-samartha*). If the same reality could change and produce a clear image in one case, and a dim one in another, it would not be uuique (*rūpa-dvayam syāt*). The author of the Ṭipp., p. 36. 14 ff., asks, «But is it not a generality that, being perceived at a distance, appears in a dim image? it is not the particular (point-instant)». And he answers that a generality by itself is something unreal, it does not exist in the sense of being efficient, efficiency always belongs to a point-instant of efficiency. And further, p. 37.3 ff., «The clear or dim image of the blue patch is not transcendentally real (*vastu* = *paramārthasat*), but that blue which represents the atom, (the underlying point-instant) which is capable of being efficient (is the real object); the clear and dim images are produced by the underlying substratum. . . ., the real object (*arthasya* = *paramārthasataḥ*) appears as clear or dim not by itself (*paramārthataḥ*), but (indirectly) through the clearness or the dimness of the image (*jñānasya*); an

(13.8). Further, why is the particular the exclusive object of sense-perception?[1] Indeed, do we not realize in distinct thought a fire (when its presence is indirectly inferred from smoke), as something capable of being experienced, (as a permanent possibility of sensation)?

14. That alone (which is unique) represents ultimate reality.

(13.11). Ultimately real means something not constructed, not imagined. What so exists is the ultimately real. That object alone (which contains no construction), which produces an impression sharp or dim, according as it is near or remote, is the only real. Since it is just that thing which is the object (producing) direct perception, therefore the particular, (i. e., the unique moment, the thing in itself) is the exclusive object of sense-perception.

(13.14). Why again is this (absolute particular, the non-constructed point-instant) alone the ultimate reality?

15. Because the essence of reality is just[2] efficiency.

(13.16). What is aimed at is the object. It is either something to be avoided or something to be attained. The first repels, the second attracts. The object, i. e., the aim, has an action, i. e., produces something. The efficiency, i. e., the capacity to produce something, is a force. Just that is the character, or the essence[3] of reality, (viz. to be a centre of forces). The test (of reality) is to be a force producing action (attracting or repelling something). For this reason (the unique,

---

universal (*sāmānyasya*), on the contrary, does not (change) in its image as clear or dim». (Read, p. 37. 5, *jñānam na bhavati*). According to Vinītadeva *asphuṭa* would mean dim in the sense of abstract, imagined, absent.

1 The following words are an answer to an objector who thinks that whatsoever produces a reflex (*pratibhāsa* = *pratibimbana*) in us is real, the universal (*sāmānya*) produces a corresponding reflex, therefore it is also real. It is answered that the efficient point-instant is alone ultimately real, the universal does not possess any separate efficiency of its own. The existence of a reflex is not a proof of reality, because by the influence of the force of transcendental illusion (*avidyā-balāt*) unreal things can evoke a reflex. A mental image does not exactly correspond to any efficient reality, because the image of a universal can be produced without the real existence of the universal (*vināpi sāmānyena*), simply by the force of inherited mental habit (*vāsanā-balāt*), cp. Ṭipp., p. 38. 2—9.

2 Read, p. 13. 15, — *lakṣaṇatvād eva vastunaḥ*. Cp. Hemacandra's Pramāṇa-mīmāṃsā, I. 1. 32—33.

3 *rūpam* = *svarūpam*.

i. e., the point-instant is the only reality). The term «real object»[1] is synonymous with «ultimate reality».

(13.18). The following is meant. We apply the term «ultimately real» to anything (that can be tested) by its force to produce an effect.[2] Such an efficient object (is always localized, it) is either near or remote. Depending on (its localization) it produces different impressions.[3] Therefore such (a localized point) is the ultimately real. (13.20). This indeed is the reason why purposive actions are realized in regard of objects directly perceived, not in regard of objects constructed (by imagination). (13.21). This explains the fact that an imagined object, although we can in thought realize it as something *quasi* visible, is by no means directly perceived, because no purposive action is possible upon (such fancied image). (14.1). A (really) perceived object, on the other hand, produces purposive action. Consequently real is only the particular (i. e., the unique point of efficiency, the thing in itself), not the constructed object (of imagination).[4]

16. Different from it is the universal character (of the object).

(14.4). The object of knowledge which is other than the unique (point), which does not represent the unique point, is its general character. An object, indeed, which is distinctly conceived by synthetic imagination does not produce different impressions when it is (imagined) in a near or in a remote place. (14.6). An imagined fire owes its existence to imagination, and it is imagination that makes it near or remote. When it is imagined, may it be as near or as remote, there is no different impression on the mind in regard of vividness. Therefore it is said to be different from the particular (from the unique). (14.8). The universal character of something is that essence which exists owing to generality, i. e., that essence which belongs equally (to an indefinite number of) points of reality. Indeed, (the fire) existing in imagination refers equally to every possible fire. Therefore it represents the universal essence.

---

1 *vastu.*

2 *artha-kriyā-samartha.*

3 Lit. «reflexes», *jñāna-pratibhāsa.*

4 Although Time, Space and Causality are regarded as constructions, but their underlying efficient point-instants are the ultimate reality, cp. *infra*, p. 69,11 (text). They correspond to the second conception of a «thing in itself», cp. above, p. 34 n.; it is partly different from the Kantian one.

(14.10). (The author) now states that this universal essence can be apprehended by indirect knowledge. He says,

17. It is the province of indirect knowledge (inference).

(14.12). It is the province of indirect knowledge, i. e., it is *prima facie* apprehended[1] (by inference).[2]

For convenience's sake this remark about the object of inference is inserted in the chapter on direct perception, because if it were intended to discuss the general essence as the object of inference in the (second chapter), it would have been necessary to repeat the whole passage in which the essence of the particular is treated.[3]

§ 7. The result of the act of cognizing.

(14.15). After having repudiated misconceptions regarding the object of perception, (the author) proceeds to clear away that wrong theory which assumes a (difference between cognition and its) result.

18. This direct cognition itself is the result of cognizing.

---

1 *grāhya-rūpa*.

2 Lit., p. 14.12. «The pronoun has assumed the gender of the (word denoting) the subject-matter».

3 As the object cognized through inference we must here understand its immediate, *prima facie* object (*grāhya-rūpa*) which is always an imagined (*vikalpita*), unreal (*anartha*) object. When we, e. g., infer the presence of fire from the presence of smoke, we imagine the fire, it is *prima facie* a fire in general. But the second step in this act of cognition will be to imagine it as a real fire, a possible object of purposive action, a possible sense-datum. Thus the particular sense-datum will also be an object cognized ultimately through inference, but indirectly. The result (*pramāṇa-phala*) of both modes of cognition from this point of view is just the same, cp. ch. II.4. Inference is *sārūpya-lakṣaṇam pramāṇam*, text, p. 6.10, but perception is also *sārūpya-pramāṇam*, I. 20. The divergence between the schools about the object of cognition (*viṣaya-vipratipatti*) concerns only this *prima facie* object of each, cp. Ṭipp., p. 36.5—6, *grāhya eva viṣaye sarveṣām vipratipattiḥ*. Since all the exposition is here made with a view to combat divergent opinions (*vipratipatti-nirākaraṇārtham*), therefore, when it is stated that the object cognized through inference is the universal, we must understand only that the first stage in indirect cognition of reality is not that pure sensation (*nirvikalpaka*) which is characteristic in sense-perception. In this there is divergence with the Realists who assume a direct contact (*sannikarṣa*) between the senses and the Universal.

(14.16). Just that direct knowledge which has been described above is the result of the act of cognizing. (There is no difference between the act of perception and the percept).[1]

(14.18). In what sense is it a result?

19. It has the form of a distinct cognition.

(14.20). Distinct cognition means determinate knowledge.[2] When direct knowledge assumes this form it possesses the essence of distinct cognition. This circumstance is the reason why (the result does not differ from the act of cognition). (4.21). The following is meant. Right knowledge is efficient knowledge.[3] The faculty of being efficient (i. e., capable of guiding men's purposive action) is not produced exclusively by its dependence on the presence of some object (i. e., by passive reaction from some object). A sprout, e.g., is invariably connected with a seed, but it is not capable (of cognizing it).[4] Therefore cognition, although produced by some object, (is not a mere reflex), but it necessarily has to accomplish some spontaneous function of absorbing the object, which alone when achieved makes the object distinctly cognized (i. e., assimilated). (15.3). And this is just (what we call) the result of

---

1 It is clear from the whole exposition that the author assumes two different stages in perception, a first indefinite moment of sensation and a following mental construction. Since the second is called forth by the first, it can be called its result. But here the problem is envisaged from another point of view. The Realists consider the act of cognizing as an act of «grasping» the external object by the senses and of conveying its «grasped» form through the intellect to the Soul which alone is self-conscious. For the Buddhists there is no «act» of «grasping», no «grasped» form, no Soul and no adequate external object, but in every idea (*vijñāna*) there is immanent self-consciousness. A distinct idea (*pratīti*) may *by imputation* be regarded, just as the case may be, either as a source, an act, an instrument (*pramāṇa*) or as an object, a content, a result of cognizing (*pramāṇa-phala*). The result of cognizing is cognition, cp. the notes on p. 42, 43, 46, and 49—50. Cp. Ṭipp., p. 39 ff. There is a difference between *chitti* and *chidā* in the act of cutting, there is no difference between *paricchitti* and *jñāna* in the act of cognizing.

2 *pratīti* = *avagama* = *bodha* = *prāpti* = *paricchitti* = *niścaya* = *adhyavasāya* = *kalpanā* = *vikalpa* are all nearly synonyms. Cp. Tātp., p. 37.20, 38.2, 87.25. They all contain an element of *smṛti* or *saṃskāra*.

3 Cp. above, text., p. 3. 5 ff.

4 *aprāpakatvāt*, according to the context, means here *aniścāyakatvāt* = *ajñāpakatvāt*. The example then means that there is an ordinary case of causation between a seed and a sprout, the latter is the result of the former, but in cognition the product *cognizes* the object which is its cause, and this act of cognition is also the result. The author of the Ṭipp., p. 40. 16 ff., suggests another explanation of this example.

right knowledge. When this (result) is reached, knowledge becomes efficient. (But this does not mean that the efficiency-function is something different from knowledge itself). (15. 3). We have indeed stated above [1] that the efficiency function of efficient knowledge is nothing but the fact that it makes manifest the object of possible purposive action. Just the same perceptive knowledge[2] possesses (both) the character of being a distinct cognition of the object and of pointing to (the presence of the object in one's ken). Therefore the result of cognizing is but cognition itself.

(15. 6). But then, if knowledge as a cognizing act [3] is the result of cognition, what indeed is the instrument, (the source) of that act?

20. The source of cognizing consists in coordination (between the constructed image and its real) object.

(15. 8). The fact of coordination,[4] or conformity between cognition and its object, this is (a fact that might be interpreted as a kind of)

---

[1] Text, p. 3. 5 ff., transl., p. 4.

[2] *pratyakṣa* is here used not in the meaning of sensation, but it is comprehensive of definite perception (*savikalpaka*) also.

[3] *pramiti-rūpa.*

[4] There is a coordination of the «thing in itself» with all the elements constituting the superimposed image or Universal. The term *sārūpya* is suggestive of a special theory of Universals. The Buddihsts are neither Realists, nor Conceptualists, but extreme Nominalists *(apoha-vādinaḥ)*. The school of Nyāya-Vaiśeṣika represents in India an extreme Realism, they use the term *sāmānya* and admit the objective reality of classes *(jāti)*, individual forms *(ākṛti)* as well as particular things *(vyakti)*. The Sāṅkhyas deny *sāmānya* and admit *sārūpya*, cp. my Central Conception, p. 56, 57, 64. The Mīmāṃsakas, very characteristically, admit both *sāmānya* and *sārūpya* (= *sādṛśya)*; as two separate *padārthas*, the latter is said to be relative, while the former represents the positive content of general features residing in an individual thing, its «form» *(ākāra)*. The Buddhists of the Sautrāntika and Yogācāra schools likewise admit, but with very important qualifications, the «forms» of our ideas, they are *sākāra-vādinaḥ*. Pure consciousness alone *(vitti-sattā)* could never produce a distinct cognition, because it is not differentiated *(sarvatra-aviśeṣāt)*. But «similarity» *(sārūpya)*, or generality, «entering» into it *(tām āviśat)* is capable of giving it a form *(sārūpyavattvam ghaṭayet)*, i. e., of prodncing a clear and distinct idea. However we cannot, on this score, characterize the Buddhists as Conceptualists. Their Universals are purely negative, or relational *(atad-vyāvṛtti-rūpa)*. Their scope, their content, is always determined by the greater or lesser amount of negations, of contrasts or «coordinations» which they may include. An elephant and a dog, although quite dissimilar, may be united as belonging to the «class» of «non-antelopes». The class «cow» is formed by contrasting it with horse etc. The Universals are relative and therefore unreal, the human mind's imagination. They obtain

a source[1] producing knowledge. For us[2] (Buddhists, when we say that) a cognition has sprung up from an object, this (simply) means that this cognition is a fact which is coordinated to a (momentary) object, as, e. g., the cognition *produced* by a patch of blue colour is *coordinated* to (the substratum of) this blue.

This coordination is described (in other terms) as an idea,[3] or representation[4] (of the object).

(15. 11). But then, is not coordination just the same thing as cognition? In that case, the same cognitive fact would be the source and the resulting (content) of cognition? Howerer, it is impossible that the same entity should be its own cause and its own effect.[5] In what sense then is this fact of coordination an act?

21. Owing to this, a distinct cognition of the object is produced.

(15. 14). «This» means coordination. «Owing to this» means through the influence of the fact of coordination. The distinct cogni-

---

some reality only through a substratum, the efficient focus *(artha-kriyā-kāri)*, the point-instant *(kṣaṇa)*, the «thing in itself» *(svalakṣaṇa)*. A distinct cognition is thus produced from two sources: its coordinations, arranged by the human mind according to its own laws, and au indefinite «thing in itself». The «object-intentness» *(viṣayatā)* of our knowledge does not consist in «grasping» *(grahaṇa)*, but it is the expression of these two facts *(tat-sārūpya-tad-utpattibhyām viṣayatvam)*. Opponents have stigmatized this theory as a «purchase without paying the price *(a-mūlya-dāna-kraya)*», since the supposed reality receives perceptibility *(pratyakṣatām labhate)*, i. e., becomes a clear and distinct perception, but «does not pay any equivalent», i. e., does not impart its «form» to this perception, since it is itself formless. Translating this phrasing into Kantian terminology we could say that the empirical object consists of an uncognizable substratum, the «thing in itself», and a superstructure which our reason imposes upon it according to its own categories of understanding. The best exposition of this theory is by Vācaspati, Nyāyakaṇikā, p. 256 ff., 289 ff., (reprint), he also several times alludes to it in the Tātparyaṭīkā, e. g., p. 102. 14 ff., 269.9 ff., 338 ff. Cp also my Soul Theory, p. 838.

1 *pramāṇa.* 2 *iha.*

3 *ākāra.*

4 *ābhāsa.* This *ābhāsa* = *pratibhāsa* possesses the immanent feature of being *sārūpya-saṃvedana* through which *bodha* = *pratīti* is attained, it can be regarded as *a kind* of *pramāṇa* = *sādhakatama* = *prakṛṣṭa-upakāraka*, cp. Ṭipp., p. 42. 3.

5 In Vinītadeva's *avataraṇa* there is no question of the same entity being its own cause and its own result, he simply asks what will be the process of (definite) perception, if perceptive knowledge is regarded as a result, and answers that the process consists in coordination or in contrasting.

tion of the object means a self-conscious idea[1] of it. Coordination is the cause producing (distinctness). (15.15). Direct cognition[2] of an object in the form of a perceptive judgment[3] is possible, i. e., (the object is really) being cognized, owing to the coordination (of an image with a point of external reality and its contrast[4] with correlative images). (15.16). Indeed, as soon as our awareness[5] (begins to present itself as) an image[6] of something blue, only then can we judge[7] that we have a distinct cognition of it (in the form «this is blue», «it is not non-blue»). It then is (really) cognized.

(15.17). The senses, indeed, and[8] (the object which together) produce (in us an indefinite) sensation[9] are not equal (to the task) of determining it as an awareness of the presence in us of a self-conscious image[10] of something blue. But as soon as we become aware of its similarity with (other) blue (objects and its contrast with everything non-blue), it then can be determined as a self-conscious image of (what is) blue.

(15.18) However, the relation (which is here admitted to exist between coordination) as producing and (cognition) as obtaining (distinctness) is not founded upon a causal relation (as between two things). It would be a contradiction (to assume such a relation in what, in our opinion), is but the same entity. On the other hand, the relation of being determined (as a content) and of determining it (as a process can be assumed to exist in what is essentially but one thing).[11]

---

1 *avabodha* is the term preferred by Mīmāṃsakas, = *adhigama* = *pratīti* = *prāpti* = *adhyavasāya*, cp. N. Kaṇikā, p. 161. 25, 167. 21.

2 *vijñāna* means here *jñāna*, cp. sūtra I. 18, = Tib., p. 35. 4, *šes-pa*.

3 *pratīti* = *adhyavasāya* = *kalpanā*, cp. above, p. 20 n. 6.

4 *sārūpya* = *anya-vyāvṛtti* = *apoha*.

5 *vijñāna* = Tib., p. 35. 6, *rnam-par-šes-pa*, includes the abhidharmic sense of pure sensation.

6 (*nīla*)-*nirbhāsa* = *pratibhāsa* = *ākāra*.

7 *avasīyate*, hence *pratīti* = *adhyavasāya*, *avasīyate* = *pratītam bhavati*.

8 *ādi* refers to *ālambana*, since according to the abhidharma two *pratyayas* produce sensation, *ālambana* and *adhipati* (= *indriya*).

9 *vijñāna* includes here also the abhidharmic sense of pure sensation, the Tib. p. 35. 7 has *šes-pa* instead of *rnam-par-šes-pa*, cp. above, p. 6 n. 3.

10 *saṃvedana* = *sva-saṃvedana*.

11 In this and the following passage we must distinguish, 1) the relation between perceptive knowledge as a mental act (*pramiti-rūpa*) and perception as an instrument (*pramāṇa*) of cognizing through the senses, and 2) the relation between the initial, indefinite moment of sensation (*nirvikalpaka*) produced by the object and the final construction of its image by synthetic thought (*savikalpaka*). The

(15.20). (This depends upon the point of view). If we therefore admit that the same entity has the (double) aspect of being, to a

---

first question should not astonish us, it is something similar to a problem which European psychology has also discussed, the question whether perception shonld be envisaged as a content or as an act or as both, cp. B. Russel against Meinong, Analysis of Mind, p. 16 ff. Just as this author, Dharmakīrti maintains that there is no difference bewteen perception as a mental content and perception as a mental act. It is the same thing, it can be viewed either as a mental content or as a mental act, this depends upon the view-point. When constrasted with other processes, it is a process of coordination. When contrasted with other contents, it is a coordinated content. This evidently refers to the final stage of the synthetic image, and by no means to the initial sensation. The Indian realists, the Mīmāṃsakas and Naiyāyikas, clung to the idea that cognition is an «act of grasping» which must have an instrnment and a separate result, just as the «act of cutting wood» has an instrument — the axe, and a result — the fissure. Cognition and self-consciousness were for them a property produced in the Soul by the outer and the inner senses. This was opposed already by Dignāga who maintained (Pr. samucc., I, 9—10) that, 1) the «act» and its «resulting» content are two different aspects of the same cognition; 2) the «result» is also *(yañ-na)* a self-conscious image *(rañ-rig = sva-saṃvedana = anuvyavasāya)*. Self-consciousness is not the property of a Soul which does not exist altogether, but it is inherent in every image, whatsoever it may be. That such is the meaning of the much discussed Buddhist theory about cognition as containing in itself its own result is very clearly stated above by Dh. himself, cp. p. 5 (transl.). Perception is here taken in its final form, as a unity, not as a consecution of moments, *anākalita-kṣaṇa-bheda* (cp. Nyāya-kandalī, p. 191. 3). That the momentary aspect of existence must be very often left out of account when considering Buddhist logical theories has been stated above, p. 8, n. 4 (transl.). But when the relation between the first moment of sensation and the subsequent clear image is considered, this momentary aspect can by no means be disregarded. The first is evidently the cause of the second. Dh. himself states it, since on p. 9 (transl.) he speaks about the *two* different moments of sensation and distinct perception, and when treating of mental sensation *(mānasa-pratyakṣa)* he clearly says that the first is the cause *(upādāna-kṣaṇa)* of the second. He also characterizes perception as a process where sensation is followed by construction *(sākṣāt-kāra-vyāpāro vikalpena anugamyate*, cp. p. 3. 13-14, 11. 12, text). The whole trend of Dharmakīrti's system reqnires ns to admit here two entities, two moments, and the first is clearly the cause which produces the second, if we understand Causality in the Buddhist sense as a consecution of discrete moments in an uninterrupted flux, cp. Vācaspati's exposition of the problem in Appendix about *mānasa-pratyakṣa*. The fact that a distinct perception is at once «obtaining and bestowing» distinctness without being causally related has been misunderstood and has given to opponents an opportunity of easy triumph. Hemacandra remarks that «one undivided moment cannot contain in itself two things, the one obtaining and the other bestowing distinctness», cp. his Commeut upon Syādvāda-mañjarī in the Yaśovijaya Series, № 30, p. 120. Cp. also Haribhadra's Anekāntajayapatāka. Vinītadeva's comment is quite simple, it avoids all the difficulties raised by Dh.; its translation is given in an Appendix.

certain extent, a process of cognition and, to a certain extent, a resulting content of it, this will not involve us into contradiction.

(15. 21). Coordination is indeed the cause imparting distinctness to our cognition. Our self-conscious image of (e. g.) a blue patch is, on the other hand, the content obtaining distinctness. And if it is asked how is it possible for the same cognition to be (at once) obtaining and imparting distinctness, we shall answer as follows.

(15. 22). When we become aware of the similarity of our cognition (with other blue objects), it then appears (as though) grasping something blue in a definite judgment, («this is blue»).[1] But (at the same time our cognition is being determined as a self-conscious image of the blue, (it may then be regarded as a content which is being grasped and thus) obtains distinctness.

(16. 3). Therefore coordination, when (it is regarded as a process and) contrasted (with other processes which are) not coordination, becomes the cause conferring distinctness (and self-consciousness on our cognitions). But when (the process has been, as it were, stabilized and) our cognition appears as a self-conscious image of the blue, it is then contrasted (with other ideas which are) not images of the blue (and it then can be regarded as a content) obtaining distinctness.[2]

(16. 4). What imparts distinctness (to our cognitions) is a constructed image. It must be regarded as something which is called forth (in us) by the influence of (pure) sensation.[3] But it is not itself (strictly speaking) a sense-perception,[4] because the latter is (passive), non-constructive[5] and therefore it is not capable of delineating its own self in the shape of a self-conscious image of the blue patch.[6]

(16. 6). Although our sensation which has not yet been determined in the judgment[7] («this is blue») really exists, it is nevertheless

---

[1] *niścaya-pratyaya* = *kalpanā*, cp. above p. 20 n. 6.

[2] Lit., p. 15. 22—16.4. «Because this cognition (*vijñāna*), being experienced (*anubhūyamāna*) as similar, is settled in a thought of ascertainment as grasping the blue, therefore similarity, when it is grasped, is the cause of establishing. And this knowledge, when being established in a thought of ascertainment as a self-conscious cognition (*saṃvedana*) of blue, is (the result) which is being established. Therefore similarity is a cause establishing cognition by excluding the non-similar. And its having the form a conscious idea (*bodha*) of blue is being established by excluding the idea of non-blue».

[3] *pratyakṣa-bala* = *nirvikalpaka-bala*.

[4] *pratyakṣam eva*.

[5] *nirvikalpakatvāt*.

[6] *nīla-bodha*.

[7] *niścaya-pratyayena*.

quasi altogether non-existent,[1] (if we want it to represent) the self-conscious idea of the blue patch. Therefore our cognition (begins) really to exist as possessing its essence of a self-conscious image of the blue[2] only when it is being definitely shaped in the judgment («this is blue»).[3] (Coordination is then immanent to the image).

§ 8. Perception is a judgment.

(16.7). (Pure) sense-perception thus becomes a (real) source of our knowledge only when it has elicited a judgment. As long as the judgment has not been produced, our cognition has not been determined in its essence of a self-conscious idea of the blue.

(16.9). Thus it is that without such judgment cognition is resultless, since its essence, the distinct image of the object, has not been elicited. Such a mental (process) cannot even be regarded as cognition, since the most characteristic feature of cognition is here in abeyance. (16.10). But when the definite judgment («this is blue») has been elicited (internally) and the mental process contains the self-conscious image of the blue patch as determined through its coordination, it is then proved that just this coordination is the (real) source of our knowledge, since it is the cause which gives it distinctness.

(16.12). If it is so, then sense-perception becomes a (real) source of our knowledge only in combination with a (constructed) judgment and not (in its genuine form of) a pure (sensation). Not (quite) so. Because in a perceptive judgment which is produced on the basis of a sensation, we judge that we see the object, but not that we imagine it.[4] (16.13) «Seeing» is the function of direct cognition, we call it presenting the object directly (in our ken). «Imagining», on the other hand, is the function of constructive (synthetic) thought.[5]

(16.14). Indeed, when we mentally construct an absent object, we imagine it, we do not see it. Thus it is that our own experience proves that

---

1 *asat-kalpam eva.*

2 *nīla-bodha-ātmanā.*

3 *niścayena = kalpanayā.*

4 Lit., p. 16.13. «Because by a judgment (*adhyavasāya*) which has been produced by the influence of sensation (*pratyakṣa = nirvikalpaka*) the object is definitely realized (*avasīyate*) as seen, not as imagined».

5 *vikalpa = kalpanā.*

the procedure of constructive thought consists in imagination.[1] (16.16). Therefore, when we have a perceptive judgment (concerning the presence) of an object (in our ken), (although it is a construction, nevertheless) our synthetic thought conceals (as it were) its proper function, and gives prominence to the function of direct presentation. We then (usually say) that it is just perception alone that has brought us this knowledge.[2]

End of the first chapter of the Short Treatise of Logic.

---

[1] Lit., p. 16. 15—17. «Thus from experience (*anubhava*) they resolve that the function of thought is (productive) imagination. Therefore in what object judgment (*adhyavasāya*) preceded by sensation (*pratyakṣa*), after having concealed its own function, presents the function of sensation, there just pure sensation alone is the source of knowledge (*pramāṇa*)».

[2] This concluding passage might have been easily misunderstood as suggesting that the discussion about the process and the result of cognition refers to the relation between the sensation and the following construction, or judgment, but it is not so. The trend of the discussion is to show that self-consciousness is not the attribute of a Soul, but it is immanent to every cognition without exception, it is neither a substance, nor the attribute of a substance, it is *kṣaṇika*. Pure sense-perception, says Tattvas., p. 390.7, although containing no construction, possesses the force of evoking a construction, or a judgment, *avikalpakam api jñānam vikalpotpatti-śaktimat*. As stated above, p. 43 n, there is here a causal relation between two facts. The Buddhists do not in the least deny that in cognition the first indefinite sensation (*nirvikalpaka*) is followed by the construction of a definite image or idea (*savikalpaka* = *pratīti*), and the latter by a purposive action (*artha-kriyā*). They do not deny that the preceding step is the cause and the following the result, (with the proviso of the Buddhist conception of Causation). But in considering the question of the result they neglect the separate moments (*pūrvāparayoḥ kṣaṇayor ekatvādhyavasāyāt*, Ṭipp., p. 41. 1), they take cognition as a unity and maintain that the result of the act of cognizing is cognition, or the self-conscious idea. As against the Realists they maintain that we do not know the external object, our images are not constructed by the external world, but the external world is constructed according to our images, that there is no «act of grasping» of the object by the intellect, that our idea of the object is a unity to which two different aspects are imputed, the «grasping» aspect (*grāhaka-ākāra*) and the «grasped» aspect (*grāhya*). This same idea is also the idea of the potential purposive action (*prāpaṇa-yogyī- karaṇa-ākāra*). In this sense there is no difference between the act and the result of cognition, between *pramāṇa* and *pramāṇa-phala* and we may by imputation speak of a coordination (*sārūpya*) of the blue with a recognizable point of reality, and its distinction from the not-blue, as a kind of source of our knowledge, cp. below the note on p. 49—50.

CHAPTER II.

INFERENCE AS A PROCESS OF THOUGHT.

§ 1. DEFINITION AND RESULT.

(17. 1). After having done with perception, (the author) proceeds to analyse inference and says,

1. Inference is twofold.

(17. 3). Inference is twofold, i. e., there are two different inferences. Now, what is the reason for (our author) to start suddenly by pointing out this division, when we would expect a definition? We answer. Inference «for others» consists of propositions, (it is a communication). Inference «for oneself» is an (internal) process of cognition. Since they are absolutely different things, no inclusive definition is possible. (17. 5). Thus it is intended to give (two different) definitions, each appertaining to one class only, (and for this aim it becomes necessary) to start with a division. For a division is an indication (of the number) of instances. When this has been done, it becomes possible to frame definitions suited to each case separately. Not otherwise. Thus to state a division means (here) to divide the definitions.[1] Having realized that it is impossible to do it (here) without previously indicating the number of instances, the author begins by setting forth the division.[2]

---

1 Lit., p. 17. 7. «Therefore the statement about the division of species is (here) nothing but (*eva*) a means (*anga*) of distinguishing between the definitions».

2 Dignāga's reform in logic aimed at a distinction between logic as a theory of cognition and logic as a teaching about various dialectical methods. The logic of the early Naiyāyikas was exlusively dialectical. Dignāga therefore deals with dialectics under the heading of inference «for others». The three-membered syllogism belongs only indirectly to the province of epistemological logic along with other dialectical methods. But inference as a process of thought distinguished from sense-perception is quite a different thing. Our terminology is so much influenced by Aristotle that we cannot free ourselves enough to find terms corresponding to In-

(17. 9). What are these two varieties?

2. For one self and for others.

(17. 11). (Internal inference is) inference «for one self». When we cognize something (internally) for ourselves, the inference is an internal (process of cognition). (Its formulation in speech) is inference «for others», it is (a method) of communicating knowledge to others.

(17. 13). Between these two inferences, for oneself and for others, what is the characteristic of the first? The author says,

3. A cognition which is produced (indirectly) through a mark that has a threefold aspect, and which refers to an object, (not perceived, but) inferred—is internal inference.[1]

(18. 2). The threefold aspect of the mark will be treated later on.[2] A (logical) mark is that by which something is *marked off*, which conveys something, (from which something indirectly follows). (18. 3). The words «produced from this threefold mark» characterize internal inference by its origin. (18. 4). The words «referring to an inferred object» characterize it from the objective side. What is produced by this threefold mark is also an object upon which the threefold mark is directed. (18. 5). Thus the definition will be—internal inference is cognition[3]

dian conceptions. Every synthetic operation of thought, *sārūpya-lakṣaṇam pramāṇam anumānam*, as opposed to the non-synthetic ideal sense-perception, is inference. Kant's conception about two transcendental sources of knowledge, the senses and the intellect, comes much nearer to Dignāga's standpoint than our usual ideas about sense-perception and inference. In *Pr. samucc.*, II. 1—2, the reason is given why inference alone receives a double treatment, as a process of thought and as a mode of communicating it, whereas perception is treated only as a process of cognition: perception namely is *inexpressible* (*abhilāpa-kalpanā-apoḍha*). About a similar division in the Vaiśeṣika school cp. H. Jacobi, Indische Logik, p. 479 ff, my article in Muséon 1904, L. Suali, Introduzione, p. 417, Faddegon, The Vaiśeṣika-system, p. 314 ff.

[1] Read p. 18. 1 *tat svārthānumānam.*

[2] On the three aspects of the logical reason see *infra*, § 2. They are here mentioned, as Vinītadeva remarks, p. 56, in order to distinguish a valid inference from logical error which is always produced by a deficiency in one or several aspects of the mark.

[3] The word *jñānam*, according to the same author, lays stress npon the fact that the logical mark (*linga*) or reason (*hetu*) produces cognition when it is definitely cognized. Sensation (*nirvikalpaka-pratyakṣa*), indeed, works automatically (*sva-sattayā, sva-rasikatayā*), whereas a logical mark leads to a conclusion when it has been definitely cognized (*jñātatvena*). Inference or indirect knowledge represents thus the spontaneous, synthetic, definitely conscious element in cognition.

produced by a three-aspected mark and concerning an inferred object.

(18.7). This is (our author's) answer to the different definitions (of other schools). He now proceeds to repudiate the misconception about (the supposed difference between inference and its) result.

4. The distinction between a source of cognition and its result is here just the same as in the case of perception.[1]

(18.9). (The problem of a special) result produced by the act of cognizing must be solved here, in the case of inference, just in the same manner as it has been done for perception. (18.10). Indeed, when we have some (indefinite) sensation (and) begin to feel that it is coordinated with the object «blue», (our sensation) then takes the shape of a definite self-conscious idea[2] of the blue. We thus (may regard) the fact of coordination of our cognition with its object «blue» as (a kind of) cognitive activity producing distinctness. (The same cognitive fact) viewed as a definite self-conscious idea of the blue (may be regarded as) the resulting (mental content) obtaining distinctness.[3]

---

[1] Vinītadeva's comment on this sūtra, p. 56.16 ff., runs thus. «Just as in the case of perception this very cognition (i. e., the definite presentation) has been said to be the result of that cognitive method, just so in this case (i. e., in inference) just the cognition of the inference (*anumānasya jñānam*) is the result of cognition (*pramāṇa-phalam*), since it has the character of definitely ascertaining the object (*artha-viniścaya-svabhāvatvāt*). Just as coordination (or similarity, *sārūpya*) with the perceived object is a mode of (definite) cognition, just so coordination of the inferred object is a mode of (definite) cognition, because through it (i. e., through coordination) the definite ascertainment of the object is established».

[2] *nīla-bodha* = *nīla-saṃvedana* = *nīla-anubhava* = *nīlam iti vijñānam*, cp. above, p. 16 n. 1.

[3] The realistic systems pondered over the problem of a special result for every special mode of cognition and considered it as a series of steps in the act of cognizing, the following step being a result of the preceding one. The result of the inferential mode of cognition of an object consisted in the conclusion of the inference, it was considered as the result of the preceding step, the minor premise (=*tṛtīya-linga-parāmarśa*). A further result was the idea of a purposive action and that action itself. Without at all denying the existence of these steps and their character of cause and effect, the Buddhists applied to them their conception of Causality (*pratītya-samutpāda* = *nirvyāpārāḥ sarve dharmāḥ*, cp. Pr. samucc. I. 10 and Kamalaśīla, p. 392. 12). But the problem of the result, as has been stated above, p. 39, they considered from an altogether different standpoint. The result of cognizing, they declared, is cognition. In this respect there is no difference between perception and inference. The latter is not then regarded as consisting of a sequel

(18. 11). Just the same (can be maintained in regard of the object cognized through) inference. (Supposing we have cognized through an

---

of judgments, but as a single judgment or even a single idea, *ekam vijñānam*, cp. Nyāya-Kanikā, p. 125.2 ff. In perception we cognize the object in its own form directly, in inference we cognize it indirectly through its mark. But the result is the same, it is a self-conscious idea coordinated with some external reality. This idea has a double aspect, the object-aspect (*grāhya*) and the self-aspect (*grāhaka*). There is no difference between cognizer, instrument, act, object aud result, they are merely different aspects of the idea (*vijñāna*). Thus these Buddhists are called Idealists (*vijñāna-vādin*). When we, e. g., cognize through an inference the presence somewhere of fire, the selfconscious idea of the fire is the result. In its inchoative state it is just a feeling of something either desirable or undesirable, this is its self-aspect which through coordination develops an object-aspect (Pr. samucc. I. 10). The difference between perception and inference is not in their result which, from this standpoint, is the same, but in their essence and in their respective objects, says Dignāga, Pr. samucc., II. 1. The essence of perception is to give a vivid, immediate image. This vividness is inexpressible in speech. If, comments Jinendrabuddhi, f. 95. a. 4, it could be so expressed, then the blind could see colours through verbal testimony. Inference produces an abstract, dim, non-vivid image of the object. As regards the *prima facie* object, in perception it is the particular, in inference the universal, the abstract, the imagined which is always dim. The self-conscious idea being the only result can nevertheless be viewed in different aspects. Coordination of the image with a recognizable point, the judgment «this is blue», produces its identity and distinctness, its contrast with everything else. This aspect can be regarded as the act or the source of knowledge (*pramāṇa*), because this feature appears as the most decisive factor of cognition, *prakṛṣṭa-upakāraka* (Ṭipp., p. 42.3) = *sādhakatama-kāraṇa* = *adhipati-pratyaya*. The self-conscious distinct idea (*pratīti* = *bodha* = *saṃvedana* = *vijñāna*) can be regarded as a kind of result (*pramāṇa-phala*).—The statement that the result of inference is the same as the result of perception reminds us of the view expressed, among others, by B. Bosanquet that «the task of drawing a line between what is and what is not inference is an impossible one» (Logic, II. 16). When this author further states that «at least a suggested distinction» is as «between direct and indirect reference to Reality» (ibid. II. 27), we see at once that this is quite the view of Dignāga. When we also read that «the processes of Recognition, Abstraction, Comparison, Identification, Discrimination ... are characteristics which no judgment or inference is without» (ibid. II. 20), and that perception always contains some inference, we are reminded of the rôle attributed to *sārūpya* and *vyāvṛtti*. When it is stated that «every idea which is entertained must be taken to be ultimately affirmed of reality» (ibid. I. 6, 76 ff., 146 ff.) we are reminded of the rôle of *sva-lakṣaṇa*, and when the sanscritist reads that «consciousness is a single persistent judgment» (ibid, I. 4), he cannot but think of *adhyavasāya* = *niścaya* = *kalpanā* = *buddhi* = *vijñāna*. — Some details about the interesting fact of a certain similarity between Dignāga's Logic and that form of this science which it has received in Germany, under the influence of Kantian ideas, at the hands of Lotze, Schuppe and Sigwart and in the works of B. Bosanquet and others in England, will be found in the Introduction.

inference the presence somewhere of a patch of blue colour.)[1] This image of the blue arises (at first indefinitely); it is then settled as a definite self-conscious idea of a blue patch (by the way of its contrast with other colours which are not blue). Thus the coordination of the blue, (its contrast[2] with other colours, may be regarded) as the source of such a (definitely circumscribed image), and the imagined[3] distinet representation will then appear as its result, because it is through coordination (and contrast) that the definite image of the blue is realized.

(18. 15). The misconceptions about the number (of varieties), the essence and the result (of indirect cognition) have thus been repudiated. The misconception concerning the object cognized through inference has been repudiated in the chapter on perception.[4]

§ 2. Invariable Concomitance or the three aspects of a valid logical mark.

(18. 16). When specifying the definition (of an internal inference), the three aspects of the logical mark have occasionally been mentioned. They are now defined.

5. The three aspects of the mark are (first)—«just» its presence in the object cognized by inference.

(18. 18). The three-aspected mark means that the mark has three aspects. We must understand[5] that they will now be explained. The (author) accordingly goes on to explain what these three aspects are. (18. 19). What an object of inference (a minor term) is, will be stated later on. The first aspect of the mark consists «just» in its presence in this object, (i. e., in its presence there in any case, but not in its presence exclusively there.[6] This presence is) «necessary».

---

1 A patch of blue colour is the usual example of sense-perception. But here it is taken as an object whose presence is not perceived, but inferred. As a matter of fact, any real object can be cognized either directly by sense-perception or indirectly through inference or verbal testimony. Vinītadeva refrains from this example.

2 *sārūpya = atad-vyāvṛtti = anya-vyāvṛtti = anya-yoga-vyavaccheda = ākāra = ābhāsa.*

3 *vikalpana.*

4 See above, p. 37.

5 Lit., «we must add (*śeṣaḥ*)».

6 The usual example of an inference is the following one,

Wherever there is smoke there is also fire,
On this spot there is smoke,
Hence there is fire.

(18. 20). Although the word «necessary» is not expressed in the definition of this (first aspect), it nevertheless (will be) found at the end, (when defining the third aspect). It must be equally referred to both the preceding aspects. (19. 1). Because the mark produces a cognition of an absent object (by logical neccessity), not by a possibility to do it, as e. g., a seed (which is capable of) producing a sprout. (The seed, even if we do not perceive it, is fit to produce a sprout).[1] But smoke, (the mark of fire), if we do not perceive it, will never produce the cognition (of the presence of fire in a given place). (19. 2). Neither is the mark comparable to the light of a lamp (when it reveals the presence) of, e. g., a jar. (Such) revelation of concealed objects is a cause (producing) knowledge of anything (that happens to be present). (There is no necessary bond between the lamp and the jar).[2] Supposing, indeed, (smoke) is perceived, nevertheless we will not know (the presence of fire) if we know nothing about its necessary[3] concomitance (with

---

The object of the inference, or minor terms must necessarily posses, «just» the presence of the mark, or middle term, smoke, i. e. smoke must be «just» present, not absent. The particle «just» (*eva*) lays stress on that word of the sentence to which it is attached and thus changes the meaning of the sentence altogether. In the sentence «on this spot there is „just" presence of smoke» the intention of the speaker is to express that smoke is really present, not absent. If it were said that «„just" the smoke is present», this would mean that the speaker's intention is to deny the presence of something else. If it were said that «the smoke is present „just" on this spot», the intention of the speaker would be to deny its presence elsewhere and to assert its presence exclusively on one spot. Every word of this definition is full of meaning, because each of them precludes some special logical error in the complete system of fallacies. Special fallacies will ensue 1) if the middle term will not be present at all, 2) if it will not be «just» present, i. e., present in one part of the minor and absent in the other, and 3) if its presence is not necessary, i. e., problematic. The translation of *eva* by «just» is resorted to for want of another.

1 Cp. Ṭipp., p. 40. 16.

2 Lit., p. 19. 1—2. «Because the mark is not the cause of the cognition of the concealed by possibility, as the seed of the sprout, since from an unseen smoke fire is not known. Neither is it an illumination of concealed objects depending upon (the production) of a cognition (having) its own object, as . . .», cp. Tib., p. 42. 4.

3 The Buddhist conception of concomitance is that it represents an invariable and necessary connection. They then give what they suppose to be an exhaustive, although very simple, table of all possible logical connections. This is part of their general idea about the validity of knowledge, *pramāṇa-viniścaya-vāda*, cp. above p. 7. Vinītadeva says, p. 58. 2, that concomitance is a necessary bond, because such is the nature of knowledge, *yathā-pramāṇa-svabhāvena.* There is a divergence on this point between the Buddhists and the Naiyāyikas. The first maintain the «necessity», *avinābhāva*, *nāntarīyakatva*, of invariable con-

the latter)[1] (19. 3). Therefore the function of the logical mark, owing to which it is able to create cognition of absent things, is nothing else than the necessity of an invariable concomitance between (the perceived mark and) the absent object. (19. 4). It follows that the word «necessary» must be referred to all the three aspects in which the mark manifests itself, since all these three forms, viz. 1. the positive concomitance of the mark with the deduced predicate, 2. its contraposition (or the inverted concomitance of their negations) and 3. the presence of the thus characterized mark upon the subject of the conclusion — all these three connections, since they represent the essence of the function performed by a logical mark, must be ascertained as being necessary.

(19. 6). The word «presence» (in the above definition) aims at excluding a (quite) unreal (non-existing) mark, as e. g., the mark of being amenable to the sense of vision (in an inference like the following one),

Thesis. The (spoken) word is non-eternal[2]

---

nection founded on an exhaustive table of necessary *a priori* existing principles (*tādātmya-tadutpatti*, cp. below p. 52, text). The second admit invariable connection *sahacarya*, *avyabhicāritva*, but not necessity, since «the devil of a doubt» (*śankā-piśācī*) can never be completely removed; they deny the exhaustive table of connections (*sambandho yo vā sa vā bhavatu*) and maintain that the connections are various and can be cognized by induction, by the method of agreement and difference (*anvaya-vyatireka*), by summarizing (*upasaṃhāreṇa*) some observed facts, cp. Tātparyaṭ., p. 105 ff. The characteristic *na yogyatayā hetuḥ* (*lingam*) is repeated below, p. 47. 9 and 49. 15. The comparison with a lamp is admitted by the Naiyāyikas.

1 One of the words for a logical reason, or mark, is in sanscrit *hetu* which also means cause. It is here distinguished as not being a producing cause (*utpādaka-hetu*) like the seed of a plant, since it does not operate automatically (*sva-sattayā*) like the senses, but only when cognized (*jñātatayā* = *dṛṣṭatayā*). Neither will it be quite right to call it an informatory cause (*jñapaka-hetu*, *jñāna-utpādaka*, the Tib. translates, p. 42. 4, *jñānāpekṣa* as if it were *jñānotpādaka-apekṣa-*) comparable to the light thrown upon an object in the dark, because it is an ascertaining reason (*niścāyaka*), a fact whose connection is «necessary».

2 The syllogism deducing the impermanent, evanescent character of the spoken word, and of the sound in general, from the fact that it is produced by special causes, for whatsoever has a beginning has also an end, — this syllogism performs, in the manuals of Indian logic and in all countries which have borrowed their teaching of logic from India, the same function as the syllogism about the mortality of Socrates in European logic. The orthodox brahmanic school of Mīmāṃsakas have exhibited their religious zeal by establishing a theory according to which the sounds of the words of their Holy Scriptures were eternal substances, something comparable to Platonic ideas, the actually spoken words were then explained as the accidental manifestations of these unchanging substances. The

Reason. Because it is perceived by vision, etc.[1]

(19. 6). The word «just» aims at excluding a mark which is partly unreal, (which is present in one part of the subject only) (19. 7), as e. g., in the inference,—

Thesis. Trees are sentient beings.
Reason. Because they sleep.[2]

Trees, the subject of the inference, (the minor term), possess sleep which is manifested by the closing of their leaves (at night). But in one part of them this mark is non-existent. Indeed all trees do not close their leaves at night, but only some of them.

(19. 8). The definition lays stress upon the circumstance that the mark, or middle term, must in any case be connected with the minor term, the subject of the conclusion, (i. e., the minor premise must be in any case realized). If, on the contrary, the emphasis were put on the word «object», (i. e., the object of the inference, or the subject of the conclusion, the minor term), then the definition might have been misunderstood as intimating that the middle term must represent something which is the exclusive property of the minor term, in which case an inference like the following one,—

Thesis. The spoken word is non-eternal,
Reason. Because it is apprehended by the sense of audition,

might have been regarded as a valid inference.[3]

(19. 10). The word «necessary» aims at excluding every problematic mark[4] of whose presence in the object of inference we can have no certainty.[5]

Indian logicians and all unorthodox schools assailed this theory vehemently, it became thus the principle point of dissention between the early logicians. This syllogism was thus introduced, with infinite subtle variations, as the usual example in manuals, and retained its place, although the theory to which it owed its origin had lost very much of its importance.

[1] Read, p. 19. 6, *cākṣusatvād ity ādi*.

[2] This syllogism is the argument by which the Jains establish the animation of plants in accordance with their idea of universal animation.

[3] Lit., p. 19. 8—10. «By putting the word «just» after the word «presence» an exclusive quality (*asādhāraṇo dharmaḥ*) is set aside. If it were said «the presence «just» in the object of inference, then «just» audibility would be a reason».

[4] *saṃdigdha-asiddha*.

[5] As e. g., in «someone is omniscient, because he speaks», cp. p. 56 n. 1.

6. Its presence only in similar cases.

(19. 12). The definition of a similar case will be given later on. The second aspect of the logical mark consists in its *necessary* presence *only* in similar cases. Here likewise (every word of the definition aims at precluding some logical fallacy). The word «presence» aims at excluding a contrary mark. Such a mark is absent in similar cases.[1] (19. 13). The word «only» sets aside non-exclusive marks, for such marks are not present in similar cases «only», but in both the (similar and dissimilar ones).[2] (19. 14). The emphasis is put on the word «similar», (the mark is present in similar cases «only», never in contrary cases. This does not mean that it must be present in every similar case without exception, but it means that it must be found in similar cases only, never in contrary cases). Thus the mark of «voluntary production» will be valid (in the following inference,—

Thesis. Words are non-eternal.
Reason. Because voluntarily produced).

This mark (of production at will) does not extend to every case of non-eternality, (but it never occurs in eternal substances).[3]

(19. 15). If emphasis were put on the word «presence», the meaning would have been, «just» the presence, (i. e., presence always, never absence), and the mark of «voluntary production» would not have been valid, (since it is by no means present in all non-eternal entities).

(19. 16). By the word «necessary» an uncertain logical mark is set aside, a mark of whose direct concomitance (with the predicate) we have no certainty, e. g.,—

---

[1] As e. g., «there is here fire, because there is water», or «words are eternal, because they are voluntarily produced».

[2] Lit., p. 19. 13. «By the word «just» the general-uncertain (is set aside)», i. e., an uncertain reason (*anaikāntika*) which is overcomprehensive (*sādhāraṇa*), it is found in similar and in dissimilar cases, as e. g.,—

Thesis. Our words depend upon volition,
Reason. Because they are impermanent.

Impermanent things are found in similar cases, in objects whose production depends upon volition, and in dissimilar cases, e. g, in lightning whose production does not depend upon human volition.

[3] Lit., p. 19. 14—15. «By putting the emphatic word before mentioning «presence» the validity (*hetutva*) of «dependence on an effort» is indicated, which possesses existence not embracing (all) similar cases».

Thesis. Someone is omniscient.
Reason. Because he speaks.[1]

The similar cases are cases of omniscience. (The existence of omniscient beings is problematic, hence it never) can be made out with certainty whether they speak, (or not).

7. Its absolute absence in dissimilar cases is necessary.

(19. 20). What a dissimilar case is, will be stated later on. The third aspect of a logical mark consists in its absolute absence in dissimilar cases, (such absence being characterized by) necessity. Here the word «absence» aims at excluding a contrary mark, since the contrary is present in dissimilar cases. (19. 21). By the word «absolute» an overwide[2] mark is excluded which embraces (all similar cases and) part of the dissimilar cases (as well), e. g.,

Thesis. Words are produced voluntarily.
Reason. Because they are impermanent.

In this example the mark (impermanence) is present in one part of the dissimilar cases, such as lightning etc. (which are not voluntarily produced and are impermanent), and absent in another one, e. g., in Space (which is not voluntarily produced, but is eternal). Therefore, it must be necessarily rejected (as a valid mark). (20. 1). If instead of saying «absolute absence in dissimilar cases» the author would have put emphasis on the word «dissimilar» cases, the meaning would have been the following one — «this is a valid mark which is absent in dissimilar cases *only*». Then (in the above example) the quality of «being produced voluntarily» would not make a valid mark, because it is really also absent

---

1 The origin of this strange-looking inference is probably the following one. The Buddhist Saint, the ārya, the Bodhisattva, is credited with the faculty of apprehending the Universe *sub specie aeternitatis*, cp. p. 32 n. When he has reached the *dṛṣṭi-mārga* all his habits of thought are changed and he directly intuits by mystic intuition (*yogi-pratykṣa*) that condition of the world which reveals itself to the monistic philosopher. This is called omniscience (*sarva-ākāra-jñatā*, *sarva-jñatā*). But this outlook is something beyond verbal expression (*anirvacanīya*). Therefore whosoever puts his teaching into words cannot be omniscient in this sense of the term. Cp. Nyāya-kaṇikā, p. 110. 15 ff. and 181. 25 ff. The problem reflected in this example is that Omniscience is beyond our knowledge. The terms have then been arranged in every possible, positive and negative, combination, as will be seen later on, ch. III, sūtra 76, ff. Cp. also Kamalaśīla, p. 882. 7 and 890 ff.

2 *sādhāraṇa*, «over-embracing».

in (some) of the similar (i. e. impermanent) cases (such as lightning).[1] Therefore the words «in dissimilar cases» have not been emphasized. (20. 3). The word «necessary» (absence) sets aside a problematic mark, a mark whose absence in dissimilar cases is uncertain.

(20. 5). The following question arises. When the presence of the mark «only» in similar cases has been stated, its «absolute» absence in dissimilar cases must evidently follow by implication.[2] Why is it then, that two different aspects of the mark have been mentioned? (20. 6). The answer is as follows. Either the positive concomitance[3] (of the mark with the predicate) or (its contraposition, i. e.), the inverted concomitance (of their negations),[4] should be actually used.[5] But both must be without exception.[6] Not otherwise. In order to emphazise (this necessity) both aspects have been mentioned. (20. 7). If however both were actually used without being applied strictly, we would have the following result — «a mark which is present in similar and absent in dissimilar cases is valid», and then we would have a valid inference in the following example,

> Thesis. The (child in the womb of this woman) has a dark complexion.
> Reason. Because it is her child.
> Example. Just as her other children whom we see.

In this example the fact of being the son of this woman would be a valid mark, (although this is not the case, since the complexion of the future child depends upon the diet of the mother).[7] (20. 9). Therefore, either the positive concomitance or its contraposition must be actually used in inference. But both must needs be without exception

---

[1] Lit., p. 20. 1—2. «(Supposing) the emphatic word precedes the word absence, the meaning would be the following one, «that is a reason which is absent in dissimilar cases only». But the «being produced by a voluntary effort» is also absent in some of the similar cases, (i. e., in some impermanent objects), therefore it would not be a reason».

[2] Lit., p. 20. 5. «But when it is said the presence «just» in similar cases, does it not necessarily follow that in the dissimilar cases there is «just» absence?»

[3] *anvaya*, corresponding to the major premise of the first figure of Aristotle's syllogism.

[4] *vyatireka*, contraposition.

[5] *prayoktavya*, lit. «formulated».

[6] *niyamavān*, limited, necessary.

[7] When a pregnant woman feeds on vegetables the complexion of the child is supposed to turn out darker than when she keeps a milk diet. This is the usual example of an unsufficiently warranted generalization.

in order that the necessary connection of the proving (mark) with the derived (predicate) should be established. (20. 10). And since they must necessarily allow of no exception, only one of them should actually be expressed, not both together. Thus it is that these two aspects of the logical mark are given (out of practical considerations), in order to teach precision in using either the positive concomitance of the mark with the predicate or its contraposition.

§ 3. MINOR TERM. INDUCTION FROM SIMILAR AND DISSIMILAR INSTANCES.

(20. 13). When giving an account of the three aspects of the logical mark, (the terms) «object of inference», «similar case», «dissimilar case» have been mentioned. Their definition shall now be given. What is here understood under object of inference?

8. The object (cognized in) inference is here the substratum whose property it is desired to cognize.

(20. 16). The word «here» means that the object of inference appears as a substance (a substratum) when the definition of its mark is considered, (the mark being an attribute of this substance). But from another standpoint, when the deduced (conclusion) is realized, the subject of the inference would be a complex (idea of the substratum together with its property).[1] (20. 17). And when the invariable concomitance (between the middle and the major terms) is considered, then the inferred fact appears as an attribute[2] (of this substance, as the

---

[1] *anumeya*, «the thing to be inferred». In a general sense it may mean an object which possesses the united properties of the major, the minor and the middle terms, e. g., «the mortal man Socrates», it is then *ekam vijñānam*. It may also mean the major term or the conclusion separately, as well as the thesis which is also the conclusion (= *pakṣa* = *sādhya*). In a special sense it means the minor term, the subject of the conclusion,and even, more precisely, the underlying substratum (*dharmin*), the efficient point-instant, that underlying point of reality upon which any amount of interconnected qualities may be assembled as a superstructure. The Buddhists do not admit the transcendental reality of the relation between substance and quality (*dharma-dharmi-bhāra*). The snbstratum alone is reality. the qualities are construction. Therefore in the formulation of inferences the subject of the conclusion, the minor term, since it contains a reference to this indefinite substratum, is usually expressed by «here», «now», «this». And even when not so expressed it is always so understood in every judgment or inference, cp. B. Bosanquet, Logic. I. 146.

[2] *dharma*, not *dharmin*, i. e., the major term, the inferred, the deduced quality.

major term). In order to point out (these differences) the word «here» has been used. We call «object of inference» an object whose property, or specification, it is desired to cognize.

What is a similar case?

9. A similar case is an object which is similar through the common possession of the inferred property.

(20.21). A similar case is a similar object. An object which is similar, which is analogous to the object of the inference, which metaphorically is called its copartner. It is characterized by the word «similar».[1] (20.22). All right! But what is this similarity which unites one part with its counterpart? The answer is, (they are similar) by the common possession of a quality which is the logical predicate. It is (the predicate), the thing to be proved, since it is not yet proved (as long as the inference is not concluded), and it is a property, because its existence depends upon a substratum from which it differs. Thus it is a predicated (or derived) quality, (a property whose existence is being deduced). (21. 2). No particular can ever make a logical predicate.[2] It is (always) a universal. Therefore, it is here stated that the thing to be cognized, (the logical predicate) is a common property. It is a predicated property and it is general. The similar case is similar to the object of the inference, because both are comprehended in the universality of the predicated quality.

(21.5). What is a dissimilar case? It is said,

10. A case which is not similar is dissimilar— (it can be) different from it, contrary to it or its absence.

(21.7). That which is not similar is dissimilar. What is it that cannot be similar? That what is different from the similar, what is contrary to it, and what is equivalent to the absence of a similar case. (21.8). Both the being different and the being contrary cannot be conceived so long as the concrete absence[3] of the similar case is not realized. (21.9). Therefore the conceptions of being different and of

---

[1] Lit., p. 20.22. «The word *sa* is a substitute for *samāna*».

[2] Particular (*viśeṣa*) is here called what we would call substance (= *dharmin*), since it is contrasted with every predicate. In sūtra II. 8, on the contrary, *viśeṣa* = *dharma*, it refers to a general quality which characterizes a particular.

[3] *svabhāva-abhāva*, this refers to the second *virodha*, cp. III. 77; *viruddha* of II. 10 would then refer to *sahānavasthānam*, cp. p. 70.22.

being contrary include the conception of the absence of a similar case, because through the analysis of these two conceptions (the third one) is revealed.[1] (21. 10). Thus it is, that absence is conceived as something representing the non-existence of a similar case directly. Difference and contrariety are conceived as representing it indirectly. Therefore all three are dissimilar cases.

§ 4. THREE KINDS OF LOGICAL MARKS. CLASSIFICATION OF INFERENCES.

11. And there are only three varieties of the three-aspected mark.

(21. 13). Owing to its three aspects the logical mark is threefold. Another division in three varieties is now added (in the words «and there are only three varieties of the three-aspected mark»).[2] The questioner[3] has first asked about the three aspects of the mark, now he has (another) question concerning (the varieties of) the three-aspected mark. Of them the three aspects have already been defined. The three varieties are next going to be defined. The threefold marks are just three, i. e., there are *only* three varieties (of the mark). What are they?

12. Negation, Identity and Causation.

(21. 18). The predicate (is either denied or affirmed), when it is denied, negation[4] (is its mark and it has) the three aspects. When it is affirmed, (its mark is either) existentially identical[5] with it, or (when it is different, it represents) its effect. (Both) possess the three aspects.

(21. 20). An example of Negation is (now) given.

---

1 Lit., p. 21. 10. «Therefore by the force of the realization of the «other» and of the «contrary», the other and the contrary are realized as possessing the form (or essence = *svarūpa*) of the non-existence of the similar».

2 Lit., p. 21. 13. «The word «and» aims at the addition of another (group of three) which will be indicated».

3 This interpretation of the word *pareṇa* is supported by the Tib. transl. Otherwise it seems more natural to translate, «one threefold division has been given above, another threefold division follows».

4 *anupalabdhi; upalabdhi* = *jñāna*, cp. text p. 22. 6, i. e., definite cognition, *savikalpaka*.

5 *svabhāva*, own existence, essence. One thing, e. g., *śiṃśapā*, is said to be the «own existence» of the other, e. g., «tree», when it contains the latter in its intension (comprehension, connotation) and is itself contained under the latter's extension,

13. Between these (three, the formula) of Negation is as follows.

Thesis. On some particular place there is no jar.

Reason. Because it is not perceived, although the conditions[1] of perception are fulfilled.[2]

(22. 3). Formula[3] means generalization.[4] Any other instance of negation is such as this one, not this alone. A «particular place» is a place before the eyes of the observer, but not every such place (happening to be before his eyes). It is added «some» (particular place).

---

being subaltern (*vyāpya*) to the latter. Both are then said to be «existentially identical (*tadātman*) and become subject and predicate of an analytical judgment, e. g., «Ašoka is a tree». According to the Buddhist conception it is not a judgment or proposition with two terms, but an inference with three terms, since a point-instant of reality, a localisation in time-space, must be added, or understood, in order to make it a real cognition, or a cognition of Reality. It then receives the form of «this is a tree, because it is an Ašoka». «Tree» is analytically connected or deduced from «Ašoka». This conception of identity is the counterpart of the Buddhist conception of «otherness». According to the law of otherness (*viruddha-dharma-saṃsarga*), as has been mentioned above, p. 8 n., existence is conceived as split into chains of discrete moments (*kṣaṇa*). Two consecutive moments in the existence of what appears to us as the same thing constitute two different realities, every moment is «another» object. All the characteristics which can be given to an object at the same moment are called «existentially connected» or «identical». Thus Ašoka, tree, hard body, thing, substance, existence etc. will be identical in this sense, we would say analytically connected. This relation of Identity is contrasted with the relation of Causality which is a relation between two moments *following* one another. The relation between seed and sprout, fire and smoke is a relation of two consecutive moments. Every relation which is not causality is regarded as a relation of identity. This of course does not exclude the existence of different local, temporal and logical relations, even very complicated ones, such as the *catuḥ-koṭi* logical relation of two terms, but they are secondary or derivate relations. The primary relation of every point-instant of reality (*kṣaṇa*) is either its identity or its otherness in regard of the preceeding moment. The right translation of *svabhāva-linga* would thus have been—a mark which is existentially identical with the fact deduced from it, since both are the characteristics of the same moment of reality. Cp. Sigwart's remarks on «essence» — das Wesen, die Natur des Dinges, — *op. cit.* I. 264, and notes below on p. 64, 65, 69 and 73.

1 *lakṣaṇa* = *sāmagrī* (text p. 22. 6) = *hetu-pratyaya-sāmagrī*.

2 *prāpta* = *janakatvena antarbhūta* (text p. 22. 7); *prāpti* and *aprāpti* are conceived in abhidharma as two special forces (*viprayukta-saṃskāra*) which either bring an element (*dharma*) of existence into its right place in a complex phenomenon, or prevent it from appearing in an undue place, cp. Abh. Koša II. 35 ff.

3 *yathā*, the exact term for a syllogistic formula is *prayoga*, it is very often replaced by simple *yathā*.

4 *upadaršana* is here = *vīpsā*.

The object[1] of the inference is constituted by a particular spot, visible to the observer. (22. 5). «No jar», this is the predicate.[2] Perception[3] means (here) knowledge. The totality of causes producing knowledge are essential[4] to it, because they constitute its essence. An object included[5] among these (causes is so called), because it is included among this totality, as (one of the causes) giving birth to (cognition). (22. 7). An object which is in the condition of cognizability is (nothing else but) a visible object, (an object which could be visible). The words «because we do not perceive any» contain the reason (or middle term).

(22. 8). Now, (it can be questioned), how is it possible for a (jar) to be perceptible in a place from which it is absent? It is said to be perceptible, although it is absent, because its perceptibility is imagined. We imagine this object in the following way: «if it were present on this spot, it certainly would have been perceived». In this case an object, although absent, is *ex hypothesi*[6] visible. (22. 10). And what is the object which can be so imagined? It is the object whose (empty) place (is perceived), all the causes of this perception being present. And when can we judge that the causes[7] are all present? When we (actually) perceive another object included in the same act of cognition. We call «included in the same act of cognition» two objects, dependent upon one another, amenable to the same organ of sense, (two objects) upon

---

1 *dharmin* = *anumeya*, cp. sūtra II. 8.

2 *sādhya*, the thing to be proved, to be deduced, to be inferred, the major term, it is also called *anumeya*, cp. comment on sūtra II. 8, since the inference, or conclusion, represents the minor and major term combined. Subject and predicate, *anuvāda* and *vidhi* or *vidheya*, are the terms of a proposition. Since Indian logic distinguishes sharply between judgment and proposition the term predicate is used only for want of another one.

3 *upalabdhi* is cognition in general, but *anupalabdhi* is non-cognition or negation conceived as the absence of sense-perception (*dṛśya-anupalabdhi*), therefore it can be here rendered as perception, cp. text, p. 37. 5 — *upalabdhiḥ* = *vidhiḥ*.

4 *lakṣaṇa* = *lakṣyate anena*.

5 *prāpta* = *antar-bhūta*.

6 *samāropya*.

7 *sāmagrī* or *hetu-pratyaya-sāmagrī* are the four *pratyayas* which also include the *hetus*, *hetu-pratyaya*, *ālambana-*, *samanantara-* and *adhipati*. The *ālambana* or *artha* being here reckoned separately remain the three conditions, the *adhipati* — the organ of sense, the *samanantara* — the preceding stream of consciousness, the *hetu* or *sahakāri-pratyaya*, light and other circumstances. Under *kāraṇa-hetu* the whole condition of the universe with respect to a given moment is included, cp. my Nirvāṇa, Index.

which the eye or another organ (can be simultaneously) fixed with attention. (22.12). Indeed, when two such objects are (before us) we cannot confine our perception to one of them, since there is no difference between them as regards possibility of perception.[1] (22.13). Therefore if we actually perceive only one of them, we (naturally) imagine that if the other were present, we should likewise perceive it, because the totality of the necessary conditions is fulfilled.[2] Thus something fancied as perceptibile is imputed. The non-cognition of such an object is called negation of a hypothetical visibility.[3] (22.15). Therefore that very spot from which the jar is absent and that cognition which is intent upon it are both styled negation of a possible visibility, since they are the real source of negative judgments.[4]

(22.16). Indeed we must at first be able to assert the presence of the (second) object which is a part of the same perception, and (then be able to assert that we have) this cognition. As long as (these two judgments are not made) we will never be able to assert the absence of something that could be present.[5] (22.17). Consequently what we call negation is (not absence of knowledge, but) a positive reality,[6] and an (assertory) cognition of it. (22.18). The simple unqualified absence of cognition, since it itself contains no assertion at all, can convey no knowledge. But when we speak of negation whose essence[7] is a negation of hypothetical perceptibility, these words may be regarded as necessarily implying[8] a bare place where there is no jar and the

---

[1] *yogyatā.*

[2] Lit., p. 22. 13—14. «Therefore when one (thing) combined in one cognition is visible, if the second would possess the whole totality of vision, it wonld be just (*eva*) visible».

[3] *dṛśya-anupalabdhi*, it is contrasted with *adṛśya-anupalabdhi*, negation of such objects which can never be visible, which we therefore cannot imagine as visible, i. e., transcendental objects, as e. g., an omniscient being whose existence can neither be affirmed, nor denied, since it is something nnknown to experience, it cannot be imagined as being experienced. Negation is a source of real knowledge (*niścaya*) only in regard to objects experimentally known.

[4] Lit. «the cause of a judgment (*niścaya*) about non-cognition of the (hypothetically) visible (*dṛśya*)». About *niścaya* as jndgment cp. above, p. 20 n. 6.

[5] Lit., p. 22. 16—17. «Indeed as long as the object combined in one cognition is not asserted (*niścita*) and its knowledge (is not asserted), so long there is no assertion of a non-cognition of the (hypothetically) visible».

[6] *vastu.*

[7] *rūpa.*

[8] *vacana-sāmarthyād eva.*

cognition of that same bare place. (Negation means the presence of a bare spot as well as the fact of its cognition).

(22. 20). Further, what is meant by the presence of (the totality) of conditions producing cognition?

14. The presence of (all) the conditions of cognition consists in the presence of an individual entity and the totality of all other conditions of cognition.

(22. 23). The conditions of cognition are present,—this means that the totality of the causes producing the perception, e. g., of a jar, is present. The words «the totality of all other conditions» have the following meaning. The cognition of a jar is produced (partly) by the jar itself, (partly) by other factors, the sense-organs etc. The words «other conditions» refer to the conditions other than the perceptible jar itself. The «totality» of them means their presence. (23. 1). The existence proper, that what distinguishes (one thing) from another, that peculiar (fact), i. e., separate (discontinuous, individually distinct existence).[1] Thus it is that an individually distinct existence and the presence of all other conditions must be both considered as constituting the perceptibility of jars and other (individual objects).

What is an individual? The (author) says,

15. It is a thing which, being present, is necessarily perceived when all other conditions of perceptibility are fulfilled.[2]

---

[1] *svabhāva-viśeṣa* means an individual in Locke's sense (Essay, XXVII. 4), existence individually distinct, «existence itself» (*svabhāva eva*), existence which is «the same as long as it is continued», existence determined by the *principium individuationis*, or Grundsatz der Individualisierung (Erdmann, *op. cit.*, p. 143). It must be distinguished from the extreme concrete and particnlar momentary thing (*svalakṣaṇa* = *kṣaṇa*) which has no duration and which is characterized by Locke, in a truly Indian manner, as «each perishing the moment it begins» (*yasminn eva kṣaṇe utpadyate tasminn eva vinaśyati*). Rgyal-thsab says, f. 25, *ghaṭo bhūtalāt svabhāva-viśiṣṭaḥ*, i. e., when a jar stands out in relief so as to be distinguished from its place, it is an individual, otherwise — according to Leibnitz' principle of Identity of Indiscernables it would not be an individual. Vinītadeva explains it as sensible existence, a possible sense-datum, not metaphysical, *na viprakṛṣṭaḥ* = *śakya-darśanaḥ* = *dṛśyaḥ*. The notions of sensible existence and individual existence are here characteristics of the same fact. Cp. also Kamalaśīla, p. 476. 1 and 481. 15.

[2] According to Dh., p. 23. 7, the Tib., p. 51. 7, Vinītadeva, p. 62. 5 and Rgyal-thsab, f. 25. a. 2, the sūtra reads — *satsv apy anyeṣu upalambha-pratyayeṣu yaḥ svabhāvaḥ san pratyakṣa eva bhavati.*

(23.6). An individual means an entity which, being present, necessarily is perceived when all other conditions of perceptibility, i. e., the causes other than the perceptible jar itself, are fulfilled. The following is here meant[1]. It is a definition of perception made from the standpoint of an individual observer. (23.8). Indeed, if a man is actually observing something, the perceived thing possesses the two (above mentioned requisites of perception). But things imperceptible, whose place, time and essence are inaccessible,[2] have no distinct reality for him, although all other conditions of perceptibility be fulfilled. (23.10). The (subjective) factors which allow the observer to see are, indeed, present. (Even if he sees nothing of the sort) they are present when he looks.[3] But if he does not look at all, objects, although they be in a place amenable to his senses, cannot be perceived. The distinct object is then present, the remaining conditions are not fulfilled. Things remote in time and place will then lack both conditions of perceptibility. (23.12). Thus it is that if somebody is looking on, the distinct thing might be absent, but all other conditions are not absent. If he does not look on, then an object, situated in his ken, (an object) which he could perceive, (but does not perceive), is deficient with regard to the other (the subjective) conditions of perceptibility. (23.14). All other objects (the remote and the inaccessible) are then deficient in both respects.

(23.15). After having done with the example of negation, (the author) proceeds to give an example of an analytical reason (founded on Identity).

16. Identity is a reason for deducing a property when (the subject) alone is by itself sufficient for that deduction.[4]

---

[1] Mallavādī, fol. 49, says—*nanu deśa-kāla-svabhāva-viprakṛṣṭāḥ piśācādayo 'smad-ādi-pratyayāntara-sākalyavantas, tathā taddeśa-tatkāla-varti-puruṣasya piśāca-rūpa-apekṣayā apratyakṣāś ca, teṣām apy upalabdhi-lakṣaṇa-prāptatvād upalabdhi-lakṣaṇa-prāptasyeti yad viśeṣaṇam* (22.1) *deśādi-viprakṛṣṭa-vyāvartakam tad anarthakam evety āśankya āha tad ayam iti* (23.7). Cp. text, p. 33.20 ff.

[2] *deśa-kāla-svabhāva viprakṛṣṭa* refers to things metaphysical, uncognizable, neither by the senses nor by the reason (=*adṛśya*, not *adṛśyamāna*), cp. *infra* sūtras II. 28, 48, 49, III. 97 and Kamalaśīla, p. 476.3. Mallavādī, f. 49, has *adṛśyeti*, not *adṛśyamāna*. Vinītadeva seems not to involve *viprakṛṣṭa* here.

[3] *nanu yadā cakṣur-ādibhir merv-ādīn na paśyati, tadā katham cakṣur-ādayaḥ sannihitāḥ, padārtha-jñānena sānnidhya-anumites teṣām ity āha, ataś ceti* (23.10), cp. Mallavādī, fol. 49—50. Read *ataś ca sannihitā yair*...

[4] Lit., p. 23.16. «Own existence (*svabhāva*) is a reason for a deduced property (*sādhya-dharma*) which exists in its own (the reason's) existence only (read *sva-*

(23. 17). The essence of a thing (can be a valid) logical reason. This is the idea.[1] What kind of logical reason consists in its merely being contained in its own predicate? The predicate possesses the characteristic of existing wheresoever the mere existence of the reason (is ascertained). (23. 18). A predicate whose presence is dependent on the mere existence of the reason, and is dependent upon no other condition besides the mere existence of the fact constituting the reason— such is the predicate which is inseparable from the reason (and can be analytically deduced).

(23. 20). When such (a predicate) is deduced, the reason represents the same fact of existence as the predicate, it is not different, (it is identical).

(23. 21). An example is given.

---

sattā-mātra-bhāvini)». Cp. Sigwart, *op. cit.* I. 264, «wo ein Subject für sich ausreicht (= *sva-sattā-mātra*) seine Bestimmugen (= *sādhya-dharma*) nothwendig zu machen ... fassen wir die Nothwendigkeit (*niścaya*) als eine innere». The subject in an analytical judgment is thus the «sufficient reason» for deducing the predicate. It is therefore rightly characterized here as a reason (*linga, hetu*). It will also appear as «subject» of the major premise in the fully expressed formula of a deductive reasoning. When two characteristics are essential and coexist in the same object, at the same moment, the mere fact of the existence of the object (*sva-sattā-mātra*) is then sufficient for deducing the presence of its essential property. The analytical judgment «Aśoka is a tree» is thus conceived as an inference in the form of «this is a tree, because it is an Aśoka; whatsoever is an Aśoka is also a tree». The major premise in this inference is an analytical judgment. Its subject represents the reason (*hetu*), its predicate the major term (*sādhya*). Their connection is a connection of Identity (*tādātmya*). Between the tree and the Aśoka-tree there is no difference in the underlying point of reality, the Aśoka is existentially identical with the tree. Dharmakīrti, therefore, characterizes their relation, in this sense, as founded on Identity (*tādātmya*), cp. sūtra II. 23—25. Kant, Kritik d. r. V.[2], p. IV, calls analytical those judgments where the connection of the predicate with the subject is conceived «through their identity». Wundt, Logik[2], I. 234, calls it «partielle Identität», Bosanquet, Logic, I. 14 — «identity in difference», Sigwart, *op. cit*, I. 111, objecting to Kant's view, prefers to call it «agreement» (Uebereinstimmung). The last named author, *ibid.* I. 264 ff., gives also expression to the view that the necessity of everything existing is deduced either out of its essence or out of its origin (aus dem Wesen und der Ursache); this would correspond to Dharmakirti's division of affirmation as founded either on Identity or Causation (*tādātmya-tadutpatti*), cp. also Schuppe, Logik, p. 128. All judgments which are not founded on a causal relation between the terms, and which are not negative, can be reduced to such a formula where the minor term is a point-instant, the major is the predicate, and the middle, which is the subject in the analytical judgment, represents the justification for predication.

[1] *sambandha.*

17. As e. g.—Thesis. This is a tree.
Reason. Because it is an Ašoka.

(24. 2). The word «this» points to the subject (of the conclusion), the words «a tree» contain the predicate, the words «because it is an Ašoka» contain the reason. This means,—this object is fit to be called a tree, because it is fit to be called an Ašoka. (24. 3). Now, if some unintelligent man who does not know the proper nse of the word Ašoka (would reside) in a country where such trees are abundant, and if somebody would point out to him a high Ašoka and say «this is a tree», then the man, being unintelligent, will think that the height of the Ašoka is the reason why it is called a tree. Looking at a small Ašoka, he would think that is not a tree. (24. 6). This unintelligent man must be induced (to use the word tree properly, as being) the general mark of every Ašoka. It means that not the height or some other special mark are the reasons for nsing the word tree, but (its essence alone), the mere fact of its being an Ašoka, its (general) characteristics, its boughs and other attributes, are the reason.[1]

(24. 9). In order to exemplify (a deduction by causality, where the reason is) an effect, the author says.

18. The effect is as follows.
Thesis. Here is fire.
Reason. Because there is smoke.

(24. 11). «Fire» is the predicate (major term). «Here» is the subject (minor term). «Because there is smoke» is the reason (middle term).

Causality is a conception familiar in common life.[2] It is known to be derived from experience (of the presence of the cause wherever there is an effect present), and from the negative experience (of the absence of the effect when its cause is deficient). Therefore the defini-

---

[1] Judgments referring to the extension and comprehension of concepts are thus brought under this head. Vinītadeva gives here no example at all. The formula of Dharmakīrti refers to all analytical judgments or inferences, and not to snch cases of name-explaining alone.

[2] This of course does not mean that the every-day conception of causality is admitted. Dharmakīrti develops his views on that subject in Pramāṇaviniš-caya. The exposition in Sarvadarš. S. (p. 5 ff.) is borrowed from that source. Cansality exists only between point-instants (*kṣaṇa*) which are not producing, but merely following one another. Dharmottara alludes to this theory above, text p. 10. 12 and in the sequel, p. 70 ff. But predication, inferring, purposive action, cognition, and consequently causation are examined in logic mainly from the empirical point of view.

tion of causality is not given, in contradistinction from the analytical reason (whose definition has been given).

§ 5. How are synthetic and analytic judgments possible.

(24. 13). (The consistency of a division into Negation, Identity and Causality) might be questioned. (If they are quite different) three principles, we cannot at all speak of one logical reason (in general). And if they are the different varieties (of one genus), then (the varieties may be endless), because the various cases of an analytical deduction alone are innumerable, and it becomes impossible to reckon only three varieties of logical deduction. To this we answer that (the principle of the division) is the following one.

19. (Cognition) is either affirmation or negation, (and affirmation) is double, (as founded either on Identity or on Causation).[1]

(24. 16). The word «here» means «among these three different logical reasons». Two reasons establish realities. They are the foundation, or justification,[2] for an affirmative judgment.[3] The (remaining) one is the reason, or justification, for a negative judgment. It must be kept in mind that by negation we mean (all deductions of) absence and the practical value of negation in life.[4] (24. 18). The meaning is the following one. (The reasons are different not by themselves, but indirectly,

---

1 Lit., p. 24. 15. «Here two are establishing real things (*vastu*), one is the reason of negation».

2 *gamaka*.

3 Very noteworthy is here the identification of reality (*vastu*) with affirmation (*vidhi*). The following terms must be regarded as synonymous *vastu* = *paramārtha-sat*, cp. p. 13. 18, = *svalakṣaṇa*, cp. p. 13. 10, = *kṣaṇa*, cp. p. 12. 18, = *artha-kriyā-kāri*, cp. p. 13. 15, = *vidhi*; cp. Tātp., 430. 19 p. — *bāhyasya* = *svalakṣaṇasya* = *vidhi-rūpasya* = *paramārtha-sataḥ*, and Tarkabhāṣā, p. 31 (Bombay ed.) where *sāmānya* is characterized as *pramāṇa-nirasta-vidhi-bhāva*.

4 *abhāva-vyavahāra*. This point is insisted upon because negation is also interpreted as the cognition of a point-instant of efficient reality (*vastu*), cp. text p. 28. 22—*artha-jñāna eva.... ghaṭasya abhāva ucyate*. It is the result of the first formula of negation, while *abhāva* is deduced in the remaning ten formulae, cp. *infra*, text p. 29. 22—24 and 38. 4—5. Ācārya Šākyabuddhi objects to this sūtra. In the inference «the word is not eternal, because it has an origin» the reason is positive, the conclusion negative, and in the inference «there is fire removing cold on the mountain, because we see smoke», the conclusion is positive, if the presence of fire be the main thing, it is negative, if the absence of cold is intended as the main thing, cp. Rgyal-thsab, Rigs-thigs-ḥgrel, f. 26 (Lhasa ed).

through the difference in the things they help to establish). The reason is subordinate to the deduced predicate. Its aim is to assert the existence of the predicate. The predicate constitutes the main (independent) part. Therefore the reason which is subordinate to the predicate is split into varieties not by itself, but in accordance with a division of the main part, the predicate. (24.19). The predicate is sometimes positive, sometimes negative. Since affirmation and negation represent attitudes mutually exclusive,[1] the reasons for them both must be different. (24.20). Affirmation[2] again, (i. e., the reality which is asserted, can only be) either different from the fact from which it is deduced or identical[3] with it. Difference and non-difference being mutually opposed by the law of contradiction, their justifications must also differ. (25.1). Therefore, there is altogether no inherent difference in the reasons *qua* reasons,[4] but when the deductions[5] (that follow) are exclusive of one another, their reasons become different (indirectly).

(25.3). Why again is it that these three (relations) represent logical reasons? Why are there no other (relations) representing valid reasons?[6] In his answer (the author) shows both why the three mentioned varieties are alone valid reasons, and why the others are not.

20. Because one thing can convey the (existence of) another one when it is existentially dependent (on the latter).

(25.6). Existentially dependent means dependent in its own existence. Existential (and necessary) dependence means dependent existence.[7] When the cause of something is to be deduced (synthetically), or an essential quality[8] is to be deduced (analytically), the effect is in its existence dependent upon its cause, (and the analytically deduced) fact is by its essence dependent upon the fact from which it is deduced. (25.8). Both

---

1 *paraspara-parihāra* is the second mode of the law of contradiction, cp. below, sūtra III. 77.

2 Here again affirmation (*viddhi*) means object of which the existence is affirmed, *vidhīyate iti vidhiḥ* (*karma-sādhana*).

3 *abhinna*, cp. p. 48.9 — *sa eva vṛksaḥ, saiva śiṃśapā.*

4 *svata eva.*

5 *sādhya.*

6 The Naiyāyikas assume an indefinite variety of relations (*sambandho... yo vā so vā bhavatu*) established by experience, Tātp., p. 107.10.

7 Lit., p. 25.6—7. «Being tied np by one's own existence means having one's own existence tied up. The composite nonn is according to the rule, Pāṇini II.1.32».

8 The term *svabhāva* is here used in two different senses, *svabhāva-pratibandha* is existential tie which *includes* the relation of the effect to its cause. But

these (connections) are contained in the one expression «existentially dependent.»[1] (25.9). (This means that) because the fact (expressing) the reason can prove the existence of the fact (corresponding to) the predicate, only if it is existentially dependent (on the latter), therefore, the above mentioned three relations alone can prove something, and there are no other relations which would allow to deduce (one fact from another).[2]

(25.11). Now, why is it, that we can deduce one fact from another, only if there is existential dependence?

21. Because a fact which is not so dependent upon another one, cannot be invariably and necessarily concomitant with the latter.

(25.14). «So dependent» means existentially dependent. A fact whose existence is not dependent upon another one, is not so dependent. (25.15). If one fact is not existentially dependent on another one, it is independent, and there can be no regularity[3] in its concomitance with the latter. Such a fact, representing that part from which the other part depends, cannot itself be subject to a rule of concomitance.[4] (25.17). The meaning is the following. If a fact is not tied up

in *svabhāva-anumāna* this term means identity in the sense indicated above, p. 66, it then is *exclusive* of the relation of causality. We must distinguish between *svabhāva-linga*, identity and *svabhāva-pratibandha*, dependence. Smoke is *svabhāvena pratibaddha* with fire, but they are two different *svabhāvas*, it is synthesis. On the other hand Aśoka, although likewise *svabhāvena pratibaddha* with tree, includes the latter in its *svabhāva*, the *svabhāva* is one, it is analysis. In the latter sense *svabhāva* refers to the intention, the essential properties, of a term. Thus, e. g., *śiṃśapā* is *vṛkṣa-svabhāvā* = *vṛkṣa-vyāpyā*, but not *vice versa*, *vṛkṣaḥ* is not *śiṃśapā-svabhāvaḥ*.

1 Lit., p. 25.7—8. « When cause and essence must be established, the essential tie (*svabhāvena pratibandha*) of the result and of essence (*svabhāva* in the sense of identity) is not different, thus both are comprehended in one composite word. The word *hi* has the sense of «because».

2 Since internal inference (*svārthānumāna*), as stated above p. 66 n., corresponds rather to our judgment, the classification of affirmative judgments (*vidhi* cp. text, p. 24.16) in *svabhāvānumāna* and *kāryānumāna* corresponds to our classification of judgments in synthetical and analytical. That the judgment «this Aśoka is a tree» is analytical will not be denied. All non-analytical, i. e., synthetical judgments are conceived as judgments of causality, because, as just mentioned, every regular connexion between two point-instants of reality is regarded as causation.

3 *niyama*.

4 Lit., p. 25.15—16. «What is not tied up to what, by its essence, for this not tied up to that, there is no rule (*niyama*) of non-divergence in that. Non-diver-

by its existence to another one, it cannot be necessarily concomitant with the fact to which it is not tied up. Therefore, there is no rule of their invariable concomitance, i. e., of the impossibility of the one being existent without the other.

(25.18). The possibility of deducing one fact from the other[1] reposes upon an invariable rule precluding the existence of the one without the existence of the other. (25.19). For we do not admit, that the logical mark is comparable to the light of a lamp which occasionally[2] brings to our knowledge some unperceived objects.[3] On the contrary (the logical mark is always a fact whose invariable connection) is ascertained beyond the possibility of exception.[4] (25.20). Therefore if (two facts) are existentially connected, we can assert that one of them cannot exist independently from the other, and therefore from the presence of the one follows the presence of the other. Hence it is established that the existence of one fact can convey the existence of another only when it is existentially dependent on the latter, not otherwise.

(25.22). Now, if among two facts one depends upon the other, there must be a dependent part and an independent part.[5] And here, between the logical reason and the logical predicate, who is dependent upon whom?

22. This is a dependence of the logical reason upon the fact which is deduced from it, (upon the predicate).

---

gence in that, is non-divergence in this object of being tied up, its rule....» Read *pratibandha-viṣaya* = *ḥbrel-pai yul gañ yin-pa de-la*.... According to the Tib. p., 57.8, we would expect *yaḥ pratibandha-viṣayas tasminn avyabhicāras tad-avyabhicāraḥ*; *pratibaddha* is the term of lesser extension, e. g., the Ašoka tree, *pratibandha-viṣaya* is the term of greater extension, e. g., the tree in general; *apratibandha-viṣaya* = *ma-ḥbrel-pai yul*, Tib. 57.11, is an object from which there is no dependence, with which another object is not invariably concomitant, cp. text p. 26.3. The logical mark, or middle term, is always a term of lesser extension as compared with the deduced fact, or major term. Therefore it is «tied up» or dependent.

[1] *gamya-gamaka-bhāva*. [2] *yogyatayā*.

[3] About invariable concomitance cp. above, p. 52 n. 3; it is here characterized as necessary; cp. also below, p. 72 notes 6 and 7.

[4] *niścaya* is here used as a synonym of *niyama*, cp. p. 25.16, just as above, p. 18.20, and below 26.16. Otherwise it is also used as a synonym of *kalpanā*, *vikalpa*, *adhyavasāya* and then means assertion, judgment cp. above, p. 47 and Tātp., p. 87.25.

[5] Lit., p., 25.22. «And is it not a tie of the dependent on the other upon the independent on the other»?

(26.2). This existential dependence is (a dependence) of the logical reason upon the fact (corresponding to the predicate). The logical reason, being the subordinate part, is dependent. On the contrary, the fact corresponding to the predicate is not subordinate, and therefore it is (the principal part), the part on which the mark depends,[1] and which is itself independent. (26.3). The meaning is the following. Even in those cases, where there is (an analytical deduction founded on) Identity[2] (of the predicate with the reason, there always is a dependent and an independent part). It is the dependent part that possesses the power to convey the existence of the other. The (independent part, that) to which the other is subordinated,[1] is the deduced part. (26.4). If the essence of an attribute[3] is such that it is invariably concomitant[4] with something else, it is dependent upon the latter, e. g., the fact of «being produced by a voluntary effort» is invariably concomitant with, (and dependent upon, or subordinate to), the fact of «not being an eternal entity».[5] On the other hand, a quality whose essence admits of being sometimes concomitant, and sometimes not, does not depend; it represents the fact upon which the other depends, e. g., the quality called «non-eternity» *versus* the quality of «being a voluntary product», (for there are other non-eternal objects besides those produced by a voluntary human effort). (26.7). The possibility of deducing one fact from another reposes on a necessary connection.[6] The essence of a thing produced by a voluntary effort is never to represent an eternal (substance), this is a necessary characteristic (of such things). (26.8). Therefore it (represents) just the fact which invariably is concomitant with the fact of impermanence. Thus it is that concomitance cannot be anything but the (necessary relation) of a determined object.[7]

---

[1] *pratibandha-viṣaya.*

[2] *tādātmya-aviśeṣe,* lit. «in non-difference of identity»; about identity between the terms of an analytical judgment cp. above, p. 66 n.

[3] *dharma* [4] *niyataḥ svabhavāḥ.*

[5] Whatsoever is voluntarily produced is non-eternal, as e. g., a jar, but not *vice versa,* a thing can be non-eternal without being voluntarily produced, e. g., lightning, although not created by human effort, is evanescent.

[6] Lit., p. 21. 7. «The relation of deducer and deduced (*gamya-gamaka-bhāva*) refers indeed to necessity»; *niścaya* = *niyama.*

[7] Lit., p. 26. 8. «Therefore the relation of deduced and deducer possesses just a determined object, not otherwise». The anthor insists repeatedly (text pp. 19, 26, 47, 49 etc.) that logical concomitance is a necessary relation. Invariable concomitance is always of the middle with the major term, it is *niyata-viṣaya,* i. e., it refers only to the middle term. The reason is always a dependent fact, and because it is dependent, it proves the reality of the other fact *upon which* it is dependent.

(26. 10). Further, why is it that the mark, (i. e., the reality underlying the reason) is existentially so related to the predicate?

23. Because, as regards (ultimate) reality, (the entity underlying the logical reason) is either just the same as the entity (underlying) the predicate, or it is causally derived from it.[1]

(26. 12). In reality (there are only two necessary relations, Identity and Causation). «Identity» with the predicated fact means that (the mark) represents (the predicate) itself, its essence. Since (in those cases) the essence of a logical reason is contained in the predicate, therefore it is dependent upon the latter (and invariably concomitant with it).[2]

(26. 13). The question arises, that if they are essentially identical, there will be no difference between reason and predicate, and then the argument will be (a repetition or) a part of the thesis?[3] Therefore it is said, «as regards reality», i. e., the two are identical with reference to what is the ultimately real essence, (i. e., the sense datum underlying both facts). (26. 15). But the constructed objects, those (conceptions) which have been superimposed (upon reality), are not the same (in the

---

1 Lit., p. 26. 11. «Because in reality there is identity with, and production from. the thing predicated». The author insists that there can be only two kinds of logical relations. The priuciple of his division is this. Existence is split in point instants. Every efficient point-instant can be the substratum of a variety of characteristics. It can be a tree, an Ašoka-tree, a solid body, a substance, etc., etc. All such characteristics refer to the same entity, they are simultaneous, they will be, according to the terminology of the author, identical. But if a tree is characterized as produced from a seed, this will be a relation between two realities, two underlying point-instants, since there is a causal relation only between the last moment of the seed and the first moment of the sprout. Therefore there can be only two relations between the terms in cognition, either the one is contained in the other, or it is produced from it, either analysis or synthesis, either identity or causation.

2 Lit., p. 26. 12—14. «From reality etc.; of what this *probandum* is the Self, the own existence, that is (the possessor) of its Self. Its condition is its-selfness, (the Self of one thing belonging to another thing); for this reason. Since the *probans* possesses the own Self of the *probandum*, therefore it is existentially tied up. This is the meaning. If the *probans* possesses the own existence of the *probandum*,...».

3 The thesis will be, e. g., «this is a tree», and the reason «because it is an Ašoka-tree». The reason «Ašoka-tree» contains the predicate «tree», or Ašoka-tree is a part of trees in general; *pratijñā* is here the same as *sādhya* or *pakṣa*, cp. III. 40 The analytical judgment being reduced to the formula «the Ašoka-tree is a tree» seems utterly useless. This problem continues to puzzle European philosophers The Indiau solution is here hinted, it will be reconsidered *infra*, in sūtra III. 20

facts constituting) the reason and the consequence.[1] (26.16). (We have already mentioned that)[2] the possibility of deducing one fact from the other always reposes upon a necessary (connection between them). Therefore their difference (in an analytical deduction) concerns exclusively those (constructed) conceptions which have been superimposed (upon the same reality) and which are necessarily (connected).[3] The (underlying) reality is the same.

(26.17). But Identity is not the only (possible relation between, a logical mark and what can be deduced from it). There is moreover (the relation of Causality). The mark can represent an effect of the fact (whose existence is then) inferred from it. The logical reason (middle term) can be existentially dependent on, (and therefore invariably concomitant with), another fact, the existence of which is deduced from it, because (the reason) owes its existence to it.[4]

(26.19). Why is it that a logical connection can be the outcome of no other relation[5] than these two, (Indentity and Causality)?

24. Because when a fact is neither existentially identical with another one, nor is it a product of the latter, it cannot be necessarily dependent upon it.

(26.21). If one fact is a characteristic of the same (underlying) existence as another one, they are (here said to be) existentially iden-

---

1 Lit., p. 15—16. «But the object of mental construction (*vikalpa*), that essence (*rūpa* = *svarūpa*) which has been superimposed by imagination (*samāropita*), with respect to it, there is a split between the reason and consequence».

2 Above, p. 26. 7.

3 Lit., p. 26. 16. «Therefore their difference is all right (*yukta*) only when referred to (that their) essence which is situated upon (*ārūḍha*) necessity (or assertion, *niścaya*)».-It has been noted above, p. 7 n., that the conception of *niścaya* or *niyama* is assimilated to *pramāṇa* and *samyag-jñāna*. All definite knowledge (*pratīti* = *bodha* = *adhigama* etc.) is constructed knowledge, *kalpita* = *vikalpita* = *samāropita* = *vikalpa-ārūḍha* = *niścaya-ārūḍha* = *buddhy-avasita*. Every definite assertion is thus contrasted with the indefinite, transcendental character of ultimate reality. And because all assertions are founded upon some invariable concomitance between constructed concepts, the term *niścaya* implies both necessity (= *niyama*) and judgment (*adhyavasāya* = *kalpanā*).

4 Lit., p. 26. 17—18. «Not alone from identy, but also there is origination of the mark from that deduced object, and because of origination from it, there is an essential tie of the mark to the deduced object».

5 *nimitta*,

tical, if not, they are existentially non-identical.[1] If one fact represents the effect of another one, it is a product of the latter, if not, it is not its product. (26.22). Now, a fact which is neither existentially identical, nor is it an effect (of another definite fact), cannot be necessarily dependent on the other fact which is neither its cause, nor existentially the same reality. For this reason (there can exist no other basis for a necessary logical connection than either Identity or Causality).[2] (27.3). If the existence of something could be necessarily conditioned by something else, something that would neither be its cause, nor essentially the same reality, then only could a necessary connection repose on another relation, (besides the law of Identity and the law of Causation). (27.4). Necessary (or essential) connection, indeed, means dependent existence.[3] Now, there is no other possible dependent existence (than these two, the condition of being the effect of something, and the condition of being existentially identical with something). Therefore the dependent existence of something (and its necessary concomitance) is only possible on the basis either of its being the product (of a definite cause) or of its being essentially (a part) of the same essence.[4]

(27.6). Now let us concede the point and admit that there is no other necessity in our knowledge than that which is founded either

---

1 Lit., p. 26. 21. «Of what this is the essence, it is (possessor) of that essence, not having that essence is possessor of an essence other than that».

2 Lit., p. 26. 22—27. 3. «What is not having the essence of what, and not having origination from what, for this not having the essence of that, and not having origination from that, there is an essence not tied up to that, to the not having that essence and to the non-producer, thus this is (the fact) whose essence is not tied up, (not dependent). Its condition is the possession of independent own-existence. Therefore (i. e.) because of the independent condition (of every fact which is neither analytically nor causally dependent)....».

3 This is a repetition of what has been said above, text p. 25. 7. The author insists that relation (*pratibandha* = *saṃsarga*) means dependence, this interdependence directly affects the constructed conceptions of our productive imagination, and indirectly the underlying «things in themselves», between which also these two relations of identity and causality are assumed.

4 The commentary of Vinītadeva upon this sūtra, p. 65. 10—15, runs thus. «What does not possess the same (underlying) essence with the predicate, and what does not originate from the entity (corresponding to) the predicate, in what way could it be said to be connected? What is not connected is not a mark, because an universal absurdity (*atiprasanga*) would follow, (everything could be deduced from anything). Therefore we can assert a (logical) connection only on the basis of an identical (fact of existence) or on the basis of causality, not otherwise».

on Identity or on Causation. But how are we, nevertheless, to explain the circumstance that nothing but a comprehended fact or a produced effect have the force necessarily to establish the existence of something by inference.[1]

25. It is (simply) because Identity and Causation (causal origin) belong just either to a comprehended property or to an effect. Inferential reference to Reality is possible exclusively on this basis.

(27.10). Since the possibility of deducing one fact from another is based exclusively upon these two relations of (underlying) Identity and Causation, and since they (in their turn) are founded exclusively upon either the presence of a (comprehended) attribute (allowing analytical deduction of the comprehensive fact), or upon the fact that a result (must have a cause), therefore the establishing of reality, or affirmation, is possible only upon the basis of these two relations, Identity and Causation.[2]

---

[1] Lit., p. 27. 6—7. «Let it be, for sure, that the Own-existence-bond comes only from Being-originated-by-this, but how is it that Own-existence, (i. e., the subordinated *svabhāva*, the comprehended property) alone (and) the effect (alone) are conveyors?»

[2] Lit., p. 27. 8—11. «And these Identity-with-that and Origination-from-that belong to the «own existence» and to the effect alone, thus from them alone is reality (*vastu*) established.—And these etc. The word *iti* in the sense of «therefore». Since Identy and Causation have their stand on «own existence» and result only, and conditioned by them is the relation of deducer and deduced, therefore from them alone, from «own existence» and result, comes establishing of reality or affirmation».—The fact of being a tree (*vṛkṣatva*) is included in the fact of being an Aśoka *śiṃśapātva*), the first fact «depends» (*pratibaddha*) upon the latter, it is invariably concomitant with the latter, because the latter is «its own existence» (*svabhāva*), i. e., both are characteristics of the same underlying reality (*vastu* = *paramārtha-sat* = *svalakṣaṇa* = *kṣaṇa*). We have here two terms so related that by the analysis of the one we get the other, by analysing the term of greater comprehension (*vyāpta*) we get the term of greater extension (*vyāpaka*). This relation is here explained as «identity» (*tādātmya*) of existence, since both terms ultimately refer to the same underlying sense-datum. A result, on the contrary, points to another reality which is the cause from wich it is derived. These two relations alone point to realities. Upon such a basis alone can we establish inferential reference to reality or truth. The term *vastu* «reality» is used as a synonym of *vidhi* «affirmative judgment», cp. text, p. 24. 16 and 27. 11. All affirmative judgments, so far they represent cognition of reality, can be reduced to these two patterns, «this is a tree, because it is an Aśoka», and «there is fire there, because there is

§ 6. The principle of negative judgments.

(27. 12). Now, why is it that we do not consider non-cognition of a thing[1] unimagined as the cause of success, (when purposive action is evoked) by a negative judgment?[2]

26. The success of negative behaviour is only owing to a negative cognition of the form described above.

(27. 14). The success of negative behaviour reposes exclusively upon such a (process of) repudiating in thought the imagined presence of an object. No other basis for it is therefore given.

(Two questions are now raised, 1) why does it repose upon such a basis, and 2) why no other basis, e. g., no real non-cognition of a real non-existence is possible)?

(27. 16). First, why does it repose upon such (a process)?

27. Because when a real object is present (it is perceived and it) becomes superfluons (to imagine its presence).

(27. 18). Because if the object to be denied[3] were present, (this would be perceived and) it would be impossible to deny its imagined presence.[4] This proves that negation is founded upon such (a process of repelling some suggestion).

---

smoke». It will be noticed that judgments, or inferences, abont future results are not considered as valid, e. g., «there will come a rain, because there are clouds» is a valid inference for the Naiyāyikas, but not for the Buddhists, because they assume that causes are not always followed by their results, cp. text, p. 40. 8. Resnlts necessarily must have always some canse or causes, therefore there is «necessity» (*niścaya*) in such affirmations, but no necessity in deducing a future result from its possible cause.

1 *adṛśya-anupalabdhi* is always problematic, cp. *infra*, p. 78 ff.

2 *pratiṣedha-siddhi* = *pratiṣedha-vyavahāra-siddhi* = *pratiṣedha-vaśāt puruṣārtha-siddhi*.

3 E. g., the visible jar (Rgyal-thsab); for Dh. this seems to refer to *viprakṛṣṭa-vastu*, cp. p. 28. 9.

4 The Indian realists maintained that negation is a cognition of real absence. Just as affirmation is cognition of real presence, they thought that negation is a non-cognition of real absence. The Mīmāṃsakas viewed non-existence as a reality *sui generis* (*vastvantaram*) and admitted *yogya-pratiyogy-anupalabdhi*, though not as *anumāna*, but as a special *pramāṇa* which they called *abhāva*. The Nyāya-Vaiśesika school viewed it as a special category (*padārtha*), a reality cognized by the senses owing to a special contact (*viśeṣya-viśeṣaṇa-bhāva-sannikarṣa*). The Sānkhyas

(27. 20). Why this alone is the basis, (and why is negation of unimaginable things impossible)?

28a. Because otherwise, (sc. if the absent thing has not been imagined as present, its absence, and the entailed successful actions, cannot follow with logical necessity).[1]

(28. 3). Because otherwise etc. The word «otherwise» implies — «because unimaginable (sc. metaphysical or problematic) negation is possible even if the (corresponding) entity be present». That is the reason why successful negation (in life) is founded on no other (but imaginable) denial. But why is that so? Why is it that even admitting the reality (of metaphysical entities), their (non-perception by the senses) can be (only problematic).[2]

28b. Because when entities do not conform to the conditions of cognizability, when they are inaccessible in space and time and (invisible) by nature, since all human experience is then excluded, apodictic negative judgments are not possible.[3]

(28. 5). We have stated above[4] that an object is said to be satisfying to all conditions of perceptibility, 1) when all the accompanying

---

applied their idea of *pratikṣaṇa-pariṇāma* and viewed *ghaṭa-abhāva* as a *pariṇāma-kṣaṇa* of *bhūtala* which, as all *pariṇāma-bheda*, is cognized, they maintain, by sense perception.

1 *anyathā ca*, according to Vinītadeva, p. 66. 18, and Rgyal-thsab, f. 27, = *dṛśyānupalabdhim anāśritya*, according to Dh., = *adṛśya-anupalabdhi-sambhavāt*.

2 Vinītadeva, p. 67 and Rgyal-thsab, f. 27, interpret sūtra II, 28 as meaning «because otherwise there can be no definite assertion (*niścaya*) of non-existence (*abhāva*) concerning...».

3 The *anupalabdhi* of the Sāṅkhyas, e. g., is an *adṛśya-anupalabdhi*, it refers to entities which are not sensibilia, not individually distinct. They maintain that their Matter (*pradhāna*) and Souls (*puruṣa*) are metaphysical (*sūkṣma* = *atīndriya*). Their non-perception alone (*anupalabdhi* = *pratyakṣa-nivṛtti-mātram*) does not entail apodictic negative judgment (*abhāva-niścaya*). They are cognized by *sāmānya-to-dṛṣṭa-anumāna* which is explained as *adṛṣṭa-svalakṣaṇasya sāmānya-viśeṣasya-darśanam*, cp. S.-t.-kaumudī *ad* K. 5—6. The Buddhists admit valid denial only if there is some *svalakṣaṇa* = *vidhi-rūpa* = *vastu* = *artha-kriyā-kāri*, i. e., in regard of such objects which can alternately be perceived and not perceived, present and absent, cp. *infra*, text, p. 38. 13. Cp. also, sūtra III. 97 where the judgment «he is not omniscient», being metaphysical, is proved to be problematic.

4 Sūtra II. 14; on Dh.'s interpretation of *viprakṛṣṭa* cp. notes on p. 64 and 65.

necessary conditions are fulfilled, and 2) when the individually distinct object itself is present. When one or the other of these clauses is deficient, the object is said to be in a condition of non-perception. The words «do not conform to the conditions of cognizability» point here to the absence of the first clause. The words «inaccessible in space, time and invisible by nature» point to the total absence of individual distinctness.

(28.9) There can be no certainty about the absence of such objects. We contend that we never could know it with certainty, eveu if such entities did really exist.[1]

(28.10). Why is it that there could be no such certainty? It is impossible, because human experience of such objects is excluded.

(28.11). Since human experience[2] in respect of (metaphysical objects) which do not satisfy to the conditions of possible experience is excluded, and there can be no apodictic knowledge of their non-existence,[3] therefore, even supposing that such objects really exist, only a metaphysical[4] negation regarding them is possible, a negation whose essence is to be beyond human experience.

(28.12). Thus the basis of negative judgments is that (process of thought which we have) described above.

(28.14). The time to which such cognition, if it is valid,[5] refers its essence, and its function will next be stated.

29. Negative behaviour[4] is successful when a present or a past negative experience of an observer has happened, provided the memory of this fact has not been obliterated.

(28.17). The preception by somebody of an object, e. g., of a jar, has not happened. This is called negative experience. This means that the essence of negation is the fact of some experience having not happened.[6]

---

1 Lit., p. 28.9—10. «Even if reality exists, its non-existence is admitted». *tasya abhāvaḥ = niščayasya abhāvaḥ, sati vastuni = pratiṣedhye sati vastuni.* *vastuni = pratiṣedhye sati vastuni* — *ātma-pratyakṣa-nivṛtti = vādi-prativādi-pratyakṣa-nivṛtti* (Rgyal-thsab).

2 *ātma-pratyakṣa-nivṛtti = vādi-prativādi-pratyakṣa-nivṛtti* (Rgyal-thsab).

3 *abhāva-niščaya-abhāva*; no assertion as of a reality (*vastu*), *ibid.*

4 *adṛšya = svabhāva-višeṣa-viprakṛṣṭa*, cp. sūtra II. 15.

5 *pramāṇa.*

6 *abhāva-vyavahāra*, a negative judgment, a negative proposition and a corresponding successful purposive action are suggested by this term, cp. text, p. 29, 22—23, for abbreviation we may express it as negative behaviour.

(28. 18). For this reason negation is not really deduced (by an inference), because simple negation, (being its fundamental aspect), is established (by direct perception). (But how can non-existence be perceived by the senses? It is perceived in imagination!)[1] An object, e. g., a jar, although absent, is nevertheless said to be perceived, because it is imagined as perceived, as being cognized in all normal conditions[2] of perception, upon a place which appears as part of the same act of cognition.

(28. 20). Therefore what we call negative experience[3] is this object (the substratum) itself appearing as part of the same cognition, and the cognition of such a substratum. Because on the basis of this perceived substratum and of its cognition we arrive at the judgment[4] on the absence of an object which is being imagined as perceived in all normal conditions of a (possible) experience.

(28. 22). Consequently when we assert the absence of the perceptible jar, we necessarily assert something positive, (we assert the presence of the bare place and the fact of its cognition).[5]

---

1 Lit., p. 28. 17—18. «The object jar etc. perceptible to the observer; its absence is non-cognition; its essence means so much as the absence of this (object). Just this non-existence is not deducible, because «non-perception of own existence» (the fundamental first formula of negation) is established (itself)». *abhāva-vyavahāra* is deduced in the first formula, *abhāva* is deduced in the remaining ones, cp. text p. 38. 4.

2 *samagra-sāmagrīka.*

3 *pratyakṣa-nivṛtti.*

4 *avasīyate = niścīyate = vikalpyate = pratīyate = prāpyate* etc.

5 Lit., p. 28. 22. «Therefore just (positive) cognition of a thing is called non-existence of a perceptible jar». Cp. Bradley, Principles², p. 117,— «every negation must have a ground and this ground is positive», it is affirmation of a quality *x* which «is not made explicit», and, p. 666, he even maintains that the negative is *more* real than what is taken as barely positive; B. Erdmann, Logik³, p. 500,— «die Urtheile mit verneinendem Prädicat sind trotzdem bejahend». According to the Indian view every judgment reduces to the form «this is that», *sa eva ayam*, it is an arrangement (*kalpanā*), or a conjunction (*yojanā*) at the same time it is a resolve, or a judgment in the real sense of the word (*adhyavasāya*) and a choice, a distinction, a contrast, the result of a disjunction (*vikalpa*). These terms describe the same fact (*anarthāntaram*, Tatp., p. 87). Now, in the conjunction of the two parts «this» and «that», of Thisness and Thatness (*idamtā* and *tattā*, cp. N. Kaṇikā, p. 124) the part «this» refers to Reality, to the point-instant, to the «thing in general» (Ding überhaupt), or «thing in itself» (*svalakṣaṇa = vastu = vidhi-svarūpa*). This is an intrinsic affirmation (*vastu = vidhi*, cp. above, p. 68 n. 3, *nāstīty anena na sambadhyate*, Tātp., p. 340. 11). The judgment is made up by the second part, by

And[1] since we are dealing here[2] (with inferential knowledge as far as it controls our purposive actions), absence is not the bare (phantom) of a non-Ens, because this alone could not produce an ascertainment of the absence of a (definite) perceptible thing.

(29. 1). Now,[3] (if) the absence of a visible thing[4] is ascertained through sense perception,[5] (and not through an inference, the practical importance of negation as a guide of our actions, could be derived from the same source)? Quite true! (It could be so derived). However,[6] (inference likewise plays a part, from the following point of view. At first) an object is imagined as visible (in the following manner), «if a jar did (really) exist on a place which would be a part of the same cognition, this jar would certainly be visible», and then, on the basis of such (a hypothetical judgment), we ascertain our negative experience.[7] (29. 3). When it has been ascertained that an object perceptible (by its nature) is not being perceived, we just *eo ipso*[8] realize its absence. If the visible object would have been present, its non-perception would never have occurred.[9]

«thatness», which contains no intrinsic affirmation (*nirasta-vidhi-bhāva*), it can be both, affirmation and negation (*gaur asti, gaur nāsti, ibid.*, p. 340. 10). It is always a universal (*sāmānya-lakṣaṇa*). a construction, not «a thing in itself», it involves a choice, a contrast, a distinction. A judgment without any reference to reality (i. e., to sensation) in the element «this», will be, as the Indian says, a lotus growing in the sky. All real cognitions are, in this sense, positive, whether they be expressed in the affirmative or in the negative. Cp. also H. Bergson, Evolution Créatrice,[11] pp. 297 ff.; S. Alexander, Space, Time and Deity, p. 198 ff.

1 *tu-śabdaḥ punar-arthe* (Mallavādī).

2 *iheti linga-prastāve* (*ibid*).

3 *nanu yathā bhūtala-grāhi-pratyakṣam ghaṭa-abhāve pramāṇam, tathā abhāva-vyavahāre'py astu, kim dṛśya-anupalambhena linga-bhūtena kāryam, iti parākṛtam prakaṭayann āha nanv ityādi* (p. 29. 1) (*ibid*).

4 *dṛśya-nivṛttir ghaṭa-abhāvaḥ* (*ibid*).

5 *dṛśya-anupalambhād iti kevala-bhūtala-grāhi-pratyakṣād iti tato 'abhāva-vyavahāro 'pi tataḥ syād iti parāśayaḥ* (*ibid*).

6 *nanu yady asmad-uktasya satyam ity ādinā* (p. 29. 2) *anumatis, tadā dṛśyā-nupalabdhi-lingatā na yuktā, ity āśankya āha, kevalam ity ādi, kiṃtu samānādhikaraṇyam iti* (*ibid*). *samānādhikaraṇyam* here evidently means that the same fact can be viewed either as a sense-perception or as an inference, cp. Kamalaśīla, p. 481. 12—*yatrāpi kevala-pradeśopalambhād* (*pratyakṣād*) *ghaṭa-abhāvaḥ siddhaḥ, sāpi ghaṭānupalambha-kārya-anupalabdhir eva* (*anumānam*). The absence of noise is perceived by *kāryānupalabdhi*, *ibid*.

7 *dṛśyānupalabdhir*. 8 *sāmarthyād eva*.

9 Lit., p. 29. 1—4. «And is not absence of the visible ascertained from non-perception of the visible? This is quite true! However, if on a visible (place) united in the same cognition there were a jar, it necessarily would be visible, thus the

(29. 4). Therefore,[1] when we have realized the non-perception of the object after having imagined its presence, (this process contains) by implication [2] the idea of its non-existence. However, this idea has not yet been translated into life.[3] It can therefore receive practical application on the basis of (an inference whose middle term is) non-perception.[4] (29. 6). Consequently we must keep in mind that what is called negation (has a positive ground in) the associated bare place and in the fact of its being perceived, because this can be regarded as the middle term in an inference which repels the suggested presence of a visible object.[5]

---

visible is imagined, from it non-perception of the visible is ascertained, and just from the capacity of the ascertainment of non-perception of the visible, the non-existence of the visible is ascertained».

1 *ata evambhūtād dṛśya-anupalambha-niścayād iti samānādhikaraṇyam* (*ibid*).

2 *sāmarthyād.*

3 *vyavahṛta.* — On the practical importance of negation in life (*abhāva-vyavahāra*) B. Erdmann delivers himself, Logik[3], p. 500, as follows, «das formulierte Denken findet... Anlässe für die Bildung kontradictorischer Artunterschiede, eben weil es das Wirkliche vom Standpunct der practischen Weltanschauung aus deutet, der das anschaulich und *practisch - teleologisch* Hervortretende vor allem ins Auge fallen lässt». Cp. H. Bergson, *op. cit.*, pp. 297, 312, 315, 321.

4 *atha yadi dṛśya-anupalambhena kevala-bhūtala-grāhi-pratyakṣena dṛśya-ghaṭa-abhāvo niścīyata eva, na vyavahriyate, tarhi kena vyavahartavya ity āha dṛśyetyādi* (p. 29. 5), *dṛśya-anupalambhena linga-bhūtena vyavahartavya ity arthaḥ* (*ibid*). Cp. Kamalaśīla, p. 481. 18, — *tasmāt sarvatra svabhāvānupalabdhir asad-vyavahāra-hetuḥ paramārthataḥ kāryānupalabdhir eva draṣṭavyā.*

5 Lit., 29. 6—7. «Therefore another thing which is being perceived and associated in one cognition and its cognition, since they are the logical reason (*hetu*) for the ascertainment of the absence of the perceived (thing). should be regarded as called absence of the perceived». — The fully expressed-formula of a negative inference is given in III. 9. — All these subtleties are probably the outcome of controversies with the Mīmāṃsakas who also admitted «repelled suggestion» or «challenged imagination» (*dṛṣya-anapalabdhi*) as a method of cognizing real non-existence (*vastu*), though they viewed it not as an inference, but as a third, independent source of our knowledge, cp. note 3 on p. 77. For the Buddhists the reality (*vastu*) is the bare place which is cognized by the senses. The Mīmamsakas retorted that the place is also perceived when the jar is present. We would then have the absurdity that the absence of the jar must also be perceived if the jar be present. Therefore, they concluded, absence must be a reality *sui generis* (*vastvantaram*). — Among European logicians Sigwart inclines to the view that negation is really an inference («secundärer und abgeleiteter Ausdruck», *op. cit.* I. 167), J. N. Keynes, in despair, thinks that «the nature of logical negation is of so fundamental and ultimate a character that any attempt to explain it is apt to obscure rather than to illumine», cp. Formal Logic[4], p. 120.

(29.7). And just as a jar, although absent, (can be now) imagined s present on a perceived spot which is part of the same perception, we can likewise remember the absence of a jar in the past). The haracter[1] of the jar is the same, it is a non-existing jar, it is imagied on a present, or remembered on a former, place, it is appertaining) the same cognition, provided the memory of the latter has not been bliterated.[2]

(29.9). Thus the essence of logical negation[3] has been explained, , is the perception of a jar that has not happened. And this is a eal fact established (by introspection).[4] Thus the non-existence of a ır cannot be deduced, but the negative judgment, as mentioned above,[5] s deduced (from that fact).

(29.11). «Not obliterated» refers to an impression[6] produced by n experience and having the capacity of evoking a recollection. This efers to a past experience of some human individual, and a present xperience of such an individual is likewise referred to. (29.13). But he qualification of «non-obliterated» memory does not refer to the resent cognition. It occurs that an impression produced by a spot vithout any jar upon it leaves no traces, neither is the imagined jar

---

1 *tad-rūpam*.

2 Lit, p. 29.7–9. «And just as the perceptibility of a jar on a perceived place) united in one cognition, although it does not exist, just so on this (place) nited in one cognition past, if the memory-impression has not been obliterated, nd present, this form of the jar is imagined although non-existent, thus should t be considered».

3 *dṛśya-anupalabdhi*.

4 *sā ca siddhā*, p. 29.10 = *sā ca siddhā*, Tattvas., p. 481.2, cp. 479.22, it. «it really exists», «it is established as an objective reality», the reality s the bare place. The realists who maintained that negation is a negative ognition of real absence (*adṛśya-anupalabdhi*) contended that the Buddhist dea of a non-Ens had no corresponding objective reality, that it was *asiddha*, *uccha*. The Buddhists answered that their view was proved and the objective eality of their idea of a non-Ens established as an active principle of cognition and onscious behaviour (*abhāva-vyavahāra*), by both perception and introspection (*sva-aṃvedana*), perception of the bare place and introspective awareness of that perception. Cp. Mallavādī, fol. 58,—*atha bhavadīyāpi anupalabdhiḥ parokṣa-nivṛtti-nātra-tuccha-rūpa-anupalabdhivad asiddhā syād ity āśankya āha, sā cetyādi* p. 29. 10). *kevala-bhūtala-grāhi-jñāna-rūpāyā anupalabdheḥ sva-saṃvedana-pratyakṣa-siddhatvāt, kevala-bhūtala-rūpāyāś ca kevala-bhūtala-grāhi-pratyakṣa-jñāna-siddhatvāc ceti.*

5 p. 29.5.

6 Here the term *saṃskāra* = *smṛti-bīja* is used in the Naiyāyika sense, as the pecial faculty included in the *smṛti-janaka-sāmagrī*.

remembered, nor the fact of the failure to perceive any. But a present spot, when there is no jar on it, cannot escape memory. Neither the imagined jar, nor the failure to perceive it can then be forgotten Therefore the qualification of non-obliterated memory is not meant as a characteristic of a present negation.[1] A present object is never severed from the trace which it leaves in memory.[2]

(29.18). What is meant is this. Negation is valid in regard of a past object, if this is clearly remembered, and in regard of a present one. We can cognize «there was here no jar, because we did not perceive any», «there is here no jar, because we do not perceive any». But the judgment «there will be here no jar, because we will not perceive any» is impossible, since a future non-perception is problematic. The time of valid negation has thus been defined.

(29. 22). Its function will be next indicated. It consists in making use of the idea of non-existence (by applying it to life). (It includes) 1) the judgment «there is not», 2) the words expressing it, and 3) successful purposive action, consisting in moving about with the certainty (not to fall upon the absent object). The last case is the physical[3] use of the idea of non-existence. When a man knows that there is no jar (in the place), he moves about without expecting (to find it). This threefold practical application[4] of the idea of non-existence is based upon non-perception of the hypothetically visible.

(30. 1). But has it not been stated above that the judgment «there is no jar» is *produced* by (sense-perception, by the perception of) the bare place?[5] (And now we include this judgment into the practical consequences *deduced by inference* from this perception). (30. 2). (Yes, we do not deny that!). Since the bare place is cognized by sense-perception, and since the negative judgment «there is here no jar» is a judgment produced by the direct function of perception, (that function which makes the object present to our senses), therefore (it is quite

---

[1] Vinītadeva has interpreted this passage as if the qualification of «non-obliterated memory» could refer to both the present and the past experience, cp. p. 68. 1—5, (but not in 69. 14). Dharmottara takes great pains apparently to redress this slight inconsistency.

[2] Lit., p. 29. 17—18. «For this very reason the word «and» has been used, «and of the present», in order that it should be known that the «present» without any qualification is combined together with the past as possessing qualification».

[3] *kāyika.*

[4] *vyavahāra.*

[5] *anupalabdher*, p. 30. 1, is explained by Mallavādī as = *bhūtalād.*

rue) that the negative judgment immediately following on the perception[1] of the bare place is a perceptual judgment. (30.4). Indeed, the negative judgment, according to what has been said above, is directly produced by sense-perception, because (qualified) perception has just the capacity of producing a judgment as to the existence (before us) of a bare place.[2] (30.5). However,[3] (the proper function of negation consists in the next following step). Objects might be not perceived, but this only gives rise to doubt, (the feeling arises as to which of them) might be present? So long as this doubt has not been removed, negation has no practical importance, (it cannot guide our purposive actions).[4] (30.6). (Imagination then steps in, and) it is thus that negation, (as a negative deduction), gives practical significance to the idea of a non-Ens. Since an object which I imagine as present on a given place is not really perceived, just therefore do I judge that «it is not there». (30.7). Consequently this negation of an imagined presence (is an inference which) gives life to the ready concept of a non-Ens, it does not newly create this concept itself. Thus it is that (the author) maintains that the negative judgment receives its practical significance (through an inference) from challenged imagination,[5] although it is really produced by sense-perception and only applied in life (through a deductive process of an inference whose logical reason consists in the fact of) a negative experience.[6] A negative inference, therefore, guides our steps when we apply in life the idea of a non-Ens.[7]

---

[1] *pratyakṣa-vyāpāra* = *nirvikalpaka-pratyakṣa*, *tad-anusārī niścayaḥ* = *savikalpaka-pratyakṣa*, in the sense explained above, text p. 16, transl. p. 45.

[2] *dṛśya-anupalambha-śabdena* (p. 30. 4) *bhūtala-jñānam bhūtalam coktam* Mallavādī.

[3] *kevalam*, the *cheda* after *sambhavāt* must be dropped.

[4] *vyavahartum* = *pravartayitum*.

[5] *anupalambhāl liṅgāt*, *ibid.*

[6] *anupalambhena liṅga-rūpeṇa*, *ibid.*

[7] Lit., p. 30. 1—30. 9. «And although the cognition «there is no jar» appears just from non-cognition and just this is an ascertainment of non-existence, nevertheless, since by perception the bare place is cognized, and therefore the ascertainment of non-existence follows on the function of perception thus «there is here no jar», therefore the ascertaining of non-existence which follows on the function of grasping the bare place is done by perception. And moreover, non-existence is ascertained just by perception in the above mentioned manner, just by its capacity of making an ascertainment of the non-cognition of the visible. (30. 5). However, since (things) non-perceived can also exist, through the doubt of existence he is not able to use non-existence. Therefore non-cognition makes us use non-existence. Since the visible is not perceived, therefore it does not exist. (30. 7). Therefore non-cog-

(30. 10). Why is it then that negation is valid (only) in regard o past or present events? The (author) says,

30. It is exclusively on the basis of sucl (negation) that absence can be ascertained (witl logical necessity).

(30. 12). The absence (of a thing) is ascertained only from it, i. e exclusively through a negation of a determined time, as has been indi cated above. A future negative experience has always the nature c being itself problematic. Since it is itself uncertain,[1] a negative jud gement[2] cannot be (sufficiently) founded on it, but a past or presen (non-perception is a sufficient reason for deducing a negativ judgment).

§ 7. THE DIFFERENT FORMS OF NEGATIVE JUDGMENTS.

(30. 14). The different varieties of negation are next shown.

31. This (negation) has eleven varieties, accoı ding to difference of formulation.

---

nition of the visible turns out the ready made cognition of non-existence, but do not make the unmade. Therefore the ascertainment of non-existence, although tu: ned out by non-cognition, is made by perception, it is said to be turned out by noı cognition. Thus non-cognition is directing the run of non-existence».— Mallavā calls attention to the circumstance that this passage should not be regarded as mere repetition of the argument contained in the passage *nanu ca* etc. on p. 29. and explains that the objector in 29. 1 ff. contended that the practical use of the id of a non-Ens is produced directly from the perception of the bare place, just as tl idea itself (*abhāva-niścaya*) is produced. The solution, in the passage *kevalam* et p. 29. 2 ff., is that sense-perception *produces* a negative perceptive judgment, tl negative inference *deduces* its practical applications. In the second instance, in tl passage *yady api ca* etc., p. 30. 1, the objection is that the judgment «there is no is also comprized under the practical applications of the idea of a non-Ens (*abhā vyavahāra*) and must be, accordingly, characterized as inferential, not as perceptu We are thus seemingly landed into a contradiction, since the negative judgme which was at first said to be produced by sense-perception and just its practi consequences deduced through the help of an inference, is now also included amoı these practical consequences. The distinction established in the first passage is th jeopardized. The solution is given in the passage beginning with *tathāpi*, p. 30. and establishes that the negative judgment is *produced* by sense-perception. B this does not prevent its being actually in life *deduced* from a negative logi reason, i. e., from a repelled suggestion, — *tathāpītyādinā pratyakṣa-kṛtatv samarthya anupalabdher abhāva-sādhakatvam uktam iti* (fol. 61).

[1] *asiddha*.

[2] *abhāva-niścaya*.

(30. 16). This negation, such (as has been here described), has eleven different varieties. What produces this difference? It is a difference of formulation. We call formulation the method [1] of expressing something in speech. Speech indeed may sometimes express (negation indirectly, through) what *prima facie* [2] would be an affirmation of something else, or it may some times express a negation, (but also an indirect one, a negation) of something else. Nevertheless (a repelled suggestion), the negation of an assumed perception,[3] will always be understood, even if not expressed (directly). Consequently there are different varieties of negation according to the different methods of expressing it. This means that in its essence [4] it is not (different, it always reduces to the same formula).

(30. 20). The different varieties are (now) explained.

32. (The first formula) is existential (or direct) negation, it is the following one.

(Thesis). There is here no smoke.

(Reason). Since, the conditions for its perception being fulfilled, none is perceived.

(31. 3). (Simple negation), or non-cognition of the existence of the denied object, is exemplified.[5] «Here» is the subject of the inference.[6] «No smoke» is the predicate. «Because of non-perception of (an imagined smoke) which nothing would prevent to perceive, if it existed», this is the logical reason. It must be understood as explained above.

(31. 6). (The second formula) expresses the absence of an effect from which the absence (of the cause) is deduced. An example (follows).

---

[1] Lit., p. 30. 17. « Application or appliance is called the denoting power (*abhidhāna-vyāpāra*) of the words ».

[2] *sākṣāt*.

[3] *dṛśya-anupalabdhi*.

[4] *svarūpa*.

[5] Lit., p. 31. 3. « What is the own existence (*sva-bhāva*) of the thing to be denied, its non-cognition is as follows ».

[6] *dharmin*, « the possessor of the quality », i. e., the real substratum (*svalakṣaṇa*) of the constructed cognition (*kalpanā*).

[7] Lit., « Because of non-cognition of the contained in the essence of cognition thus the reason ».

33. Negation of an effect is as follows.

(Thesis). There are here no efficient causes producing smoke

(Reason). Because there is no smoke.

(31.9). «Here» is the subject. Unchecked, i. e., efficient. «Causes whose efficiency in producing smoke is not checked, are not present», this is the predicate. «Because there is no smoke» is the logical reason.

Causes, indeed, do not necessarily produce their effects. Hence, when we observe the absence of the effect, we can infer only the absence of such causes whose efficiency has not been interfered with, but not of other ones. Causes whose efficiency remains unopposed are the causes which exist at the ultimate moment (of the preceding compact chain of moments), because the possibility of all other (preceding moments) being checked (in their efficiency) never can be excluded.

(31.12). (This method) of negation of an effect is resorted to in cases where the cause is invisible, because, if it were visible, the method of direct negation (first formula) would have been adopted.[1]

(31. 13). The following (is a case where this method must be applied). (Supposing a man) stands on the roof of a palace wherefrom he fails to perceive the court grounds. He looks at the upper extremities of the walls enclosing the court on its four sides, and at the same time he sees the space which is called the range[2] of his sight, free from smoke. (31.15). Since he is sure that there is no smoke in this space, he must conclude that there is (also) no fire, the efficiency of which to produce smoke is unchecked, in a place wherefrom the smoke would reach the court.[3] (31.17). The smoke which would be produced by a fire situated in the court would be present in the space (visible to him). Therefore he must conclude that there is no fire in that place. (33.18). Then the man standing on the roof (produces a judgment) the subject of which is the court, surrounded by the walls, as well as the space, surrounded by the upper parts of the walls, the space which constitutes his range of sight and which is free from smoke. (31. 19). Therefore the subject consists here of a particular space actually perceived and of an

---

1 Lit., «Just non-perception of the perceptible is valid (*gamikā*)».

2 *āloka*.

3 Lit., p. 31. 15—16. «Because of the certainty of the absence of smoke in that (place), we must learn the absence of fire whose efficiency is unchecked, by which fire, in which place situated, the produced smoke would be in this place».

un-perceived part, (not of the perceived part alone). It is a complex of something cognized directly and something invisible. It has the power of bringing about a judgment on the absence of fire. The word «here», which points to perception, refers to the visible part.

(31. 21). The subject of an inference (or the substratum of a judgment) is a combination of a part perceived directly and a part not actually perceived not only in the present case, but in other cases also. E. g., when it is being deduced that the sound represents (a compact series) of discrete momentary existences,[1] only some particular sound can directly be pointed to, others are not actually perceived. Just the same occurs in the present example. The subject of an inference (or of a judgment) represents a substratum, (an underlying reality), upon which a conception (corresponding to) the predicate (is grafted).[2] On the present example it has been shown to consist of a part directly perceived and a part unperceived. That the same is the case in the following formulae of negation (the reader) will be able to make out by himself.

(32. 3). The third formula represents negation of a fact of greater extension from which the absence of a subordinate fact is deduced. An example is given.

34. Negation of a term of greater extension is as follows.

(Thesis). There is here no Aśoka tree,
(Reason). Because there are no trees.

(32. 5). «Here» is the subject. «No Aśoka tree», i. e., the absence of such trees, is predicated. «Because there are (altogether) no trees», i. e., the term of greater extension is absent. This is the logical reason. This formula of negation is used when a subordinate term

---

1 *kṣaṇika*.

2 Lit., p. 31. 21—32. 1. «And just as the subject (*dharmin*), being the substratum for the cognition of the probandum (*sādhya-pratipatti-adhikaraṇa*), is here shown to consist...». The real subject of a judgment (*adhyavasāya* = *niścaya* = *vikalpa*), whether it be an inferential or a perceptual judgment, is always a point of reference to reality which in speech is expressed pronominally as «this», «there» etc., it then corresponds to the Buddhist «thing in itself» (*svalakṣaṇa*), or it may also include some characteristics, it then consists of a visible and an invisible part, and is expressed by a noun. Cp. the remarks of Sigwart, *op. cit.* I. 142, upon the judgment «this rose is yellow» which reduces to the form «this is yellow» the real subject being expressible only by the demonstrative «this», the actually perceived part.

like the Aśoka tree is not being perceived. If it were in a condition affording possibility of perception, simple negation of the hypothetically visible, (i. e., the first formula), would be sufficient.

(32. 7). Now (let us imagine before us) two contiguous[1] elevated places, the one covered with a forest, the other consisting of mere rock, without tree or bush. (Let us imagine) an observer capable of seeing the trees, but not capable of discerning their species, Aśoka or other. For him the presence of trees is perceptible, but the presence of Aśoka trees is not. (32. 10). Then (turning) to the treeless place which consists of bare rock, he produces a judgment.[2] («I cannot discern Aśoka trees in this wood, but on that place beyond there are surely none, because there are altogether no trees»). The absence of trees he ascertains through simple non-perception,[3] because they would be visible, the absence of Aśoka trees — (indirectly) through the absence of the pervading term, the trees.

(32. 11). This method of negation is resorted to when non-existence is predicated in cases analogous to (the example here given).

(32. 12). (The fourth formula) consists in the affirmation[4] of something which by its nature is incompatible with the presence of the negatived fact. It is exemplified.

35. Affirmation of something incompatible (with the fact which is being denied) is as follows.

(Thesis). There is here no sensation of cold.

(Reason). Because there is fire.

(32. 14). «Here» is the subject. «There is no sensation of cold», i. e., a negation of such a sensation, is the predicate. «Because there is fire» is the logical reason. This variety of negation must be applied where cold cannot be directly experienced. Otherwise simple negation would be sufficient.[5] Hence it is applied in such cases where fire is directly perceived by seeing a characteristic (patch of) colour, but cold, because of its remoteness, although present, cannot be felt.

---

1 *pūrva-apara-upaśliṣṭa.*

2 *avasyati = niścinoti = kalpayati.*

3 *dṛśya-anupalambhāt.*

4 *upalabdhiḥ = vidhiḥ*, cp. *infra*, p. 37. 5.

5 Lit., p. 32. 15. «Because, when it is perceptible, non-perception of the perceptible is applied».

(32.18). (The fifth formula) consists of the positive perception of the effect of something whose presence is incompatible with the presence of the fact denied. This gives valid[1] (negative judgments).

36. **The affirmation of an incompatible effect is as follows.**

(Thesis). **There is here no sensation of cold.**

(Reason). **Because there is smoke.**

(32.20). «Here» is the subject. «There is no sensation of cold», i.e., the absence of such sensation, is the predicate. «Because there is smoke» is the logical reason.

(32.21). In those cases where cold could be felt directly, its simple negation will give a valid judgment. Where fire which is incompatible with such sensation is directly perceptible, (the fourth formula), the affirmation of the incompatible, must be resorted to. But when both are beyond the range of sense-perception, we can avail ourselves of (this fifth method, consisting) in an affirmation of an incompatible effect, (i. e., in deducing the absence of something from the absence of something else, this second thing representing the result of a cause whose presence is incompatible with the presence of the denied fact).

(33.1). (This happens, e. g.), in following cases. Supposing somebody perceives a thick column of smoke coming out of a room. This allows him to infer the presence of a fire capable of removing cold from the whole interior of the room. After having inferred the presence of such an efficient fire, he concludes that there is no cold. In this case the subject consists of the visible place in the door together with the whole interior of the room, as has been noticed before,[2] because, when realizing the predicate[3] (absence of cold), we must conform (to its peculiar character of filling up the whole interior).

(33.5). The (sixth formula of a negative reason) consists in the affirmation of a fact which is subordinate to (or less in extension than) another fact, when the latter is incompatible with the presence of the fact denied. An example will be given.

37. **(A negative reason consisting in) the affirmation of something subordinate to an incompatible fact is as follows.**

---

1 *gamaka.*

2 Cp. above, p. 89.

3 *sādhya-pratīti.*

(Thesis). The evanescent character, even of such things which have an origin, is not something constant.

(Reason). Because (their destruction) depends upon a special cause.[1]

(33. 8). Constant is what necessarily, constantly, occurs. «Not constant», i. e., the denial of constancy, is the predicate. «Evanescence» is the subject. «Even of such things that have an origin» is a qualification of the subject. (The opponents of the Buddhist theory of Universal Momentariness maintain that) the impermanent character of products, i. e., of things that have a beginning, is not something constant. Still stronger are the reasons for denying constant evanescence in unproduced (eternal) substances.[2] That is why the qualification «even» (even of things that have an origin) has been added. (33. 10).

---

[1] The next example is apparently chosen with the aim of meeting the objection that, if every negation is nothing but a repudiation of imagined visibility, then objects and processes which are invisible to ordinary men by their nature, will never be liable to this kind of negation. The objectors maintain non-perception of the invisible (*adṛśya-anupalabdhi*), cp. above p. 81 and infra sūtra II. 48—49. Since the Buddhists are advocates of Universal Momentariness (or destruction) the author seems willing to tell his opponents «if you wish to repudiate my idea of imperceptible constant destruction, yon can do it only by denying a visible, sensible form of constancy, not an invisible, metaphysical one». Mallavādī says—*athaivam vyāpaka-anupalabdhir dṛśya-śiṃśapātve prayujyate, adṛśye cety āśankyāha*, *op. cit.*, fol. 64. Rgyal-thsab introduces the example with the follwing, words, *op. cit*, fol. 30,—*log-togs dgag-pai-ched-du thal-bai-sbyor-ba-smras-par zad-kyi, ñes ḥphans-pa ni, dños-po chos can, ḥjig-par-ḥgyur-ba-phyis-byuñ-gi rgyu-la bltos-pa-med de, ḥjig-ñes yin-pai-phyir ces-pao; thal-ba-ltar rañ-rgyud-dpe-la sbyar-na, ras dkar-po chos-can... = vipratipatti-nirākaraṇārtham prasanga-prayoga-vacana-mātram, niścayas tu, bhāro dharmī, vināśa-hetvantara-anapekṣaḥ, vināśa-niyatatvād iti; yathā-prasangam svatantra-udāharaṇam prayuñjānaḥ, paṭaḥ śukla (iti) dharmī...* The *vipratipatti* alluded to by Rgyal-thsab is evidently the view of the Sānkhyas, the Naiyāyikas and the Mīmāṃsakas that metaphysical entities and processes are *anupalabdha = adṛśya = apratyakṣa*.

[2] All Indian systems, except the Buddhists, assumed the existence of several eternal and ubiquitous substances. The early Buddhists postulated the reality of three eternal, i. e., unchanging, unproduced, permanent elements (*asaṃskṛta-dharma*), viz., empty space and two kinds of eternal blank supervening after the total extinction of all forces in the Universe. In Mahāyāna they are declared to be relative and therefore unreal. The Sautrāntikas and Yogācāras identified existence with constant change (*kṣaṇikatva*).

A special cause[1] is a cause different from origination,[2] e. g., a hammer (by whose stroke a jar is destroyed). Evanescence (according to Realists) is dependent upon such a (special cause). «Because it so depends» is the logical reason. (33.11). Now, (the fact of being) dependent on a special cause is not something constant,[3] e.g., the colour of a cloth depends upon a fortuitous process of dyeing which is not constant. Non-constancy is the opposite of constancy. (33.13). Evanescense (interpreted) as the fact of having an end, is assumed (by Realists) to depend upon special causes.[4] They therefore deny its constancy, on the ground of experience, (which teaches) that it depends upon special causation, (and this fact of accidental causation disproves constancy), proves the opposite (of constancy).[5]

---

1 *hetv-antara.*

2 The Buddhist theory of Universal Momentariness *(kṣaṇikatva)*, converting the universe into a kind of cinema, maintains that there is no other cause of destruction than origination, entities disappear as soon as they appear, the moment when the jar is broken by a stroke of a hammer does not differ in this respect from all preceding moments, since every moment a new or «other» jar appears, constant destruction or renovation is inherent in every existence which is really a compact series of ever new moments. The realistic opponents of the Buddhists admit the duration *(sthāyitva)* of entities from the moment of their origination up to the moment of their destruction by a special cause *(hetv-antara)*. The Sānkhyas established the theory of constant change *(pariṇāma-nityatā)* of Matter. The Buddhist theory of Universal Momentariness is once more alluded to below, sūtra III. 11 ff., cp. notes.

3 Lit., p. 33. 11. «Dependence upon a special cause indeed is contained under *(vyāpta)* non-constancy».

4 Lit., p. 33. 13. «And destruction, being the very essence of the destructible, is admitted to be dependent on another cause». The Tib., p. 75. 11, emphasizes in repeating *ḥjig-pa yaṅ.* According to the realists destruction which they call *pradhvaṃsa* is a reality *sui generis* (*bhāva-svarūpa* = *bhāvāntara*), according to the Buddhists it is a name for the thing itself, for the momentary thing, since every existence is a flow of discrete moments, *bhāva eva vinaśyati iti kṛtvā vināśa ity ākhyāyate* cp. Kamalaśīla, p. 137. 22. This simply means that every duration is really a motion and that causal connection exists between moments only, a conception of causality which is not unfamiliar to students of European philosophy. From the Buddhist standpoint the *hetvantara* can be only the preceding moment, (cp. p. 88 and Tattvas, kār. 375), but not *mudgarādi.* Hence, if *vināśa* is the *svabhāva* of existence, it cannot depend upon a special cause. The passage therefore means «the things which we, Buddhists, hold to be evanescent every moment by their nature, you, realists, assume to possess duration and to be destroyed by special causes»

5 Lit. p. 33. 13—14. «And destruction whose essence is to possess an impermanent nature is admitted to depend upon another cause. Therefore observing dependence upon another cause, (this dependence) being subordinate to what is incompatible *(viruddha)* with (constancy), constancy is being negatived».

(33. 14). For us[1] (Buddhists) constancy is permanence (eternity), non-constancy impermanence.[2] Since permanence and impermanence are (qualities) exclusive of one another,[3] it would be a contradiction to assume their (simultaneous) presence in the same place. (33. 15). In such cases, if one of the two contradictory qualities is present, the presence of the second must be *eo ipso* denied.[4] (33. 16). But such negation is possible only in regard of an (object) whose perceptibility is hypothetically assumed. When denying the reality (of the predicate) we, indeed, must argue in the following manner.[5] «If the fact before us were permanent, we would have some experience of its permanent essence, but no permanent essence is being experienced, therefore it is not permanent».[6] (33. 18). It follows that when we deny permanence this denial refers to objects of a possible experience.

---

1 *iha*, cp above text, p. 10. 12.

2 The argument is that the real thing being one (*unus numero*), cannot possess two such contradictory characeristics as origination and destruction *niramśa eva bhāvaḥ... katham tasya uttarakālam kāraṇāntaraiḥ svabhāvāntaram ādhīyate*, Kamalaśīla, p. 134. 3. The real thing can be either *nitya*, eternal and unchanging or *anitya* = *kṣaṇika*, momentary — *apracyuta-anutpanna-sthiraikasvabhāvam nityam ākhyāyate, prakṛty-eka-kṣaṇa-sthiti-dharmakam cānityam* (Anekānta). p. 13). The Realists and the Jainas assume a limited duration of some things which in that case possess both characteristics of origination and destruction. The Sānkhyas assume *pariṇāma-nityatā*, an ever changing substance, the Buddhist — a constant change without any substantiality, simple momentary flashes. Since *vināśa* is the name for such a flash, and *adhruvabhāvin* is the same as *anityatva*, the problem here alluded to amounts at asking whether *anityatva* is itself *anitya*, a problem the solution of which attracted the attention of the Buddhists already in the Kathāvatthu, XI. 8, just as in later times they were interested in the problem whether *śūnyatva* is itself *śūnya*, cp. my Nirvāṇa, p. 49 ff.

3 *paraspara-parihāra*, cp. below, text p. 69. 20.

4 *tādātmya-niṣedha*, lit., «its identity (i. e, its presence in that thing) must be denied» This expression means evidently the same as *ekatvābhāvaḥ* or *ekātmakatva-virodhaḥ* on p. 70. 11—12 (text), cp. below the notes on the translation of that passage. Between *vṛkṣa* and *śiṃśapātva*, as noted above, p. 73 ff., there is no *tādātmya-niṣedha* with regard to the *vastu*, but between two consecutive moments of the same thing there is one.

5 Lit., p. 33. 17. «Because the denial of the identy (of the fact constituting the predicate, i. e., of permanence) is done thus».

6 Lit., p. 33. 17. «If this thing we look upon were eternal, it would appear in its eternal essence (*rūpa* = *svarūpa*), but it does not appear in an eternal essence...». The term *darśana* is used where we would say «experience», *darśanāt* means «because we know from experience». Cp. the use of that term in the Kārikā of Dharmakīrti quoted in Sarvad, p. 22 (Bombay S. S. ed; incor-

(33. 19). Even (supposing we have) a really invisible thing, such as, e. g. a ghost, we could deny its identity with some other (visible) object, e. g., a jar, only after trying to imagine (for a moment) its own visibility.[1] (We then are doing it in the following manner). «If this visible object were identical with a ghost, we would perceive the ghost, but we dont perceive him, therefore it is not a ghost». (33. 21). When we intend to deny the identity of a visible real object, say a jar, with some other object, (it does not matter whether the latter) be real or unreal, amenable to perception or not, we must begin by hypothetically assuming its perceptibility, (thus merely can we arrive at the judgment «this is a jar», «it is *not* a ghost»).[2]

(34. 1). If this is true, then just as we deny the presence of a jar only after having (for a moment) imagined it as visible, just the same are we doing (when we realize the «otherness» of something according to the law of contradiction). Wheresoever we deny the presence of an object which is «other» than the object perceived, we do it only on the basis of (a negative judgment, i. e.) non-perception of something hypothetically visible.[3] Consequently (if we interpret) this formula in the manner just described, it is (virtually) included in (the first formula, i. e.,) direct negation of what hypothetically is visible.

(34. 4). (The seventh formula of a negative reason) consists in the affirmation of something incompatible with the effect of the denied fact. An example is given.

38. Affirmation of something incompatible with the effect is as follows —

---

rect reading in the B. I. ed., p. 7), where positive and negative experience (*darśana-adarśana = anvaya-vyatireka*) are contrasted with logical necessity (*niyama*). Here *dṛśyamāna* means an object we look upon, *nitya-rūpa dṛśyeta* means that we must have some real experience of what permanence or eternity is in order to predicate it.

1 Upon this point, namely that the invisible things in our knowledge are nothing but repelled hypothetical visibilities cp. the somewhat parallel argument in Husserl's, Logische Untersuchungen, II, p. 313 — «Jupiter stelle ich nicht anders vor als Bismark . . .»

2 Lit., p. 33. 21—34. 1. «And the negation of identity is preceded by assuming identity with the perceived in a perceived entity, a jar etc. (whether it be the negation of identity) of a real or unreal, a perceptible or unperceptible thing».

3 Lit., p. 34. 1—2. «And if it is so, just as we deny (the presence) of a jar after having assumed its (possible) per. eption on (the basis of) just non-perception of visibility, just so on the (the basis of) that very non-perception of visibility, the denial (is made) of every mutually incompatible thing, (the denial of its presence) in something else (which would be) perceptible».

(Thesis). There are here no efficient causes of cold.

(Reason). Because there is a fire.

(34.7). «Here» is the subject. «Causes of cold», i. e., causes whose efficiency to produce cold has not been arrested, this is the predicate. «Because there is a fire» is the reason. (34.8). We can avail ourselves of this formula in those cases where neither the causes producing cold, nor the cold itself are directly felt. Where cold is felt we will use the (second formula), the formula of denying the result («there are here no causes of cold, since there is no cold»), and when its causes are amenable to sensation, we will use the formula of a simple negative judgment, (the first formula, «there are no causes of cold, because we do not perceive them»).

(34.10). Consequently this is also a method of deducing non-existence. We avail ourselves of it in cases where the observer is situated at a distance. He can neither feel the cold, nor perceive the causes which would produce cold sensation, but fire, notwithstanding the distance, is perceived through its refulgence.

(34.12). (The eighth formula of a negative judgment) consists in affirmation of something incompatible with a fact of greater extension than the fact denied. An example will be given.

39. Affirmation of something incompatible with a fact of greater extension is as follows —

(Thesis). There is here no sensation produced by snow.

(Reason). Because there is a fire.

(34. 14). «Here» is the subject. «No sensation of snow» is the predicate. «Because there is a fire» is the reason. This method (of proving the absence of snow) is used in cases where neither the fact of lesser extension, the snow, nor the fact of greater extension, the cold, can be directly experienced, because when they can be experienced directly, either (the first formula), the simple negation (of snow), or (the third formula), the negation of the fact of greater extension (i. e. of cold) will be resorted to. (34.16). Consequently this is likewise a method of deducing non-existence. For a remote observer any variety of cold lies beyond the range of sensation, and the sensation produced by snow is but a variety of the sensation of cold. Fire, on the other hand, owing to its specific refulgence, is seen even at a

distance. Hence from the presence of fire the absence of cold in general is deduced, and from it the absence of its variety, the sensation produced by snow, is ascertained, because the specific sensation is included in the general one. This method will accordingly be resorted to in specific cases.

(34.20). (The nineth formula of a negative reason consists in) a negation of the causes of the denied fact. An example is given.

40. Negation of causes is as follows.

(Thesis). There is here no smoke.
(Reason). Because there is no fire.

(35.2). «Here» is the subject. «No smoke» is the predicate. «Because there is no fire» is the reason. This method is used when the effect of something, although existent, is not directly perceived. When perceptible, we will avail ourselves (for denying it) of the method of simple negation of the hypothetically perceptible, (the first formula). Consequently this is likewise a method of deducing non-existence. (35.4). (It occurs, e. g., in following cases). Supposing we have a pond covered by an extensive sheet of motionless water which in the dim twilight in winter time emits vapour. Even if some smoke were present, it would not be possible to discern it (in the darkness). Nevertheless its presence can be denied through non-perception of its cause. For if there were fire, (in a piece of wood) swimming on the water, it would be visible through the characteristic refulgence of its flames. (35.6). Even supposing it is not flaming, but lingering in some piece of wood, then this fuel being the place where fire is concealed could be visible. Thus fire would be in any case visible, either directly or through the object in which it is concealed.[1] In such cases this formula is applied.

(35.9). Next comes an example (of the tenth variety) which consists in affirmation of something incompatible with the cause of the denied fact.

41. The affirmation of a fact incompatible with the causes of something is as follows.

(Thesis). He betrays no symptoms of cold, such as shivering etc.
(Reason). Because there is an efficient fire near him.

---

[1] *ādhāra-rūpeṇa.*

(35. 12). «He» is the subject. «Shivering», chattering teeth etc. are special symptoms produced by cold. They are different from the expressions of fear, devotion and other (emotions), therefore they are called special symptoms. Their absence is predicated. An efficient fire is a fire which is distinguished from other fires by its capacity of removing cold. For there are fires which are not capable of that, as e. g., the fire of a lamp. In order to set aside such fire, a qualification has been introduced, «a proximate good[1] fire». Its presence is the logical reason.

(35. 16). This formula is applied in those cases where cold, although existent, cannot be directly felt, and its symptoms, like a shivering produced by it, can neither be seen. When these symptoms can be perceptible, direct negation of the hypothetically visible (the first formula) is used. When cold can be directly felt, the negation of the cause is applied. Consequently this is also a method of deducing non-existence. (35. 19). Indeed, fire is perceived at a distance owing to its specific refulgence when neither the cold can be felt nor the shivering observed directly. Therefore their absence is deduced (indirectly), from seeing (a fire) which is incompatible with their cause. In such cases this formula is used.

(35. 21). (The eleventh formula of negation consists) in affirmation of an effect of something which is incompatible with the cause of the fact denied. An example is given.

42. Affirmation of an effect of something incompatible with the cause is as follows.

> (Thesis). In this place nobody exhibits symptoms of cold, such as shivering etc.,
> (Reason). Because there is smoke.

(36. 3). «This place» is the subject. It is devoid of men exhibiting shivering and other symptoms of cold, this is predicated. «Because there is smoke» this is the reason. When the shivering can be observed, we use direct non-perception, (the first formula). When the cause, the sensation of cold, can be directly felt, we use (the nineth formula), the formula of non-perception of the cause. When the fire is perceptible, we use (the tenth formula), the formula of the perception of the thing incompatible with the cause. But when all the three cannot

[1] *dahana-viśeṣa*

be directly perceived, we use the present formula. Hence, this is also a way of establishing non-existence.

(36. 7). This formula is a suitable means of cognition in those cases, when neither the fire nor the cold nor the shivering can be directly perceived by a remote observer, but smoke is perceived directly. Such smoke is here meant which points to a fire capable of extinguishing the cold in that place. If fire in general is inferred from the presence of some smoke in general, then neither the absence of cold nor the absence of shivering can be ascertained. Thus it must be borne in mind that the reason does not consist in the mere presence of some smoke in general.

§ 8. The importance of the formulae of negation.

(36. 12). If there is only one reason, (i. e., one logical process) of negation, how is it that we have enumerated eleven (different) reasons from which non-existence can be deduced?

43. All these ten formulae of a negative judgment, beginning from the second, are (virtually) included (in the first), the (direct) non-perception of the existence of something.

These, i. e., the formulae of negation. The word «these» points to the formulae which have just been specified. How many of them are meant? The non-perception of the result (the second formula) and the following ones. Three or four or how many out of their number are meant? He says, ten. Are the ten examples alone meant? He says, all. (36. 18). The following is meant. Although not mentioned, but similar to those which are mentioned, are all (the cases of negation). Thus it is that since the word «ten» comprises all the adduced examples, their totality is suggested (through this word alone, the word «all» becomes superfluous). However, since the totality of the quoted examples is already suggested by the word «ten», the additional word «all» refers (to another totality), the totality of the cases similar to the examples.[1] They are identical with simple

[1] This superfluous remark is probably directed against Vinītadeva who has, quite naturally, interpreted the word «all» as meaning that all the ten varieties of negation, without any exception, can be reduced to one fundamental formula, the first one, cp. p. 78. 16. As usual, Dharmottara seizes every possible subtle occasion to find fault with Vinītadeva.

negation, and therefore included in it, i. e., their essence is direct negation.[1]

(37. 1). However there is a difference between the formula of direct negation (the first formula) and the formulae of non-perception of the result, (i. e., the second) and other formulae. Therefore how can they be included in the former? He says,

44. Indirectly. There is a difference of formulation, (a fact is denied indirectly) through affirmation or negation of something else.

(37. 4). Although there is a difference of formula, i. e., of verbal expression, nevertheless they are included. How is this different formulation to be understood? (Our author) says, through affirmation and (negation of something else). In the (fourth formula), the formula of affirmation of something incompatible with the existence of the object denied, we have, e. g., a positive cognition, or affirmation,[2] of something different from the denied object. In (the second formula), the formula of non-perceived result and similar formulae, we have a negation (of something different from the object which it is intended to negate). (37. 6). Thus by affirmation of another, (i. e., of an incompatible) fact, and by negation of another, (i. e., of a connected) fact, the formulae are different.

(37. 7). If in different formulae some connected facts are either affirmed or denied, how is it that they are included? He says: indirectly, i. e., mediately. (37. 8). The following is meant. These (ten) formulae do not directly express a negation of imagined visibility, but they express an affirmation or a negation of something else, and this invariably leads[3] to simple negation of the hypothetically visible. Therefore, they are included in simple negation not directly, but mediately.

(37. 11). Now, if the difference is one of verbal expression, this should be discussed under the head of inference «for others» (or syllogism)? Difference of formulation is, indeed, difference of verbal expression. But speech (is not internal inference or judgment, it) is external

---

[1] Lit., p. 36. 21—22. «They go through identity into inclusion in the non-cognition of own-existence, this means that they possess own-existence of non-cognition of own-existence».

[2] *upalabdhi* = *vidhi*.

[3] *avyabhicārin*.

inference (or syllogism). In answer to this question (the author) says,

45. The formulae have been specified under the head of internal inference, because by their repeated consideration the distinct conception of what a negative judgment[1] represents internally (as a process of thought) becomes thus also clear to the (scrutinizing individual) himself.

(37. 15). Formulae are scientific constructions. The repeated occurrence of their cognition, again and again, also leads the cognizing individual himself to a right conception of what limitation or negation is, in the way which has been analysed just above.[2] (37. 17). The meaning is the following one. By a study[3] (of these different) formulae we ourselves also in the way thus (indicated) arrive at understanding (what negation really means).[4] Therefore, since (the study) of the different formulae (does not exclusively serve the purpose of communicating knowledge to others, but) since it also serves the purpose of our own analysis[5] of them, they have been considered (in the chapter) devoted to internal inference (or inferential judgment). On the contrary (the methods) which are exclusively used to communicate with others will be necessarily examined (in the last chapter), as a verbal expression of inferences,[6] (not as a process of thought).

---

[1] *vyavaccheda* is properly limitation, contrast or distinction, but here it is explained, p. 37. 17, as =*pratiṣedha*.

[2] Lit., p. 37. 15—17. «Consideration of the formulae etc. Of the formulae which have been constructed in science (*śāstra*) the consideration, the knowledge. Its repetition, its reoccurrence again and again. Therefore, for (this) reason. Also for himself, i. e, also for the cognizer himself. Thus, in the above mentioned manner. Of the contrast (*vyavaccheda*), of negation, the distinct knowledge (*pratīti*) arises. The word *iti* in the sense of «therefore».

[3] *abhyāsa*.

[4] i. e., that it means «contrasting» (*vyavaccheda*), and since a contrast is involved in every act of definite cognition, negation is inherent in every clear thought. About the importance of *pariccheda* and *vyavaccheda* in cognition cp. below, text p. 69. 22 ff. and Tātparyaṭ., p. 92. 15 ff.

[5] *pratipatti*.

[6] *parārthānumāna*, as stated below, text p. 40, is not an inference, but only ist formulation.

§ 9. Negation founded on sensible experience.

(37.21). However, it may be questioned, how are these formulae all implied in the (first one), in the negation of a (hypothetically) visible object? Indeed, in such formulae as, e. g., the (fifth) which represents the non perception of a result, the presence of causes is denied which are anything but perceptible, because in cases when something that might be perceptible is denied, we are obliged to use the formula of direct negation. If such be the case, their denial, (it would seem), is not made on the basis of an imputed perceptibility?[1]

The answer is as follows.

46. Negation is the process through which either the absence of something or some practical application of the idea of an absent thing is deduced. Whether the facts be denied by way of an affirmation of something incompatible with them or through the negation of their causes etc., everywhere negation, on analysis, refers to possibilities of sensation.[2]

(38.4). Absence and its application (are here mentioned, because in the first formula), in direct negation, the deduction refers to the practical application (of the idea of an absent thing, of a non-Ens, as produced by sense perception), in the remaining formulae the absence (of the denied facts) is itself deduced. The negative cognition on which both are founded (always refers to sensations actual or possible).

(38.6). All the formulae of negative deduction reduce to the formula of direct negation, because whatsoever be the facts denied in

---

1 Lit., p. 37.21—23. «And how is it that there is negation of just imperceptible causes etc. in non-cognition of effect etc., since there is the consequence of the formula of non-cognition of own-existence in the negation of the perceptible, and, if it is so, there is no negation of them from non-cognition of the perceptible, therefore how are these formulae included in non-cognition of the perceptible?».

2 Lit., p. 38.1—3. «And everywhere in this non-cognition which establishes non-existence and the application of non-existence, (the things) whose negation is expressed through cognition of the incompatible with own-existence etc., and through the cognition of causes etc., their cognition and non-cognition must be understood exclusively as of (things) reached by the essence of (sense-) perception».

all of them, they are all *sensibilia*,[1] i. e., objects susceptible of sense-perception.[2]

(38.7). How is it proved that they are all sensibilia? They are all sensibilia because in all these formulae there is either affirmation of the contradicting counterpart of the denied fact or the denial of its cause etc., (and the laws of Contradiction and Causation refer to sensibilia only).[3]

(38.10). To be sure, negation is expressed in them either by the affirmation of something essentially incompatible (with the fact denied) etc. or by the negation of its cause etc. But nevertheless, does it follow that negation refers to sensibilia only?

(38.11). They refer to sensibilia only for the following reason. In order to establish the subalternation of two facts or their causal relation, and in order to know what will contradict these relations, we necessarily must have had some experience of them, i. e., we must have had some perception of their presence and some experience of their absence, preceded by a perception of their presence.[3] Objects which have been alternately perceived and not perceived are necessarily perceptible.

(38.14). Consequently when incompatible and other facts are being denied either by the way of an affirmation of their correlative part or by an elimination of their causes etc., we must know that this refers to sensibilia only, to such objects whose presence and absence have been alternately observed.[4]

---

1 *dṛśya*. The term *sensibilia* as contrasted with sense-data we borrow from B. Russel, Mysticism, p. 152.

2 *upalabdhi lakṣaṇa-prāpta*.

3 It is interesting to compare on this topic the view of Herbert Spencer (apud Stuart Mill, Logic 8 I, p. 322) — «the negative mode cannot occur without excluding a correlative mode: the antithesis of positire and negative being, indeed, is merely an expression of this experience». According to the Buddhists the concrete content of every single case of contradiction, as of causality, is provided by experience, the causal laws have an application to sensibilia only, but whether the laws themselves are mere generalizations from experience is another question, cp. p. 69. 11 (text).

4 Lit., 38. 5—15. « And everywhere. The word *ca* is used in the sense of « because ». Because everywhere, in non-perception of what (facts) the negation is expressed, of them the negation (refers to objects) reached by the conditions of cognition of the perceptible, therefore it is included in non-perception of the visible. Why is it that this (refers) only to perceptibles? He says, own-existence etc. Here also the word *ca* has the meaning of cause. (38. 8). Because negation is expressed by affirmation

(38. 15). Thus a series of questions have been raised (and answered) conjointly. Since such and such are the answers, the corresponding objections are discarded. Therefore these answers have been arrayed together.

(38. 18). Further, why is it that (the existence of both) a positive and a negative sense-perception must be assumed whenever the denial of an incompatible fact or of a (cause or effect) is made.

47. Because (the laws of) Contradiction and Causality do not extend their sway over other (i.e., over metaphysical) objects.[2]

(38. 20). Objects different from those which (alternately) are perceived and non-perceived are (metaphysical) objects which are never

---

of those (facts) among whom the essentially incompatible is the first, and by non-perception of those (facts) among whom the cause is the first, therefore negation is only of the perceptibles. This is meant. (38. 10). If, to be sure, negation is expressed by affirmation of the essentially incompatible etc., and by non-perception of the cause etc., nevertheless why is negation of perceptibles only? Cognition etc. Here also the word *ca* means the cause. Since the contradictories are known as being inclusive and included, as being cause and effect, just necessarily their perception and non-perception preceded by perception must be understood. Those that possess both, perception and non-perception, are necessarily perceptibles. (38. 14). Therefore by perception of the essentially incompatible etc. and by non-perception of the cause etc., the negation being made of the incompatibles etc. as possessing perception and non-perception, must be considered as being made of perceptibles only ».— The interpertation of the three *ca*'s as «because», and the coordination of the three different questions seems artificial. Vinītadeva has nothing of the sort. Mallavādī does not comment upon this passage.

[1] Lit., p. 38. 15—17. «Because many objections have been gone through, the word *ca* which has here the meaning of collecting the answers together has the meaning of «because», (therefore) «because we have such and such answers, therefore such and such objections are not right», this is the meaning of *ca*».

[2] In the text of sūtra 47 the word *abhāva* must be inserted before *asiddheḥ*, cp. Tib. This *abhāva* is interpreted as *abhāvaś ca vyāpyasya vyāpakasya abhāve.* The Tib., p. 88. 1, has no equivalent for *vyāpyasya.* This word *abhāva* would thus refer to the fourth formula, the *vyāpaka-anupalabdhi*, cp. sūtra II. 34; but Vinītadeva, p. 82. 10 ff., divides *virodha-kāryakāraṇa-bhāvābhāvau* and explains it as *virodhasya bhāvaś ca abhāvaś ca, kāryakāraṇatvasya bhāvaś ca abhāvaś ca.* This explanation seems preferable, since the *vyāpaka-anupalabdhi* can be regarded as included in *virodha.* The lit. translation of the sūtra, as nnderstood by Dh., is—«because Contradiction, Causality and Subalternation of others are not established»; as understood by V., it is—«because the existence and non-existence of Contradiction and Causality of others is not established». Dh.'s interpretation seems artificial and is probably due to his polemical zeal.

perceived. Their contradiction with something else, their causal relation (to something else), their subalternation[1] it is impossible (to imagine). Therefore it is impossible to ascertain what is it they contradict, and what are they causally related to.[2] For this reason contradicting facts (causes and effects) are fit to be denied only after their observation has been recurrent.[3] Therefore, since the impossibility of contradiction or of causal relation is established, the incompatible facts can be denied only when they refer to objects which alternately are perceived and non-perceived. Those which are open to both (perception and non-perception are called sensibilia), they are necessarily capable of being experienced. Therefore, negation refers only to objects of possible experience.[4] (39. 1). The following is the meaning. Contradiction, Causality, Subalternation are necessarily based upon negative judgments, (upon non perception of sensibilia). (39. 2). Contradiction is realized when on the presence[5] of one term we distinctly cognize the absence of the other. Causal relation is established when the fact which we accept as the result is absent, if another fact which we accept as cause is also absent. Subalternation is established when it is precisely known that on the absence of the term which is admitted to possess greater extension the less extensive term is definitely absent. We must indeed be alive to the fact that the extension (and comprehension of our concepts) are founded on Negation. The (comparative) extension (of the terms tree and Ašoka) is fixed when we know that, if on a certain place there are no trees, there are also no Ašokas. (39. 6). The knowledge of the absence of something is always produced only by the repudiation of an imagined presence. (39. 7). Therefore, if we remember (some cases) of Contradiction, of Causality or of different extension, we needs must have in our memory some negative experience. (Negation is) the foundation of our concept of non-existence which is underlying[6] our knowledge of (the laws) of Contradiction, of

---

1 Lit., p. 38. 21. «And absence of the contained (the term of lesser extension) when there is absence of the container (the term of greater extension)».

2 Lit., p. 38. 22. «Therefore, for the cause of non-establishment of the contradicting, of the relation of cause and effect and of non-existence (of the subaltern)» (according to Dh.). The real meaning is probably «because the absence of the contradicting and of causal relation is not established».

3 Lit., p. 38. 22. «Can be negatived contradicting (facts) etc. only when they possess perception and non-perception».

4 *dṛšyānām eva.*

5 *samnidhi* in the sense of presence (not nearness as in sutra I. 13).

6 *viṣaya.*

Causality and of Subalternation. (39. 9). If we do not have in our memory some negative experience,[2] we will not remember contradiction and other (relations), and then, in that case, the non-existence of a fact[3] would not follow from the affirmation of an incompatible fact or from the negation (of its cause) etc. Since the negative experience which we have had at the time when we first became aware of the fact of incompatibility or (of a causal relation) must necessarily be remembered, (it is clear) that a negative cognition is founded exlusively on such (a repudiation of imagined visibility). (39. 11). Thus, although the negative experience is not occurring at present, it did occur at the time when the incompatibility of the facts and their other relations have been first apprehended. Its presence in our memory is the real foundation of our negative judgments.[4] (39. 13). The negation of the result, (i. e., the second) and following formulae, differ from the (first) formula, the direct repudiation of an imagined presence, in that they deduce the absence of something from a past negative experience,[5] but since, by the affirmation of the presence of an incompatible fact or by the negation of the presence of the cause, they implicitely refer[6] to a negative experience, therefore (in these cases also) negation[7] is based just on such a repudiation of an (imagined) presence which occurred at another time, but is nevertheless present in memory, and therefore these formulae are (virtually) included in the (first) formula of sensible negation. Thus it is clear that the whole (of the preceding discussion) proves that the ten formulae of negation are at the bottom[8] nothing but negative experiences of sensibilia.

§ 10. The value of negation in metaphysics.

(39. 18). Negation which has been here analysed (as reducing to a negative experience of sensibilia) is a valid cognition of the absence

---

2 *dṛśya-anupalabdhi.*

3 *itara-abhāva.*

4 *abhāva-pratipatti.*

5 Lit., p. 39. 13—14. «Therefore — there is no perception of the visible now— thus by proving non-existence the formulae of non-perception of a result etc. differ from the formula of non-perception of the visible».

6 *ākṣipta.*

7 *abhāva-pratipatti.*

8 *pāramparyeṇa.*

(of the denied objects) and (a source of the corresponding) purposive actions.[1] Now, what may be the essence and what the function of a negation of *non-sensibilia*?[2]

48. Negation of objects inaccessible (to experience) is the source of problematic reasoning, since its essence is exclusive of both direct and indirect knowledge.

(39. 21). An object can be inaccessible in three respects, in time, in space and in essence. Negation regarding such objects is a source of problematic reasoning.[3] What is the essence of such reasoning? It is repudiation of both direct and indirect knowledge.[4] This means that they are not (knowledge at all, because) the essence (of knowledge is to be an assertory) relation between cognition and its object.[5]

(40. 1). However, cognition[6] proves the existence of the cognized, therefore it would be only natural to expect that absence of cognition would be a proof of the absence of the cognized?[7] (This question) is now answered.

49. When there are altogether no means of cognition, the non-existence of the object cannot be established.

(40. 4). When a cause is absent the result does not occur and when a fact of wider extension is absent, its subordinate fact is likewise absent. But knowledge is neither the cause nor the extensive fact, in regard of the object of cognition. Therefore, when both the ways of cognition (the direct and the indirect one) are excluded,[8] this

---

1 *abhāva-vyavahāra.*

2 *adṛśya*, i. e., objects unimaginable as present to the senses.

3 *saṃśaya-hetu*, i. e., doubtful reasons or non-judgments.

4 *pratyakṣa-anumāna.*

5 *jñāna-jñeya-svabhāva.*

6 *pramāṇa.*

7 This was the opinion of the Naiyāyikas and of European science up to the time of Sigwart.

8 It is clear from this passage that *viprakṛṣṭa=tribhir viprakarṣair viprakṛṣṭa= deśa-kāla-svabhāva-viprakṛṣṭa* refers to metaphysical entities which are *eo ipso* declared to be uncognizable by their nature = *na jñāna-jñeya-svabhāva*, they are uncognizable neither by sense-perception=*atīndriya*, nor by inference =*pratyakṣa-anumāna-nivṛtti-lakṣaṇa*, cp. Kamalaśīla, p. 476. 3. The example of such a meta-

does not prove the non-existence of the object, and since (this absence of knowledge) proves nothing, the negation of the non-imaginable[2] is the source of problematic reasoning, not of (assertory) judgments.[3]

(40. 7). But on the other hand it is only right to maintain that the existence of a (suitable) source of knowledge proves the existence of the correspondent object. A right cognition[4] is the product of its object. A product cannot possibly exist without a cause. But causes do not necessarily carry their results. Therefore the existence of right knowledge proves the existence of real objects, but absence of knowledge cannot prove the non-existence of (the corresponding) object.

End of the second chapter of the Short Treatise of Logic.

---

physical, declared to be uncognizable entity, as is clear from sūtra III, 97, is an Omniscient absolute Being, a Buddha. This agrees with the views of Dharmakīrti as expressed in other contexts, cp., e. g., the concluding passage of Santānāntarasiddhi. Such entities are also characterized as *anupalabdhi-lakṣaṇa-prāpta* (II. 28), *svabhāva-viśeṣa-rahita*, p. 23. 9, 28. 8, and *adṛśya*, p. 39. 18. In regard of such entities no judgments, no deductions which would possess logical necessity (*niścaya*) are possible. A negative judgment in regard of them is possible only by *tādātmya-niśedha*, i. e., by assuming for them a kind of visibility for a moment, as explained under sūtra II. 37.

[2] *adṛśya*, the non-sensible.

[3] *niścaya-hetu*, the reason of an inferential judgment. A problematic judgment from the Indian point of view, is a *contradictio in adjecto*, a judgment is a verdict, the solution of a problem, as long as there is no solution, there is no judgment (*niścaya* = *adhyavasāya*).

[4] *pramāṇa*, in the sense of *pramā*.

CHAPTER III.

SYLLOGISM.

§ 1. Definition and varieties.

(41. 1). Between the two classes of inference, (internal) «for oneself» and (verbal) «for others», the first has been explained. The (anthor) now proceeds to explain the second.

1. Inference «for others» (or syllogism) consists in communicating the three aspects of the logical mark (to others).

(41. 3). Communicating the three aspects of the logical mark, i. e., (the logical mark appears here also in) three aspects[1] which

---

1 The three aspects are those mentioned in ch. II, sūtra 5—7. Its first aspect (II. 5) corresponds to the minor premise (*pakṣa-dharmatva*), its second aspect (II. 6) — to the major (*anvaya*), and its third aspect (II. 7) — to the coutraposition of the major premise. It will be noticed that, although the tree aspects of the logical mark are the same in internal inference and in syllogism, their order is difference. Inference starts with the minor premise and ascends to a generalization corroborated by examples, it looks more like a process of Induction. Syllogism, on the other hand, starts with a general statement in the major premise, whether positive or negative, and then proceeds to its application in a particular case. It represents Deduction, although the examples are always mentioned as a reference to the inductive process by which the major premise has been established. In the third posthumous edition of his monumental work on Logik, the late Prof. B. Erdman has decided to reverse the traditional order of the premises in all syllogisms, because the traditional order of beginning with the major premise is in contradiction with «the real connexion of the premises in the living process of formulated thought» (p. 614). The Indian inference when treated as a process of thought also starts with the minor premise (*anumeye sattvam lingasya*) and proceeds to a generalization of similar cases (*sapakṣe eva sattvam = anvaya = vyāpti*). But when syllogism is regarded as a method of proving a thesis in a controversy, the exposition begins with the universal proposition or major premise and the minor premise occupies the second place.

are called (respectively) direct concomitance[1] (or major premise expressed positively), its contraposition (or the same premise expressed negatively)[2] and (the minor premise or) the fact of the presense of the mark in the subject (of the inference, i. e., the fact that the subject of the inference is characterized by the logical mark).[3] (41. 4). The logical

[1] *anvaya*, e. g., «wherever there is smoke, there is fire», or «whatsoewer is a product is non-eternal», it corresponds to the major premise of the first figure of Aristotle.

[2] *vyatireka*, means that subject and predicate, or the middle and major terms, exchange their places and change quality at the same time, it is a conversion of the negations of both the subject and predicate of the major premise, e. g, «wheresoever there is no fire, neither is there smoke», or «whatsoever is eternal, (i. e., not non-eternal) is not a product». Although one of the premises, the judgments «there is no smoke» and «it is not a product» are negative, the inference itself will not, according to the Indian view, be a negative process of cognition, because the conclusion is positive, e. g. —

Major premise. Wheresoever there is no fire, neither is there smoke.
Minor premise. But there is here smoke.
Conclusion. Hence there is here fire.

The conclusion, and therefore the inference, i. e., the inferred cognition of some reality, is exactly the same as when the major premise was not contraposed. Under a negative syllogism, or negative inferred cognition, something quite different is understood, as has been explained above, ch. II, p. 77 ff. and will be exemplified below, ch. III, p. sūtra 9 ff

[3] *pakṣa-dharmatva* does not correspond to Aristotle's minor premise exactly, for it not only ascertains the presence of the middle upon the minor, but it refers to such a middle term whose invariable concomitance with the major has already been ascertained in the foregoing major premise, e. g., «there is here that very smoke which is known to be invariably concomitant with fire». Therefore there is practically no need of expressing the thesis and the conclusion in separate sentences, they are both understood without being explicitely stated, cp. below, sūtra III. 36 ff. The syllogism of the Naiyāyikas counts five members, because both the thesis (*pratijñā* = *pakṣa*) and the conclusion (*nigamana* = *sādhya*), although they are equivalents, appear as separate propositions, and the minor premise appears twice, once in the ascending process of Induction and once in the descending process of Deduction, e. g., 1) the mountain has fire, 2) because it has smoke, 3) just as in the kitchen etc. smoke is always concomitant with fire, 4) this very smoke is present on the mountain, 5) the mountain has fire. The Indian syllogism is thus the verbal expression of the normal type of ratiocination which is always inductive and deductive, cp. J. S. Mill, Logic[8], I. 228 ff. Dignāga in his reform has dropped thesis conclusion and the double appearance of the minor premise. Thus the Buddhist syllogism reduces to two members since the major and its contraposition express exactly the same thing. It consists of a general statement and of its application to a given particular case. The general statement is always followed by examples, positive

mark possesses these three aspects and they are being expressed, (i. e., communicated). Expression is (an expedient) through which some thing is being expressed or communicated. (41. 5). And what is this (expedient)? Propositions.[1] Indeed the three aspects of the logical mark are communicated to others by propositions. Therefore it is called «inference for others».

(41.7). An objection is raised. Has not inference been defined as (a variety) of knowledge, (viz. as indirect cognition)? How is it then that it is now said to consist of propositions? The (author) answers,— (propositions are given the name of an inference) —

2. Metaphorically, (by naming) the cause instead of the effect.

(41. 10). When the threefold logical mark has been expressed (in propositions, the person to whom it has been communicated) retains them in memory, and his memory produces an inference (in him). Of this inference the propositions expressing the logical mark are the indirect[2] cause (through his memory). Thus the propositions are the cause and the inference the result, there is a metaphor, an imputation of the latter upon the former. (41.12). By dint of such a metaphor propositions are called inference, (whereas they really are its) cause. This means that they are an inference metaphorically, not in the literal[3] application of the term. (41. 13). Nor should it be supposed that whatsoever is capable of being indirectly indicated by the word

---

and negative, which correspond to the part performed in modern European logic by Induction. Thus the full form of the Buddhist syllogism will be represented in the following example,

1) Major premise. Wheresoever there is smoke there is also fire, e. g., in the kitchen where both are present, or in water where there is no smoke, becaus there can be no fire.

2) Minor premise and conclusion combined. There is here such a smoke indicating the presence of fire.

The ultimate result is an inferred judgment (*niścaya = adhyavasāya*), i. e., a reference of a mental construction to a point-instant of external reality (*svalakṣaṇa = paramārtha-sat*).

1 *vacana*. We see that the question which has been so long debated in European, especially in English, logic, viz. the question whether logic is concerned with judgments or with propositions, is here clearly solved by a distinction between what is the part of a thought-process and what the part of its verbal expression.

2 *paramparayā*.

3 *mukhya*.

inference will be here discussed. (41. 14). On the contrary, the aim being to explain what inference is, its essence should be elicited, and its cause found out.[1] This cause is the three-aspected logical mark, (the middle term and its concomitance) which produce inference either when cognized directly or when communicated by another (42. 1). Therefore both the essence of the logical mark and the words by which it is communicated must be elucidated. The first has been done (in the preceding chapter), the second will be done now. (42. 3). Hence, the full meaning[2] is the following one. Our Master (D i g n ā g a) has given the name of inference to propositions,[3] in order to suggest that (the methods of) expressing inference must necessarily be discussed.

(42. 5). The varieties of this kind of inference «for others»[4] are now given.

3. It is twofold.

(42. 7). «It» means syllogism.[5] It is «twofold», i. e., it has two varieties.

(42. 8). Why has it two varieties?

4. Because it is differently formulated.

(42. 10), Difference of formulation is difference in the expressive force of words. Formulation,[6] or expression, means (the capacity of words) to express a meaning. (The verbal formulation) of an inference is divided into two varieties according to a difference in the expressive force of the words, (they can express the same meaning differently).

(42. 12). In order to show this difference, produced by the method of expression, the (author) says.

---

1 Lit. «Because the essence (*svarūpa*) of inference must be explained, its cause should be explained».

2 *paramārtha.*

3 *śabda,* it is reckoned in the majority of schools as a separate source of knowledge including Scripture.

4 It would have been more precise to call it an inference «in others», sc. in the hearers, cp. text p. 41. 10.

5 *parārtha-anumāna.*

6 *prayoga* has the meaning of a formula, or mode of a certain syllogistic figure, cp. p. 37. 15 (text); here and above, p. 30. 15, it is identified with *abhidhā* or *śakti,* i. e., the direct expressive force of words is compared with their capacity of indirect suggestions (*lakṣaṇā, vyakti*). The two methods of inference are here ascribed to a difference in the direct meaning (*abhidhāna-vyāpāra*) of the propositions composing a syllogism.

5. (Method) of Agreement and (method) of Difference.

(42. 14). To agree means to possess the same attribute. The (corresponding) condition is agreement. To disagree means to possess a different attribute. Difference is the condition of one who possesses attributes which do not agree. (42. 15). When there is an agreement, produced by (the common possession of) the logical reason (middle term), between the subject[1] of the conclusion and the similar cases[2] (from which the positive form of the general proposition is drawn by induction), we call it Agreement. But when there is a contrast, produced by the logical mark, (between the subject and the examples, i. e., when the examples are negative), we call it the method of Difference.

(42. 16). Out of these two (methods, the method of Agreement) consists in propositions proving[3] this agreement (directly), as e. g. —

(Major premise). (All) products[4] are impermanent.
(Example). Just as a jar (etc.).
(Minor premise). The sounds of speech are such products.
(Conclusion. They are impermanent).

(42. 18). The directly expressed meaning is here the agreement between the subject of the inference (or minor term) and the similar cases[5] (the jars etc.), an agreement on behalf of the fact that both are products.

(42. 19). But when the (*prima facie*) expressed meaning is disagreement, we call it (the method) of Difference, as e. g. —

---

1 *sādhya-dharmin.*

2 *dṛṣṭānta-dharmin;* the agreement is, more precisely, between two substratums (*dharmin*) upon which concomitant qualities (*dharma*) have been superimposed by constructive thought.

3 *sādhana-vākya,* or simply *vākya,* is the term more closely corresponding to our syllogism, as a complex of propositions proving something; when the method of agreement is used, the analogy, between the given case and those cases from which generalization is drawn, is expressed directly (*abhidheya*), the *prima-facie* meaning is agreement. When the method of difference is resorted to, the *prima facie* meaning is divergence, the examples are negative, but the result is the same.

4 *kṛtaka* corresponds to what in Hīnayāna is called *saṃskṛta* or *saṃskāra,* e. g., in *anityāḥ sarve saṃskārāḥ.*

5 Lit., «between the two possessors (*dharmiṇoḥ*) of the similar and of the inferred qualities».

(Major premise). Eternal entities are known not to be products.

(Example). As e. g., Space.[1]

(Minor premise). But the sounds of speech are a product.

(Conclusion. They are impermanent).

(42.20). These (propositions) express (*prima facie*) a divergence between the sounds of speech, the subject of the conclusion, and Space, the example. The divergence is produced by the fact that the one is and the other is not a product.[2]

(42.22). If the (*prima facie*) meaning expressed in both these syllogisms is different, how are we to understand that (the conclusion is not different, i. e., that) they express the same logical (connection) in its threefold aspect?

---

[1] Space (*ākāśa*) is a reality (*vastu* or *dharma*) only in Hīnayāna where it is entered into the catalogue of Entia as *asaṃskṛta-dharma* № 1 along with *nirodha* or Nirvāṇa which in these Buddhistic schools represents a lifeless reality. The Mahāyānistic schools and the intermediate school of the Sautrāntikas did not admit the reality of eternal, unchanging (*asamskṛta*) elements, because they did not fit in their definition of reality. But although unreal, Space could be used as a *negative* example to confirm a universal major premise. For negative examples the rule is laid down that *vastv avastu vā vaidharmya-dṛṣtānta iṣyate*, cp. text, p. 87. 3. In the Brahmanical systems *ākaśa* means Cosmical Ether, it is either one and indivisible or atomic and entering in the composition of material bodies.

[2] The Methods of Agreement and Difference have been established by J. S. Mill in European Logic as methods of experimental inquiry. They are treated under the same heading by Sigwart, *op. cit.* II. 477 ff. But A. Bain, Logic[2], II. 51, calls the Method of Agreement — «the universal or fundamental mode of proof for all connections whatever... for all kinds of conjunctions». The same, no doubt, applies to its corollary, the Method of Difference. It is in this generalized function that we meet both methods in Indian Logic. They are used not only for singling out the cause of an event, but also for establishing the limits of every notion. Since those methods are methods of Induction, it is clear that Indian Logic, especially its Buddhist variety, considers every process by which anything is inferred as consisting of an Induction followed by a Deduction. This is, according to J. S. Mill, *op. cit.*, I. 232, the «universal type of the reasoning process» which «is always susceptible of the form, and must be thrown into it when assurance of scientific accuracy is needed and desired». The methods of Concomitant Variations (*pratyaya-bheda-bheditva* or *tad-vikāra-vikāritva*) and of Residues (*śeṣānumāna*) are very often discussed in Indian Logic, in the Nyāya, the Vaišesika and in Pr. samuccaya, but they are not given the fundamental importance of the first two methods and are not put on the same level. Both methods are already mentioned in the Nyāya-sūtras, I. 1. 34—35, cp. below p. 126 n. 5.

6. There is no virtual difference between the two (meanings).

(43. 2). The meaning is the aim (of the syllogism), the real fact which must be expressed by it, the fact concerning which both the syllogisms are drawn. (43. 3). There is no difference whatsoever in the fact which they aim at establishing.[1] Indeed, (the aim) is to express a logical connection[2] which (always has) a threefold aspect. For that purpose both (methods) are used. (Although they represent) two (different methods), they express (just the same fact of one) logical connection having three aspects. The idea[3] which they should express is just the same. From this side there is no difference whatsoever.

(43. 6). But then, indeed, we would neither expect any difference in expression? It is answered (that there is no difference) —

7. Except the difference of formulation.

(43. 8). Formulation is verbal expression. Except a difference merely verbal, there is no other difference, no difference in the aim.[3] (43. 9). The meaning is the following one. The *prima facie* meaning[4] is one thing, the aim for which it is used another one. The expressions differ so far the *prima facie* meaning is concerned, but regarding the (aim) for which they are used there is no difference. (43. 10). Indeed, when the (direct or positive) concomitance has been expressed (in the major premise), its contraposition follows by implication. The method (of this contraposition) will be explained later on.[5] And likewise, when the converted (i. e., contraposed) concomitance has been expressed, its positive form follows by implication. (43. 11). Thus it is that the threefold logical reason which should be expressed remains unchanged. Indeed the implied meaning does not always change when the words expressing it are different. (43. 12). For if we have two propositions: «the *fat* Devadatta does not eat at day-time» and «the *fat* Devadatta eats at night»,[6] although the direct

1 Lit. «Between both no difference whatsoever from the aim (*prayojanāt*)».

2 *linga*.

3 *prayojana*.

4 *abhidheya*. 5 Cp. sūtra III. 28 ff.

6 This is the usual example of the method of Necessary Implication (*arthāpatti*), a method of proof very much in vogue in the school of Mīmāṃsakas. They applied it wherever the consequence seemed to them immediate and quite unavoidable (*anyathānupapatti*), the contrary being simply impossible (*sambhava-abhāva*). The Naiyāyikas reduced all such cases to simple inferences in which one proposi-

meaning is different, the intention is quite the same. Just so is it in the present case. Although the words are different, the conveyed real fact is quite the same.

§ 2. The method of agreement.

8. **Among these two (methods, the method) of Agreement (is now illustrated by examples).**

(43.16). The first to be exemplified among the two (methods) of Agreement and of Difference is the method of Agreement. The author gives an example of a negative deduction [1] (in the formulation of agreement).

---

tion is deduced from another, because it is virtually contained in the latter (*samudāyena itarasya grahaṇam*), cp. N. bh., II. 2. 2 ff. European logic treats these deductions mostly under the head of immediate or apparent inferences. How difficult it is to draw a line of demarcation between immediate and mediate inference is proved by the fact that in modern times some logicians are trying to reduce all inference and even the whole field of logical relations to Implication (Bradley, Bosanquet, and New Realism, p. 82). The Buddhists make a distinction between propositions which are virtually synonymous and those which contain real deductions. The criterium is the fact of external reality about which the proposition contains a communication. Speech is at once a result of external reality and of the intention of the speaker, cp. below text p. 60. 11 ff. If the fact communicated is absolutely the same as, e. g., the fact that Devadatta eats at night, in the above example, the propositions are logically synonymous. The major premise is synonymous with its contraposition. But if the facts are however slightly different, it is a deduction, e. g., when the part as contained in the whole is deduced from it, or even when absence or negation is deduced from non-perception.

[1] The «three-aspected mark» (*trirūpa-linga*) is but an other word for concomitance (*vyāpti*). Three kinds of such logical connection have been established which are respectively called Negation (*anupalabdhi*), Identity (*tādātmya*) and Causation (*tadutpatti*, more precisely, the fact of being necessarily caused by something). Thus the middle term, or logical reason, i. e., the fact used as a logical reason, may be either 1) the fact of non-perception of something that could be visible (*dṛṣya-anupalabdhi*); all negative deductions are reduced to this simple fact as has been explained above; 2) or the fact of greater comprehension and lesser extension from which a fact of lesser comprehension and greater extension can be deduced; the reason is called Identity, because it is inherent in the same entity as the deduced term; all analytical processes of thought are reduced to this type, (*vyāpya-vyāpaka-bhāva*) and 3) the fact that every event has necessarily a cause or causes; all synthetic or causal cognitionitions are reduced to this type (*kārya-kāraṇa-bhāva*). Each of them can be expressed according to the method of Agreement or the method of Difference. We will thus have six principal types of reasoning which the author is now going to illustrate.

9. (Major premise). Wheresoever we do not perceive the presence of a representable thing, we exhibit corresponding behaviour towards it.

(Example). Just as when we fail to perceive another thing known from experience to be quite unexisting, though representable, e. g., the horns on the head of a hare etc.

(Minor premise). On a certain place we do not perceive the presence of a jar which is representable.

(Conclusion. We behave without expecting to find it there).[1]

(43.21). «A thing (known) to be essentially perceptible»,[2] i. e., a thing which can be imagined as perceived, and «is not perceived» — these words represent the subject[3] (of the major premise), it is the fact of the absence of a cognition of something representable.[4] (43.22). This is a case when we are justified to behave in accordance with its non-existence,[5] i. e., we can take action knowing that it is absent. (44.1). Thus it is stated that the fact of not perceiving (the presence) of a representable object is necessarily associated with the possibility of negative purposive action towards it. This means that a representable object not being perceived affords an opportunity for a corresponding negative action.[6] (44.2). Now, the statement that the logical reason is necessarily associated with its consequence is a statement of invariable concomitance; this is according to the definition — invariable concomitance (between a subject and its predicate or a reason and its

---

1 Lit., p. 43.18—20. «What, being contained in the essence of perception, is not perceived, it is established as an object of non-Ens-dealing; just as some other established hare-horn etc.; and on some special place a jar contained in the essence of perception is not perceived».

2 The word *lakṣaṇa* is here rendered in Tib. by *rig-bya* = *jñeya* = *viṣaya*, and *prāpta* by *gyur-pa* = *bhūta*, thus *upalabdhi-lakṣaṇa-prāpta* = *jñāna-viṣaya-bhūta*, i. e., an object which does not transcend the limits of our knowledge, which is representable, is not something transcendental, cp. above, transl. p. 107 ff.

3 *anūdyate*.

4 *dṛśya*.

5 Lit., p. 43.22. «This is the established object of (our) dealing (*vyavahāra*) with non-Ens, it means we can behave with the thought (*iti*) „it is not"».

6 Lit., p. 44.1. «Through this predication is made of the fitness (*yogyatva*) of the (object) for non-Ens-dealing».

consequence) consists in 1) the necessary presence (never absence) of the predicate upon the subject, and 2) in the presence of the subject exclusively in the sphere of the predicate, (never beyond it).[1]

(44. 4). The example (points to induction), to the evidence by which the invariable concomitance has been established.[2] In order to indicate it, it is said «just as (when we fail to perceive) another object» etc. This means that the example is some other object, different from the subject of the conclusion (or minor term). (44. 5). «Known from experience» (to be quite unexisting) means ascertained by evidence. The horns (on the head) of a hare have indeed never been perceived by vision nevertheless they are imaginable, and this is the evidence owing to which we conclude that we will never have an opportunity of experiencing (them as efficient). These (utterly unexisting) horns are indeed an evidence proving that the idea of a non-Ens has a practical value (for our purposive actions) and it is exclusively founded on our capacity to imagine their existence and then to repudiate that suggestion. This

---

[1] Lit., p. 44. 3—4. «Concomitance is necessary presence (*bhāva eva*) of the embracer (*vyāpaka*) there and the presence of the embraced (*vyāpya*) necessarily there (*tatra eva*)», e. g., in the judgment, or the deduction, «the Ašoka is a tree» concomitance requires the necessary presence of the term of greater extension, the «embracer», «the tree», with the subaltern, or embraced Ašoka, but it may be also found outside the Ašokas, in other trees, whereas Ašoka, the term of greater comprehension and lesser extension, is necessarily present among trees only, not among non-trees. Reduced to Aristotle's phrasing this rule means that a universal affirmative judgment is not convertible otherwise than *per accidens*. Now, the negative judgment, or negative deduction, in its basic form, is not a tautology of the form «there is no jar because there is none», but it is a deduction of the form «there is no jar because there is a bare place». It is a cognition of an underlying point instant of reality and this makes it a true cognition or judgment (*niščaya*). The term «a bare place» (*dṛšya-anupalabdhi*) is greater in comprehension and less in extension than the affirmation of non-Ens which is deduced from it, since there are other non-Ens'es which are not associated with a bare place (*adṛšya-anupalabdhi*, transcendental objects, unimaginable concretely, cp. sūtra II. 48—49. Cp. H. Bergson, *op. cit.*, p. 319— «De l'abolition (= *dṛšya-anupalabdhi*) à la négation (= *nāsti iti*), qui est une opération plus générale, il n'y a qu'un pas».

[2] Lit., p. 44. 4. «The example is the sphere (*viṣaya*) of proof (*pramāṇa*) establishing concomitance». It is clear that the example performs the part of Induction from paricular instances; *pramāṇa* thus has the meaning of evidence, of an ascertained fact, *pramāṇa-siddham trairūpyam* means concomitance established upon ascertained facts or upon experience (*avisaṃvāda*); *dṛṣṭa*, *daršana* corresponds to our experience, *pramāṇena niščita*, or sometimes *pramāṇa* simply, means an established fact, induction from particular facts, cp. the meaning of this term in p. 45. 1, 61. 10, 80. 21, 81. 1—2, 81. 20, 86. 11 etc., cp. below p. 147 n. 7.

alone is the evidence. (44. 8). By this proposition (containing a reference to the evidence proving the general law), we must be satisfied that the invariable concomitance is (fully) expressed.

(44. 9) After having established the general concomitance (in the major premise), the (author) now proceeds to state its application[2] to the subject (in the minor premise). He says «and we do not perceive (the presence of a jar somewhere on a definite place)». A place is one (definite) place on earth. It is «just this place» because it is distinguished from other places.[3] One definite place means the place upon which (there is no jar). «Somewhere» means a place

---

[1] Lit., p. 44. 6—8. «Bnt by evidence (*pramāṇena*), by non-perception of the imagined, it is known to be fit for non-Ens-dealing. The hare-horn is the first (example) of an object of a non-Ens-dealing, it is so expressed. On the hare-horn etc., indeed, the non-Ens-dealing is proved by evidence to depend on nothing but non-perception of the imagined. Just from this evidence». *tata eva pramāṇāt* — is a separate sentence.—The horns of a hare or of a donkey, the son of a barren woman, a lotos flower in the sky are the usual examples of absolute nnrealities. They differ from the absent jar which is a contingent unreality. The author lays stress on the fact that even absolnte unrealities are representable and have some negative importance in guiding our purposive actions, this being the test of reality. It is real absence, it is not nothing (*tuccha*), because nothing could not guide our actions even negatively. Bnt it is not a reality *sui generis* (*vastvantaram*), as the realists maintain, it is imagining (*dṛśya*). Unimaginable are metaphysical entities, e. g., Buddha or Nirvāṇa in their Mahāyānistic conception (*sarvajñatvam hy adṛśyam*, p. 71. 3). Mallavādī, fol. 75—77, expatiates on this example as proving that negative behaviour (*asad-vyavahāra*) has no other logical reason, i. e., no other necessary reason than imagination of a thing absent or unreal. Others, says he, have maintained that the absence of a perception (*ghaṭa-jñāna-abhāva*), the fact that we do not name it (*ghaṭa-śabda-abhāva*), the fact that we do not use the jar for fetching water (*jala-āharaṇādi-kriyā-abhāva*) are the reasons for availing oneself of the idea of a non-Ens in practical life. Bnt these facts of non-existence are either simple nothings (*tuccha*), they are then unreal (*asiddha*) and can have no influence on our actions; or they are meant for their positive connterparts (*pratiyogin = paryudāsa*) which is cognized, as stated above, p. 30. 8, by sense-perception, when the perceptual judgment «there is here no jar» is the outcome. But when the facts of speaking of other things, not of the absent jar, and the fact of doing something else than fetching water in a jar (*paryudāsa*) are the outcome, this is already a practical consequence of the idea of the absent jar, and it thus, being itself purposive action, cannot be the reason of that very purposive action (*na hi sādhyam eva sādhanam bhavati*). Therefore the only reason of our negative hehaviour is imagination.

[2] *pakṣa-dharmatva*.

[3] Cp. H. Bergson, *op. cit.*, p. 301— «quand je dis que l'objet, une fois aboli, laisse sa place inoccupée, il s'agit... d'une *place*, c'est à dire d'un vide limité par des contours précis, c'est-à-dire d'une espèce de *chose*».

lying before the eyes of the observer. (44.12). Although it is «some» place, but that place alone is the object of a negative purposive action which is present to the observer, not any other place. (A jar) satisfyng to the conditions of perceptibility [1] means a jar which can be imagined as perceived.[2] (44.13). The manner in which a non-existing jar is placed by imagination in all the necessary conditions of perceptibility has been explained above.[3]

(44.15). In order to give the formula of an analytical reasoning [4] according to the Method of Agreement [5] the (author) says —

10. The analytical reasoning can be expressed according to the same (method).

(44.17). Just as the negative deduction has been formulated according to (the method of) Argeement, just so will an analytical deduction now be formulated accordindg to this same (method).

11. (Major premise). Every thing that exists is momentary.

(Example). Just as a jar (representing a compact chain of momentary existences).

(Minor premise. The sound exists).

(Conclusion. It is a chain of momentary existences).

This is the formula of a simple (unqualified) analytical deduction.

(44.19). «What exists», i. e., existence, is the subject. «Every thing» is momentary», i. e., momentariness is predicated. The words «every thing» are inserted for emphasis. All is impermanent, there is nothing which is not impermanent. What exists is necessarily impermanent. Over and beyond impermanence, there is only eternity and that is no existence.[6] (44.21). Thus it is declared that existence is necessarily dependent on

---

1 *upalabdhi-lakṣaṇa-prāpta.*

2 *dṛśya.*

3 Cp. text p. 29, transl. p. 81 ff.

4 *svabhāva-hetu.*

5 *sādharmyavat.*

6 Different definitions of what is meant by existence, or reality, have been current at different periods of Buddhist philosophy. In the Hīnayāna the Sarvāstivādins and other schools defined existence as whatsoever has a character (*dharma-svabhāva*) of its own (*sva-svabhāva-dhāraṇād dharmaḥ*). This involved a pluralistic view of the Universe. The Mādhyamikas defined existence as non-relative (*anapekṣa*),

the predicate of impermanence, (i. e., momentariness).[1] Consequently the (major) premise expresses their invariable concomitance. (45. 1). The words «just as a jar etc.» is a statement concerning the evidence by which the general law is established. This is the formula of a simple analytical reason.[2] «Simple» means without qualifications.

(45. 3). In order to give the formula of a qualified analytical reason, the (author) says —

absolute reality, this involved a monistic view of the Universe. Cp. my Nirvāṇa, p.40 ff. The Santrāntikas and the later Yogācāras, the Buddhist Logicians, defined reality as efficiency (*artha-kriyā-kāritva*) cp. above, sūtra I. 12—14. This involved the theory that ultimate reality is represented by the focus of efficiency, the point-instant (*kṣaṇa*). Thus every existence without exception is split in discrete moments. Every stability, every duration is, on the contrary, a construction, an integration of moments (*kṣaṇa-santāna*). Impermanence (*anityatva*) is here an equivalent of momentariness (*kṣaṇikatva*). There is nothing between eternity and momentariness, *nityam=apracyuta-anutpanna-sthira-eka-svabhāvam*, *anityam=prakṛtyā eka-kṣaṇa-sthiti-dharmakam*, see Haribhadra Anekānta-jaya-patākā, f. 2. a. 31 (Ahmedabad City Printing Press), cp. Jayanta, p. 115. 3.

[1] That jars etc. are suitable examples where universal momentariness is established by Induction may seem strange to us, but this is proved by a very subtle argument which is reproduced by Mādhavācārya in Sarvadarś p. 20 ff. (Poona 1925) where it is borrowed from Dharmakīrti's Pramāṇaviniścaya. It has been translated by Cowell and by Deussen (in his History of Philosophy), but I doubt whether these literal translations can affor d much help in understanding the real argument of Dharmakīrti. Virtually his argument is very similar to the one stated by B. Russel, Mysticism, p. 184 ff., in the following words—«if the cause is purely static... then, in the first place, no such cause is to be found in nature, and in the second place, it seems strange — too strange to be accepted, in spite of bare logical possibility, that the cause after existing placidly for some time, should suddenly explode into the effect, when it might just as well have done so at any earlier time, or have gone on unchanged without producing its effect», cp. =*kadāpi na kuryāt*, *op cit.*, p. 21. The conclusion is drawn that there is an imperceptible change going on in the jar at every moment of its existence, the supposed duration of the jar, assumed by the realists, from the moment of its production by the potter up to the moment of its destruction by a stroke of a hammer, is an illusion. Rgyal-thsab, fol. 34, translates *sarvam sat* in this passage very characteristically by *dños-par-yod-pa=vastutaḥ sat*, thereby indicating that the absolutely real, the point-instants (*svalakṣaṇa=kṣaṇa*) are here taken as the subject of the general proposition. The example in Sarvad., p. 20. is a cloud (*jaladhara-paṭala*), but this makes no difference. Since it is established that there can be no other causation but between moments, hence a jar is a series of momentary existences where every preceding moment is the cause of the following one. This subtle theory is criticized at length by Vācaspatimiśra in Tātparyaṭ. p. 379 ff. and very often alluded to almost in every Indian philosophical work.

[2] This argument is directed against the Mīmāṃsakas who assumed that the sounds of speach are but a manifestation of eternal entities. The non-eternality of

12. The formula of an analytical syllogism with a middle term which is differentiated by a qualification existentially identical with it, is the following one —

(Major premise). Whatsoever has an origination is impermanent.

(Example). (Just as a jar etc.).

(Minor premise). (The sounds of our speech possess origination).

(Conclusion). (The sounds of our speech are impermanent).

(45.5). «Origination» means assuming one's own essence.[1] The words «what has an origination» express the subject (of the major premise). The words «is impermanent» express the predicate. Thus the invariable concomitance of everything having an origination with impermanence is expressed.

(45.7). This is a formula whose *raison d'être*[2] (as compared with the preceding one) consists in a special qualification which (however) is existentially identical,[3] essentially the same, (as the preceding one). An entity is called «having an origination» when contrasted with beginningless entities, (which is the same as permanent, eternal entities). When we wish to give expression to a contrast independent from

---

sound is deduced here out of a special conception of existence. This is a specific argument of the Buddhists, the advocates of Universal Momentariness or Continual Flow of Existence. The realistic Naiyāyikas and Vaišeṣikas, in combating the Mīmāṃsaka theory of eternal sounds of speech, deduce the non-eternity of words from the fact that they are products and even wilful products of man. These arguments are also admitted by the Buddhists, but they begin by a deduction from their general idea of existence as a flux and continue by deductions from its subaltern or narrower characteristics, such as production, wilful production etc.

[1] *svarūpa-lābha* = *svabhāva-lābha* = *ātma-bhāva*, usually rendered in Tib. by *lus* = *šarīra* (the sentence is here omitted, in the Tib. transl., cp. p. 101.15).

[2] *hetūkṛtya.*

[3] We have noticed above, transl. p. 70 n., the two different meanings of the term *svabhāva*, in *svabhāva-pratibandha* where it includes causation and *svabhāva-hetu*, where it excludes causation and means «inherent property». In sūtra II. 15 we had *svabhāva-višeṣa* meaning «an individual». Here we have a further differentiation of the second meaning. Inherent property is divided in *svabhāva* proper and *upādhi*. The first is an inherent property which «seems to mean something» (*vyatirekiṇīva*), but means nothing additional, it is synonymous. Since existence according to the Buddhist theory of Universal Momentariness is nothing but permanent origination without any stability, origination and existence practi-

any other (real) contrast, (a contrast limited to expression), it is called apparent contrast,[1] as e. g. «the beginning of existence», (existence is nothing but permanent beginning). A (momentary) reality qualified by a beginning which is only apparently different from the (reality itself) is described as something having a beginning. (45.10). Thus the analytical reason here formulated must be regarded as characterized by an attribute which is included in the same thing itself and can be distinguished only in abstraction (i. e. in imagination).[2]

13. The formula of an analytical syllogism with a middle term containing an additional (accidental) qualification is the following one —

(Major premise). Whatsoever is a product is impermanent.

(Examples). (As a jar etc.).

(Minor premise). (The sounds of our speech are products).

(Conclusion). (The sounds of our speech are impermanent).

(45.13). The attribute of «being a product» is the subject, «impermanence» is the predicate (of the major premise). It expresses that the fact of being a product always includes[3] in itself the notion of

---

cally become synonyms. The second is an inherent property which really means something additional, something different (*vyatirekin*). The difference however is only of the point of view, since both the attributes of «origination» and «production from causes» are conterminous and coinherent in every existing thing. From one point of view every thing appears as constantly changing and haviug no duration at all, but without any reference to causal laws. From the other point of view every thing represents a constant change in coordination with antecedent moments according to causal laws. For the Buddhists they are correct inferences supported by the totality of the similar cases and contrasted with the dissimilar, or eternal, cases, since the latter have no existence. For the Realists who admit the existence of both the eternal and non-eternal entities they will be logical fallacis (*anupasaṃhārin*).

[1] *vyatirekiṇīva.*

[2] The difference between Aśoka-tree and tree in general is also said to be produced by imagination (*kalpita-bheda=vikalpa-viṣaya* cp. above, text 26. 15, cp. 48.9), it is logical, not real, since both these concepts are different, although they appear as the characteristics of the same moment of reality (*vastutaḥ*). Here, on the contrary, the difference is produced not by different concepts, but only by two expressions which, taking into account the theory of Universal Momentariness, are synonymous.

[3] *niyata=pratibaddha*, lit., «the being a product is fastened to impermanence», i. e., the notion of being a product is subaltern to the notion of imperma-

impermanence. Therefore it shows that there is an invariable concomitance between every product and impermanence. This is the formula of the analytical reason with an additional (accidental) qualification.[2] (45.15). «Qualification» means characteristic. An analytical reason characterized by a difference of qualification, by an (accidental property) which is different from it, is here formulated. (45.16). Now, sometimes (in life) we name a thing simply, sometimes accompanied by a characteristic which ist not separate from the object itself, sometimes accompanied by a characteristic which is separate. E. g., «Devadatta» is a proper name, «long-eared» is a name by which he is characterized through both his ears which are not beyond him. «The owner of a brindled cow» is a name by which he is characterized by (the accidental characteristic of the ownership) of a brindled cow which exists beyond him. (45.18). Similarly the word «existence» is a simple designation (of a fact). «Having origination» is (a designation of the same fact) through a characteristic which does not differ from it. «A product» is a characteristic (of the same fact) through something (additional), that lies beyond it, (viz. through its causes).

(45.20). The following objection (will be perhaps made). In the example of the «owner of a brindled cow» there are two words expressing the qualification (of Devadatta), the word brindled and the word cow. In the example («a product is impermanent») a single word «product» is used without any qualifications. (How can it represent a qualified reason?)».[3] The answer is as follows.

14. «A product» means an existence (viewed as something) which for its own concretisation is

---

nence, it is contained in the latter, it is greater in comprehension and less in extension (*vyāpya*) than the latter (the *vyāpaka*). This would mean that the proposition «all products are impermanent» is convertible *per accidens*, that momentary entities are assumed which are not products, but from III. 128 it seems that both conceptions are conterminous.

[2] Lit., p. 45. 14—15. «Through a difference of the condition (*upādhi*), the words «formula of self-existence (*svabhāva*)» are connected (from the preceding sūtra)».

[3] This introduction of Dharmottara does not refer to the fact that the qualification is expressed by two words in *citra-gu*, this seems quite immaterial, it might have been expressed by one word as well. Important is only the fact that the accidental characteristic is expressed. Vinītadeva's *avataraṇa* states that in the word «prodnct» there is no qualification perceptible (*mṅon-pa* = *sākṣāt*), and explains that it is not expressed but understood, p. 88. 1—2.

dependent upon the efficiency (of entities) other (than itself).

(46.2). The efficiency[1] of causes other (than the entity itself) is needed for the appearance of a (concrete) entity.[2] This is the reason[3] (why the word product contains this meaning). Since we call produced (an entity) which depends on the efficiency of something else, therefore we say that the analytical reason[4] is qualified by something (additional, something) lying beyond it.[5] (46.4). There is here no word corresponding to this additional characteristic, nevertheless it is implied in the word «product» itself. That is why this word has the shape of a technical term,[6] since grammar enjoins to build technical terms in this way.[7] In those cases where the attribute is implied there is no necessity of using a special word for it.

(46.8). Sometimes the (accidental) attribute is understood (but not expressed), as e.g., if we say «a product» we understand «produced by causes». In such cases, the word «causes» is sometimes expressed and sometimes not.

15. The (expression) «variable concomitantly with a change in the causes» and other (similar expressions) must be understood in the same way.[8]

(46.11). (The accidental characteristic) is expressed by a corresponding word, e.g., in the expression (a function) «variable concomitantly

---

1 *vyāpāra.*

2 *svabhāva* in the sense of *svabhāva-viśeṣa* «an individual» cp. sūtra I. 15.

3 Lit., p. 46. 3. «The word indeed (*hi*) in the sense of because».

4 *svabhāva* here in the sense of *svabhāva-hetu.*

5 *vyatiriktena viśeṣeṇa.*

6 The term *kṛtaka*, as stated above, corresponds to the Hīnayānist term *saṃskṛta*= *kāraṇaiḥ* (= *samskāraiḥ*) *sambhūya kṛtam.* The connotation in Hīnayāna is different, since reality is there divided in *saṃskṛta* and *asaṃskṛta* elements, whereas in the Mahāyāna and in the Sautrāntika school the definition of reality having been changed, the *asaṃskṛtas* including Nirvāṇa have no separate reality, cp. my Nirvāṇa, p. 42.

7 Lit., p. 46. 6. «Because the suffix *kan* is prescribed for names», cp. Pāṇini IV. 3. 147.

8 This sūtra, according to Vinītadeva, p. 88.9, included the word *prayatnānantarīyakatva* also. This would make two further arguments for proving that the sounds of our speech are not unchanging metaphysical eternal elements, as maintained by the ancient Mīmāṃsakas, viz. 4) whatsoever exhibits concomitant variations is impermanent, and 5) whatsoever is produced by a conscious effort is impermanent.

with a change in the causes». Here the words expressing it are «concomitantly with a change in the causes». This expression and other similar ones, as e. g., the expression «invariably dependent on volition»[1] are instances of the analytical reason[2] where this reason is accompanied by an indication of an additional (accidental) attribute,[3] just as in the word «a product». (46.13). The sounds of our speech vary according as the causes (producing them) change. Their conditions or causes[4] being different, being variable, they have themselves the nature of changing concomitantly, according as the conditions vary.[5] (46.15). Thus from the fact that the sound is variable, dependent on a change in its causes, it is deduced that it is a product. From the fact that it «invariably depends on volition» its impermanence is deduced. (46.16). In the first instance the words «concomitantly with a change in the causes» and in the second the word «volition» express such qualifications which are additional (to the fact adduced as a reason).

(46.17). We have thus shown that there can be a threefold difference in framing the analytical reason, it may be simple, essentially and accidentally determined. This we have insisted upon in order that no one

1 *prayatna-anatarīyakatva.* This attribute is introduced here by Dh. as an instance alluded to by the word *ādi* of the sūtra, but in the text commented upon by Vinītadeva it was included in the sūtra.

2 *svabhāva-hetoḥ prayogāḥ.*

3 *bhinna-viśeṣaṇa-svabhāva-abhidhāyin.*

4 *pratyaya* condition and *kāraṇa* cause are here used synonymously.

5 We find the method of Concomitant Variations for the first time applied in Indian Philosophy in the Abh-kośa, I. 45, (cp. V.S.II. 2. 29), where it appears under the name of *tad-vikāra-vikāritva*, i. e., «the fact of (this thing) undergoing a change when there is a change in that thing». It is there applied as a proof of the connection between the senses and feeling, i. e., as we can put it, between the brain and the mind. European logicans will be perhaps astonished to see that a similar statement of Prof. A. Bain, Logic², II. 63, was anticipated by Vasubandhu. They will perhaps be still more astonished when they have fully realized the implications of the fact that the Buddhists were lead to this conclusion by their conceptions of Causation (*pratītya-samutpāda* = *asmin sati idam bhavati*) of which the psycho-physical parallelism is an illustration. Indian philosophy has thus abandoned the anthropomorphic view of Causality at a very early date, and replaced it by the idea of what in mathematics is called a function, cp. my Nirvāṇa, p. 39 ff., *pratyaya-bheda-bheditva* is of course just the same as *tad-vikāra-vikāritva* and Vācaspatimiśra thinks that we must interpret *upacāra* in N. S. II. 2. 13 as *śabda-bheda-pratyaya.* Of course the Method of Concomitant Variations is not treated here as a separate method, in coordination with the fundamental methods of Agreement and Difference; it appears here as a method of proof subordinate to the method of Agreement.

should be misled by a difference in the wording when using the analytical reason (i. e., a reason from which the predicate is analytically deduced).[1]

16. The sounds of speech are existent, they have a (real) origin, they are produced — these are the minor premises.[2]

---

[1] Dh. warns us against committing mistakes in using the term analytical or essential reason (*svabhāva-hetu*). The latter has been defined above, sūtra II. 16, as a reason which alone by itself is a sufficient ground for deducing the consequence, the consequence is contained in the reason, no other additional or accidental condition is needed (*na hetu-sattāyā vyatiriktam kamcid dhetum apekṣate*, p. 22. 19). We were, accordingly, justified in assigning to the major premises of Dharmakīrti's analytical syllogisms a place among the class of propositions in which the predicate is of the essence of the subject. But now we are warned that if an accidental or additional attribute (*upādhi*) is contained in the reason (or subject), the judgment will nevertheless remain analytical. The analytical reason can, in its turn contain either an essential or an accidental attribute (*vyatiriktena viśeṣaṇena viśiṣṭaḥ svabhāvaḥ*, p. 46. 4). The judgments «whatsoever changes concomitantly with a change in its causes, is a product of these causes» and «whatsoever is consequent on an effort is impermanent» are, according to Dharmakīrti. analytical or essential judgments, the predicate is included in the subject. Now what is contained in the subject and what is not yet included in it is very often questionable, and accidental attributes may become essential when the observer has satisfied himself from experience that the subject always possesses that attribute. The extension and intension (*vyāpya-vyāpaka-bhāva*) of attributes, is determined by their definitions founded on observation (cp. text, p. 39. 5 ff.). The subject is thus supposed to include all those attributes, whether essential, previously known, or accidental, newly added to it as a result of assent to a judgment, which are co-inherent in him. It has been acknowledged in European philosophy that the line of demarcation between attributes essential and accidental is constantly shifting. In India all attributes known (*siddha*) to be coexistent are considered as constituting the essence of the thing. The difference is between coexistance and succession.

[2] The ancient Mīmāṃsakas (*jarad-mīmāṃsaka*) in their speculations on the nature of sound established a theory according to which the sounds of speech (*gakārādi*) were imagined as unchanging eternal appurtenances inherent in the cosmic aether (*ākāśa*), their existence occasionally manifested itself when a concussion of air was produced by the conjunction or disjunction of objects, cp. Tātp., p. 307. The Naiyāyikas, N. S. II. 2. 13 ff., cp. V.S.II.2.32, opposed this theory by three arguments, 1) the sounds of speech have a real beginning or causes, 2) they are perceived not in the place of their origin but when having reached the organ of audition, hence the existence of a series (*santāna*) of momentary sounds must be assumed in the interval, and 3) these sounds are variable in intensity and character, hence at every moment we have a different sound (this is the meaning of *kṛtakavad upacārāt*, according to commentators). The last argument, Uddyotakara remarks, is Buddhistic, since it implies Universal Momentariness — ***sarva-anityatva-sādhana-***

§ 3. Analytical deductions are deductions of coexistence.

(46.21). Follows the question, can these analytical reasonings be used when the connection of the reason (with the deduced property) is already known or when it is not known? In order to show, that they must be used in such cases where the connection (of the subject and the predicate) is already known, (the author) says —

17. All these attributes (which are given as) reasons[1] (for the deduction of corresponding predicates) should be conceived (as logical reasons) for deducing only such predicates[2] whose necessary dependence on nothing but (the presence of) the reason is established by proofs,[3] (whatsoever they may be) suiting every special case.

(47.3). They are called reasons, since they prove (the presence of something else), and they also are attributes, since they inhere in

---

dharmaḥ, and Vācaspatimiśra, *loco. cit.*, p. 313, identifies it with a reference to the Buddhist «law of otherness» (*viruddha-dharma-saṃsarga*) according to which every variation in time, place and character makes the object «another» object, cp. above note 2 on p. 8. The Buddhists start with a deduction of the non-eternity of the sounds of speech from their conception of every existence in general as a run of momentary events having only apparent stability, and then proceed in order to refer to the 1) fact of having a beginning, 2) causality, 3) concomitant variability, 4) dependenee on a wilful effort. The first and 4th of these arguments correspond to the 3d argument of the Naiyāyikas, and the 2d and 3d are contained in their first one (*ādir* = *kāraṇam*). There is more logic in the Buddhist arrangement. The first argument contains in itself all the others, the second directly (*svabhāvena*) the third and others — indirectly (*upādhinā*). All these conceptions, existence, origination, causality, concomitant variation, dependence on the will are analytically connected, in the Indian sense of the term *svabhāva*, the first includes all the others, it is of greater extension and less intension than the others which are its subalterns. The extension and intension of all these attributes are determined, according to what has been stated above, p. 38—39 (text), transl. p. 108 ff., on the basis of actual observation, on the basis of «perception and non-perception». From this point of view all judgments of Coexistence, or co-inherent attributes, are also founded on experience, just as those which are founded on uniformity of Succession or Causation.

1 *sādhana-dharmāḥ*. 2 *sādhya-dharme*.

3 *pramāṇa* is here an equivalent of *dṛṣṭānta*, cp. above p. 44. 8 (text) cp. below p. 147 n. 7.

something else.[1] These attributes «alone»,[2] i. e., nothing but their mere (presence is sufficient for making the deduction of other co-inherent attributes). By the words «nothing but»[3] every additional circumstance which should be taken into account is excluded. (47.4). Their «necessary dependence»[4] means their following, their flowing[5] (necessarily from the nature of the fact representing the reason).

(47.5). The necessary dependence upon nothing but the presence of (the fact representing) the reason which is here mentioned is «established».[6] By what is it established? By corresponding proofs. Every predicate is established just by that proof which is the proper proof (for the given generalization). (47.6). Since the reasons by the analysis of which[7] (the predicate of impermanence) may be established are many, the proofs establishing the (analytical) tie[8] are likewise many, therefore they are mentioned in the plural.

(47.8). (The deduced or predicated attribute is characterized as) «deduced» because it is made to follow (from the presence of the reason), and it is also an attribute, because it is inherent in something else, (it is co-inherent with the attribute representing the reason).

(47.8). What the (author) means is really[9] this. A logical reason does not produce cognition (of some unobserved fact) accidentally, as e.g., a lamp (producing knowledge of such unobserved objects which it accidentally happens to illumine).[10] But it produces knowledge (by

---

1 *dharma* is here used in the ordinary (and original) sense of a quality belonging to some substance. It does not follow that the objective reality of the categories of substance and quality (*dharma-dharmi-bhāva*) is admitted, but the Hīnayānistic view that there are only *dharmas* and no *dharmins* at all, that, as Yašomitra puts it, *vidyamānam dravyam* (cp. my Central Conception, p. 26), this view is forsaken, and replaced by the admittance of a logical connection between a substratum and all the variety of its possible attributes, this logical connection has also an ontological meaning so far the ultimate substratum of all logical constructions, the ultimate *dharmin* is the point-instant as the thing in itself (*svalakṣaṇa*).

2 *eva*.

3 *mātra*.

4 *anubandha*.

5 *anvaya*.

6 *siddha*.

7 *svabhāva-hetu*, as, e. g., the three conceptions of «existence», of «having an origin» and of «being produced from causes» through the analysis of which the predicate non-eternal is deduced.

8 *sambandha* = *pratibandha*, cp. Jayanta, p. 114. 9 — *nanu cānyaḥ sambandhaḥ, anyašca pratibandhaḥ*.

9 *paramārtha*.

10 Cp. text p. 19. 2 and 49. 15.

logical necessity) as an ascertained case of invariable concomitance. (47.9). The function of the logical reason is, indeed, to produce the cognition of an unobserved fact, and this is just (what is meant by) ascertainment of the reason's invariable concomitance with the latter. (47.10). First of all, (as a preliminary step), we must be certain that the presence of our logical reason is necessarily dependent upon the presence of the predicated consequence, (we must verify it by trying to find) contradictory facts.[1] We then can proceed to syllogize and avail ourselves of the general proposition recorded in our memory, (the proposition) intimating that its subject is invariably concomitant with its predicate, e. g. —

Any object produced (according to causal laws) is non-eternal.

(47.12). After that we can connect this general record with the given particular case —

That causal origin which is a characteristic of the sounds of our speech necessarily coexists with the attribute of non-eternity.

(47.13). Between these (two premises, the major) contains the mnemonic record, it is a knowledge of the logical reason (and its concomitance, acquired by whatsoever evidence). The syllogism (proper is contained in the next step, when we in the minor premise) assert[2] that

---

1 *bādhakena pramāṇena.* We take *pramāṇa* here as meaning *dṛṣṭānta* as in 44.4, 61.10, 80.21, 81.1—2, 81.20—21, 86.11, 87.5. Rgyal-thsab, f. 35, explains it as meaning that the denial of an analytical judgment is impossible, since it would be a contradiction, «eternal (i. e., immutable) substances cannot produce anything, since they cannot be efficient, neither gradually, nor at once» cp. Sarvad, p. 21—24. Another verification, according to the same author, would be a reference to the Buddhist doctrine of Universal Momentarines — *rañ-yod-tsam-nas ḥjig-pa rañ-gi ño-bo-ñid-du rjes-su ḥbrel-te.* The author of Pramāṇa-vārtika-alaṃkāra (Rgyan-mkhan-po), Prajñākaragupta, Bstan-ḥgyur, Mdo, vol. 99—100, thinks that this doctrine is an extraordinary intuition of great men (*anāsrava-jñāna* of Mahātmas) which cannot be arrived at in the ordinary way. According to Rgyal-thsab, sūtra III. 17 suggests (evidently in the words *yathā-svam-pramāṇaiḥ*) that the usual methods of induction indicated in sūtra II. 6ff. (*sapakṣe sattvam eva* etc.) do not apply in these cases, that the reasoning starts here with the general proposition — *go-byed-du-ḥgyur-ba ḥbrel-ba thsad-mas khoñ-du-chud-pa-la bltos-pa* = *gamaka-bhūta-sambandha-pramāṇa-pratīti-apekṣa.* Thus we would have here, according to the author of the Alaṃkāra, «ratiocination independent of any previous induction» (cp. J. S. Mill, Logic, book II, ch, 2, § 4). This however is not the general view. Mallavādī has here a lacuna.

2 Lit. «remember». Rgyal-thsab, f. 35, mentions that the interpretation of the syllogism here as two acts of memory belongs to Dharmottara, (the minor premise is usually represented as a judgment by analogy, cp. Tātp., p. 40. 7).

the causal origin which is inherent in the particular case of the sound is necessarily coexistent with the attribute of non-eternity. (47. 15). If that is so, then cognition (or communication) of an unobserved fact is, for sure, nothing but a cognition of invariable concomitance. It is therefore stated that analytical deductions (or deductions of coexistence) can be resorted to when the deduced fact is known (by whatsoever evidence) necessarily to be present wheresoever the mere fact of the presence of the reason is ascertained, and not in any other cases.[1]

(47. 17). If that is so, (what we have to do in ratiocination) is to ascertain the connection of the logical predicate with the logical reason. But here the predicate (necessarily) follows on the mere fact of the presence of the attribute representing the reason. Why is it then that something already quite certain is being (here) sought-after? (An analytical deduction is it not a *petitio principii?*).[2] (No,—)

---

[1] Lit., p. 47. 9—16. «The reason is not like a lamp, producing cognition as a possibility, but it is ascertained as an invariable concomitance, for the function (*vyāpāra*) of the reason to convey a cognition of the probandum consists just in an ascertainment of (its) invariable concomitance with (this) probandum, it is nothing else. At first through a contradicting proof the dependence of the reason on the probandum must be ascertained, «the attribute (— *tva*) of being produced, namely, possesses the essential attribute (*sva-bhāva*) of non-eternity». Then, at the time of syllogizing, he joins the meaning (*artha*) remembered in general with the particular case «this attribute of being produced which is inherent in the sound possesses also the essential attribute of non-eternity». Among them (*tatra*) the memory of the general is cognition of the reason, and the memory of the particular, of production inherent in the sound as possessing the essential attribute of non-eternity, is cognition of the syllogism (*anumāna* = *parārthānumāna*). And if it is so, the fact of communicating an unobserved thing is just a cognition of invariable concomitance. Therefore it is said that «own-existence» -reasons (or co-existence reasons) must be applied for a probandum which follows the mere (presence) of the (probans), not anywhere else».

[2] Dh.'s introduction to sūtra III. 18 suggests that in this sūtra we shall have an answer to the objection very much urged in Europe by the assailants of the syllogistic doctrine, namely that the syllogism contains in the conclusion nothing that has not been stated in the premises, that it is therefore a *petitio principii*, *niścito mṛgyate* = *siddha-sādhanam*. This is repeated by Rgyal-thsab, fol. 36— *ñes-par ḥbrel-ba btsal-bar-bya-ba yin-te*. We would expect an answer somewhat similar to that which has been given in European logic, (cp. J. S. Mill, *loco cit.* § 5) namely, that the syllogism contains an extention of the general proposition to unobserved and new individual cases (*parokṣārtha*, p. 47. 15). But we then find in the sūtra III. 18 only a restatement of the doctrine that (in analytical judgments) the subject by itself is a sufficient reason for deducing the predicate. This is by no

18—20. Because (what we call an analytical reason) is just the fact that the predicate is a natural outflow of the reason, (not a fact outside it), it is contained in the essence of the latter. The underlying reality is the same for both (the reason and the fact deduced from it). If the reason could exist without the predicate, the latter would not be contained in the essence of the former.[2]

(47.19). Such connection alone represents its, (the analytical reason's), essence.[3] «Such (connection) alone» means the established fact of a necessary concomitance (of the logical predicate) with every case where the property representing the reason is present. «Represents its essence» means, belongs to the essence of the attribute representing the reason. Indeed, wherever a fact is deduced which is necessarily inherent in every instance of the reason, it is necessarily (comprehended) in the essence of the latter. No other (property can be so deduced).

---

means a satisfactory answer to the accusation of begging the question. Vinītadeva's introduction. p. 90. 14 ff., is much more reasonable. According to him sūtra III. 18 answers the question why is it that the deduced property here follows (on the mere fact of the presence of) the attribute representing the logical reason? And the answer is then quite natural, viz. because in reality (V. adds *dños-su-na* = *vastutas*, as in sūtra III. 20 which he omits) the deduced property is already contained in the reason.

1 Lit., p. 47. 17—18. «If thus the tie of the deduced (*sādhya*) with the reason (*sādhana*) must be ascertained, why is it that the following, which is certain, of the deduced from the fact (*dharma*) (representing) the reason, is sought for? He says . . .»

2 Lit., sūtras III. 18—22. «Because just this (following upon the mere reason) is its (the reason's) essence. (19) And because this essence (of the reason) is the reason. (20) Because in reality they are identical. (21) Because the non-appearing when this appears is not its essence. (22) And because of the possibility of divergence».—Sūtra III. 20 is omitted by Vinītadeva, but the word *vastutas* is added in sūtra III. 18.

3 *svabhāva* here in the sense of essential property as indicated above. This means that the proposition «Aśoka is a tree» is susceptible only of a *conversio per accidens*, the *śiṃśapā* is *vṛkṣa-svabhāvā*, but *vṛkṣaḥ* is not *śiṃśapā-svabhāvaḥ*, therefore the sūtra emphazises *tasyaiva; tat-svabhāva* is here felt as a *tat-puruṣa*, *sādhyam* (= *vṛkṣatvam*) *tasya* (= *sādhanasya* = *śiṃśapātvasya*) *svabhāvaḥ*, we can change the expression and say *sādhanam sadhya-svabhāvam*, then the last word will be a *bahuvrīhi* as in 47. 12 — *kṛtakatvam anityatva-svabhāvam*. cp. N. Kandalī, p. 207. 20, Jayanta, p. 114. 10.

(47.23). All right! Let this be just the essence (of an analytical deduction)! Why should we then deduce this essence? Why should we have recourse to logical reasoning for deducing from the reason what is already given in the reason?[1]

(48.2). Because the essence is the reason, (i.e., we deduce out of the reason its inherent property).

(48.2). We are dealing here just with (the analytical reason which is a reason in whose) essence (the deduced property is included). Therefore we can deduce merely such facts which are included in the essence of the fact (serving as a reason). Now, this essential property can be nothing else but a fact present wheresoever (the other fact representing) the reason is also present.[2]

(48.4). But if the deduced fact is included in the reason (the deduction will be a tautology), the argument will be included in the thesis?[3] (Yes), because in reality they are one. (48.6). «In reality» means from the standpoint of the ultimately real.[4] (Viewed as properties of an underlying reality, both) the deduced property and the property from which it is being deduced are identical. They are different by imputation.[5]

(48.7). The logical reason and the logical predicate are (here), indeed, two aspects (of the same underlying reality). (These two aspects) have been constructed in our judgments.[6] But a logically constructed aspect is (always relative). By such an imputed differentiation (reality) becomes split (in two parts seemingly) exclusive of one another. Thus the attribute representing the reason is one thing, and the attribute representing the consequence is another one, (but in reality the one

---

1 Lit., 47.23. «Why the application of a reason for deducing (*sādhya*) of just one's own essence?».

2 Lit., 48.3. «And essence (*svabhāva*) is following upon the mere fact (*dharma*) of the reason».

3 *pratijñā*, e.g., «this is a tree», *hetu* «because it is an Aśoka-tree». In the adopted phrasing the «thing to be deduced» (*sādhya*) means predicate, conclusion, major term and thesis as well, whereas *hetu* means reason, middle term, subject (*anuvāda* in the major premise) and argument also.

4 *paramārthataḥ*.

5 *samāropita*.

6 Or, as J. S. Mill, in discussing a problem somewhat analogous, expresses it, according to his ideas on propositions and names, *op. cit.*, § 6, «have been added as a result of assent to a proposition». To the Indian realists both conceptions are realities, there is no existential identity between them, an identity would have been between synonyms *vṛkṣa* and *taru*, not *vṛkṣa* and *śiṃsapā*, cp. Tātp., p. 309.5.

is wrapt up in the other). (48.8). Indeed when we at a distance observe an object having twigs and (leaves), we assert «it is a tree», we cannot assert «it is an Ašoka tree». Next to that, (when we are near the object, we assert) «just the same thing is a tree and an Ašoka». The (underlying) reality is thus quite the same, but our judgment imposes upon it a construction which makes it appear as divided (between two notions) different only by the contrasts (implied in them).[1] (48.10). Therefore reason and consequence are here different (not as realities), but on account of those conceptions which have been superimposed upon reality by constructive judgments.[2]

(48.11). In this sense (analytical) reasoning (is not a tautology), the argument is not a portion of the thesis. But the (underlying) reality is identical.

(48.12). Further, why is it that the deduced essential attribute is necessarily coexistent in every particular instance where the attribute representing the reason is found? It is said,

21. (If it were not co-existent, if the consequence) could have appeared without the reason having also appeared, it could not represent an inherent property of the latter.

(48.14). If one thing is not necessarily implied in the other, it can be absent when the other is present. Such an attribute which can

---

1 *vyāvṛtti-bhedena* «through a difference of contrasts», e. g., when we characterize an object as «Ašoka» we have in mind its contrast with birches, pines and other trees, but when we characterize the same object as a «tree», we have in our mind its contrast with houses, mountains, rivers etc. The reality is the same, only it is put in a different light by a difference of those objects with which it is being contrasted, cp. Tātp., p. 340. 19 ff. A similar difference mnst be assnmed between the notions of «being produced» and «beind impermanent», the first means produced from causes and conditions (*hetu-pratyayaiḥ kṛtam*), it is contrasted with space or a motionless cosmical Aether (*ākāšā*); the second means inherent evanescence, every moment a new thing (*ḥjig-pai rañ-thsul-can-gyi rañ-bzhin = sva-rasa-vināša-svabhāva*), it implies a denial of the ordinary view of a limited duration of empirical objects, cp. Vinītadeva, p. 90. 17 ff.

2 Lit., p. 48. 7—10. «Indeed the relation of deduced and deducer are two forms (*rūpe*) which are lifted up upon certainty (i. e., superimposed upon reality by constructive thought, *niščaya = vikalpa = kalpanā*). And a form which is imputed certainty by an imputed division produced by mutual exclusion of one another becomes divided, thus the deducer (reason) is one thing, the deduced part another thing... Therefore certainty (i. e., constructive thought) points out to us as divided in a division of mutual exclusion a reality (*vastu*), although it is not divided».

be absent at the time when the reason is present cannot be its inherent property. (48.15). Indeed, presence and absence is the same as existence and its denial. Existence and non-existence (are correlative), they have their stand in mutual exclusion. (48.16). If there could be a unity betveen what has already appeared and what has not yet appeared, then the same thing could be at once existent and non-existent. (48.17). However existence and non-existence, being contradictory of one another, can impossibly be united. Becanse absence of unity (or «otherness») consists in assuming attributes exclusive (of one another). (48.18). Moreover, a thing appearing after another one (not only possesses a different time attribute, but) is produced by other causes, since every difference of the effect presupposes a difference in the causes. (48.19). Therefore a thing which has already appeared and a thing which has not yet appeared represent a difference consisting in having attributes exclusive of one another, and a difference of causes which produce the difference of these attributes. How is identity then possible? Consequently an (analytically) deduced inherent property[1] is (coexistent with the reason), it necessarily is present wheresoever the fact constituting the reason is present.

(48.21). All right! We admit that the subsequent fact cannot be an inherent property of a foregoing fact. However why should (the subsequent fact) not be deducible (from the foregoing fact)?

22. Because they can exist separately.

(49.2). A thing appearing later can exist separately, quite distinctly,[2] from a thing appearing before. Because of such a possibility the later fact (the effect) is not (analytically) deducible from the former one.[3]

---

[1] *sādhyaḥ svabhāvaḥ.*

[2] *parityāga* = *paraspara-parihāra* = *virodha.* Between every two moments in the existence of a thing there is thus divergence (*vyabhicāra*), incompatibility (*parityāga*), mutual exclusion (*paraspara-parihāra*), contradiction (*virodha*) «otherness» (*viruddha-dharma-saṃsarga*). It will be noted that the terms «opposite», «contrary» and «contradictory» cannot be used strictly in the Aristotelian sense since these conceptions are here applied not to terms and propositions, but to cognitions of the type «this is blue», blue and not-blue are opposed directly, blue and yellow also opposed, because yellow is only part of the «not-blue». A tree and an Aśoka-tree, although identical for the underlying reality, are opposed (*vyāvṛtta*, cp. p. 48. 8) logically, they are mutually «other». On the «law of Otherness» cp. above p. 8 n. 2, on the law of Contradiction cp. below, text p. 69 ff.

[3] Vinītadeva, p. 91. 12 ff., gives the folloving example, «if a product did exist (= *kṛtakatve siddhe*) and afterwards by a cause like a stick impermanence

(49. 3). Therefore (analytically) deducible is only such an inherent property which is always coexistent with the (fact representing the) reason.

(49. 4). And thus it is fundamental that analytical reasoning should be applied only to such cases where an inherent property is already known to be always coexistent with the fact from which it is deduced.[1]

§ 4. Syllogism of Causality in the Method of Agreement.

(Next comes the reasoning from causality, where the logical reason corresponds to the result and the logical predicate to the cause).

(*anityatva*) would be produced, then divergence would be possible, since sticks and similar objects are likewise produced from their own causes. Thus it necessarily (must be admitted that) if something is not a product it cannot be annihilated». Thus existence and evanescence are coinherent and the latter conception can be analytically deduced from the former. But in order to make this deduction we must previouly know by appropriate arguments (*yathāsvam-pramāṇaiḥ*) the exact meaning of both conceptions. How the Buddhist theorem of existence is proved has been hinted above, p. 121 n.

[1] The argument in sūtras III. 17—22, expressed freeely in terms of modern philosophy, seems to be the following one. There are analytical judgments, they are concerned with co-inherent or coexistent attributes. When the subject of a general proposition contains in itself a «sufficient reason» for an affirmation of the predicate, when the mere presence of the thing denoted by the reason necessarily implies the presence of the connoted consequence, then wheresoever the first is found, the second is necessarily present. The connotation of the subject can be established by whatsoever methods, by definitions founded on observation, by an extraordinary intuition (*anāsrava jñāna*), testimony, Scripture or some complicated analysis (as the one by which Dharmakīrti has established the theory of Universal Momentariness). Whatsoever its origin the general proposition establishes that the reason A contains in itself the predicate B, because (18) B is the inherent property (*svabhāva*) of A. But (19) A, the reason, is also the essence (*svabhāva*) of the consequence B. Does that mean that the analytical judgment is a tautology? No, because (20) the identity is of the underlying fact of existence, the logical superstructure is manifold but coinherent in this underlying reality. (21) If it were not coexistent, the consequence would not be the inherent property and (21) it would then be a separate existence. — Some difficulty of interpretation arises from the double meaning of *svabhāva*, in sūtra III. 19 *svabhāvaḥ* = *hetuḥ*, in p. 48. 4 it is = *sādhya-dharmaḥ*, in p. 23. 20 we have *hetuḥ* = *svabhāvaḥ sādhyasya* and in p. 47. 21—23 *sādhya-dharmaḥ* = *svabhāvaḥ*, *svabhāve* = *sādhye*. The solution can be found in the fact that as *sādhya*, *svabhāva* means essential property and as *hetu* it means identity of that reality in which both the *hetu* and the *sādhya* coinhere.

23. (The deduction by causality, where) the reason represents the effect, has the following formula, also (expressed by the method of Agreement) —

(Major premise). Wherever there is smoke there is fire,

(Example). As e. g., in the kitchen, etc.,

(Minor premise). Here there is smoke,

(Conclusion). (Here there is fire).

(49.8). This is a formula where an effect (takes the place of) the reason. It follows from the context that this formula is expressed according to (the method of) Agreement. «Wherever there is smoke» means that smoke is the subject (of the general proposition). «There is fire» means that fire is its predicate. Their connection should be conceived as a necessary one,[1] (not an accidental one), just as in the preceding case (of the analytical tie). (49.9). Consequently this (proposition) represents an invariable concomitance based upon the law of causality.[2] (49.10). Pointing to the sphere of observation from which this concomitance is established [3] (by Induction), it is said, «just as in the kitchen etc.». In the kitchen and similar cases it is established by positive and negative experience,[4] that there is between smoke and fire an invariable connection representing a causal relation. The words «here there is (smoke)» wind up [5] (the syllogism by applying) to the subject of the inference [6] its deduced characteristic [7] (i. e., they contain the minor premise).

24. Here also, we can assert that an effect is the logical reason for deducing from it the cause, only when the fact of their causal relation is already known (in general).

(49.14). The words «here also» mean that not only in the case of analytical deductions, but also here, when the syllogism is founded

1 *niyamārtha.*

2 *kārya-kāraṇa-bhāva-nimitta.*

3 *vyāpti-sādhana-pramāṇa-viṣaya.*

4 *pratyakṣa-anupalambhābhyām*, cp. above p. 38.13, 39.7 (text), transl. p. 103—105.

5 *upasaṃhāraḥ.*

6 *sādhya-dharmin.*

7 *pakṣa-dharma = sādhya-dharma.*

on causation. The words «is already known» mean that the existence of a causal relation (must) be ascertained[1] (by induction from particular. cases).

This certainty must necessarilly be established, because, as we have said,[2] the logical reason conveys a deduction not accidentally, but on the basis of an invariable concomitance.

§ 5. Deduction by the Method of Difference.

(49. 17). The analytical, causal and negative syllogism according to the method of Agreement have been thus exhibited. The author proceeds to exhibit the (method) of Difference.

25. The method of Difference[3] (will be now exhibited). Negation represents then the following formula —

> (Major premise). What exists, all conditions of perceptibility[4] being fulfilled, is necessarily perceived.
>
> (Example). As, e. g., the particular case of a patch of blue colour[5] etc.
>
> (Minor premise). But on this (spot) we do not perceive any existing jar, although all conditions of perception are fulfilled.
>
> (Conclusion). (Therefore there is here no jar).

(50. 4). The method of Difference (will now be demonstrated). «What exists, all conditions of perceptibility being fulfilled», means what exists and is perceptible; (hence) existence is taken as the subject of (the general proposition). «Is perceived», i. e., perception is predicated.

---

1 *niścita*, characterized by necessity, *i. e.*, the major premise must be shown by an induction from particular instances, no counter-instance being producible, cp. above, p. 19 ff. (text). The necessity consists in the fact there is no effect without a preceding cause. Therefore, strictly speaking, permissible are only the deductions of causes from effects, not *vice versa*, of future effects from causes, cp. above text p. 31. 10, transl. p. 88.

2 Cp. text, p. 19. 1 ff. and p. 47. 9.

3 Read *vaidharmya-*, instead of *vaidharma*.

4 *upalabni* misprint in stead of *upalabdhi*

5 *nīlādi-viśeṣa* = *nīlādi-svalakṣaṇa*, the latter in the third sense indicated transl. p. 34 n. 4.

(50. 5). Thus this (proposition) expresses that the existence of something perceivable, (the totality of the conditions being fulfilled), is invariably followed[1] by perception. Existence is the negation of non-existence,[2] and cognition the negation of non-cognition. Hence (we have a contraposition), the negation of the predicate is made the subject, and the negation of the subject is made the predicate.[3] (50. 7). Thus the (general proposition) expresses that the negation of the consequence is invariably concomitant[4] with the negation of the reason, because it is necessarily dependent[5] upon the latter (i. e., wheresover there is some sense-perception, there necessarily is some existence). (50. 8). If the deduced fact (the consequence or major term) were not to be found with the subject of the inference (minor term), neither would the reason (middle term) be there present, because the absence of the latter necessarily involves the absence of the former. But the reason is present, (hence its consequence must also be present).[6] (50. 9). Consequently the negation of the reason is the term of greater extension to which the negation of the consequence, being the term of lesser extension, is subordinate.[7] When (the first) is absent, it follows

---

1 *vyāpta*. Lit., «is embraced in the fact of being and object of perception».

2 P. 50. 6 read — *kathitam, asattva-nivṛttiš ca sattvam, anupalambha* ...

3 i. e. the contraposition of the same major premise as formulated according to the method of agreement in sūtra III. 9, transl. p. 117. There it was said, «the possibly visible, if not perceived, is absent», here it is expressed by contraposition «the possibly visible, if it is present, is necessarily perceived». Both these formulations represent expressions of the principle underlying every negative deduction. Howsoever complicated, the negative deduction can be reduced to it. The method of this reduction has been explained in sūtra II. 43—46, p. 116 ff., and a classification of all negative deductions has been given there, II. 31—42. The Naiyāyikas have remained faithfull to their theory of the perception of non-existence, or absence, by the senses. They accordingly reject the Buddhist theory of negation. But this does no prevent Vācaspatimišra very often to formulate complicated negative deductions according to one of the formulae prescribed by Buddhist logic, cp., *e. g.*. Tātp., p. 88. 12, 88. 17 etc.

4 *vyāpta*.

5 *niyata* = *pratibaddha*.

6 This conclusion that right cognition (*pramāṇa*) is a proof of existence has been already mentioned above, text p. 40. 7. Cognition is conceived as an effect of an objective reality and the principle is laid down that we always conclude from the existence of an effect to the necessary existence of its cause, but not *vice versa*. Since a possible cause does not necessarily produce its effect, the conclusion about a future effect is always more or less problematic for a non-omniscient being.

7 Lit., 50. 9—10. «Therefore, since the embracing non-existence of the reason

that the (second) is also absent, hence (we arrive at the absence of the absence of the consequence, i. e.), at its affirmation.[1]

(50.10). The following rule is therefore established, — when a deduction is made according to the method of Difference it always must be shown that the negation of the deduced consequence necessarily involves the negation of the reason.[2]

(50.12) The formula of an analytical deduction according to the method of Difference is next given.

26. (Major premises). What is changeless is neither existent nor has it an origin nor can it be a product.

(Example). (As e. g., the Cosmic Ether etc.).

(Minor premises). But the sounds of speech exist, have origination, are a product (of causes).

(Conclusion). (Hence they are impermanent).

(50.15). The consequence to be deduced (i. e., the major term), is here the impermanence (or non-eternity of the sounds of speech).[3] Its negation necessarily involves[4] the absence of the logical reason. By this (proposition) it is expressed that the negation of the consequence necessarily involves[5] the negation of the reason, in all the three cases

is absent, the embraced non-existence of the consequence is non existent, thus there is ascertainment of the consequence (*sādhya*)».

1 *sādhya-niścaya* = *sādhya-vidhi*.

2 Thus the major premise in a negative deduction, i. e., the fundamental formula of it, is always an affirmation. The fact that subject and predicate have been substituted by their negations and have changed places does not affect the quality of the judgment, it remains affirmative. But the minor premise, as well as the conclusion, are negative.

3 As against the view of the Mīmāṃsakas, cp. above, p. 127 n. 2.

4 *niyata* = *pratibaddha* = *vyāpya*, e. g., «wheresoever there is no fire, as in water, there necessarily is no smoke», or «wheresoever there are no trees, there necessarily are no Aśoka-trees».

5 *vyāpta*, lit., p. 50. 16, «the absence of the consequence is embraced by the absence of the reason». In the major premise, as in every judgment, the predicate or major term is greater in extension (*vyāpaka*), it «embraces» or contains the subject or middle term. But it is also «bound up» (*pratibaddha*) *to* the latter, because the presence of the latter involves necessarily the presence of the major term, which becomes «necessarily following» (*niyata, anubaddha, pratibaddha, anvita*). In a contraposed major premise the same relations obtain between the ne-

of analytical deduction.[1] (50. 16). «The sounds of speech exist, have origination, are a product» — these words refer to the presence of the reason in the subject of the conclusion, (i. e., to the minor premise), equally in all three cases. (50. 17). Here again it is (thus) stated that in the present case the absence of the reason is missing, (i. e., it is stated that the reason is present). And since the absence of the reason contains in itself the absence of the consequence, (this latter absence being subordinate to the former), it follows by implication that the absence of the consequence must also be missing. The absence of the absence of the consequence (i. e., its double negation) is equivalent to its affirmation. (Hence the presence of the consequence is proved).[2]

(50. 19). The formula of a causal deduction according to the method of Difference is next given.

---

gation of the predicate and the negation of the subject. Expressed as a Mixed Hypothetical Syllogism *modo tollente* the present example must be thrown in the following form —

> If a thing has an origin, it is non-eternal,
> Non-eternity is absent, e. g., in the Cosmic Ether.
> Hence origin is also absent.

But this is equivalent merely to the contraposed major premise of the Indian syllogism, which gives rise to a new mixed hypothetical syllogism, —

> If a thing is non-non-eternal (i. e., permanent), it has no origin,
> The attribute of having no origin is absent in the sound,
> Hence the attribute of non-non-eternity is also ebsent, (i. e., sound is impermanent).

When all double negations are stripped off, the conclusion is affirmative, «sound is impermanent». But in its negative form —

> Sound is not non-non-eternal,
> Because it has not the quality of non-origin,

it is a negative syllogism according to the third figure (*vyāpakānupalabdhi*, cp. sūtra II. 34, because *sādhanābhāva* is *vyāpaka* in regard of *sādhyābhāva*).

[1] A full *cheda* is needed after *hetuṣu* and the one after *uktaḥ* must be dropped.

[2] Lit., p. 50. 15—18. «Non-eternity being absent etc. Here it is expressed that the non-existence of the consequence, of non-eternity, is necessarily dependent (*niyata*) on the absence of the reason. By this it is said that the absence of the consequence is embraced by (or contained in) the absence of the reason, in the three «own-existence» reasons also. The sound is existent, has an origine, is a product— thus the presence (— *tva*) of (these) attributes in the subject (*pakṣa*) is indicated. Here also the non existence of the non-existence of the reason, (which non-existence of the reason) is the container (*vyāpaka*), is stated. Hence also the contained (*vyāpya*), the non-existence of the consequence, is precluded. Thus the existence of the consequence (is proved)».

27. The formula of a reason representing an effect is as follows —

(Major premise). Where there is no fire, there neither is smoke.

(Example). (As e. g., on the water of a lake, etc.).

(Minor premise). But there is here some smoke.

(Conclusion). (Hence there must be some fire).

(50. 21). Here also it is stated that the absence of fire involves[1] the absence of smoke.[2] The words «but there is here some smoke» express that the involving[3] part, the negation of smoke, is absent. Hence the involved[4] part, the negation of fire, is likewise absent. And when (the negation of fire is denied, its affirmation, i. e., the presence) of the consequence becomes established.[5]

§ 6. Equipollency of the Methods of Agreement and Difference.

(51. 1). The following question is now answered. How is it that in the formulae expressed according to the method of Agreement, the contraposition of the general proposition is not expressed, and in those which are expressed according to the method of Difference the original form[6] of it is not stated? How can it then (be maintained that syllogism) is an expression (in propositions of all) the three aspects of a logical relation, (concomitance, contraposition and minor premise)?

28. From a formula of agreement the corresponding formula of difference follows by implication.

---

[1] Lit., *vyāpta* «is embraced», is included, is involved, is subaltern, is less in extension, i. e., there can be no smoke without fire, but fire may be present where there is no smoke, as e. g., in a hot iron-ball.

[2] Hence the absence of fire involves the absence of smoke, but not *vice versa*.

[3] *vyāpaka*, embracing, including, containing, pervading.

[4] *vyāpya*, embraced, included, contained, pervaded.

[5] *sādhya-gati*.

[6] *anvaya*.

(51.4). When a formula directly[1] expresses agreement (i.e., the positive concomitance of the reason with its consequence), their difference, i.e., the contraposition (of the general proposition) follows virtually,[2] i.e., by implication. Therefore (each formula) is a verbal expression of the three aspects of the logical mark.[3] (51.6). Although the contraposition of the general proposition is not directly expressed when the concomitance is expressed in the original form, it nevertheless is understood[4] as implied in the latter.

Why?

29. Because if that were not so, the reason could not be invariably concomitant with the consequence.

(51.8). If the contraposition of the general proposition were not ascertained in thought,[5] neither could the positive concomitance of the reason with the consequence be so ascertained. (51.9). When the original general proposition[6] testifies that the reason is invariably concomitant[7] with its consequence, no doubt is possible as to the presence of the reason where the consequence could be absent, otherwise it could never be invariably concomitant with the latter.[8] (51.10). The contraposition is realized when it is realized that in the absence of the consequence the reason is likewise absent. Thus when stating in the original general proposition that the reason is invariably concomitant with its consequence, it is also implied[9] that their contraposition holds good.[10]

---

1 *abhidheyena.*

2 *arthāt.*

3 The three-aspected logical mark (*trirūpa-linga*), as explained above, sūtra II, 5 ff., is equivalent to an induction from particular instances, no counter-instance being producible.

4 *avasīyate = niścīyate = gamyate = jñāyate.*

5 *buddhy-avasita* is here an equivalent of *niścaya-avasita*, *niścaya-ārūḍha*, *niścaya-apekṣa*, cp. p. 26. 16.; the term *buddhi* thns refers to *savikalpaka-jñāna*, *buddhy-ārūḍha* = *niścaya-arūḍha* (p. 48. 7) = *vikalpita*. But in other cases *buddhi* = *saṃvid* especially in *kārikās*, may refer to *nirvikalpaka-pratyakṣa*, cp. Tipp., p. 31. 6.

6 *anvaya-vākya.*

7 *niyata.*

8 Lit., p. 51. 10. «Otherwise (the reason) would not be conceived (*pratīta*) as necessarily tied up to its consequence».

9 *sāmarthyāt.*

10 *avasita.*

30. Similarly (when the deduction is expressed) by the method of Difference, the original (positive) concomitance follows (by implication).

(51.13). If we apply the method of Difference, the direct concomitance (of the reason with its consequence), although not *prima facie*[1] expressed, follows simply by implication, just as in the case when direct concomitance is expressed, (its contraposition follows also by implication).

(51.14). Why?

31. Because otherwise the absence of the reason in cases where the[2] consequence is absent would not be established.

(51.16). If the general proposition, in its original form, would not be present to the mind,[3] the absence of the reason when the consequence is absent could not be established, i.e., could not be ascertained. (51.17). If it is realized, through the contraposition of the general proposition, that the absence of the consequence is invariably concomitant[4] with the absence of the reason, it cannot be expected that the consequence will be absent where the reason is present. Because otherwise it could not be known,[5] that the absence of the consequence is invariably concomitant with the absence of the reason. (51.18). The concomitance is realized[6] when it is realized that in the presence of the reason its consequence is invariably present. (51.19). Therefore when in a contraposed general proposition it is directly expressed that the absence of the consequence is invariably concomitant with the absence of the reason, the positive (original) form of the concomitance is also conveyed[7] by implication.

(51.21). (When constant change is being deduced from the notion of existence), space and other (immutable substances are adduced as negative examples proving) the absence of the reason wherever the

---

1 *anabhidhīyamāna.*

2 *tasmit* misprinted for *tasmin.*

3 *buddhi-gṛhīta* is here the same as above, p. 51.8, *buddhy-avasita*, but in other cases *grahaṇa* is the opposite of *adhyavasāya*, both are contrasted, cp. the explanations of sūtra I. 12.

4 *niyata.*

5 *pratīta = niścita = adhyavasita = buddhi-gṛhīta.*

6 *gati.*

7 *anvaya-gati.*

consequence is absent. Does it follow that (these examples) can likewise prove the presence of the consequence when the reason is present?[1]

32. (No!) If their concomitance[2] is not (ascertained), then the absence of one term cannot necessarily follow from the absence of the other.

(52.2). (Concomitance is based upon) an essential dependence (of one thing upon another). If there is no such dependence (between two things), the negation of one of them, of the logical consequence, does not necessarily imply the negation of the other one, of the reason (or middle term).

33. It has been stated above[3] that there are only[4] two kinds of dependent existence, whatsoever the case may be. (The dependent part represents either existentially) the same thing or the effect of (another existent).

(52.5). Whatsoever (be the content) of the dependent part, (the form of the dependence is of (one of) two kinds. The essence or the cause (of one form of dependence) is Identity (of existence). The essence or the cause (of the other one) is the fact of being an Effect (produced by causes). If one (existence) is dependent upon some other (existence), the thing upon which it is dependent represents either (essentially) the same fact of existence or a cause. (52.7). To be dependent upon something else is impossible. Therefore has it been stated (above) that there are (only) two kinds of dependence.[5] (52.8). And we have

---

1 Vinītadeva's introduction to the next sūtra is much simpler. He says «if it be asked why is it that when there is no concomitance the contraposition is not valid, (the following sūtra gives the answer)». (*anvayābhāve vyatireko' siddha ity etat kutaḥ*) Dharmottara's *avataraṇa* means lit., p. 51.21—22: «If really in space etc. in the absence of the predicate (major term) there is absence of the reason (middle term), nevertheless for sure (does it follow) that in the presence of the reason the predicate is present? To this he answers».

2 *svabhāva-pratibandha* = *vyāpti*.

3 sūtra II. 25. Lit. «consisting in identity-with-that and consisting in origination-from-that».

4 *caḥ* (p. 52.4) *punar-arthe, evārthe vā, tena dvi-prakāra eveti yojanīyam* (Mallavādi, f. 85).

5 Cp. B. Russel, Mysticism, p. 152— «the only way... in which the existence of A can be *logically* dependent upon the existence of B is when B is part of A». This is the same as the Indian view. The notion of a tree (B) is an inherent

on that occassion also stated[1] that the dependent (part is the fact represented by) the reason, (it is dependent upon the fact corresponding to) the deduced consequence.[2]

34. It follows therefore that if the (concerted) absence (of two terms) is expressed, their interdependence must reveal itself. Therefore the contraposed general proposition always contains an indication of their interdependence. This indication is nothing but the general proposition (in its positive form). Thus it is that one single general proposition, either directly or in its contraposed form, declares that the logical mark is present in similar and absent in dissimilar cases. Therefore it is not indispensable to express both these propositions.[3]

---

part of the notion of a *śiṃśapā* (A) and it is the latter that is logically dependent on, i. e., subordinated to, the former. The foundation of this dependence is Identity of the underlying reality But, according to the Indian view, it is not the «only way». There is a dependence of Coexistence and a dependence of Succession. Every thing is the result of some causes, it is therefore *logically*, or *necessarily*, dependent on its causes. But a cause does not necessarily produce its effect. Therefore there is never logical necessity (*niścaya*) in the predication of a future result, cp. transl. p. 108.

[1] sūtra II. 22.

[2] It is here again pressed with emphasis that there is no other logical dependence than the dependence founded either upon what is here termed Identity (*tādātmya*) and explained as coexistence of coinherent attributes, or on Causation which is explained as a logical necessity for every entity to have a cause (*tadutpatti*). Every fact is thus either coexistent and coinherent with another fact, or it is its product. Thus the general proposition either expresses a Uniformity of Coexistence or a Uniformity of Succession. It follows that whatever be the method applied, whether it be the method of Agreement, or the method of Difference, a logical deduction or logical thought in general cannot possibly express something else than what either directly represents or finally reduces to these two kinds of logical relations. Contraposition is therefore equipollent with the original proposition.

[3] Lit., p. 52. 9—13. «Since (it is so), therefore who speaks abolition must show connection. Therefore the proposition of abolition (the negative proposition) is just an indirect showing of suggested connection. And what is suggestion of connection, that is just expression of concomitance. Thus by one proposition formulated with a concomitance-face or with a contraposition-face the presence-absence of the mark in the similar-dissimilar cases is declared Thus the formulation of two propositions is not necessary. *hi* in the sence of „because"».

(52. 13). When (two facts) are essentially interdependent,[1] the absence of the one conveys the absence of the other. Therefore, if it is shown that the reason is absent wherever the consequence is also absent, the interdependence of both these absences[2] will be shown. (52. 14). If the reason is dependent upon its consequence, then it will necessarily be absent wheresoever the consequence is absent.[3] (52. 15). And since it is (impossible not to) indicate the dependent (character of the reason), therefore the proposition indicating the absence of the reason, if its consequence is absent, contains[4] an implied indication[5] of its dependence. (52. 16). This indication is nothing but the general proposition (or major premise) itself.[6] The interdependence (of reason and consequence) must necessarily be stated, but (this does not mean that it should always) be made in the positive form, because the example will always establish the interdependence by induction,[7] and this will represent nothing else but the general proposition in its positive form. (52. 18). Therefore when the negation of something depends upon the negation of something else, the interdependence of both these terms must reveal itself, and this becomes simply a cognition of their positive concomitance.[8] (52. 20). Since the positive concomitance implies its contraposition and (*vice versa*) the contraposition implies the original proposition, therefore one[9] of them is (sufficient) to declare the pre-

---

1 i. e., when one fact represents either the identity of the underlying reality or its production from another reality.

2 *nivartya-nivartakayoḥ pratibandhaḥ*, lit., «the dependence of the stopped and the stopper».

3 as e. g., smoke being dependent upon fire, is not to be found in places where there is uo fire.

4 *ākṣipta* = *saṃgṛhīta*.

5 *upa-darśana*.

6 Lit, p. 52. 15—17. «And because its dependence must be shown, therefore the proposition about the non-existence (*nivṛtti*) of the reason when the predicate is absent, by this (proposition) an indirect indication (*upa-darśana*) of the dependence is suggested (*ākṣipta*). And what (represents) the indirect indication of the dependence suggested by that, just this is the concomitance-proposition».

7 *pramāṇena*. Concomitance must be shown by an induction from particular instances, no counter-instance being producible, these particular instances are termed *dṛṣṭānta* or *pramāṇa*, cp. the use of this term in the ff. passages, 44. 5, 45. 1, 58. 1, 61. 10, 64. 1, 80. 21, 81. 1, 81. 2, 81. 20, 81. 21 (*apramāṇa*).

8 Lit., 52. 19—20. «Therefore the connection (interdependence) of an abolished and the abolisher must be known, and thus just (*eva*) concomitance is known. The word *iti* in the sense of „because“».

9 The word *vākyena* must be inserted after *ekenāpi*, cp. Tib. p. 119. 9, *thsig gcig-gis kyaṅ*.

sence of the mark in similar cases and its absence in dissimilar cases.[1] (53. 1). The positive concomitance may be *prima facie* expressed. It is one method of expressing it. Similarly the contraposition may be *prima facie* expressed.[2] But since a single proposition conveys both (these meanings), there is no strict necessity for the formulation of both in every single syllogism.[3] (53. 4). Words are used to convey a meaning, when the meaning is conveyed, what is the use of (superfluous) words?

(53. 4). Thus it is that either the original form of the general proposition must alone be used or its contraposition, (but not both together).

35. (This rule applies) also to (Negation, i. e., to a deduction of absence whose reason is) non-perception. When we state (the contraposed formula[4] of negation, viz.) —

> «Whatsoever exists, all conditions of perceptibility being fulfilled, is necessarily perceived»,
>
> the original concomitance —
>
> «If such an object is not perceived, it is absent»,
>
> is established by implication.

(53. 8). Even[5] in a (proposition expressing Negation founded on) non-perception, the original positive concomitance follows when the contraposition is expressed. «Whatsoever exists all conditions of perceptibility being fulfilled» — these words express that the predicate (in the formula of simple negation) is cancelled, i. e., the possibility of such behaviour (which follows upon a perception) of absence (is

---

[1] i. e. the induction from particular instances, no counter-instance being producible.

[2] Lit., p. 53. 1—2. «Positive concomitance is the face, the means, because it is directly expressed, this is a proposition whose face is positive concomitance. Thus (also the proposition) whose face is contraposition. The word *iti* in the sense of „because"».

[3] *sādhana-vākya.*

[4] *anvaya*, the positive or original concomitance. Negation in contraposition will be double negation, i. e., affirmation. The formula of negation expressed as direct concomitance in a general proposition will be «non-perception is concomitant with absence», its contraposition will be «non-absence is concomitant with non-non-perception» or «presence is followed by perception».

[5] *na kevalam kārya-svabhāva ity arthaḥ* (Mallavādī, f. 86).

denied). It means essentially the same as the existence of something perceivable. «Is necessarily perceived»—these words express the absence of non-perception. It means essentially the same as perception.[1] (53.10). Thus it is shown that the absence of the consequence (or predicate) is invariably concomitant with the absence of the reason.[2] Supposing the consequence could be absent even if the reason were present, then the absence of the consequence would not be invariably concomitant with the absence of the reason.[3] (53.11). Indeed, when we realize the (contraposed) concomitance, we must (also) realize that the presence of the reason is invariably concomitant with the presence of its consequence. (53.12). Therefore (the negative conclusion) is drawn in the words «if such an object, i. e., a representable object, is not perceived, it is absent». Since this (conclusion) is cognized, since it is simultaneously present to the mind,[4] the original concomitance (of the formula of negation) is thus ascertained.[5]

§ 7. Is the conclusion a necessary member of the syllogism?

36. When either of these two (methods) is applied, it is not always necessary explicitly to mention the thesis (or the conclusion).[6]

---

1 *upalambha-rūpa*.

2 i. e., we cannot deny the existence of something when it is present in the ken of our sense-faculties.

3 The absence of the consequence means here the presence of the object in the range of our senses, the absence of the reason—its perception. If the object could be present without being perceived, then we could not maintain that its presence (accompanied by all other factors of perception) is invariably followed by its perception.

4 *sam-pratyayāt*.

5 *anvaya-siddhi*.

6 The term *pakṣa* means here the standpoint of the disputant, it includes both the thesis and the conclusion. In sūtra III. 41 it is identified with *sādhya* which is also as *sādhya-dharma* the name of the major term. In the five membered syllogism of the Naiyāyikas both the thesis (*pratijñā*) and the conclusion (*nigamana*) are admitted as separate members, beside the reason, the major and the minor premises. The Mīmāṃsakas and the later Naiyāyikas were inclined to reduce the members of their syllogism to three, roughly corresponding to the three members of Aristotle. But Dignāga makes a distinction between inference as a process of thought (*svārtha*) and syllogism as a method of proof in a controversy, and points to the fact that very often when the point under discussion is evident out of some former argumentation,

(53. 15). (The core of a syllogism is) the logical reason (or middle term), its invariable concomitance with the deduced property must be expressed, and this again, (as we have shown), is based either upon necessary co-existence or necessary succession between the facts corresponding to the reason and the deduced property. Whether we apply the method (of Agreement or the method of Difference), in both cases the fact to be deduced is the same. Therefore there is no absolute necessity of expressing separately (the thesis or) the conclusion. (Supposing) the reason has been cognized as invariably concomitant with the deduced property, (we then know the major premise). If we then perceive the presence of that very reason on some definite place, (i. e., if we know the minor premise), we already know the conclusion. (What is then the use of mentioning this fact once more?) The repetition of the deduced conclusion is of no use![1]

(53. 18). That just this[2] (principle) applies to the formula of a negative deduction (as founded on a repelled suggestion), will be next shown.

37. In our[3] formula of Negation, expressed according to the method of Agreement, it is likewise (superfluous to mention the conclusion separately). When it is stated that —

> (Major premise). Whatsoever is not perceived, although being in conditions of perceptibility, is practically non-existent.

---

suffices it to state the major and minor premises, the conclusion or thesis being then implicitly contained in the minor premise. Mallavādī, f. 87, introduces this section with the words, *atha matāntaravad bhavan-mate'pi pakṣaḥ kimiti na nirdiśyate?* — an allusion to N. S., I. 1. 33.

[1] Lit., p. 53. 15—17. «And because in both formulations the *probans* (*sādhana*) must be understood as tied up to the *probandum* (*sādhya*) from «identity with it» and «production by it», therefore the stand point (*pakṣa*) must not be just necessarily specified. What *prabans* is cognized as confined to the *probandum*, just from it when it is perceived upon the substratum (*dharmin*) of the *probandum*, the *probandum* is cognized. Therefore nothing is (achieved) by the specification of the *probandum*».—According to the Tib. *pratīteḥ* is perhaps to be read instead of *pratītiḥ* in p. 53. 17. *sādhya-nirdeśena* = *pakṣa-nirdeśena*. If we have ascertained by induction the invariable concomitance of the smoke with its cause the fire, and then perceive smoke upon some remote hill, we then have present to our mind the judgment «there it is, this very smoke which is invariably concomitant with fire». It becomes quite superfluous to repeat the conclusion, cp. p. 152, n. 6.

[2] Read *etam eva*.

[3] Read *atra* in stead of *yasmāt*, cp. Tib. transl.

(Minor premise). On this place no jar is perceived, although all other conditions for its perceptibility are fulfilled.

(The Conclusion) «There is here no jar» follows entirely by implication.

(53. 22). In (negation) expressed according to the method of Agreement (the conclusion) «there is no jar on this place» follows entirely by implication.[1] The (author) shows the process of implication. (53. 23). The words «whatsoever is not perceived, although being in conditions of perceptibility», refer to a negative experience as a subject. The words «it is an object practically non-existent» refer to the possibility of our behaviour towards it as non-existent. (54. 1). Thus it is shown that the non-perception of something imagined (as present) is invariably concomitant with corresponding purposive actions.[2] (54. 2). The words («a jar) is not perceived» prove that the logical mark is present upon the subject of the conclusion (on the minor term).[3] If the deduced fact would not have been present upon that substratum, neither could the logical reason be there present, because the latter is invariably concomitant with the former.[4] This is how the (conclusion) is implied.

38. The same refers also (to this formula expressed according to the method) of Difference—

(Major premise). Whatsoever is present (as an object of our purposive actions) and is in conditions of perceptibility, is necessarily perceived.

(Minor premise). But on this place no such jar is being perceived.

Through mere implication (the conclusion) follows that as an object of our purposive actions this thing is absent.[5]

---

1 *sāmarthyād eva.*

2 Lit., p. 54. 1—2. «If it is so, the non-cognition of the visible is shown to be contained in the fact of being fit for a non-Ens deal».

3 *sādhya-dharmin.*

4 *sādhya-niyatatvāt tasya.*

5 Lit., p. 54. 6—7. «Just by connotation (*sāmarthyād*) it becomes „there is here no object of dealing as existent with"».

(54. 8). In the formulation according to the method of Difference, the conclusion «there is here no jar as an object for our purposive action» follows by mere implication. It is the same conclusion as in the formula (expressed according to the method) of Agreement. The (author) then proceeds to indicate the pocess of implication. (54. 9). A thing which can be an object of purposive action means a thing which is present.[1] An object being in the conditions of perceivability means an object imagined as present. This represents the negation of the deduced consequence.[2] (54. 10). The words «is necessarily perceived» express the negation of the logical reason.[3] Thus it is shown that the absence of the consequence is invariably concomitant with the absence of the reason. (54. 11). The words «no such (jar)» etc. mean that on this place the possible perception of a jar has not happened in the manner in which other perceivable objects (usually) are perceived. Thus it is proved that upon the subject of the conclusion, (i. e., on a definite place) there is absence of the reason (i. e., of perception) which invariably involves the absence of the deduced consequence (i. e., of the jar). (54. 13). Supposing the consequence would not be present upon the subject of the conclusion, neither could the reason be there present. But the fact[4] representing the reason is present, (hence the consequence must also be present). This is (how the conclusion) is implied. (54. 14). Therefore, since it is implied, there is no need of explicitly stating it, because we understand (without such a statement) that «there is here no jar».

(54. 15). Similarly in the formulae of an analytical or causal deduction (the conclusion) becomes simultaneously present to the mind[5] by implication. There is, consequently, no necessity of stating it explicitly.[6]

---

1 *vidyamāna.*

2 The deduced consequence is the absence of the jar.

3 The logical reason is non-cognition, its reverse (*nivṛtti*) is cognition.

4 *dharma.* 5 *sam-pratyaya = sama-kālīna-pratyaya.*

6 Pārthasārathimiśra remarks, Śāstra-dīpika, p. 239 (Benares, 1908) that the Buddhists, thinking that the Naiyāyikas have introduced superfluous details in their 5-membered syllogism, have reduced it to two members, major and minor premises (which he calls *udāharana-upanaya*). After having remembered the major premise «what has a cause is non-eternal», and then having merely mentioned «the sounds have a cause», it is quite superfluous to repeat the conclusion that «the sound is non-eternal», because this is implied in the minor premise. Cp. Sigwart, *op. cit.* I, p. 478 n. — «Ebenso setzt... der Untersatz die Conclusion voraus; denn wo bliebe die Wahrheit des Untersatzes, dass Socrates ein Mensch ist, wenn es noch zweifelhaft wäre, ob er... die Sterblichkeit hat die der Obersatz als allgemeines Merkmal jedes Menschen aufführt».

§ 8. Definition of a thesis.

39. Nevertheless what is it that we can call a (sound) «thesis»?

(54.18). It must be nevertheless explained what is the meaning attached to the word thesis.

40. A (sound) thesis is (a proposition to be maintained by the disputant, i. e., a proposition) which he himself accepts «just as such», (i. e., just as the point he *bona fide* intends to maintain, if from the start) it is not discredited (by self-contradiction).[1]

(54.20). «Just as such» means just as (the proposition) to be maintained. «Himself» means the disputant. «Accepted» means that (the proposition) is not only expressed in words, but also (*bona fide*) accepted (to be true). Such a topic, if it is not invalidated (from the start) by perception or other proofs, is called a thesis.

(54.21). But if the thesis is not to be explicitly mentioned (in the conclusion or at the beginning of a syllogism), why do we give the definition of such a (member) which can be dispensed with? We give the definition not because it should be a (necessary) member of the syllogism,[2] but because there are (logicians) who mistake a wrong thesis for a right one and *vice versa.*[3] Therefore, in order to set aside misconceptions about what can and what cannot be a (sound) thesis,[4] the definition of a proposition to be maintained is given.

(55.4). The words «as such» are next explained.

41. «As such» means accepted as (the proposition) to be maintained.

---

[1] Lit., p. 54.19. «What is accepted just as the proper form and not repudiated, is a thesis».

[2] *sādhana-vākya-avayava.*

[3] This remark is directed against N. S. I. 1. 33 and possibly also hints at both the schools of the Mādhyamikas. The Prāsangika school was prepared to defend any amount of theses, bnt not *bona fide*, its aim being to undermine logical methods altogether and to demonstrate the hopeless contradictions of the principles npon which logic is built. The other Mādhyamika school, the Svātantrikas, the followers of Bhāvaviveka, although admitting logic, have established a series of quite incredible theses in contradiction to common sense, cp. my Nirvāṇa, p. 115,

[4] *sādhya = pakṣa.*

(55.6). Since the thesis represents (the proposition) which must be deduced, there is nothing else[1] (to which we could give that name). Therefore its essence[2] consists in its being deduced.

(55.8). In order to explain the meaning of the word «just»,[3] it is said —

42. «Just as such» means accepted as the fact which must be deduced, in contradistinction) from the reason from which it is deduced.

(55.10). It might perhaps be asked why do we not take[4] the word «just» separately? Why do we repeat it in the combination «just as such»? We answer. The word «just» is a particle of emphasis. It emphasizes the quality contained in another word. Therefore it is repeated together with the word which points to the emphasized part. (55.12). (The thesis is the fact which it is intended to deduce), not also the fact which is admitted to represent the reason. What is expressed as being the reason, is also accepted as being the reason. (55.13). When the reason is not accepted (by the opponent), he may also regard it as something that requires a proof, (as a fact which must be deduced). But this is excluded. The word «just» is an indication (that not every unproved thing is a thesis).[5]

(55.15). An example —

43. Supposing the non-eternal character of the sounds of speech must be established (as against the Mīmāṃsaka), and the reason would be, (say), its visibility. Since the visibility of sounds does not exist, it might be regarded as

---

1 *aparam rūpam.*

2 *sva-rūpam.*

3 *eva.*

4 *praty-ava-mṛś*, «to reconsider singly».

5 The definition of the Naiyāyikas «a thesis is a statement of what wants to be proved», N. S. I. 1. 33, was assailed by Dignāga on the ground of his theory of the purely relative character of the meaning of all words (*apoha*). If the expression «wanting a proof» only excludes the things proved or real (*siddha*), then every reason and every example, especially if they are quite absurd (*anupapadyamāna-sādhana*) can be characterized as being in want of a proof and would be included in the definition, as e. g., «sounds are eternal because visible», — *sādhyayor hetu-dṛṣṭāntayor api prasango, yathā nityaḥ śabdaḥ cākṣuṣatvāt*, cp. N. bhāṣya, p. 40, N. vart., p. 113 and Tātp., p. 183 ff.

a fact which is in need of proof. But it is expressed as the reason, therefore it is not here intended to be proved, (albeit it is unproved).

(55.18). Supposing the non-eternal character of the sounds of speech is to be proved, and (someone would point to their) visibility as a (possible) reason. Since the existence (of visible words) is not established, one (could be misled to suppose) that it is just the thing which (the disputant) wishes to establish. (55.19). Therefore it is said that «this», i. e., visibility, «here», i. e., in regard of the sounds of speech, is not admitted as just the point to be established. It is said that there is no necessity (to envisage it here) as something that is intended to be established, since it is expressed as the reason. Whatsoever is expressed in the form of a reason is also admitted to represent the reason, but not the consequence.[1]

(55.22). The word «himself» is next pointed to and explained.

44. «Himself» means the Disputant.

(56.3). «Himself» is a pronoun.[2] «Disputant» is the proximate (subject to which it refers).[3]

(56.6). Who is this Disputant?

45. That one who at this occasion sets forth an argument.

(56.8). «At this occasion» means at the time of some philosophical disputation. He sets forth an argument. As there can be many disputants, this is a specification of the disputant, denoted above by the word «himself».

---

[1] Therefore the Naiyāyika definition in N. D. I. 1. 33, *sādhya-nirdeśaḥ pratijñā*, has been corrected by Dignāga in adding *eva*.

[2] *nipāta* = *thsig-phrad-kyi sgra*, «a particle meaning some relation».

[3] Lit., p. 56.2—5. «The word «himself» is a particle which is used for the (reflexive pronoun) «self» in the Genitive and in the Instrumental cases. Now, here the word *svayam* is used in the sense of the word self in the Instrumental case. Moreover the word self is a pronoun (*sambandhi-śabda*). And the disputant is near. Therefore of whose disputant the self is endowed with the sense of the Instrumental case, just that one is specified as endowed with the sense of the Instrumental case: «by the disputant». But «by the dispntant» is not here the synonym of «himself». — This perfectly useless explanation is characteristic for Dharmottara's scholasticism. Vinītadeva (p. 102) links this sūtra with the following and simply says, «a thesis is only that topic which (the author) proves himself, but not the one that is established by the originator of the system (*śāstra-kāra*)».

(56. 9). If that is the case, the meaning is (simply) that the thesis is what the disputant wishes to prove. What is the use of such a statement? This means that only that fact is a (real) thesis which a definite disputant, at the occasion of a (definite) disputation, intends to prove, and not any other fact. It is equivalent to saying that we cannot force anybody to defend a cause which he himself does not care to defend.[1]

(56. 12). But at what juncture could it occur that (the disputant would be expected) to prove (not the thing he would himself care to prove, but) something else? To guard against what has it been necessary to make this specification?

46. The following is meant. Supposing someone takes his stand on a definite system and quotes arguments accordingly. Supposing the framer of the system has admitted several facts characterizing the same subject. Nevertheless the thesis will be represented by that fact alone which at a given occasion, a definite disputant himself chooses to argue, not by any other one.[2]

---

1 Lit., p. 56. 11. «The result of these words (means) so much as a repudiation (*nivartana*) of the advocation (*sādhyatva*) of an undesirable feature (*aniṣṭa-dharma*)».

2 Since in the laconic style of the sūtras every superfluous syllable must be avoided, Uddyotakara declares that the word «himself» is quite useless. He exclaims «there you are! so keen upon finding the fault of superfluous syllables in others, you make this mistake in your own proposition... no reasonable man will say «I am *myself* going to wash», cp. N. vart. p. 120. According to Dignāga «myself» in this case means «not another one». His principle is that every word includes a negation (*apoha*), the disputant «himself» means «not the initiator of the system to which the disputant adheres». The point of Dignāga is apparently directed against dogmatism, he wishes to vindicate the freedom of the philosopher to choose his arguments, he is not bound to quote only the arguments accepted in the school to which he belongs (*abhyupagama-siddhānta*). This is denied by the Naiyāyikas. If, says Vācaspatimiśra, someone known to be an adherent of the Vaiśeṣika system would appear in a learned society (*pariṣad*) and advance the tenet that the sounds of speech are eternal entities, which is a tenet of the Mimāṃsaka school against which the Vaiśesikas always protested, neither the society nor the official opponent would care to listen. He would not even be allowed to state his argument, he would be declared beaten as soon as he had pronounced the thesis, ap Tātp., p. 187. 5 ff.

(56.16). The possibility of some other fact[1] being deduced in regard of the same subject arises when the author of a system, accepted by the disputant, has admitted several facts characterizing the same subject (about which a variety of discordant views are current).[2]

(56.17). It is indeed quite wrong to suppose that if somebody ranges himself at the side of a definite system, he is obliged to advocate every doctrine which is there admitted. This (wrong view is here) cleared away. Many doctrines may be accepted, nevertheless that topic alone which the dispuntant (at a given occasion) chooses himself to argue will represent the thesis, but not any other one.

(56.19). The following question might be asked. Should not a logical argument[3] disregard all established doctrines and be guided (exclusively) by the weight of real facts?[4] Therefore a philosopher should never take his stand on a body of established doctrines, since they must be left out of account? (56.20). Quite right! But, as a matter of fact, even in those cases when (a philosopher) selfreliently takes his stand on a body of established doctrines, i. e., if he is an adherent of a definite system (and) quotes arguments (in accordance with that system), nevertheless only that proposition will represent his thesis which he himself chooses to advocate (at a given occasion). In order to declare this, it is stated that (the thesis is a proposition which the philosopher «himself» chooses to advocate at a certain occasion).[5]

(56.23). The word «accepts» is next taken (separately) and explained.

47. The word «accepts» (in the above definition of a sound thesis) means (that there is sometimes no necessity of expressing the thesis in words). When an argument is adduced in answer to an objection on a subject which one

---

[1] *dharma*.

[2] *tasmin dharmiṇi=vipratipatti-viṣaya-dharmiṇi*, cp. Vinītadeva, p. 102. 13. Probably an allusion to the great variety of views on the same subjects advocated in the different Buddhist schools.

[3] *linga*.

[4] *vastu-bala-pravṛtta*.

[5] Lit., p. 56. 21—22. «But although, as a consequence of infatuation, he takes his stand upon some teaching (*śāstra*), admits some teaching (and) says the reason, nevertheless just what for him is desirable, just that is his thesis (*sādhya*). In order to declare that, thus has it been told».

wishes to establish, the thesis, even if it is not expressly specified, is (understood from the context).

(56.3). «On a subject», e. g., on the existence of the Soul. (Supposing) a doctrine opposed to the existence of the Soul is being discussed, a doctrine denying the existence of the Soul, (a doctrine maintaining that) there is no Soul. Since affirmation and negation are contradictories, this doctrine contradicts the view that the Soul exists. (Supposing) that in answer to this contrary tenet an argument is adduced by someone who wishes to establish, i. e., to prove[1] the existence of this object, of the Soul. The word «accepts» intimates that this fact (the existence of the Soul) wil be his thesis (even if it is not explicitly stated).[2] (57.6). This is the meaning suggested by the word «accepts».[3] Although in a verbal inference, (in a syllogism), we would expect that the thesis to be deduced should be expressed (in a separate proposition), nevertheless, even if it is not expressed, (it is clear) what the thesis really is, because it is expressed by implication.

(57.8). Why is that?

48. Because it represents the point against which the opposite view is directed.

(57.10). «It» means that topic which is the subject (of the discussion), the subject matter against which the opposed view is directed. Because of this circumstance (the real intention of the speaker becomes evident from the context).

(57.11). The following is meant. The disputant adduces a proof in order to confute the opposed view. Therefore the tenet which the opponent aims at disproving is *eo ipso* the topic he himself wishes to

---

1 *niścaya* is here a synonym of *siddhi*, meaning something «logically proved to be real».

2 Or even if the thesis explicitly proved is different from what is really the intention of the speaker. The real thesis is the intention of the speaker. A thesis can be clearly understood out of both premises without expressing the conclusion separately. But even if it is expressed separately, it may sometimes represent the real intention of the speaker only half-way, indirectly. This happens when the speaker intends to prove his tenet surreptitiously, through an indirect suggestion, as is illnstrated by the following example.

3 Lit., p. 57. 6. «What is mentioning at the end (sūtra 49, p. 57. 17) of *ity uktam bhavati*, with regard to this place the sentence must be closed». Instead of repeating these words twice, at the end of sūtra 47 and 49, they have beeu taken only once at the end of sūtra 49.

prove. (57.12). His argument has just the aim to confute the opposed view. If this were not his thesis, where on earth could you find something as definitely representing a thesis, as this one![1]

(57.15). This case is exemplified. When an argument is advanced against an opponent, something may be understood to represent the deduced thesis without being expressly stated.

49. An example[2] —

> (Thesis). The sense of vision and other senses (are organs) to be used by someone else.
>
> (Reason). Because they are composite (substances).
>
> (Example). Just as beds, chairs and other implements (composed for the use of man).
>
> (Major premise. Whatsoever is a composite substance is not an independent existence).

The aim is to prove that (the senses) are the organs of the Soul (which is a simple and independent substance), although this is not expressly stated. Thus the thesis is not always that alone which is expressed. That is the meaning (of the word «accepts»).

(57.18). «The sense of vision, the sense of audition etc.» are the subject, (the minor term). They exist for the sake of someone else, i. e., they have dependent existence, this is the predicate, (the major term). «Because they are composite (substances)», that is the reason, (the middle term). (57.20). The words «just as beds, chairs and other implements»

---

[1] Here again, according to Dignāga's method, the word «accepts» includes a negation, «accepted» means «non-expressed», as illustrated by the next following example «the senses are the organs of some one else». The Naiyāyikas answer that this qualification is superfluous. «No one will establish what he does not accept«, says Uddyotakara, N. vārt., p. 118 and Vācaspati comments, «if the aim of the word «accepted» is to include an unexpressed intention, this cannot be done in the syllogism which would then be wrong (*ananvayo hetuḥ*). But words have always beside their direct expressive power (*vācyam*) a power of indirect suggestion (*lakṣyam*). If the words are not suggestive, they cannot point to an unexpressed intention, cp. Tāpt., p. 186.

[2] Cp. Sānkhya-kārikā, 17.

refer to the facts on which that generalization is established.[1] Beds, chairs etc. are requisites serviceable to man[2] and they are composite substances.

(58. 1). Thus, although this example[3] does not (by itself) mean that the organs of sense are employed by the Soul, nevertheless, although unexpressed, this is the thesis. (58. 2). Indeed, the Sānkhya philosopher maintains that the Soul exists. The Buddhist maintains, on the contrary, that the Soul does not exist. Thereupon the Sānkhya philosopher, starting from[4] the Buddhist view which is opposed to his own, brings forward an argument, with the aim of confuting the opposed view and of establishing his own. (58. 4). Therefore, the fact that (the senses) are in the service of the Soul represents the (real), although unexpressed, thesis (which the disputant has at heart), since the opposed view is directed against it.

(58. 5). It is not proved that beds, chairs and other requisites used by men are in the service of the Soul. The major premise[5] («whatsoever is composite is controlled by the Soul» is not proved at all). Established is only the simple fact that these composite things are made for the use of somebody, in this sense they are called objects «for use» by somebody. (58. 6). The (real) intention is to prove that the Intellect is also an organ of something else. This is suggested by the words «and other senses». This «something else» in regard of the Intellect can be only the Soul. (58. 7). Thus it would be proved that consciousness[6] is in the service of another (higher principle). The

---

1 *vyāpti-viṣaya-pradarśana*, «pointing to the scope of the concomitance».

2 *puruṣa-upabhoga-anga* has here probably a double sense, with regard to beds, chairs etc. it means the requisites serviceable to man, with regard to the Soul (*puruṣa*) of the Sānkhyas it means the experiences imputed to the Soul during its state of bondage in some particular existence, as conditioned by the deeds (*karma*) in former existences.

3 *atra pramāṇe* = *thsad-ma hdir; pramāṇa* is here used in the sense of *dṛṣṭānta*, cp. 52. 18 and 7 note to transl. p. 147.

4 *hetū-kṛtya*.

5 *anvaya*.

6 *vijñāna* = *vijñāna-skandha*. For the Sānkhya undifferentiated «consciousness», pure changeless consciousness, is an eternal substance, the Soul (*puruṣa*). For the Buddhist this same undifferentiated consciousness is pure sensation, consisting of momentary, ever changing flashes. There is thus in the argument of the Sānkhya a *quaternio terminorum*, since he understands under *vijñāna, manas, antaḥkaraṇa* unconscious, physical principles, consisting predomineutly of a special intellect-stuff (*sattva*) or nervous matter capable only to be reflected in consciousness which, in the shape of a Soul, is a quite different principle. For the Bud-

words «for the use of someone else» have been inserted in the hope that one could surreptitiously[1] prove the Intellect to work in the service of the Soul.

(58. 9). Consequently the statement that the thesis is something «accepted» (by the disputant) has the following meaning. The thesis is not always (a proposition) expressly mentioned. It might be expressed and it might be merely understood from the context, (especially) when it is something the disputant wishes to prove (surreptitiously), in answer to a contrary opinion advanced by an opponent.[2]

(58. 13). The words «not discredited (from the start by self-contradiction)» must be now explained.[3]

50. The words «not discredited (from the start by self-contradiction)» are an indication of the fact that according to this definition a (proposition) can be accepted (by the disputant as expressing) the fact to be established and nevertheless not represent a thesis, if it is in contradiction with perception, with inference, with (the identity) of a conception or with the very words (in which it is expressed).

(58. 13). «This (definition)» means the definition explained above, namely, «the thesis is a proposition which the disputant himself

---

dhists it is consciousness itself. The argument from the analogy of composite things, and the induction from chairs, beds etc. is of course very feeble, but it was admitted in the Sānkhya-school, cp. Sānkhya-kārikā, 17. Since the thesis, or conclusion, is not an indispensable member of the Buddhist syllogism, its definition may have been omitted. Nevetheless Dignāga and Dharmakīrti expatiate on it in order to show 1) that the definition of the Naiyāyikas in N. S. I. 1. 33 lacks precision and 2) to give them a lesson on the precise meaning of words, since all words according to the *apoha*-theory of the Buddhists imply negations or contrasts, — *atra anya-vyacchedam (= apoham) vākyārtham manvāno bhadantaḥ pratijñā-lakṣaṇam ati-vyāpty-avyāptibhyām ākṣipati*, cp. Tātp., p. 182. 34. The Naiyāyika term *pratijñā* «thesis, proposition» is here replaced by *pakṣa* «tenet». Dh. uses both terms indiscriminately, cp. 26. 14, 48. 4, 58. 20, 59. 14, but the Naiyāyikas make a difference, cp. N. vārt., p. 117. 14 ff. and Tātp., p. 185. 7 ff. Vasubandhu in his Vādavidhāna avails himsalf of the term *pratijñā*, cp. N. vārt, p. 121. 2.

1 *sāmarthyāt*.

2 It is evident from this example as well as from the addition of the words «accepts himself» in the definition that the term *pakṣa* refers bere to the real tenet of the disputant, not to its formulation in speech alone. Cp. N. kandalī, p. 234. 13— *vacanasya pratjñātvam, tadarthasya ca pakṣatā*.

3 This sentence must precede the sūtra III. 50.

accepts just as such etc.» The words «not discredited (from the start)» are added in order to declare that a proposition may conform to (this part of) the definition and nevertheless not represent a thesis. (58.15). What is the fact that cannot be a (sound) thesis, although (the disputant) may be willing to defend it? The (author) answers. Supposing (the disputant) intends to prove a topic which is discredited, i. e., its contrary is proved, either by perception or inference or (the identity) of a conception or his own words, this will not be a thesis.[1]

51. Among them, contradicted by perception is, e. g., (the following proposition),

The sound is not perceived by hearing.

(58.18). There are four kinds (of contradiction), viz. by perception etc. Among them what is a proposition contradicted by perception? The following is an example. It is an example because there are other cases of contradiction with perception, which must be understood just as this one. Perceptible by hearing means perceptible with the ear, «Not so perceptible» is not to be heard, not to be apprehended by the sense of audition — this is the (intended) meaning of the thesis.[2] (58.20). The non-perceptibility of the sound by hearing is contradicted by its perceptibility which is established by direct perception.[3]

---

1 These words (i.e., the four syllables, *akṣara-catuṣṭayam*, *'ni-rā-kṛ-ta*, for every syllable counts) are redundant, says Uddyotakara, p. 119, because if the word «accepts» is inserted in order to exclude unacceptable and unaccepted (*aniṣṭa*, *anīpsita*) theses, the contradictory theses are already excluded by it. Moreover Vasubandhu has also omitted them in his definition — *sādhyābhidhānam pratijñā*, cp. N. vārt., p. 121, and Tātp., p. 186. 67. Dh. thinks that a thesis may satisfy to all conditions already mentioned and nevertheless be unaceptable, not to the disputant himself, but to the audience. The judge (*madhyastha*) will then declare the discomfiture of the disputant without allowing him to continue, cp. Tātp., p. 187. 5 ff.

2 Such a thesis as «the active sense of vision does not perceive the visible» has been advanced with a special intention by the celebrated «sophist» Bhāva-viveka, cp. Madhy. vṛtti, p. 32. 9 (B. B.), cp. my Nirvāṇa, p. 115.

3 The full inference according to Dignāga is, *asrāvaṇaḥ śabhaḥ kṛtakatvād ghaṭādivat*. His idea is that this inference cannot even be admitted to discussion, because of its glaring contradiction to fact. Uddyotakara proposes another example, «the fire is not hot», cp. N. vārt., 116. 21. He thinks that «audibility» cannot be perceived directly, because the process of the operation of the sense-faculties is imperceptible, *indriyavṛttīnām atīndriyatvāt*. According to the Buddhist theory of Negation (*anupalabdhi*), if a sound is not heard it does not exist as an object influencing behaviour (*vyavahāra*). But for the Naiyāyiks the denial of audibi-

52. A thesis contradicted by inference is, e. g., (when an adherent of the Vaišeṣika system affirms),

The sounds of speech are eternal entities.

(59.2). Contradicted by inference is, e. g., (in the mouth of an adherent of the Vaišeṣika system the proposition) «the sounds of speech are eternal entities». The intended thesis, the proposition that the sounds of speech are eternal, is contradicted by their non-eternity which (the Vaišeṣika) proves by inference.[1]

53. A thesis contradicted by the (identity) of a conception is as follows,

The word «hare-marked» does not mean the moon.

(59.5). The following is an example of a proposition standing in contradiction to the (identity of the corresponding) conception. The word «hare-marked» does not mean the moon, i. e., cannot be denoted by the word moon. This is disproved by (the identity of) the conception

---

lity does not mean denial of existence, *na šabdābhāve tan-(šrāvaṇatva)-niṣedho 'vakalpate*, cp. Tātp., p. 31. 12; and even the non-existence of a sound is for them something real, *na cābhāvas tucchaḥ*, *ibid;* hence even this non-existence is apprehended by the sense of audition. For the Buddhist, on the contrary, non-existence of the sound is not a reality (*abhāvas tucchaḥ*), but its substratum is a reality, therefore it only can be inferred on this substratum by *kāryānupalabdhi*, cp. Tattvas., kār. 1689 and Kamalašīla's Comment. According to the Vaišeṣikas sound is directly perceived, cp. V. S., II. 2. 21.

1 The text commented upon by Dharmottara has *nityaḥ šabdaḥ* and this is supported by the Tibetan translation. But Vinītadeva reads *ghaṭo nityaḥ* = *bum-pa ni rtag-pao*, and this probably has been one of the current readings Dignāga originally has characterized this class of wrong theses as contrary to the accepted doctrine (*āgama-viruddha*). Owing to the ambiguity of the term *āgama* this could also mean «contrary to Scripture». Uddyotakara, p. 117. 5 then objected that the Vaišeṣikas prove the non-eternality of the sounds of speech not from Scripture, but by argument, cp. V. S. II. 2. 28 ff. This criticism has apparently been accepted by Dharmakīrti, he then has changed *āgama-viruddha* into *anumāna-viruddha*. The reading *ghaṭo nityaḥ* seems also to have found its way into some Mss. for similar reasons, cp. N. vārt., p. 117. 8. Since Dharmakīrti enumerates in this place such theses which are not worth the while of being disproved, the example of Vinītadeva seems much more natural than the Mīmāṃsaka thesis round which war has been waged during centuries. Otherwise every thesis opposed by the Buddhists would fall into the category of impossible theses The text is either to be corrected accordingly or it must be understood as referring only to a Vaišeṣika-philosopher to whom the audience will refuse to listen. This is another instance of very old text corruptions, cp. above sūtra III. 18—20,

(corresponding to both these words). (59. 6). A thing is said to be distinctly conceived[1] when it is an object (apprehended by a synthetic) mental construction.[2] To be a concept or to be conceived means to be an object of a mental construction. (59. 7). Owing to the circumstance that the thing «bearing the image of a hare» corresponds (in our speech) to a mental construction which has the form of a concept, (of a distinct image), it is established beyond doubt[3] that it can be given the name of the moon. (59. 8). Indeed, what corresponds to a constructed image[4] is capable of coalescing with a word,[5] and what is capable of coalescing with a word can be designated by a name chosen (arbitrarily) by convention. (59. 9). Consequently the possibility of giving it the name of the moon, and the contradiction[6] of denying it, are established by (the identity) of the object of mental construction, i. e., by the (identical) form of the (corresponding) image.[7]

---

1 Dignāga called this case *loka-prasiddhi-viruddha* «contrary to what is generally known». Vinītadeva and the Tibetan translators interpret *pratīti* as meaning the same as *prasiddhi* = *grags-pa*. Uddyotakara thinks that this cannot be a separate class and must be included in the preceding ones, cp. N. vārt., p. 117. 9 ff. The change of *prasiddhi* into *pratīti* by Dharmakīrti nevertheless seems intentional, cp. Tātp, p. 185. 4. Dh. thinks that this must be considered as a case of an analytical syllogism, it can then be thrown into the following form,

Major premise. Whatsoever appears as the distinct image of the moon can be given the name of the moon.

Minor premise. The «hare-marked» object appears as the distinct image of the moon.

Conclusion or Thesis. It can be given the name of the moon.

Both names represent two coexisting possibilities, the presence of the one is by itself a sufficient reason for inferring the necessary presence of the other, the denial of this would be a contradiction (*bādhita*). Vācaspati thinks that the Buddhists ought to have considered this wrong proposition as repudiated by introspection (*svasaṃvedana*), and the Naiyāyiks as a case repudiated by internal evidence (*mānasa-pratyakṣa*). The difference between these two views is that the first implies simultaneous self-cognition as inherent in every moment of consciousness, cp. above sūtra, I. 10, the second considers it as a subsequent moment, cp. Tātp., p. 185. 4—5.

2 *vikalpa-vijñāna* = Tib. *rnam-par-rtog-pai rnam-par-šes-pa;* p. 59. 8 our text has *vikalpa-jñāna*, probably a mistake for *vijñāna*, because the Tib. has, p. 134. 11, *rnam-par-šes-pa*. Cp. Tātp., 185. 4. where we nevertheless have *vikalpa-jñāna-gocaratva*. All difference between *vijñāna* and *jñāna* is here obliterated.

3 *eva*.

4 *vikalpa-jñāna-grāhya* = *vikalpa-vijñāna-viṣaya*.

5 *šabda-ākāra*. 6 *bādhaka*.

7 The interpretation of Vinītadeva is much more simple and natural. He takes *pratīti* not in its technical sense of a mental construction, but in its general

(59.11). The existence of a distinct image is here an analytical reason, because the possibility of giving some name, arbitrarily chosen, flows naturally just out of the circumstance that it is a mental construction. (59.12). Thus the possibility of giving the name of the moon, and the contradiction of denying this possibility must be considered as established by analytical reasoning.[1]

54. A proposition contradicted by the words in which it is itself expressed, is as follows,

Inference is not a source of knowledge.

(59.14). When the intended thesis[2] is contradicted by the proper words of the proposition which expresses it, it cannot be deduced, as e. g., «inference is not a source of knowledge». This proposition

---

sense of something being known to everybody. A thesis is inadmissible when it runs against the generally accepted meaning of the words. Everybody knows that the moon is called (in sanscrit) the thing «marked by a spot in the form of a hare», therefore it is impossible to deny it. He adds the very characteristic remark that this wrong thesis is also overthrown by the fact that «every word can have any meaning» (*sarvasya śabdasya sarvārtha-vācyatvam*), since the meaning of a word is a matter of conventional agreement (*sanketa*). This reminds us of a saying current among pandits *sarve śabdāḥ sarvārtha-vācakāḥ*, an allusion to the exceedingly developed metaphorical use of sanscrit words. Vinītadeva adds (p. 106.7) «you may (if you like) call the jar a moon!».

1 The comment of Vinītadeva on this sūtra, p. 109. 1—7, runs thus. «There are some who maintain the thesis that the thing having the mark of a hare is not called the moon. This (thesis) is repudiated on the ground of universal consent (*pratīti* = *prasiddhi*) that the «hare-marked» is a name of the moon. It is moreover repudiated by the fact that every object can receive any name, because the connection between a thing and its name is arbitrary (read *brdar-btags-pa*), e. g., we can give to a jar the name of a moon». — Thus, according to V., the meaning of words is founded on convention (*prasiddhi* = *sanketa*). This, of course, is not denied by Dh. But he calls attention to the fact that the possibility of giving a name is founded upon the existence of a concept (or distinct image = *pratibhāsa-pratīti*) constructed by the synthesis of our thought (*vikalpa-vijñāna* = *kalpanā*). Such a concept contains in itself the possibility of being designated by a conventional name (*abhilāpa-saṃsarga-yogya*, cp. sūtra I. 5). Therefore the judgment expressed in the proposition «every distinct conception can be given a conventional name» is an analytical judgment, since the predicate, the possibility of giving a name fixed by convention, is contained in the subject, in every distinct conception. Thus Dignāga, the Tibetans and Vinītadeva are satisfied with a reference to the conventional meaning of words (*prasiddhi* = *sanketa*), but Dharmakīrti and Dharmottara make the addition that this is founded on the existence of constructed concepts (*prasiddhi* is founded upon *pratīti*).

2 *pratijñā-artha* = *pakṣa*. This indeed has been a thesis of the Cārvākas.

means that the character of being a source of right knowledge is denied of inference (or judgment).[1] But this is contradicted by the proper words in which it is expressed, i. e., by the words «inference is not knowledge». (59.16). The fact that the speaker resorts to such a proposition is an indication that he admits the idea produced by its expression[2] to be a true one. (59.17). Indeed if the speaker intended to convey the following meaning «the idea which will be produced[3] in you by my words is a false one», he never would have pronounced them. Supposing the idea to be communicated (to my hearer) is that my words have a wrong meaning, well, my words will then (really) have a wrong meaning.[4] (59.19). Supposing somebody says «whatsoever I speak is wrong», even then the speaker pronounces this proposition in order to convey[5] that these his words (at least) have a true meaning. If this proposition is shown to be true, then his other propositions will (*eo ipso*) be shown to be false. (60.1). If this proposition were not true, his other propositions would not be declared to be false. There would then be no use of pronouncing them. He would have never pronounced them. (60.2). Consequently when a speaker pronounces a proposition he (*eo ipso*) really declares that the idea[6] produced by his words, the idea corresponding to the meaning of the proposition is a true one, (i. e., reflects reality). (60.3). If this be the case, (the speaker) can show that the meaning of his words is truth only in showing (*eo ipso*) that there is an invariable concomitance[7] between speech and external reality. It is a relation of an effect to its cause (60.4). Thus our words (can be regarded) as an effect of those objects of the external world which they denote. By using them we wish to show that the ideas communicated by them represent truth, (i. e., they express external reality, their cause). We thus clearly show that the process of understanding the meaning of a word is nothing but an inference from an effect of external reality to its cause, reality itself. (60.6). Therefore

---

[1] It has been indicated above, passim, that the *svārthānumāna* is in many cases equivalent to our judgment. Here the proposition «inference is not a source of knowledge» virtually means «a judgment is not a judgment».

[2] *śābda-pratyaya.* [3] *yo 'rtha-sampratyayaḥ.*

[4] *apārthaka.*

[5] *ādarśayan* «clearly showing».

[6] *vijñāna* is here, as well as in 60.4 and 60.5, in the sense of the old *saṃjñā*, but Tib. has in all the three cases, p. 136.5, 136.9 and 136.12, *śes-pa* = *jñāna*.

[7] *nāntarīyaka.*

if someone says «inference is not a source of knowledge», what he really says is this: «knowledge communicated by words does not apprehend reality», because not to be a source of knowledge is nothing else than not to apprehend reality.[1] (60. 7). However, the fact that we have recourse to words proves by implication that our words are necessarily connected with reality, and thus the reality of their corresponding objects is (also) proved. (60. 8). Consequently, since we conceive (i. e., imagine)[2] the words as a product of reality, we then infer the existence of this reality, (the reality) which corresponds to the idea produced by our words. This reality contradicts the unreality which is expressed in the (intended) thesis. (60. 9). The meaning is thus the following one. From the proper words of the speaker the existence of a corresponding reality is inferred. Thus the unreality which is *prima facie* expressed[3] is contradicted by those very words in which it is expressed.[4]

(60. 11). Others uphold (the following theory). Words are the result of the intention (with which they are pronounced). They produce (in the hearer) a knowledge of the speaker's intention. It is his intention (to communicate) truth. He avails himself of language (only to communicate this intention). The proposition that «inference is

---

1 Lit., p. 60. 4—7. «And it being so, who shows that the word is invariably concomitant with external reality must show that the idea produced from the word possesses a true object. Therefore that one who shows that the idea produced from the word which is an effect of the external object (that this idea) possesses a real object, has shown that verbal cognition (*pramāṇa*) is an inference produced by the mark of an effect. Therefore that one who says «inference is not cognition» has said that verbal cognition does not apprehend a real object; indeed we call «non-cognition» (*aprāmāṇya*) just the absence of a real object».

2 *kalpita.*

3 *vācyamāna.*

4 The interpretation of Vinītadeva is virtually the same, but simpler. He says that since knowledge communicated by speech is a kind of internal inference, it follows that if there were no inference the words would never have been pronounced. The words thus appear not as a product of external reality, but as a consequence of the intention with which they are spoken. Vinītadeva says «if these your words do not communicate knowledge, why do you pronounce them?» It means that the words are the product of the intention of the speaker to communicate truth. This simple interpretation Dharmottara has again complicated by introducing the difference between the real canse of speech, which is the intention to communicate truth, and the imagined, or indirect one, which is the truth itself, or external reality.

not knowledge» is contradicted by this (intention of the speaker to communicate something).

(60. 12). This is wrong! That our words are really the result of the intention with which they are spoken,[1] (we do not deny). But we do not allude here to the real (immediate) cause (which produces language).[2] We have just mentioned that the identity of a conception is a sufficient reason (for inferring the identity of the meaning of two different words), and (we now contend) that our language is a sufficient reason for inferring the existence of some real facts of which it is an expression.[3] But we take these relations in their logical,[4] not in their real (or psychological aspect).[5]

(60. 14). And further, (we admit) that if someone denies inference, he will have no right to infer the presence of fire from the presence of smoke, he likewise will have no right to infer the intention of the speaker from his words. Nevertheless we avail ourselves of speech in order to make a communication about something really existing in the external world. Therefore language is not caused by a conviction that it is an expression of our intentions.

(60. 17). And then, we do not pronounce words in order to intimate that we have the intention (of doing so), but we do it in order to make a communication about the existence of some external reality. Therefore language is caused by our conviction that it is an expression of real facts existing in the external world.[6] Thus our interpretation as given above is the only right one.[7]

---

[1] Except when he is mistsken himself or wishes to deceive others, cp. Tātp., p. 185. 10.

[2] The real cause is here evidently conceived as the last moment of the preceding series of efficient moments, all other moments can be only logically or indirectly constructed as causes, cp. above, text p. 31. 11—12.

[3] In the first case we imagine coexistence between two attributes of the same reality or an analytical relation founded on identity of the underlying reality. In the second an indirect succession of two facts.

[4] *kalpita.*

[5] Intention is viewed as the psychological cause of pronouncing words. Truth may be regarded as its logical foundation, or reason. Vinītadeva is thus guilty of not having sufficiently distinguished these two relations.

[6] The existence of real objects in the external world (*bāhya-vastu-sattva*) must be understood as explained above in the notes to ch. I, sūtras 20—21.

[7] Lit., p. 60. 11—19. «But others have said, knowledge produced from a word which is the result of intention has (this) intention for its object, the use of words belongs to a man who wishes a real meaning, by this the thesis, the fact of not

55. The four kinds of an inadmissible thesis are thus rejected.

(60.21). The words «not discredited (beforehand)» are intended to reject four impossible points.

(60.22). Next it will be shown what meaning results if the negative counter-part of every word is taken and all the negations collected together.[1]

56. Thus (a sound thesis should not be) 1) a fact already proved, 2) a fact, although not yet proved, but adduced as a reason, (not as a consequence), 3) a fact which the disputant himself does not intend to prove at that occasion, 4) it must not necessarily be a fact explicitly stated, 5) it must not be a fact impossible (by self-contradiction). (All this is excluded), and just this contrast will show that our definition (of a sound thesis) is unimpeachable, namely, 1) it is a point which the disputant himself has chosen to establish, 2) which he himself admits and 3) which is not (internally) imposible.

(61.5). «Thus» means in the manner just exposed. A thesis to be proved[2] is contrasted with a point already proved. A point which

being a source of knowledge, is contradicted. This is wrong, because here we admit the distinct idea (*pratīti*) as an imagined own-existence-reason, and one's own words as an (imagined) effect-reason, not as real. And the fact of being an effect of intention is quite real for the word. Therefore it is not taken here. Moreover, just as the one who does not admit inference does not understand the non-discrepancy (*avyabhicāritva*) of smoke with fire, just so will he not understand the non-discrepancy of the word with intention. And the word is used for communication of external reality. Therefore the use of words is not preceded by admitting an invariable connection between words and intention. And again, words are pronounced not in order to make known an intention, but to communicate the existence of external reality. Therefore the use of words is preceded by admitting (their) invariable connection with external reality. Therefore just the preceding interpretation is faultless».

[1] In order to wind up this lesson on the theory of the relative or negative meaning of words (*apoha*) the author now repeats the whole definition from the negative side by collecting together all negations implied in the positive formulation.

[2] *sādhya* = *pakṣa*, a thesis and a predicate.

must be argued in a controversy is the opposite of a point already previously established. The thing proved is contrasted with the thing unproved. Therefore a thesis to be proved cannot be something already proved.[1] (61. 7). But not every unproved point (makes a thesis). It is further contrasted 2) with the fact adduced as the proof, 3) with the fact which the disputant himself does not intend to prove on that occasion, 4) with the necessity to give it expression in words, (it can be understood without being expressed), 5) with a fact which although unproved it is imposible to prove.

(61. 9). The point which is free from these five negative characteristics (with which it is contrasted), a point which is 1) not yet proved, 2) not a reason, 3) intended to be proved by the disputant, 4) which may be either expressed or understood, 5) which is not invalidated (from the start by counter) proofs — such is the point which has been defined by the words «is intended as such by the disputant himself and not discredited».[2]

---

1 Lit., 61. 5—7. «The predicate (*sādhyaḥ*) must be envisaged by opposition, by the reason of its being the opposite to the proved. This means that to what object the proved object is opposed, this is the predicate, the proved is the opposite of the non-proved. Therefore the unproved is (the predicate) to be proved».

2 Thus the inadmissible theses are, 1) according to Dignāga *pratyakṣa—*, *anumāna-*, *āgama-*, *prasiddhi-* and *svavacana-nirākṛta;* 2) according to Praśastapāda who borrows from Dignāga, *pratyakṣa-*, *anumāna-*, *abhyupagata-*(= *āgama-*), *svaśāstra-* and *svavacana-virodhin;* 3) according to Dharmakīrti —*pratyakṣa-*, *anumāna-* (=*svaśāstra*), *pratīti* (=*prasiddhi*) and *svavacana-nirākṛta.* Śaṃkarasvāmin in his Nyāya-praveśa has added four further varieties of an impossible thesis, thus increasing their number to nine. The Naiyāyikas and the united Nyāya-Vaiśeṣika school reject the wrong theses, on the score that a thesis is never right or wrong by itself, but only on account of the reason, cp. N. vārt., p. 116 ff. and Tātp., p. 32. 2—3. They accordingly reckon two additional wrong reasons, or logical fallacies, the counterbalanced (*satpratipakṣa*) and the self-contradicting (*bādhita*), and likewise two additional aspects of a valid reason (*asat-pratipakṣatvam* and *abādhita-viṣayatvam*), since they have borrowed from Dignāga the view that the classification of wrong reasons must correspond to the number of the aspects of a valid reason, cp. my Théorie bouddhique de la Connaissance in the Muséon, V p. 42 (reprint). The *asat-pratipakṣa-* form of the reason corresponds to what in the definition of the thesis is hinted at by the words *sādhyatvena iṣṭaḥ*, cp. N. Kandali, p. 203. 10 — *pakṣo nāma sādhya-paryāyaḥ, sādhyam ca tad bhavati yat sādhanam arhati, sambhāvyamāna-pratipakṣaś ca artho na sādhanam arhati, vastuno dvairūpya-abhāvāt.* The *abādhita-viṣayatva-* form of a valid reason corresponds to the four inadmissible (*nirākṛta*) theses, cp. *ibid.* — *pratyakṣādi-viruddho'pi pakṣo na bhavati.* Therefore these both additional aspects of a valid reason are to be included in the first one (*anumeye sattvam*), *ibid.* — In the final form of the Nyāya-system

(61.12). What must thus be proved is called the thesis. The definition is thus[1] shown to be unimpeachable. There is nothing inconsistent in it.

§ 9. Logical Fallacies.[2]

(61.14). Having concluded the examination (of the syllogism which is) the verbal expression of the three aspects of the logical mark (or reason), and having incidentally dealt with the (correct) definition of the thesis, the author now proceeds to examine the logical fallacies. By way of introduction it is stated —

57. We have defined the syllogism as the verbal expression of the three aspects of the reason. Now, if even one of the three aspects is not (correctly) expressed, (the result) is a fallacy.

(61.18). The following is meant. If someone wishes to give verbal expression to the three aspects of the logical reason, he should do it with precision,[3] and precision is attained when the negative counterpart[4] of (every aspect) is likewise stated. When we know what is to be excluded, we then have a better knowledge of the other part, of what is to be accepted. (61.20). The definition of a syllogism has been given above, it is «the verbal expression of the three aspects of the logical mark». Now, i. e., in the light of this definition,[5] if even one of the aspects is not (correctly) expressed — the word «even» implies that the same consequence will follow, if two of them are not (correctly) expressed[6] — a fallacy will ensue. A fallacy is what resembles

---

as settled by Gangeša in his Tattva-cintāmaṇi the impossible theses of Dignāga appear as impossible reasons (*bādhita-hetvābhāsa*) and ten varieties of them are established.

[1] Lit., p. 61.12. «The word *iti* in the sense of „thus"».

[2] All the implications, the originality and the importance of the Buddhist theory of Logical Fallacies will be elicited only when Dignāga's Table of Reasons (*hetu-cakra*) will be analysed and translated. An edition of it with a commentary by Bstan-dar Lha-rampa and an english translation by M-r A. Vostrikoff will shortly appear in the Biblioteca Buddhica series.

[3] *sphuṭa*.

[4] *prati-rūpaka* = *prati-yogin*.

[5] Lit., «if this exists».

[6] No fallacy of omission of one of the aspects of the logical reason is mentioned in the sequel. But some examples will be given of syllogisms which although valid by themselves are not correctly formulated, cp. below text, p. 88—89. The three aspects of the logical mark are those mentioned under III. 1, but not those mentioned in II. 5—7.

a syllogism, but does not represent a (valid) syllogism. It is a fault consisting in some one of the three aspects being deficient.

58. And also (there will be a fallacy) if they are, although expressed, but either unreal or uncertain, either for the opponent or for the speaker himself.

(62.4). Fallacy is produced not only by deficient expression, but also through unreality or uncertainty of the reason, either to the hearer, i. e., the opponent or the speaker, i. e., the respondent.[1]

§ 10. Unreal reason.

(62.6). Now, what is the name of the fallacy corresponding to each unreal or uncertain form of the reason?

59. If one aspect of the reason, namely, its (first aspect), its presence upon the subject of the conclusion, is either non-existent or uncertain, the reason is called unreal.

(62.8). If one of the aspects (of the middle term), its necessary connection with the subject of the conclusion, i. e., its presence upon that subject, is either non-existent or uncertain, the fallacy is called «unreal[2] reason». Just because it is «unreal», it conveys no knowledge about the subject. It neither conveys cognition of the predicate nor of the reverse of it nor of something uncertain, it is a reason of cognizing nothing. Such cognition would never convince anyone.[3] This meaning is clearly implied just in the name «unreal».

(62.12). An example is given.

---

[1] This is the celebrated rule of Dignāga which lays down the fundamental principle that a philosophic debate must have some common ground to start with. Neither the speaker nor his opponent has the right of quoting facts or reasons that are not admitted as real by the other party. This rule proved very embarrassing to such philosophers as the Mādhyamikas who denied altogether that the Absolute, the «thing in itself» (*svalakṣaṇa*), could be cognized by logical methods. They nevertheless produced arguments, but only with the aim to show that all arguments were mutually destructive of one another. They pointed to the fact that Dignāga himself was obliged to admit that in religious matters (*āgama*) it was impossible to find a common ground between two opposed religions, cp. my Nirvāṇa p. 119.

[2] *asiddha.*

[3] This remark refers only to the first example in III. 60.

60. E. g., when it must be proved that the sounds of speech are not an eternal entity, the reason «because they are visible»—is unreal for both parties.

(62. 14). This reason is wrong for both sides, the respondent, (the Mīmāṃsaka who maintains the eternity of the sounds of speech),[1] and the opponent, (the Buddhist who denies it).

61. «Trees are animate beings» — this shonld be deduced from the fact that «they die when the entire bark is taken off». It is not accepted by the opponent. He defines death as an extinction of sensations, sense-organs and life. Such a death does not occur in trees.

(62. 18). The Digambaras maintain that trees are sentient beings.[2] They point to the fact that they die as soon as they are entirely stripped of their bark. (The reason) is unreal in the eyes of their opponent, the Buddhist. Why? Because (a Buddhist understands by death the cessation or extinction of sensations, of sense organs and of life).[3]

(63. 1). Sensations — means here visual and other sensational consciousness.[4] Under sense organs we understand some special (subtle) matter[5] in a (living) body, located on the ball of the eye and in

---

[1] Cp. above, p. 127 n. 2.

[2] The Jainas assume that plants are animate beings possessing only one sense-faculty, viz. the tactile sense, cp. v. Glasenapp, Jainismus, p. 172.

[3] Lit., 63. 1. «Sensation and organ and life is a *drandva*-compound».

[4] *vijñāna* or *vijñāna-skandha* means in Hīnayāna exclusively undifferentiated pure sensation, the mere sensation of the presence of something indefinite in the ken of our sense-faculties (*prati-vijñapti*). It is one element (*dharma*), has by itself no varieties, but distinguished into visual, auditional and other sensations according to the cause which evoked it. Cp. my Central Conception, pp. 16 and 63. In the Mahāyānistic *abhidharma* another *vijñāna* has been imagined, the *ālaya-vijñāna* which is the store house for the germs of all future ideas and for the traces left by all the former ones, but the school to which Dharmakīrti belonged seems to have rejected this theory.

[5] *rūpa* or *rūpa-skandha* means every element of matter as characterized by resistance or impenetrability, it must be distinguished from *rūpa-āyatana* which means only colour and lines, i. e., visual matter, cp. Central Conception, p. 11.

other parts of the body.[1] Its existence is inferred from the fact of the production of visual and other sensations. Under «life», in common parlance, breath is understood. The meaning attached to this term in (Buddhist) science[2] is (that of a special transcendental force determining *a priori* the term of an existence), it is here out of place.[3] Therefore life as manifested in breath is here meant. The extinction or cessation (of these phenomena) is the mark or the essence of death. This death is meant by the Buddhist when he contends (something about this subject).

(63. 5). However, why is (this reason which is advanced by the Digambaras) unreal? Because there is no such death consisting in the extinction of sensation etc. in the trees. Extinction presupposes previous existence. If someone admits the extinction of consciousness in trees, he cannot but admit its (previous) existence. Therefore, since no consciousness in trees is admitted, neither can its extinction be maintained. (63. 7). It might be objected that exsiccation is death, and this really occurs in trees. This is true. But the reason adduced (by the Digambara) is a death which is conditioned[4] by the (previous) existence of consciousness, not mere exsiccation. Hence that death which is taken as a reason is unreal, and that death which is real, consisting in exsiccation, is not the reason.

(63. 10). The Digambara takes as reason death in general, without making a difference between a death concomitant with the predicate (sentient being) or not so concomitant. Hence the respondent is here mistaken (about the connotation of the word) death which he adduces as a reason. Consequently he thinks that exsiccation is a real (reason), because experience teaches[5] that trees are subject to death from exsiccation. The opponent, on the other hand, has the right conception, therefore the reason is for him unreal.

---

1 According to the *abhidharma* an organ of sense (*indriya*) consists of an imperceptible (*atīndriya*) subtle kind of matter different in every organ, it has been compared with the nerves, cp. my Central Conception, p. 12 ff.

2 *āgama-siddha*, *āgama* includes all Buddhist literature, religious or revealed (*sūtra*) as well as scientifical (*śāstra*). But when dogmatical knowledge is contrasted with empirical (*vastu-darśana-bala-pravṛtta*), *āgama* refers to the former, cp. below, sūtra III. 116.

3 *āyuḥ-saṃskāra* or *jīvita*, one of the non-mental forces, *citta-viprayukta-saṃskāra*, cp. Central Conception, p. 105.

4 *vyāpta*, concomitant.

5 *darśanāt*.

(63.13). But if someone produces an argument which he himself also acknowledges (to be wrong), the rule is that the argument remains unreal for him, (e. g.),

62. Supposing a supporter of the Sānkhya system wishes to prove that the emotions, pleasure etc., are unconscious, and refers to the fact that they have a beginning or that they are impermanent. This argument is «unreal» for the disputant himself.

(63.16). «Pleasure etc.» means (emotions) like pleasure, pain etc. Their unconscious character it is intended to prove by pointing to the fact that they have a beginning or that they are impermanent. What has a beginning or what is impermanent is unconscious, as for instance, the elements of Matter are (in Buddhist philosophy).[1] Pleasure etc. indeed have a (perpetual) beginning and are impermanent, therefore they (must be) unconscious. Consciousness, on the other hand, is the essential attribute of Soul (which according to the Sānkhya system has no emotions).[2] In this instance beginning and impermanence are to be taken separately (as reasons), not simultaneously.[3] Both these attributes are not real from the standpoint of the disputant, of the Sānkhya. (63.20). Now, a logical reason is advanced for

---

1 Here evidently the *rūpādi-āyatana* are meant, i. e., the sense-data, *āyatana* №№ 7—11, cp. my Central Conception, p. 7. It cannot be *rūpādi-skandha*, because although they are also impermanent and momentary, but only the first of them is unconscious, all the others are intent (*sālambana*) upon an object.

2 Consciousness (*puruṣa*) in the Sānkhya system is imagined as an eternal, changeless, motionless substance, as the pure light of consciousness which is being reflected in the mental phenomena. The latter are imagined as being by themselves mere collocations of material particles (*gunas*), unconscious (*jaḍa*) in themselves. For the adept of this system whatsoever is impermanent (*pariṇāmin*) is unconscious. But from another point of view the Sānkhya declares all phenomena to be eternal (*sarvam nityam*), since they are only modifications of one Matter (*prakṛti*) with which they are identical according to the principle of identity between cause and effect (*sat-kārya-vāda*). The Buddhist, on the other hand, denies the existence of a substantial Matter, and replaces it by momentary fhashes of special elements (*dharma*), or forces (*saṃskāra*). In the present case the Sānkhya apparently wishes to deduce his idea of unconscious mental phenomena ont of the Buddhist idea of impermanent elements, assuming evidently that whatsoever is a momentary flash cannot be conscious, since consciousness includes memory.

3 This remark probably hints at the Sarvāstivādin theory that all elements (*dharma*) appear and disappear in the same moment, cp. my Central Conception, p. 40.

the sake of convincing the opponent, (the Buddhist). Therefore such a reason must be given which is valid for him.[1] The opponent admits as true that (elements) which never have existed are produced (out of nothing), and that the existent is impermanent, i. e., vanishes without leaving anything behind, (reverts to nothing).[2] Both these tenets are wrong in the eyes of the Sāṅkhya. (63. 22). In such a case the reason is fallacious for the respondent (who brings it forth), because he has no knowledge of the manner in which both the (absolute) beginning and the (absolute) extinction are argued.[3] (64. 1). If he did possess a knowledge of the arguments by which these (theories) are supported (and if he did believe in them), they would be real reasons for him, but since he has no proper knowledge of them, they are unreal from his own point of view.

(64. 3). Next comes the unreal, because uncertain, reason.

63. If doubt prevails regarding the very (fact adduced as a reason) or regarding its localization, the reason is unreal.

(64. 5). If the reason itself is subject to doubt or its localization uncertain, it is unreal (as a reason). The localization of a reason is something different from the reason itself, it is a place where it is found, a place corresponding to the subject of the conclusion. The reason must be present upon it in order to convey (the predicate).[4] When its localization is uncertain, (the fact itself) becomes uncertain.

---

[1] This point is especially controverted by Candrakīrti, cp. my Nirvāṇa, p. 118 ff.

[2] This is one of the methods of expressing the theory of Universal Momentariness or constant change. Every moment in the existence of a thing is regarded as a separate existence detached from the preceding and following moments (*pūrva-apara-kāla-kalā-vikalaḥ kṣaṇaḥ*); it then appears that at every moment the thing is produced out of nothing and reverts again to nothing.

[3] Cp. above text, p. 33. 10 ff. and 44. 20 ff. Transl. p. 9. 1 ff. and 120 ff.

[4] Lit., p. 64. 5—6. «And its localization, i. e., the localization of this reason; localization means that the reason is lodged in it, a substratum of the predicate (*sādhya-dharmin*) is indicated which constitutes the locus, which is different from the reason». — Unreal is not the fact corresponding to the reason, but the fact corresponding to the minor term (*dharmin*). All fallacies of an «Unreal» (*asiddha*) reason are what we would call fallacies of the minor premise, they refer to the absence or doubtful presence of the middle term upon the minor, i. e., to what is here called, cp. II. 5, the first aspect of a logical mark.

(64.8). (The author) proceeds to give an example (of an unreal reason represented by a fact which is) uncertain in itself.

64. If something is suspected to represent (not smoke, but) vapour etc., and if it is adduced as a proof for the presence of fire, it will be an unreal, because uncertain, reason.

(64.11). Vapour etc. means either vapour (or smoke or fog or dust) etc. When something is suspected to represent either vapour or (smoke), it is an assemblage of material elements, an assemblage of the solid (the liquid, the hot and the gazeous atoms).[1] When (sometimes) one is uncertain whether something represents vapour (or smoke), and when it is adduced as proving the presence of fire,[2] it becomes an unreal reason.

(64.13). The following is meant. (Supposing we think that we perceive) smoke, but we are not sure whether it may not perhaps be vapour. Then it is unreal (as a reason), since it lacks the proving force of certainty. What is ascertained as being smoke, since smoke is produced by fire, proves the presence of the latter. But if this is uncertain, then it proves nothing. Thus it falls under the head of logical fallacies, called (here) unreal reasons.

(64.16). An example of an unreal (fact, because of the uncertainty of its) localization, is the following one—

65. There is a peacock in this cave, because we hear its cries.

(64.18). «This cave» is the subject (or minor term of the deduction). A cave is a place covered by a rock which streches out horizontally and conceals it. The presence of the peacock is the fact to be

---

1 Matter (*rūpa* = *rūpa-skandha*) is imagined in the *abhidharma* as consisting out of four kinds of atoms, the solid (*pṛthivī*), the liquid (*ap*), the hot (*tejas*) and the levitant (*vāyu*). They are conceived as focuses of energies producing resistance, cohesion, heat and motion, the latter conceived as contiguous appearance of a series of discrete moments (*nirantara-utpāda*). The body is then either solid or liquid or gazeous (ever moving = *satata-gati*) or hot according to the intensity of the force (*utkarṣa*), since the proportion of different atoms is constant, always the same, in every bit of matter, whether it be solid or liquid or gazeous, hot or cold. Thus *bhūta-saṃghāta* or *mahā-bhūta-saṃghāta* simply means some material phenomenon, or something physical. Cp. my Central Conception, p. 11.

2 *agni-siddhau* is corrected by Dh. into *agni-siddhy-artham*.

proved. «Because we hear its cries» is the reason. Why is it unreal by localization?

66. There can be a mistake as regards the direction from which the cry comes.

(65. 2). That place wherefrom the peacock's cry comes is called the place of its origin, the place wherefrom it reaches us. When there is a mistake, or confusion, regarding the place from which it reaches us, the basis of the reason is unreal. Supposing we have a number of caves contiguous with one another, we might be mistaken whether the cry comes from this cave or from that one. This is called unreal by localization.

(65. 6). When the subject (minor term) is a non-entity, the reason is likewise unreal. An example is given.

67. And when the subject is not a reality, the reason will likewise be unreal. E. g., when the omnipresence of the Soul (of an individual) is deduced from the fact that its attributes may be apprehended anywhere, this reason is unreal.

(65. 9). Soul, (i. e., an individual Soul), is omnipresent, to be found in any place, i. e., ubiquitous. When this is to be proved, the reason adduced is the fact than its attributes can manifest themselves in any place. Its attributes such as pleasure, pain, desire, hatred etc. can manifest themselves in whatsoever a place (the corresponding living body be transferred to). For this reason (it must be ubiquitous, because a Soul cannot displace itself).[1] (65. 11). Attributes cannot exist without the substance to which they belong, because they are inherent in the latter. But Soul is motionless. Therefore if it were not ubiquitous, how could it be possible that the feelings of pleasure etc. which we experience while living in the Dekkhan should be also experienced when we move to the Midlands.[2] Consequently, (our) Soul must be

[1] The Vaiśeṣika system imagines the Soul of every individual as an omnipresent substance, conterminous with Space, motionless and unconscious by itself «as a stone», but capable of producing consciousness in the corresponding individual through a special contact with its internal organ. When the body of the individual moves from one place to another its Soul remains motionless, but the thoughts and feelings are then produced in that part of the omnipresent Soul which corresponds to the place which the body has newly occupied, cp. my Nirvāṇa, p. 57 ff.

[2] *madhya-deśa.*

ubiquitous. (65.13). Now, for the Buddhists, Soul itself (as a separate substance) does not exist, still less does the fact of its attributes being perceived anywhere exist. Thus the reason is unreal.[1]

(65.15). The difference between the two last cases is that in the former one the existence of the subject was doubtful, because its place[2] was unknown; in the latter case the subject of the conclusion itself is a non-entity.

(65.16). Thus it is, that when one form of the reason, the form concerning its presence upon the subject of the conclusion (i. e., the minor premise), is not real, we have the (material) fallacy of an unreal reason.[3]

---

1 According to the Tib. the *cheda* before *tasya*, p. 65. 14, must be dropped, it then refers not to *bauddhasya*, but to *ātmā*; *asiddhau* must be then corrected into *asiddho*.

2 Lit. «substratum», *dharmin* = *āśraya*. The ultimate substratum in every cognition (cp. comment on sūtra I. 12) is the «thing in itself» (*svalakṣaṇa*), the efficient (*artha-kriyā-kārin*), the point-instant (*kṣaṇa*), it is the pure substratum (*dharmin*) with all its attributes (*dharma*) stripped off, not the empirical thing (*samudāya* = *dharmi-dharma-samudāya*, cp. comment on sūtra II. 8). This underlyng point-instant of reality is problematic in the first case, it is quite absent in the second, i. e., when the attributes of sensation, feelings, ideas etc. are taken away there remains no point of something real to which the designation of a Soul could be applied. The construction of an ubiquitous Soul-substance, the substratum of all mental phenomena, by the Vaiśeṣikas is therefore pure imagination.

3 The division of logical fallacies (*hetvābhāsa*) which we find in the original sūtras of the Nyāya and of the Vaiśeṣika systems, as well, as in the Bhāṣya of Vātsyāyana, is substantially different from the Buddhist classification which was first established in strict conformity with his theory of the three aspects of a logical reason, by Dignāga in his celebrated little work «An Elucidation of a Table of possible Reasons» — Hetu-cakra-samarthana. The Bhāṣya of Praśastapāda has then adopted the main lines of Dignāga's classification and all the subsequent evolution of this part of the science of Indian logic is influenced by it, cp. my article «Rapports entre la Théorie Bouddhique de la Connaissance et l'enseignement des autres écoles», in the Muséon, V, cp. also Randle's article in the Mind, 1924, p. 405 ff. Since all objects in the whole universe are interconnected and logically dependent upon one another, either as uniformities of Coexistence or as uniformities of Succession, every object is *eo ipso* a logical reason and the possibilities of logical fallacies are infinite. Those that are not worth considering have been set aside, as we have seen, as impossible theses. After that come the fallacies of the reason properly speaking which are fallacies of one or of more than one of its three aspects. The cases where the first aspect alone is either wrong or uncertain are all fallacies of the minor premise. The cases when the second and third aspect of the logical reason are either wrong or uncertain

§ 11. Uncertain reason.

68. **When another aspect of the reason — its absence in counter-instances — taken singly — is unreal, the fallacy is called uncertainty.**

(65. 18). When another[1] single aspect of the reason, namely its absence in counter-instances, is (not supported) by reality, we have the fallacy of an uncertain reason. Certainty means one issue. It is the aim of (the syllogism), it becomes then conclusive. Inconclusive is uncertain. It is a case when neither the conclusion nor its negation can be ascertained, but, on the contrary, there remains only a doubt.

---

are fallacies of concomitance, or of the major premise. All the cases where the minor premise is wrong, i. e., where the reason is either totally or partly absent on the subject of the conclusion, or where its presence there is uncertain, are called «unreal» (*asiddha*) reasons. These are material fallacies or fallacies of fact, *fallacia extra dictione. Fallacia in dictione*, in the strict sense of the term, sc. fallacies of expression, where the thought is all right, but wrongly expressed, are treated as wrong examples, cp. below, text 89. 8 — *na duṣṭam vastu tathāpi vaktrā duṣṭam darśitam.* All other fallacies are also, strictly speaking, fallacies of fact, material fallacies, since they are fallacies of a wrongly established concomitance, and concomitance is always a generalization from facts. When the presence of the middle term upon the whole compass of the minor term is an ascertained fact, comes the next step of ascertaining its position between the similar and dissimilar cases. It must be present in similar cases *only* and absent from *every* dissimilar case, cp. sūtra II. 6—7. The conclusion is right *ubi non reperitur instantia contradictoria.* This again must be ascertained by facts. But these latter fallacies correspond more closely to our fallacies of undistributed middle and of illicit major and can be termed logical fallacies in the stricter sense. We thus have two main groups of fallacies which we can call fallacies of the minor premise and fallacies of the major premise. In the monastic schools of Tibet and Mongolia pupils are trained to distinguish among these two groups at once, without delay, when a series of quite fantastic combinations are proposed to them. If the minor premise is not supported by the facts, the answer must be «the reason is unreal» (*rtags ma grub = asiddho hetuḥ*). When the concomitance between the middle and the major terms is not warranted, the answer must be «concomitance is not produced» (*khyab-pa ma ḥbyuñ = vyāptir na bhavati*). Dignāga distinguished 4 varieties of *asiddha-hetu.* The number is here increased to six. Gangeśa and the logic of the united Nyāya-Vaiśeṣika system have retained the class of unreal (*asiddha*) fallacies, but the clear cut principle of Dignāga's division has been obliterated by useless details and the desire to compromise with the fivefold division of fallacies in Gotama's sūtras, cp. Suali, Introduzione, pp. 393—394.

[1] Read *aparasya.*

We call uncertain a reason which makes us fluctuate between a conclusion and its denial. Examples are now given.[1]

69. Supposing we must prove the eternal character of the sounds of speech or some other (property to be mentioned presently). If the fact of its being cognizable and other properties are quoted as their (respective) reasons, they—being present, either partly or completely, in dissimilar cases also[2] — (are uncertain reasons).

(66. 3). «The eternal[3] character or some other property». By «some other property» (the following three predicates) are alluded to, 1) the fact of not being produced by a voluntary effort, 2) the fact of being so produced, and 3) eternality (once more).

(66. 4). «The fact of being cognizable and other properties». By «other properties» (the corresponding three following reasons) are meant, 1) impermanence, 2) (once more) impermanence, and 3) (penetrability or) the fact of not being an extended body.[4] When eternality or the other (three) attributes are predicated, cognizability and the other three properties (in the order stated) are uncertain reasons, since the absence of all the four facts in counter instances is subject to doubt. (We thus obtain the four following patterns of uncertain reasoning).

(66. 7). Indeed, (first syllogism).

(Thesis). The sounds of speech are eternal.
(Reason). Because they are cognizable.
(Major premise). (Whatsoever is cognizable is eternal).
(Example). Just as Space, (cognizable and eternal).
(Counter instance). And (not) as a jar, (non-eternal, but not incognizable).

---

[1] The aspects of the logical reason referred to in this section where the logical fallacies are examined are always those which are established for internal inference, cp. sūtras II. 5—7, not those mentioned under sūtra III. 1. The latter are again taken into account when examining the wrongly expressed examples, cp. below, text p. 88—89.

[2] Lit. «in both the similar and dissimilar cases».

[3] Read *nitya* instead of *anitya* in 66. 1, 66. 3 (bis), 66. 6 and 66. 7.

[4] *amūrta* = *lus-can-ma-yin-pa*, «not possessing a body», *mūrta* means possessing a definite limited dimension, = *paricchinna-pariṇāmavat*.

The reason «cognizability» covers similar as well as contrary cases, (eternal objects, like Space and impermanent ones, like jars etc. It is inconclusive).

(66. 8). (Second syllogism).

(Thesis). The sounds of speech are not produced by an effort.

(Reason). Because they are impermanent.

(Major premise). (Whatsoever is impermanent is not produced by an effort).

(Examples). Just as lightning and as Space, (both not produced by an effort, but the one impermanent, the other eternal).

(Counter-instance). And (not) as jars etc. (which are so produced and hence ought to have been permanent, but are impermanent).

Impermanence is present in one part of the similar cases (i. e., in objects not produced by an effort). It is present in lightning etc., but it is absent (in the other part of them), in Space etc. And it includes all the contrary cases, since it is present wheresoever there is production by an effort.[2]

(66. 10). (Third syllogism).

(Thesis). The sounds of speech are produced by an effort.

(Reason). Because they are impermanent.

(Major premise). (Whatsoever is impermanent is produced by an effort).

(Example). Just as a jar (which is so produced).

(Counter-instances). And (not) as lightning and Space (which both are not so produced, but the one is impermanent and the other eternal, whereas if the reason were right they ought to have been both eternal entities).

---

[1] No such syllogism, of course, has ever been advanced *bona fide*, but the idea of the Mīmāṃsakas about eternal unmanifested sounds is twisted in every possible way for exemplification of logical rules. The Indian and Tibetan logicians think that in order to get the real force of the syllogistic formulae, it is much better to practise on propositions which are quite wrong, so strikingly wrong that they never have occurred to anybody.

[2] The dissimilar or contrary cases are objects produced by an effort, as jars etc. The contraposition of the major premise gives the proposition — «whatsoever is produced by a conscious effort is eternal».

Impermanence is present in one part of the contrary cases,[1] it is present in lightning etc., but absent in Space. It is moreover present in all similar cases, since everything produced by a conscious effort is impermanent.

(66.12). (Fourth syllogism).

(Thesis). The sounds of speech are eternal.

(Reason). Because they are not limitedly extended bodies.

(Major premise). (Whatsoever is not an extended body of limited dimensions is eternal).

(Example). Like Space and like atoms (which both are eternal).

(Counter-instances). Contrary[2] to motion and to a jar (both of which are impermanent, but the first is non-extended).

The attribute of «not being a limitedly extended body» is partly found both in similar and contrary cases. It is present partly in both, in (eternal) Space and in (impermanent) motion, (both are not bodies of limited dimensions). But in atoms which represent one part of the similar (eternal) cases, and in jars etc. which represent one part of the contrary (non-eternal) cases, it is absent. Jars as well as atoms have limited dimensions. That atoms are eternal is a tenet admitted by the Vaiśeṣika school, therefore they are included in the similar cases. (66.15). In these four examples, the (condition of) the absence of the reason in contrary cases is not realized, therefore they produce fallacies of uncertainty.[3]

---

[1] i. e., in some of the objects which, although impermanent, are not produced by any conscious effort, like lightning.

[2] Lit. «like».

[3] These are in Dignāga's system the four varieties of an overwide, or not exclusive enough (*avyatirekin*) logical mark. They have all that feature in common that the mark is not excluded from every dissimilar case. While being present, either partly or totally, in similar cases—this is only as it should be in a correct reason—it is nevertheless present, either partly or totally, in the dissimilar cases also. The third aspect of a logical reason, mentioned in sūtra II. 7, is not realized. In order clearly to show the position of the reason between the similar and the dissimilar cases Dignāga begins by giving an example where the reason pervades all things cognizable, i. e., all similar and all dissimilar cases together. This is tne absolutely overwide reason (*sādhāraṇa-hetu*). This would correspond to an inference of the form «Socrates is immortal because he is a cognizable object», an inference which by itself would not be worth considering, but it is introduced in order better to show the full score of the possible situation of a reason between similar and dissimilar instances. The second variety will be when the reason pervades the totality

70. When this aspect of the reason is dubious, the fallacy is likewise one of uncertainty.

(66.17). When this aspect of the reason, its absence in contrary cases, is unreal, the fallacy is one of uncertainty. And similarly, when this aspect is dubious, the (resulting) fallacy is likewise one of uncertainty.[1]

An example —

71. Supposing we wish to prove that a certain person is non-omniscient, or that he is subject to passions. If the fact that he is endowed with the faculty of speech (and other attributes of a man) is quoted as a reason, its absence in contrary cases (i. e., with omniscient beings) becomes problematic.[2]

---

of the similar cases and moreover trespasses partly upon the domain of the dissimilar ones. This would give us an inference of the form «Socrates is a man because he is mortal». The reason mortality not only pervades the whole domain of men, but trespasses moreover upon the forbidden ground of the dissimilar cases, i. e., of non-men. It is the ὕστερον πρωτερον of Aristoteles. In Dignāga's Table it occupies the place of the second uncertain reason, (the place at the right corner of the Table). Here and in the Nyāya-praveśa it is given the third place, but below, text p. 76.13—14 (*sandigdha-vipakṣa-vyāvṛttika*) it is rightly placed as the second. The third variety (here placed as the second) will be when the reason pervades the totality of the dissimilar cases and only one part of the similar ones. This would give us an inference of the form «Socrates is not a man, (is a non-man), because he is mortal». Here the similar cases, the non-men, are partly mortal, and the dissimilar ones, sc. men, which should be all immortal, are, on the contrary, all mortal. Finally the last combination will be when the reason is partly present on both sides. This would give us an inference of the form «Socrates is immortal, because he is an idea». Excluding all ambiguity in the terms and assuming that Socrates is taken in the sense of a man, we will have an uncertain reason, because there are ideas on both sides, mortal and immortal ones. All this schema is devised only in order to show the exact position of the right reason between the similar and dissimilar instances, as in the inference «Socrates is mortal, because he is a man».

1 Thus an uncertain or problematic judgment is always a case of incomplete induction from particular cases, counter-instances being producible.

2 The syllogisms would have the following forms,

1. Whosoever is a man is non-omniscient.
   This one is a man.
   He is non-omniscient.
2. Whosoever is a man is non-passionless.
   This one is a man.
   He is non-passionless.

(66.21). The predicate to be deduced is «non-omniscience» (i. e., limited knowledge). «A certain person», is a person whom the speaker has in view. This is the subject of the conclusion. A second predicate is the fact that he is subject to passions. When the fact of limited knowledge or the presence of passions are asserted, such attributes as the faculty of speech, (or such animal functions as) the opening and closing of the eyes etc. are inconclusive. Their absence in contrary cases (i. e., in omniscient beings) it is impossible to prove. (67.3). The contrary case is omniscience. Whether omniscient beings possess that faculty of speech (and other attributes of men), or whether they do not possess them, it is impossible for us to decide. Consequently it is never known whether a speaker is omniscient or not. Speech is an uncertain mark.[1]

(67.6). But (it might be objected) that there are altogether no omniscient speakers in existence, why then should we entertain doubts regarding their faculty of speech?

72. A negative judgment of the form «there are no omniscient speakers in existence» concerns a fact which is essentially beyond any possible experience. Therefore the absence of speech and (human attributes in omniscient beings, i. e.) in cases contrary to non-omniscience, cannot be warranted.[1]

(67.9). For this very reason the negative judgment «there are no omniscient speakers in existence» produces uncertainty. For what reason? Because it refers to an object whose essence is to be beyond any possible experience, and this (always) leads to uncertainty. (67.11). When a negative judgment refers to an object unaccessible to experience, negation then does not produce a necessary conclusion[2] but a problematic argument.[3] The absence of the faculty of speech in omniscient beings is therefore uncertain. Omniscience is the counter-instance

---

[1] About the origin of this example see above, p. 56. The idea that an omniscient being should necessarily remain silent, since human speech is incompatible with omniscience, because it is adapted to express relative, but not illimited knowledge, this idea is now being pressed in different combinations merely in order to exemplify logical rules; cp. N. Kaṇikā p. 111 ff. and the concluding part of Tattvas.

[2] *niścaya-hetuḥ.*

[3] Cp. above, ch. II, sūtra 48—49.

in regard of limited knowledge, (a case where the absence of the mark is ascertained).[1]

(67.15). (The opponent may rejoin[2] that) it is not (experience, be it) negative experience, which induces (him) to maintain that omniscient beings do not speak, but (he maintains it) because (human) speech is incompatible with omniscience?[3]

(We answer: No, because —)

73. The contraposed proposition, viz., «an omniscient being does not resort to speech» cannot be proved by negative experience, neither (can it be deduced from incompatibility with speech), because there is no contradiction between omniscience and the faculty of speech, (omniscience) being problematic.[4]

(67.16). There is no incompatibility between omniscience and the faculty of speech, and for this reason the contraposed proposition cannot be established. (67.17). The contraposed concomitance[5] is (now) quoted. «One who is omniscient (does not speak)». The subject is the negation of the predicate, i. e., omniscience. The predicate is the negation of the subject, i. e., «the absence of the faculty of speech». Thus it is intimated that the negation of the predicate is invariably concomitant with the negation of the subject, and the first is thus subaltern to the second.

(67.19). Such an inverted concomitance (of the form «whosoever is omniscient is not a man») could be accepted as established, if omni-

---

1 Lit., p. 67. 11—12. «Since non-cognition whose object is irrepresentable (*adṛśya*) is a cause of doubt, not a cause of certainty, therefore is the exclusion of speech etc. from omniscience, which is the contrary of non-omniscience, doubtful».

2 Lit., p. 67. 15. «Not because of non-cognition do we declare that speech is absent in omniscience, but because of the contradiction of speech with omniscience». This proposition must precede the sūtra III. 73.

3 Cp. N. Kaṇikā, p. 111. 11 — *sarva-jñatāyā atyanta-parokṣāyāḥ kena cid api saha pratyakṣa-pratītena virodhānavagateḥ.*

4 Lit., p. 67. 13—14. «And because there is no opposition (*virodha*) between the faculty of speech and omniscience, even if there is no experience (*adarśane'pi*) of «whosoever is omniscient does not speak», the contraposition does not really exist (*na sidhyati*), because of doubt».

5 *vyāptimān vyatirekaḥ.*

science and human speech[1] were opposed (by Incompatibility or Contradiction). But that is not the case. Therefore, the inverted concomitance does not hold good. Why? Because it is uncertain. Since there is no opposition, therefore the problem (cannot be solved). And when uncertainty obtains the contraposed concomitance is not established.[2]

§ 12. The law of Contradiction.

(67. 22). How is it that there is no opposition?[3]

74. Opposition between objects is of a double kind.

(68. 2). There is no opposition between the faculty of omniscience and human speech, because opposition can be only of two kinds, (Efficient Opposition and Contradiction) and no more. What is this double aspect of opposition?

75—76. When (one fact) has duration (as long as) the sum-total of its causes remains unimpaired, and it (then) vanishes as soon as another, (the opposed), fact appears, it follows that both are incompatible, (or efficiently opposed) just as the sensations of heat and cold.

(68. 5). Possessing unimpaired causes means having the totality of its causes present. If something owing to deficient causes ceases to exist, it cannot (efficiently) be opposed by something else,[4] (since it does

[1] The faculty of speech, as is clear from text, p. 67. 2, is only quoted as the main characteristic of a human being, all other characteristics are equally meant we could therefore translate «if omniscience and man were opposed by contradiction».

[2] Lit., p. 67. 19—21. «Such contraposition implying concomitance (*vyāptimān*) would exist between omniscience and the faculty of speech, if they would be opposed. But there is no opposition. Therefore it (the contraposition) does not really exist. Why? He says, because of doubt. Since there is no opposition, therefore there is doubt. Because of doubt contraposition is not real (*asiddha*)».

[3] In the following exposition we will translate *virodha* when it refers to both its varieties by «opposition», its first variety by «efficient opposition» or Incompatibility, its second variety by «logical opposition» or Contradiction, resp. law of Contradiction.

[4] Lit., 68. 4—6. «Because of the non-existence, in case another exists, of lasting possessor of non-deficient causes, there is a conception (*gati*) of opposition

not exist). This is (the idea) carried by the expression «unimpaired causes».

(68.7). But is it not evident that as long as the totality of the causes of something remains intact, nothing (in the world) will be able to interfere with it? How can it then be (efficiently) opposed (by anything else?)

(68.8). This is however (possible) in the following way. Let the sum total of its causes be present, the fact is nevertheless (efficiently) opposed by that other fact which, producing a breach in this totality, thus removes it.[1] If a fact is opposed to another one in this sense, it always affects it in some way or other. (68.10). Indeed if (an agency) producing cold curtails its efficiency to produce further moments of cold, it removes cold and (in this sense) is opposed to it. (68.11). Therefore to be (efficiently) opposed means just to produce a disappearing (phenomenon) by producing a breach in its causes.[2] This kind of opposition means (Incompatibility), or impossibility of contiguous coexistence. (68.12). Consequently contiguous coexistence of such mutually opposed facts in the same moment must be impossible. Such mutual exclusion obtains between two opposed (phenomena) when they

---

«Of a possessor of non-deficient causes» — thus that one is called whose causes are non-deficient, are intact. Of whom there is non-existence, through deficiency of causes, to him there is no opposition even from whatsoever».

[1] Lit., 68.8—9. «However thus. Even the possessor of undeficient causes is known (*gati*) to be in opposition to that one through the cause-deficiency-made-by-whom there is non-existence». Cp. Jayanta, Nyāyamañjarī, p. 55 — *akiṃcit-karasya virodhitve 'tiprasaktiḥ*.

[2] Lit., p. 68.10—11. «Indeed, opposed (*viruddhaḥ*) is the abolisher (*nivartakaḥ*) of cold-sensation which counteracts the force producing cold-sensation, (although) being (himself) a producer of cold-sensation. Therefore opposed is just the producer of the disappearing phenomenon (*nivartyatva*) which makes a deficiency of causes». — The idea seems to be that when cold is superseeded by heat there is a struggle between two forces. Three phases, or moments, of this struggle must be distinguished. Heat is latent in the first phase, although it latently counteracts already the forces producing cold, so that in the next phase cold will appear in a final moment, in order to be superseded in the third phase by heat. Thus it is that in the first phase cold is in a state of latently efficient opposition with the forces which will produce heat in the ultimate phase. Dh. thus maintains that the causes which produce cold in the next moment, will produce heat in the next following moment. That heat is the cause of cold means that heat is present among the causes which produce the last moment of cold. This also is an answer to the much debated question, in India as well as in Europe, whether the night which precedes the day can be regarded as the cause of the day.

are neighbours to one another, because if they are located at some distance there is no (efficient) opposition between them.

(68.13). Thus it is that when one (phenomenon) removes the opposite one, (there is a gradual change, and if the change is abrupt), it can do it in no less than in three moments. In the first moment it meets it and becomes ready to produce a condition of non-efficiency. In the second it (actually) reduces the opposite phenomenom to such a condition. In the third it removes and supersedes it.[1]

(68.16). If this is right,[2] then light, which represents a moving substance, occupies space spreading gradually by light waves (in the following manner). When it produces the moment of light which follows immediately upon darkness, it (begins) by producing in the neighbouring darkness a condition of non-efficiency. That darkness alone becomes non-efficient which is contiguous with the light, (first moment). When the non-efficient has been removed, (second moment), light springs up in the same place, (third moment). In this manner darkness can be gradually driven away by light. In the same way a hot sensation can be superseded by a cold one.

(68.19). But when light springs up (abruptly) just in the place occupied by darkness, (the series of light-moments is the direct continuation of the series of dark moments, there is no antagonism)? (68.20). (However, in that case also there is a moment of darkness which is followed by the final moment of it), the moment which produces no further darkness, and it is just this moment which (must be reckoned as) being also the birth moment of the (future) light. The antagonism[3] consists just in the fact that a condition of non efficient (feeble) darkness is produced (after which no further darkness appears). (68. 22). Therefore if the change is produced (abruptly, with the utmost) speed, darkness has disappeared in the third moment from the beginning of the process. (From this third

---

[1] Lit., 68. 13—15. «Therefore who of whom is the remover, he removes him, at the utmost, in the third moment. Coinciding in the first moment he is fit to produce a condition of non-efficiency. In the second he makes the opposed unefficient. In the third, when the unefficient has disappeared, he occupies its place», p. 68. 14 read — *avasthādhāna-yogyo*, cp. Mallavādī, fol. 95, — *asamarthā cāsav avasthā ca ksaṇāntara-janana-śakti-(ra)hitety arthaḥ, tasyā ādhāna-kṣaṇam, tatra yogyo bhavati.*

[2] *tatra ity evam sthite sati* (Mallavādī).

[3] *nivartakatvam.*

moment onwards begins a new series which is) efficiently opposed[1] (to the preceding series).[2]

(69.1). (Now, if efficient opposition is nothing but a change when) one phenomenon produces (or is followed by) another one, this efficient opposition will obtain between two phenomena having duration, not between two moments?[3] (This however could not be an efficient

---

1 *viruddho*.

2 The difference between this case of such an abrupt change and the preceding one is that in the latter we have two systems of momentary existences running parallel and a meeting point between them which can be reckoned as the beginning of efficient opposition, the incompatibility (*virodha*) is a process (*bhavana-dharman*). Every change is theoretically constructed as occupying three moments (*tri-kṣaṇa-pariṇāma*), because there is always an intermediate phase between the opposed phenomena, in contradistinction from the second kind of opposition, or logical contradiction, where the counterparts are diametrically opposed (*paraspara-parihāra, parityāga*) and there is nothing intermediate. When light is produced just in the place formerly occupied by darkness, e. g., by lighting up a lamp, there is no efficient opposition in the first phase of the process of change, because there is as yet no light, nor is there any in the third moment because there is already no darkness, (cp. below, Mallavādī's comment). The opposition reduces to a simple change just as, e. g., the change of clay into a jar, or the destruction of the jar by a stroke of a hammer, its change into splinters. According to the Buddhist idea of the Universe as an impersonal process of perpetual change where the point-instants (*kṣaṇa*) following upon one another according to causal laws may be arbitrarily united in series (*santāna*) which receive names, the series of light moments is only the continuation of the series of dark moments. Every existence has the possibility to be followed either by homogeneous or by heterogeneous moments (*sajātīya-vijātīya-ubhaya-santati-janana-śakti-yukto ghaṭaḥ*). There is thus no opposition between two consecutive moments, but only between the end of one duration and the beginning of the other. The so called incompatibility (*nivartya-nivartaka-bhāva*) is nothing but the beginning of a new series (*janya-janaka-bhāva*), it would be simple difference, no opposition. The question is solved in the sequel by pointing to the fact that there is an antagonism or struggle between two continuous phenomena trying to oust one another Cp. Mallavādī, fol. 96, — *atha yadā tatraiva pradeśe utpadyata ālokas tadā kā vārtety āha yadā tv* (p. 68. 19) *ity ādi. tata* (p. 68. 21) *iti, yataḥ pradīpādir andha-kārādy asamartham janayan nivartayati, tataḥ kāraṇāt. atha bhavatu janya-janaka-bhāvena nivartya-nivartaka-bhāvaḥ, param kim ataḥ siddham? ityāha, ataś cetyādi* (p. 68. 22). *ato janya-janakatvena nivartya-nivartakatva--- yad iti yasmād vā* (?) *yo janakaḥ kṣaṇo na sa viruddha-deśam ākramati, yaś cākramati na sa janako 'samartha-vikārādes, tat kata(ra)yor virodha ity āha, janyety ādi* (p. 69. 1). Cp. also Jayanta's Nyāyamañjarī, p. 60—61 (Vizian.).

3 Lit., 68. 19—69. 1. «But when light is produced just there, in the place of darkness, then, from which moment the birth-moment of the light of the darkness-

opposition, since causal efficiency belongs to moments only[1] and not to artificial integrations of these moments into series? Yes,) but although the serial existences are not realities, their members, the moments, are *the* reality. (69. 2). Therefore the core of the problem[2] is the following fact. There is no incompatibility between two moments, but between (two series consisting) of many (moments). Indeed (the incompatibility of heat and cold does not consist in simple difference, but in the fact that) as long as the moments of heat are present, the moments of cold, although being active (forces), are kept down (in a state of suppression).[3]

(69. 4). Efficient opposition is thus marked off by an antagonism between two phenomena having duration. All atoms (on the other hand, possess mere difference), any pair of them cannot occupy the same place,[4] but there is no efficient opposition between them, because the duration of one atom does not interfere with the duration of another one.

(69. 5). (But if light has the capacity of stopping the duration of darkness why does it not stop it completely[5])? Light is a moving substance, when it occupies a place it stops the duration of the con-

---

place is being produced, just from that (moment) the darkness which is not capable of producing other darkness has been produced. Therefore just the production of an unefficient condition (means) doing it away. And therefore in which moment is the birth-producer, in the third moment from it the opposed is stopped, if it is stopped quickly. (69. 1). And since there is relation of producer to produced the opposition is of two series, not of two moments».

[1] Cp. above notes on pp. 91 and 121. [2] *paramārtha*.

[3] Lit., «The moments of cold, albeit efficient (*pravṛtta*) have the attribute of non efficiency (*nivṛtti-dharman*)».—They are, so to say, kept in the state of *nirvāṇa*, the Hīnayānistic conception of *nirvāṇa* being just a condition when all the forces (*saṃskāra*) of life are suppressed to a condition of non-efficiency, cp. my Nirvāṇa, p. 28 and 197.

[4] Such was evidently one of the current definitions of contradiction—*ayam eva ca virodhārthaḥ, yad ekatra ubhayor anavasthānam*, Jayanta, *op. cit.*, p. 60. In the Vaišeṣika-sūtras, III. 1. 10—12, *virodha* is defined as a variety of *sambandha* and even non-existence or absence was regarded in later Nyāya as residing in its substratum by *višeṣaṇa-višeṣya-bhāva-sambandha* or *svarūpa-sambandha*. Cp. Sigwart, *op cit.* p. I. 159, — «ein Band welches trennt ist ein Unsinn», nevertheless contradiction is a relation, and a relation is a connection (*sambandha*).

[5] Cp. Mallavādī, f. 97. — *atha samīpavarty-andhakāram prati pradīpāder nivartakatve 'bhyupagamyamāne sarvāpavaraka-madhya-sthitāndhakārasya pradīpāder nivṛttiḥ syān, na ca dṛšyata ity āšankyāha.*

flicting phenomena of that place. Although the light of a lamp standing in one corner of a room is contiguous with the dark (parts of the room), it does not remove darkness altogether, because it has not the force to produce further moments of light in those parts of the room which are still occupied by darkness.

(69. 7). In order to indicate that this kind of opposition concerns only serial existences and is brought about by producing a breach in the causes (of a lasting phenomenon), it has been stated (above), that (the opposed facts) have «duration». Duration means lasting for some time without interruption. (Such) a series of moments of cold vanishes when a series of moments of heat appears.

(69. 11). There are some (philosophers) who maintain that the relation of (efficient) opposition is not a reality. To them we answer (as follows). When an effect is produced, we do not really experience causation itself (as a sensible fact). But the existence of a (real) effect presupposes the former existence of a (real) cause, therefore (indirectly) the relation is necessarily a real one.

(69. 13). And similarly when something real has been removed, we can have no direct sense-experience of opposition itself. But when a cold sensation is not followed by any further such sensation, (we know) that this is caused by (real) heat. (Efficient opposition is thus as much a reality as the relation of cause and effect).[1]

(69. 15). The example «just as the sensations of cold and heat» must be interpreted according (to the lines traced) above.

(69. 19). Turning to the second variety of opposition the (author) says,

77. There is also (opposition between two facts) when their own essence consists in mutual exclusion, as between the affirmation and negation (of the same thing).[2]

---

[1] This passage is of extreme importance as an evidence of that Kantian spirit which prevailed in the school of Dignāga and Dharmakīrti. The categories of Causation, Substance, Quality, Negation etc. are logical, mental constructions (*kālpanika, adhyavasita, niścita*) superimposed (*āropita*) upon the absolute reality (*paramārthasat*) of point-instants (*kṣaṇa*) or the extreme particular «things in themselves» (*svalakṣaṇa*) incognizable in discursive thinking (*jñānena prāpayitum aśakya*, cp. N. b. ṭ, p. 12. 19).

[2] Lit., p. 69. 20. «Or by the fact (*-tayā*) of having (*bahuvr.*) an essence which has its stand on mutual exclusion, as existence and non-existence (affirmation and

Mutual exclusion means complete separation (diametrical opposition, without anything intermediate). If two facts have the essence, or possess the nature, consisting in such mutual exclusion, they (are correlative, they) have their stand in mutual contradiction.

(69.22). When something on earth[1] is definitely cognized, (something else is always at the same time) excluded, the essence of the distinctly cognized has its stand on a contrast with the excluded. (70.1). When (a patch) of blue is being definitely cognized, its non-identity[2] (the non-blue) is (*eo ipso*) excluded. If it were not excluded we would have no cognition of blue.[3] Therefore existence and non-existence of a reality (its affirmation and negation, are correlative, their) essence is mutual exclusion,[4] (the one is nothing but the negation of the other).

---

negation)». — It is clear that in these words we have a definition of the Law of Contradiction, so much discussed in European Logic from Aristoteles through Leibnitz, Kant and Sigwart up to the modern logicians. It is therefore of the highest importance to realize the exact meaning of the Indian view. It will be noticed, first of all, that there is no difference between a contradiction of concepts and a contradiction between judgments, the terms *bhāva = vidhi = vastu,* Tib. *yod-pa = sgrub-pa = dños-po* being synonymous, cp. E. Obermiller's Index. of N. b. ṭ. The term «blue» in logic always means the judgment «this is blue», it is a synthesis of «thisness» and «thatness», it is contrasted with the mere reflex of the blue (*pratibhāsa*), an unascertained reflex which has no place in logic. Thus in the quarrel between Aristoteles and Sigwart, *op. cit.* I. 118 ff., on the one side, and Kant on the other, the Indian view will fall in line rather with the first party. The contradiction is virtually between the judgments «this is blue» and «this is not blue».

[1] *iheti jagati*, cp. Mallavādī, f. 97.

[2] *tādrūpya-pracyuti = tādātmya-abhāva* «loss of identity» or «non-identity». The term *tādrūpya-pracyuti-vyavaccheda* or, as below p. 70. 18, *sva-pracyuti* means that if A is A it is excluded that A is non A or, in other words, that the law of Identity is the counterpart of the law of Contradiction. From this point of view the law of Contradiction expresses the impossibility of contradiction between subject aud predicate of the same analytical judgment, this would correspond to the Leibnitz-Kant formulation of the law. We have seen above, p. 132 ff., that Dharmakīrti, avails himself of the term *tādātmya* to designate also a quite different identity, the existential identity which Sigwart, *op. cit.*, I. 111, calls law of Agreement. (Uebereinstimmuug).

[3] i. e., if the judgment «this is not blue» were not excluded we would not have the judgment «this is blue».

[4] Lit., 70. 2—3. «Therefore being and non-being of a real object possess an essence (*rūpa = svarūpa*) having its stand on mutual exclusion».—Since the terms *vastu, vidhi, bhāva* (Tib. *dños-po, sgrub-pa, yod-pa*) are used as synonyms, cp. the note above, the sentence means that reality and unreality, affirmation and negation, existence and non-existence are correlative.

(70. 3). Further a thing[1] which is (merely) «other» than blue cannot avoid being (included in) the negation of blue.[2] When we perceive a yellow or some other colour (that is not blue), we (*eo ipso*) do not perceive any blue. We then imagine its presence (and on the ground of a repelled suggestion) we ascertain its absence (in a negative judgment), because[3] just as the blue excludes its own negation, so also does the yellow and any other colour exclude[4] the negation (of its own self). (70. 5). Thus it is that there is a direct contradiction between affirmation and negation, (between blue and non-blue), and (only an indirect) contradiction between (blue and yellow, i. e., between the affirmations of) any pair of (different) objects,[5] in as much as they unavoidably include the one the negation of the other.

(70. 6). But[6] what is it that we can conceive as non-existent in something else? Something distinct. Not something unlimited, as e. g., the fact of being a point-instant.[7] Since the very essence of all

---

1 Lit., «a form», *rūpam*.

2 Mallavādī, f. 97, introduces this sentence thus, *yady evam nīlam svābhāvam eva pariharati, na nīlābhāvavat-pītādikam ity āha nīletyādi* (p. 70. 3).

3 Lit., p. 70. 3—4. «Because of an ascertainement of non-existence through non-perception of the blue imagined as visible (*dṛśya*) when yellow etc. is perceived». — Thus our author's theory of negation falls in line with his view of Contradiction.

3 *co hetvarthas* (Mallav., f. 97).

4 *abhāvāvyabhicārī* would mean lit. «invariably connected with non-existence» or including non-existence, but of course *svābhāva-abhāva-avyabhicārī* is meant, i. e., including the impossibility of its own non-existence or excluding its own non-existence.

5 *vastunoḥ* would mean lit. «between two realities», but this is not quite accurate, since below, p. 70. 22, it is said *sakale vastuny avastuni ca*.

6 *kasya ceti caḥ punararthe, ibid.*

7 An extreme concrete and particular (*svalakṣaṇa*), or a point-instant (*kṣaṇa*), is «other» in regard of every thing in the whole Universe (*trailokya-vyāvṛtta*), it includes no coordination (*sārūpya*), it is something unlimited (*aniyatākāra*). A patch of blue, as including already coordination with other colours and duration through a series of moments (*santāna*), may be characterized as a mental construction under the law of Contradiction, but if «non-blue» is interpreted as including every thing in the Universe except this blue, as has been sometimes done in Europe (cp. Sigwart, *op. cit.*, I. 184—185), the representation and the judgment will be infinite and senseless. H. Bergson, *op. cit.*, p. 317, characterizes the denied fact as replaced «par une certaine qualité x», and Bosanquet falls in line by maintaining, *op. cit.*, I. 305, that «A is not B may always be taken to = A is x», x is *aniyata-ākāra*. By Dh. the «non-blue» is here characterized not as an x, not as including all the point-instants of the Universe, but as the fact of the ab-

existing objects, (sc. coloured points), patches of blue etc., consists in point-instants, therefore this fact has no limits. If we exclude (all) point -instants, nothing (real will remain) that could be apprehended.

(70.9). If that is so, (viz. if this bare form of existence is unlimited and indefinite, its counterpart) non-existence will be equally unlimited? Why? (Why) indeed should it be unlimited? In so far as this non-existence has the (definite) shape of the repudiation of a real object (whose presence) has been imagined,[1] (it is not unlimited).[2]

(70.10). (And since this is an imagined concrete case of non-existence), therefore[3] when we (in a negative judgment) distinctly

---

sence of a representable blue on a substratum on which it could have been present and on which its presence can be imagined. The term *niyatākāra* means here exactly the reverse of what is designated above by the term *niyata-pratibhāsa*, text p. 8—9, although *ākāra* and *ābhāsa* (=*pratibhāsa*) are quoted as synonyms, p. 15.9—10 and N. Kaṇikā, p. 184.16. *aniyata-pratibhāsa* is meant. We find the term *aniyata* applied to an object not restricted to a present moment in Ab. Košabh. *ad* I. 23. Thus *niyatākāra* correspouds to *aniyata-pratibhāsa*. The term *nīrūpa-abhāva* which is also used as a characteristic of the excluded connterpart of an idea must be interpreted so that it should not conflict with *niyatākāra-abhāva*, cp. below, text 79.10,—*abhāvo hi nīrūpo yādṛšo vikalpena daršitaḥ*, cp. Jayanta, *op. cit.*, p. 52.3.

1 *vastu-rūpa-vivikta-ākāraḥ kalpito 'bhāvaḥ* =*kalpita-anupalambhaḥ* = *dṛšya-anupalabdhiḥ*.

2 Here evidently Dh. hits upon the problem of an infinite or unlimited (unendlich, unbegrenzt, *αοριστον*) judgment. The judgment «this is non-blue» will be according to Aristotle, Kant, Cohen and others infinite. According to Sigwart, *op. cit.*, I. 157, the predicate alone is infinite, but the judgment is affirmative. This is denied by Wundt. The infinite judgment endures the taunts of Lotze, Logik, p. 61—62 and is highly vindicated by Cohen, Logik der r. Erkenntniss, ch. I. According to Sigwart the law of Contradiction obtains only between the pair of judgments «this is blue» aud «this is not blue», the first is affirmative, the second negative. Vis-à-vis this confusion in European logic the position of the Buddhist logicians is quite clear: the judgments «this is not blue» and «this is non-blue» are both negative, they refer to the same fact. As every negation they express not something unlimited, an x (*abhāva-mātram* = *aniyata-ākāram*), but only the repudiation of a thing whose presence has been imagined (*dṛšyānupalabdhi*). As to the problem of an infinite predicate or name, *ονομα αοριστον* it is very much discussed by the Buddhists under the head of their theory of naming according to which all names, when viewed from a certain point of view, are infinite or, as Sigwart, *loco cit.*, puts it, «limitirend», not really positive, but only «limiting» (*apoha*). This theory exhibits some remarkable points of analogy with Cohen's view of the infinite judgment as the foundation of a universal category of thought. Vācaspatimišra's exposition of the Buddhist theory of naming (*apoha*) will be translated in an Appendix.

3 *tata iti yataḥ kalpito 'bhāvas tataḥ kāraṇāt* (Mallav., f. 98).

cognize (the absence of a definite object) on some definite place, we cognize it not in the form of an illimited non-existence, but in a definite form, whether this form has been actually experienced or only imagined. Thus when we deny eternity (or simple duration[1] of existence, or when we deny the presence) of a ghost[2] we should know that (these denied facts) must have a definite (representable) character.

(70.11). This Contradiction is a contradiction (or cancellation) of Identity.[3] If two facts have their stand upon mutual exclusion, (if they are correlative) they cannot be identical. This Contradiction is, therefore, called Essential Contradiction[4] (or law of Contradiction), meaning by it that it serves to establish the essence, or the nature, of (all) entities.[5] By dint of this (law of) Contradiction the essence of (every) reality is established as something «other», (as contrasted with other things).

(70.14). This (visible contrast between all objects of perception) is just the foundation[6] (of our theory of Negation). If, in perceiving something, we *(eo ipso)* deny something else, we deny it after having (for a moment) imagined its visibility. (70.15). Whether, in pointing to a yellow patch, we deny even[7] (its own) non-existence or whether we deny that it is a ghost, we can deny only a representable (concrete form of non-existence). Therefore negation is founded exclusively on a repelled suggestion. (Negation is then decided) after having (for a moment) imagined the visibility (of the denied fact).

(70.17). And if it is so, (it follows that) when an object is being definitely circumscribed[8] (by cognition), a representable form of its negation is being *(eo ipso)* repudiated, (not an illimited, infinite form).

(70.17). (Now, when yellow is denied simultaneously with a perception of a patch of blue colour, does this absent yellow include, in its turn, also a denial of non-yellow? Yes!) The definite form of non-existence which, (because it is definite), itself includes (another) non-existence,

---

1 Cp. above, p. 33.17.

2 Cp. above, p. 33.20.

3 I. e., the law of Contradiction is the counterpart of the law of Identity.

4 Cp. Jayanta, p. 59.10.

5 Here again *vastu* is used for *vastu* and *avastu*, cp. p. 70.22.

6 *ata eveti vibhaktatva - vyavasthāpanād eva dṛśyābhyupagama - pūrvakam niṣedha-svarūpam bhāvayati*, Mallav., f. 98.

7 *abhāvo' pīti na kevalo bhāva ity api-śabdaḥ*, ibid. f. 99.

8 *paricchidyate = pratīyate = jñāyate.*

is also repudiated as an imaginable (concrete form of non-existence). Therefore those objects which are excluded (according to the law of Contradiction, when something is definitely cognized), are excluded together with all the negations which they themselves include. Thus it is that the identity is denied (of all correlative objects, i. e., of all) objects the essence of which consists in mutual exclusion.[1]

(70. 20). This kind of contradiction does not prevent coexistence (in close contiguity). Thus the two kinds of opposition have different functions. By one of them the identity of cold and heat is precluded, by the other their contiguous coexistence. They also have different spheres of application. The (law) of Contradiction (is logical), it regards all objects, whether real or not. But (Incompatibility or) impossibility of coexistence refers to a limited number of real (occurrences) only. Thus they have different functions and different spheres of application. Hence (it cannot be maintained that) they mutually include one another.[2]

---

[1] Lit., p. 70. 17—19. «And the definite form possessing the non-existence of that, it is also excluded as representable; therefore, just as one's own non-existence, the possessors of non-existence are likewise excluded. Thus the possessors of an essence which has its stand on mutual exclusion are all by this denied to be identical».

[2] Thus the Buddhists have established, 1) a general law of Contradiction which has two aspects, a) what can be termed its Identity-aspect according to which every thing and every idea excludes its own non-existence, and b) its Difference aspect according to which every thing and every idea has its own character different from others. 2) Besides this the Buddhists have their law of Otherness (*viruddha-dharma-saṃsarga*), cp above p. 8, note 2, according to which every variation of place, time and quality make the object «another» object, this law reduces everything to point-instants and cancels individual identity altogether. 3) Among the «different» real objects there are some that are antagonistic inasmuch as the duration of the one is repugnant to the duration of the other (*sahānavasthāna*). 4) Among the non-repugnant attributes there are some that are coinherent, belong to the same object, they are declared to be existentially identical, (*tādātmya*), e. g., a tree and an oak. The contrary opposition which is assumed in some European logics between the extreme members of a series, as between white and black, and the contradiction between general and particular judgments is not taken notice of in Buddhist logic. Sigwart, *op. cit.* I. 178, remarks that an almost Babylonian confusion reigns in European logic in the application of the terms contrary, contradicting, opposed, repugnant etc. This makes the task of translating Indian conceptions extreemly difficult. Sigwart himself, *op. cit.*, I. § 22, establishes a difference between a predicate which is absent from the subject and a predicate which is incompatible with it, this difference, to a certain extent, corresponds to the difference established by Dharmakīrti between general opposition (or contradiction) and efficient incompatibility.

§ 13. The uncertain reason (continued).

78. Now, neither of these two kinds of opposition does exist between the faculty of human speech and omniscience.

(71.2). Admitting now that there are two kinds of opposition, (it is clear that) neither of them obtains between the faculty of human speech and omniscience.[1] (It cannot be maintained), indeed, that omniscience (as a phenomenon enduring as long as) all the conditions (producing it) are fulfilled, vanishes as soon as human speech appears. Omniscience is really irrepresentable (transcendental). And (according to what has been explained above)[2] the absence of something irrepresentable[3] can never be asserted[4] (with logical necessity). For this reason (alone) efficient opposition with such a (transcendental entity) is altogether impossible.[5]

(71.4). Neither (does the second variety of opposition, i. e., logical contradiction, obtain between these two facts, for it cannot be maintained that) the essence of omniscience consists in the absence of human speech. In this case logs of wood would be omniscient, because they cannot speak. Nor does the essence of the faculty of human speech consist in the absence of omniscience. For if it were so, logs of wood would possess this faculty, because they are not omniscient. Consequently since there is no opposition (of whatsoever a kind), we cannot deduce a denial of omniscience from an affirmation of the faculty of human speech.

(71.8). Be it so! But if there were altogether no incompatibility between (omniscience and the faculty of speech), they could have been observed as coexistent, just as a jar and a cloth. This coexistence, however, has never been observed. Could we not think, on the ground of such negative experience,[6] that (nevertheless some kind of) incom-

---

1 Lit., p. 71.1. «Further this, albeit double, opposition is impossible for speech and omniscience». *sa ceti caḥ punararthe* (Mallav., f. 99).

2 Ch. II, sūtra 48, cp. text p. 39.18, transl. p. 193 n.

3 Read *adṛśyasya*, cp. Mallavādī, f. 99 — *tata iti* (p. 71.4), *yato adṛśyasya sataḥ sarvajñatvasya nābhāvo 'vasīyate vaktṛtve sati, tataḥ kāraṇāt.*

4 i. e., no negative judgment (*adhyavasāya*) in the real sense of this term is possible, cp. above, notes on pp. 104 ff.

5 Lit., p. 71.4. «Therefore there is no knowledge (*gati* = *rtogs-pa*) of opposition with it». *aneneti sarvajñatvena*, ibid.

6 *adarśanat.*

patibility obtains between them, and then conclude, on the ground of this incompatibility, that (the presence of the one implies) the absence of the other?

This supposition is rejected in the following words.[1]

79. Even when a fact has never been observed, its non-existence cannot be deduced from the presence of another fact, if the latter has not been established (by experience) as incompatible with it.[2]

(71.11). Even if (omniscience) has never been actually observed, (in a speaker), the existence of the[3] (faculty of speech) cannot be (interpreted) as the existence[4] of something incompatible (with omniscience). Although (it is true) that both facts have never been observed together, this does not mean that there is incompatibility between them, because incompatibility is not established through the mere fact that they never have been observed together. On the contrary (it is established) through our conviction[5] that among two (equally) observable facts the presence of the one blots out the presence of the other.[6] (71.13). Therefore although (the gift of omniscience has never been observed

---

1 Lit., p. 71.8—9 «Be it (so)! If opposition does not exist at all, (we) could also observe their coexistence, just as of a jar and a cloth. But from non-observation opposition (would) follow. And from opposition non-existence (would) follow? Having thus emitted a doubt he says». — The introduction of Vinītadeva, p. 117.11—13, is, as usual, more simple: «Let there be no opposition, if it is nevertheless asked whether speech can exclude omniscience also without any opposition (between them), the answer is...» Dh. has complicated the problem by the useless example of jar and cloth. In his comment Mallavādī remarks that for the sake of argument we must imagine that a jar and a cloth are two attributes predicable of the same subject, — *(ghaṭa-)paṭayoḥ samānādhikaraṇyam syād ity api sambhāvane* (f. 100).

2 Lit., p. 71.10. «And from the affirmation of the non opposed (= non incompatible) even if there is non-perception, non-existence does not follow».—The term «affirmation» *vidhi* is here synonymous with «reality» (*vastu*) or «existence» or «presence» or a perceptual judgment, cp. above text, p. 24.16.

3 *ayam iti vaktṛtvādiḥ*, Mallav., f. 100.

4 *vidhi* = *bhāva*.

5 *(adhy-)avasāyāt*, lit. «through a judgment», in the direct meaning of the term judgment, as implying an assertory attitude towards some reality by logical necessity. Vinītadeva says, «we cannot believe» (*yid-ches-par mi nus-so*) in its absence» (p. 117.16).

6 *nivartya-nivartaka-bhāva*.

as coexisting with the gift of human speech), the presence[1] of the latter (cannot be interpreted as) the presence of something incompatible (with omniscience). Consequently the presence of the former[2] does not imply the absence of the latter.

(71. 15). Similarly we cannot deduce the presence of passions (in an individual) from the fact that he (is a human being and) possesses the faculty of speech. Because, if speech were the result of passion, we could then deduce the presence of passions from the presence of the faculty of speech, and *(vice versa)* from the extinction of passions the absence of the faculty of human speech. But human speech is not an effect of psasions.

Why?

80. — because a causal relation between passions and speech has never been established.

(71. 18). Since passions etc. have never been proved (by Induction) to be related to human speech etc. as cause to effect, therefore (speech) is not the effect of passions. Hence we cannot infer the existence of passions from the existence of the faculty of human speech.

(71. 20). Let us admit that human speech is not the outcome of passion, it nevertheless can be a coexisting (phenomenon), and then the passions being extinct, the faculty of speech can likewise disappear, (because) the accompanying phenomenon is absent? To this question we have the following reply,

81. We cannot conclude that the faculty of speech must be absent when something that is not its cause is absent.

(72. 2). If something that is not the cause[3] of speech is absent, if it is something that merely happens to be (sometimes) coexistent with it, then the other fact, viz., the absence of speech, does not follow (with necessity) Therefore it is (quite) possible that the faculty of speech and extinct passions will be found existing together.

82. Thus the faculty of speech is an uncertain mark. Its (necessary) absence in contrary

---

[1] *vidhi* = *sattva* = *yod-pa* = *sgrup-pa*, cp. Tib , p. 162. 13, 162. 15 and 163. 1.

[2] *asmād iti vaktṛtvāt.* Mallav., p. 100.

[3] Read *vākāraṇasya* in 72. 1 and 72.

cases (where there is the gift of omniscience and passions are extinct) is subject to doubt.

(72. 5). Therefore the faculty of human speech is an uncertain reason, since its absence in (all) contrary cases is subject to doubt. (The contrary cases are) omniscience which is the contrary of non-omniscience[1] and extinct passions which is the contrary of efficient passions.

§ 14. The contrary reason.

(72. 7). After having thus explained the fallacies which are incurred when a single aspect of the logical reason (viz., its first aspect or its third aspect) is either wrong or uncertain, the (author) now goes on to explain the fallacies which are incurred when two aspects together are either wrong or uncertain.

83. When the reverse of two aspects of the (adduced) reason is true, (the fallacy is called) a contrary (or inverted) reason.

(72. 10). When two forms of the reason are wrong, the reason is inverted. But the reason has three aspects. In order to specify (the two wrong aspects), it is asked,

84—86. What are the two? Its presence in similar and absence in dissimilar cases. E. g., the attributes of being a product, or of being voluntarily produced, become contrary reasons, if the eternality of the sounds of speech is to be deduced from them.

(72. 14). The two particular aspects are being specified.

(72. 17). They are the presence of the reason (only) in similar cases and its absence from (every) dissimilar case. We must connect (these words with the preceding ones and understand), when the contrary part of both these aspects is true, (the reason becomes an inverted one). The fact of being a product is an analytical reason.[2] The fact of being voluntarily produced (must be understood here) as an infe

---

[1] The syllogism is stated in sūtra III. 71, the major term is non-omniscience the dissimilar or contrary cases are cases of omniscience.

[2] Cp. above, sūtra III, 13, transl. p. 123.

rence from the existence of the effect (to the existence of its[1] cause). (72. 18). The words «produced voluntarily» may indeed (have a double meaning), they may refer to the production (of an object) or to its cognition. Production is identical with the thing produced. But cognition is an effect of the object cognized. The latter is here meant. It is an argument from causation.[2] Both these arguments,[3] (supposing they are adduced to prove the eternity of the sounds of speech), are fallacious and are proving just the contrary.

(72. 22). Why is it so?

87. Being absent in similar and present in dissimilar cases, they prove just the contrary.

(73. 2). It is certain, that neither the attribute of being produced nor the attribute of being voluntarily produced, are present in similar cases, (i. e., in unchanging eternal entities). On the other hand, their presence in contrary cases only (i. e., in impermanent objects) is certain. Therefore the reverse (of what is needed) is established.

(73. 4). Why is it, again, that when the reverse is established the reasons are contrary?

88. They are contrary, because they establish just the inverted (conclusion).

(73. 6). They prove the reverse part of the predicate «eternal», i. e., they prove impermanence. Therefore, they are called contrary.[4]

---

[1] Cp. above, text p. 46. 12, transl. p. 126, where it was quoted as an example of an analytical deduction of coexisting attributes.

[2] Lit., «Therefore an effect-reason».

[3] For his Table of Reasons (*Hetu-cakra*) Dignāga wants two varieties of reasons to the contrary, just as he has also two varieties of correct reasons. For the details of this interesting question we must refer to the impending edition and translation of Dignāga's work. Since he wanted an analytical and a causal deduction to the contrary, he modified the inference *śabdo' nityaḥ, prayatnānantarīyakatvāt* into the form of *śabdo' nityaḥ prayatnānantarīyaka-jñāna-utpādanāt*. *anityatva* is here the same as *sattva*, and existence is posited as the cause of its willful cognition. The exact interpretation of this strange example has given rise to many divergent views among Indian and Tibetan logicians.

[4] The author establishes three varieties of the fallacy of a contrary reason. Two of them contradict an explicitly stated major, viz., 1) sound is eternal, because it is a product, 2) sound is eternal, because it produces knowledge by a conscious effort. Both reasons, the one coexisting with, (analytical), the other succeeding to,

§ 15. A REASON CONTRADICTING AN ADMITTED PRINCIPLE.

(73. 8). If these two arguments, (the one analytical, the other causal), are fallacious contrary arguments, because they prove just the reverse (of what they were supposed to prove), then[1] the major term (of which the reverse is thus being proved, must) be explicitly stated in the syllogism, it cannot remain unexpressed. We have however stated above[2] that the point to be deduced is (sometimes understood) without being explicitly mentioned. Therefore an argument which contradicts a (tacitly) admitted principle will constitute a separate, (third variety of this fallacy). Alluding to this (circumstance the author) says,

89. There is a third variety of a self-contradictory argument? That which contradicts a (tacitly) admitted principle.

(73. 11). Has not a third variety of the contrary reason been given? Two of them prove the contrary of what is expressed. The third is destructive of an admitted principle which is not explicitly stated.

(73. 13), An example is given.

90. This is an example—

(Thesis). The sense of vision and othe senses are serviceable to another one' needs.

(Reason). Because they are composit substances.

(Example). Just as beds, chairs and other requisites.[3]

(73. 15). «The eye and other sense-organs», this is the subject. They participate in the production of a foreign purpose, of another's aim, or they really create such an (object). The words «they are serviceable to another one's needs» — express the consequence. Because

---

(causal), the major term, are similar, since they establish the same inverted conclusion explicitly stated, cp. Mallavādī, f. 101, — *tata iti* (p. 73. 6) *viparyaya-sādhanād īty anayoḥ samānādhikaraṇyam.*

1 Cp. Mallavādī, f. 101, — *uktam ce ti* (p. 73. 8) *cas tathārthe.*

2 Cp. sūtra III. 47, transl. p. 157.

3 Cp. above, sūtra III. 49, transl. p. 159.

«they are composite substances», this is the reason. (73.16). Indeed, the eye and other organs (are physical they) consist of an assemblage of atoms,[1] therefore they are called composite. On the other hand, beds and chairs etc. are requisites, because they are commodities to be enjoyed by man. This is the example which proves the general proposition. (On the authority of) this example the fact of having a composite nature is supposed to be subordinate to the fact of being serviceable to somebody else. Since beds, chairs etc. have a composite nature and they are serviceable to the man who uses them, therefore they are called requisites.

(73.21). How does this reason contradict an admitted principle?

91. It is a contrary reason, because it proves just the reverse of (the principle) admitted by the (disputant), viz., the reverse of an existence for the sake of a simple substance.

(74.2). To exist for the sake of something simple, means to have an aim directed towards something simple. This principle, the existence of the composite for the sake of the simple, is admitted by the disputant who is a Sānkhya philosopher. The opposite of it is existence for the sake of something composite. Since it proves the opposite the reason is self-contradictory. (74.4). (Indeed), the Sānkhya maintains that the Soul exists. The Buddhist asks, why is that? The other then adduces a proof for establishing the existence of the Soul. (74.5). Thus it is that the point to be proved is that the sense-organs are serviceable to the Soul which is a simple substance. But this principle implies just the contrary. Indeed, when one thing helps the other, it is efficient in regard of the latter. And the effect is always something composite either from the start or gradually. Thus it is, therefore, that (the proposition) «the senses are not independent substances» means, that they exist for the sake of some composite substance, (not for the sake of a simple one).

(74.9). This variety of a self-contradictory argument has been established by our Master Dignāga. How is it that you (Dharmakīrti), being the author of a Commentary on his work, have omitted it?

---

[1] E. g., the organ of vision consists in atoms of transparent matter (*rūpa-prasāda*) located on the surface of the eye-ball in concentric circles, cp. my Central Conception, p. 12 ff.

92. Why is it not mentioned here (as a separate variety)? Because it is implied in the two other ones.

(74.14). It might be objected that this contrary reason does not prove the reverse of what is expressed. How is it then, that it is included in the foregoing ones?

93. It does not differ from them, in that it proves the reverse of the consequence.

(74.16). (It is included in the former ones), because such a reason which contradicts an admitted tenet, does not differ from them, inasmuch as it proves the reverse of the predicate which it is intended to establish. Just as the previous two forms prove the reverse, so is also this one. Whether it proves or not the reverse of the words expressing it, does not matter. Therefore it is necessarily included in them.

(74.19). If someone would object that the predicate to be deduced must necessarily be expressed, and ask how it is then that the latter form (of fallacy) is identical with the preceding two in proving the reverse of the predicate, the author answers,

94. There is indeed no material difference between an expressed and an intended predicate.

(74.21). Since there is no disctinction, no difference whatsoever, between what is expressed as a predicate and what it is intended (really to prove), therefore this last form of the contrary reason is implied in the former two. Such is our conclusion.[1]

(74.22). Every section (in a scientific treatise) is devoted to some fact which has been challenged[3] by the opponent. To establish this fact is the aim (of the disputant). Whether this aim is explicitly stated or implicitly understood, makes no difference, because (according to our opinion) there is no necessity of explicitly stating the point which must be established, (when it is understood implicitly).[4] There is thus no (material) difference (between the last and the former two varieties of a contrary argument).[5]

---

1 *upasaṃhāra.*

2 *āpanna.*

3 *jijñāsita.*

4 Cp. above, sūtra III 47.49.

5 Lit., p. 75.1—2. «And what has fallen into the section is objectivized by the wish to prove it. A probandum is admitted whether expressed or not expressed, but not exclusively just the expressed is the probandum. Therefore no difference».

§ 15. Another fallacy of an uncertain reason.

(75.4). What fallacy ensues when one aspect of the reason is wrong and the other is uncertain?

95. When one of the two forms[1] is wrong and the other dubious, the reason becomes uncertain.

(75.4). When the reverse of both these aspects of the reason is ascertained, the reason is contrary. When one of them is wrong and the other dubious, the reason is uncertain.
(75.6). What form has it? The author answers,

96. An example —

> (Thesis). Someone is passionless or someone is omniscient.
>
> (Reason). Because he possesses the faculty of speech.
>
> (Major premise). (Whosoever is a human being possessing the faculty of speech, is omniscient and passionless).

The contraposition is here wrong, the positive concomitance uncertain.

(75.9). «Free from passions» is one predicate, «omniscient» is another one. «Because he possesses the faculty of speech» is the reason. The contraposition gives a wrong judgment. Our own personal experience teaches us that the reason is present in dissimilar cases, that a person who has passions and who is not omniscient is nevertheless not deprived of the faculty of speech.[2] Therefore, the general

---

[1] The second and the third aspect of the logical reason are alone here alluded to, its presence in similar cases only and its absence in every dissimilar case, *alias* the major premise in its direct and its contraposited form. The first aspect of the reason or its presence upon the subject of the conclusion, *alias* the minor premise, is here left out of account, its deficiency has been treated above in sūtras III. 59—67.

[2] Lit., p. 75. 10—11. «Just in the self which has passions and is non-omniscient, in the dissimilar case, the fact of speech is seen».

proposition is wrong when contraposited. In its positive form it is uncertain.[1] Why?

97. Since omniscience and (absolute) absence of passions are unaccessible to experience, it is uncertain whether the gift of speech coexists (with these attributes) or not.

(75. 14). Omniscient beings and beings (absolutely) without passions constitute the similar instances (from witch the generalization is to be drawn by Induction). They are unaccessible (to experience),[2] they are metaphysical.[3] The faculty of speech, on the other hand, is a faculty known from experience. Whether this faculty is present with them,[4] i. e., with transcendental omniscient and passionless beings, or

---

1 The positive form of the major premise will be,

Whosoever possesses the faculty of speech is omniscient.

Its cortraposition will be,

Whosoever is non-omniscient does not possess the faculty of speech.

Although it has been established above, sūtra III. 28 ff., that concomitance and its contraposition are equipollent and always express implicitly the same fact, nevertheless in a fallacious syllogism the one may be wrong and the other only uncertain. Here the contraposition is proved by personal experience to be wrong. This same experience, one would think, is sufficient to explode the positive form of the major premise *modo tollente*, but it is here treated as though it had the form of the proposition «all omniscient beings possess the faculty of speech» and is then rejected on the ground that omniscient beings are beyond our experience. It is a matter of course that no such syllogism has ever been maintained by any school. The Jains have maintained that the founder of their religion was omniscient because he has preached their religion. Other Jains are reported to have considered the knowledge of astronomy as a token of omniscience, cp. below sūtra III. 131. The Buddhists, on the contrary, have maintained that preaching (*upadeśa-praṇayanam*) is a mark of non-omniscience, since conceptual thought (*vikalpa*) and speech can express only limited, imputed knowledge, cp. N. kaṇikā, p. 112—113. It is nevertheless a tenet in Mahāyāna that Buddha, the Absolute Being,is Omniscient, but this cannot be established by logical methods. Here the terms are arranged in every possible combination, from a formal stand point, for didactical purposes, without any reference to real tenets. It has become usual among Tibetan logicians to choose quite senseless examples in order better to impress the rules of formal logic. An inference of the form «all goats are sheep because they are cows» is considered to be well suited to exemplify an inference where all the three aspects of the reason are wrong.

2 *viprakarṣāt.*

3 *atīndriyatvāt.*

4 *tatra.*

not, (will always remain) a problem. Therefore we will never be able to decide whether omniscience can be deduced from the faculty of speech or not. The reason is uncertain.

§ 16. What fallacy ensues when both aspects of the reason are uncertain.

(75. 17). It will now be stated, that when both the aspects of the reason are dubious, the reason is (also) uncertain.

98. When there is doubt regarding these same two forms of the reason, the fallacy is (also) called uncertain.

(75. 19). When the same forms, i. e., the general proposition and its contraposition are dubious, the reason itself is dubious.

99. (Thesis). The living body is endowed with a Soul.

(Reason). Because it possesses breath and other (animal functions).[1]

---

[1] We find the argument inferring the existence in a body of a substautial Soul from the presence in it of animal functions, already adumbrated in Vaiš. S, III. 2. 4. It was included by Dignāga in his Hetu-cakra as a logical fallacy of a conterminous (*asādhāraṇa*) reason Uddyotakara, opposing Dignāga, took it up and vindicated it as a valid reason. He thus was led to establish the theory of logical reasons supported by negative examples alone (*kevala-vyatirekin*). He also interpreted the Method of Residues (*śeṣavad-anumāna*) as an inference from negative instances only and applied to it the term of *avīta-hetu* which in the Sāṅkhya school was the current designation of the Method of Difference (*vaidharmyavat*). N. Kandalī, p. 208, Jayanta, p. 436 and 577, accepts the theory. After some fluctuations it was finally incorporated into the amalgamated system by Gaṅgeśa, cp. Tattvacintāmaṇī, p. II. 582 ff., and has become one of the characteristic features of modern Nyāya, cp. on it H. Jacobi in 99 A. 1919, p. 9 ff. and art. Vīta und Avīta in R. Garbe's Festschrift. As fallacy it occupies in Dignāga's system of possible logical reasons the central position, it is the most barren, so to say, reason, so barren that it almost is no reason at all. The function of a logical reason is to determine the position of a subject between similar and dissimilar cases and thus to connect it through similarity with its logical predicate. But in this case there are no similar and no dissimilar cases at all, the subject being conterminous with the fact adduced as a reason. Since the predicate and its negation contain in themselves all things cognizable, the supposed reason, so far it is a real fact, must be contained somewhere among them, but there is absolutely no possibility to determine whether it is contained thein one part or in the other. The argument, according to Dig-

(76. 2). «Is endowed with a Soul» is the predicate. «The body» is the subject. The «living body» is a qualification. When the body is dead, the existence in it of the Soul is not admitted (by the advocates of a substantial Soul). «Breath» means taking in breath and other attributes of a sentient being, like opening and shutting the eyes etc. The fact that the living body possesses these attributes is the reason.

(76. 5). This fact gives rise to uncertainty (as to whether a Soul really exists in it or not), since it is over-narrow,[1] (i. e., it is found in the living body exclusively, the reason is conterminous with the subject).

Indeed, the presence of the middle term upon the minor[2] produces[3] doubt (as to the presence there of the major term) owing to two causes. (The first is) that a dilemma is produced of which the two horns embrace together every thing existing.[4] (The second is) that we do not know which of these two comprehensive classes includes (the fact representing our logical reason, or middle term). (76. 7). If these two classes did not embrace together every thing existing, (if some evidence from similar and dissimilar cases would have been available), there would be no doubt, because there being other (similar) instances the minor premise[5] (would then be confirmed by evidence drawn from them), one of the horns of the dilemma would be cancelled and the doubt sol-

---

nāga, reduces to the formula «sound is eternal because it is heard», which is as valid as the contrary judgment «sound is non-eternal because it is heard». According to the Naiyāyikas there are contrary cases, viz., inanimate things, jars etc., from which animal functions are excluded, and this proves by mere dissimilarity the existence of a Soul. But according to the Buddhists there is no exclusion from dissimilar cases, if there is no inclusion in the similar ones. The Buddhists deny the existence of the Soul as a separate substance. Mahāyāna denies also the existence of all eternal substances and applies the term existence only to what is causally efficient (*artha-kriyā-kārin*). But the question whether the Soul really exists, or whether eternally unchanging substances really exist, is here left out of account, and the question is taken from the logical side only, which must be binding even to the advocates of the existence of a Soul.

1 *asādhāraṇa*. 2 *pakṣa-dharma*.

3 *hetu* = *kāraṇa* = Tib. *rgyu*.

4 Viz., the living body possessing animal functions, as according to the law of excluded middle, either is or is not the possessor of a Soul. The possessors and non-possessors of a Soul represent together all things existing.

5 The minor premise (*pakṣa-dharma*) here must be imagined as having the form of «this living body possesses those animal functions which by induction from similar cases are proved to be invariably concomitant with the presence of a Soul». Since there are no facts from which this generalization can be drawn, there is no certainty concerning the reason and minor premise.

ved.[1] (76.9). A fact which points to an indefinite position of the subject between two mutually exclusive attributes is a source of doubt. A fact which is not capable of doing even that (is no reason at all), it is a source of ignorance. A fact which points to a definite position of the subject between two (opposed) possibilities is (either a right logical reason), or it may also be just a contrary one.[2]

(76.11). Therefore, if there are only two all-embracing possibilities and no certainty that the subject is present upon only one of them, this will give rise to doubt. (76.12). On the other hand, (if there are instances) proving the presence (of the reason either in the one or in the other class), if we are certain that it is definitely present (only on one side), the reason will be, (as stated above, either a right one) or just the contrary (of a right one, in any case it will not be indefinite). (76.13). But if we are certain that it is indefinite, it then can be either 1) an overwide mark (pervading not alone the subject of the inference, but all the similar and dissimilar instances as well[3]), or 2) a reason whose exclusion from the dissimilar instances is subject to doubt,[4] or

---

1 Lit., «could not point to a subject non-disjoint from one attribute among the two», i. e., could point to a subject disjoint from one of the attributes, and consequently conjoint with the other.

2 E. g., both propositions «Socrates is mortal, because so many persons are known to have died», and «Socrates is *immortal*, because so many persons are known to have died» have that feature in common that the position of the middle term «man», although right in the first case and wrong in the second, is in both cases definite; in the first proposition it is represented as present in similar and, *eo ipso*, absent in dissimilar instances, in the second it is, on the contrary, represented as present in dissimilar cases, i. e., in cases of immortality, and absent, *eo ipso*, in similar cases, or in cases of mortality. It is indispensable to mention both these combinations because in Dignāga's system of logical reasons they fill up definite places assigned to them.

3 Example see above, text p. 66.7, transl. p. 181, «the sounds of speech are eternal entities, because they are cognizable». Cognizable are both the similar eternal entities, like the Cosmic Ether or Space, and the dissimilar impermanent entities, like pots etc. The presence of the reason is equally ascertainable on both sides, hence no conclusion is possible.

4 Example cp. above, text p. 66.10, transl. p. 182, «the sounds of speech are willfully produced, because they are impermanent». There are two classes of objects, they are either willfully produced or produced without the intervention of a personal will. Willfully produced are pots etc., and impermanence is present on them. But existing without the intervention of a personal will are both permanent objects as the Cosmical Ether and impermanent things like lightning etc. The position of the reason is uncertain, since it is only partly excluded from the dissimilar cases.

3) a reason whose positive concomitance is subject to doubt,[1] or 4) a reason whose contraposited concomitance is wrong.[2] (76. 14). (Finally,[3] when there are altogether no instances) pointing to the presence of the reason (either on one side or on the other, when the reason is conterminous with the subject of the inference), the reason will be an over-narrow, (a too peculiar), uncertain reason.[4]

---

1 Example see text p. 66. 8, transl. p. 182, «the sounds of speech are produced *without* the intervention of a personal will, because they are impermanent». The two mutually exclusive classes are the same as in the preceding example, but the position of the similar and dissimilar instances, from which the generalization is drawn, is reversed. The similar instances, the objects not willfully produced, are both permanent and impermanent. This alone would not invalidate the concomitance since the positive concomitance must be supported not by all similar cases, but only by some of them (cp. sūtra II. 6—7); provided there is no evidence to the contrary, it will be right. But in the present case the concomitance will nevertheless be uncertain, because the contraposition will give a wrong judgment. The dissimilar instances, the objects willfully produced are all impermanent. This fallacy occupies the third place in Dignāga's system.

2 Example see text p. 66. 12, transl. p. 183, «the sounds of speech are eternal entities, because they are penetrable». All objects are either eternally unchanging or perpetually changing (momentary, cp. p. 121 n.). Penetrability is represented on both sides, but only partly. The Cosmic Ether is imagined as conterminous with Space, eternal and penetrable. Atoms are assumed by the Vaiśeṣika school as eternal and impenetrable. It is not required that all penetrable (*amūrta*) objects should be eternal in order to establish the general proposition «whatsoever is penetrable is eternal». The predicate can be greater in extension than the subject. But the canons of inference (cp. sūtra II. 7) require that the reason should be totally absent in dissimilar cases, i. e., in the present instance, that the impermanent objects should be all of them penetrable, and this is not the case, because jars etc. are impermanent and impenetrable. Since the contraposition does not hold good (*asiddha*), the fallacy is called fallacy of unwarranted contraposition. It is the ninth fallacy of Dignāga's system. The logical value of this example has given rise to a great deal of controversy among the Tibetan logicians.

3 This fallacy occupies the central position in Dignāga's systematic table of possible reasons. There are neither similar nor dissimilar cases. The major premise cannot be established by Induction. Above and beneath it are the two right reasons, whose position regarding the similar and dissimilar cases is definite and correct. At the right and at the left are the two contrary reasons whose position is as definite, but the reverse of correct. In the four corners are situated the indefinite uncertain reasons. We thus have a square table with a centre and three points on every side making together 9 items (if the corner points are not reckoned double). This remarkable achievement of Dignāga will be fully elucidated by M-r A. Vostrikoff in his forthcoming edition and translation of Dignāga's Hetucakra-samarthana.

4 Lit., p. 76. 5—15. «This non-shared (by anything else fact) will be established as a cause (*hetu* = *rgyu*) of doubt. And the attribute of the subject (*pakṣa*-

(76.15). Therefore (the author now proceeds) to indicate the two causes why an attribute conterminous (with the subject of the inference) can produce no certainty.

100. Because except the class of entities possessing a Soul, and the class not possessing it, there is no (third) group where animal functions are found.

(76.18). «Possessing a Soul» is an entity wherein the Soul exists. «Non-possessing it» is that wherein it is absent. There is no group, different from them, wherein breath etc. should be present as a real attribute. Therefore it gives rise to uncertainty.

(76.21). Why is it that there is no other group?

101. Because presence and absence of the Soul embrace between them every existing object.

(77.2). Presence of the Soul is its existence. It is contrasted with non-existence.[1] Both embrace, i. e., include, every existing reality. Where Soul exists, we have an entity possessing a Soul. All other

---

dharma) is a cause (*hetu* = *rgyu*) of doubt from two causes (*kāraṇa* = *rgyu*). Because which two forms are the object of doubt in them every existing object is included, and because there is no certainty of (its) presence even in one of these two pervasive forms. There is no doubt regarding those two forms in which two forms all existing objects are not included. Because when another form occurs, the attribute of the subject will not be capable of showing the subject as non-disjoined from one attribute among the two, therefore it will not be a cause (*hetu* = *rgyu*) of doubt. (70. 9) The thing showing an indefinite existence between two attributes is a cause (*hetu* = *rgyu*) of doubt. But a thing incapable of showing even an indefinite existence among two attributes is a cause (*hetu* = *rgyu*) of non-cognition. A reason (*hetu* = *gtan-thsigs*) showing a definite position is eventually (*vā*) contrary. (76. 11). Therefore by which two (possibilities) every thing existing is included, for them there is a cause (*hetu* = *rgyu*) of doubt, if there is no certainty of the presence also in one among them. But if there is certainty of presence, if there is certainty of definite (-exclusive) presence in one place, the reason (*hetu* = *gtan-thsigs*) can eventually be a contrary one. But if there is certainty of non-exclusive (*aniyata*) existence, it will be generally uncertain or uncertain as to the exclusion from dissimilar cases or doubtfully concomitant or wrong as to exclusion. But if there will be uncertainty as to its presence even in one place, it will be a non-shared uncertain (reason)». Note the double translation in Tibetan of **hetu** either by *rgyu* = *kāraṇa*, or by *gtan-thsigs* = *linga.*

[1] Lit., p. 77. 2. «The presence of the Soul is its real existence, its exclusion is its non-existence».

entities do not possess it. There is no other (third) group. This circumstance is (one of the) causes producing uncertainty.

(77.5). After having stated that the two groups include everything existing, the second (cause of uncertainty) is next given.

102. Neither can the presence (of the reason) in one of these (classes) be apprehended with certainty.

(77.7). There is no certainty of the presence, or of the real existence, (of the reason) in one of these groups, either in the one which (is supposed) to possess a Soul or in the one which (is supposed) not to possess it. Neither is there some other place, besides these two groups, where the presence of animal functions could be found as a real attribute.

(77.8). Therefore only so much is known that (animal functions) are an appurtenance of some entities which are included (somewhere) among just these two groups. But there is no certainty about that particular group in which alone they are really present. That is the meaning. Therefore (the author) says, — (the reason is uncertain).

103. Since neither in the entities supposed to possess a Soul, nor in the entities known not to possess it, is the presence of animal functions certain.[1]

(77.12). There are no real objects in which either the presence or the absence of an (eternal) Soul would be (empirically) ascertainable and universally accepted, and in which (at the same time) the absence of animal functions would be an established fact. Therefore the reason is uncertain, since its concomitance is not ascertained. These two causes make an attribute conterminous (with the subject) an uncertain reason. They have been thus indicated.

(77.15). Every logical reason being present upon the subject of the conclusion[2] (constitutes the minor premise, but it) becomes uncer-

---

[1] In sūtra III. 103 read *asiddhes* instead of *asiddhiḥ*, the following words *tābhyām na vyatiricyate* must be transferred to the end of the next sūtra, where likewise *asiddheḥ* is to be read instead of *asiddhiḥ*.

[2] The minor premise (*pakṣa-dharma*) would have been «the living body possesses animal functions». But the author introduces it in the form of a part of the conclusion, saying in sūtra III. 104 «*therefore* the breath etc. being present in the living body» etc. The term *pakṣa-dharma* is often used as a synonym of *hetu*, Dandar Lha-ramba calls the *Hetu-cakra Phyogs-chos-khor-lo* = *pakṣa-dharma-cakra*.

tain when it is either overwide (trespassing into the sphere of dissimilar instances, whether embracing all of them or only a part), or when it is over-narrow (conterminous with the subject). The (author) now introduces the minor premise, giving it the form as though it were a conclusion.

104. Therefore, since it is not proved that animal functions inherent in a living body exclude it either from the class of all objects possessing a Soul or from all objects not possessing any, (it is impossible to point out that one among) these two groups in which they are necessarily absent.

(77.19). The words «animal functions inherent in a living body» point to the minor premise. Since there is no certainty of the absence of the mark in neither of both groups, therefore it does not exclude (the living body, neither out of the one group, nor out of the other). If it were a real attribute necessarily present in one of the two all-embracing groups, it (*eo ipso*) would have been absent in the other. Therefore it is said, «since it is not established that (animal functions in a living body) exlude it either from all entities having a Soul or from all entities not having any Soul etc....». Animal functions are absent in some objects only, e. g., in jars etc. So much alone is certain. But we do not know precisely whether it is absent in all objects having or in all objects not having a Soul. We do not know that it is necessarily absent in the whole of the one or (in the whole) of the other group. It cannot, therefore, be necessarily excluded out of neither of them.

(78.5). But then perhaps the positive concomitance of animal functions with one of the two groups is certain?

105—106. Neither is there any positive concomitance, because (the necessary presence of the reason) in one of the groups is also not established.

(78.7). No! animal functions are not necessarily concomitant with either of the (two groups), neither with the group of those having a Soul, nor with the group of those who have none. Why is that? (78.10). Because its presence in one of the two groups, either in that where there is a Soul, or in that where there is no Soul, is not established. That animal functions are a real attribute to be found somewhere among the two groups, this is certain. But it is not certain that they necessarily coexist with a Soul, or that they necessarily are incompatible with Soul. How can then their concomitance (with the Soul) be ascertained?

(78.13). Now, the Buddhist denies the existence of Soul altogether. For him there can be no question whether animal functions really exist in those beings which (are supposed) to possess a Soul. On the contrary, for him there is only certainty that we can speak neither of the presence nor of the absence of such functions in them. (Does that mean that he can deny both their presence and their absence with the non-existing Soul?)[1] This suggestion is answered (in the following passage),

107—108. Whether the Soul exists or whether it does not exist, we cannot in any case deny at once both the presence and the absence of animal functions (in soulless beings), because the denial of the one implies the affirmation of the other.[2]

(78.17). If there are real beings endowed with a Soul, we can impossibly be (simultaneously) certain of both the presence and absence in them of animal functions. (Nor is the contrary possible). If there are no (real beings) endowed with a Soul, we neither can deny (at once) the presence and the absence (in them of those functions).[3] Why is that? (78.21). Because just the denial[4] of the one — whe-

---

[1] Lit., p. 78.13—15. «And is it not that for the opponent there is nothing possessing a Soul? Therefore there is neither concomitance nor exclusion of this reason in the possessor of a Soul. Thus there is certainty of the non-existence of both concomitance and exclusion in the (non-existing) possessor of a Soul, but not doubt of its real existence. Having put this question he says». — *vyatireka* is here used not in the sense of contraposition, but of exclusion or absence, = *abhāva*, cp. text p. 79. 7. From the fact that there are no Souls altogether, the disputant draws a *deductio ad absurdum*, that animal functions whether present or absent will always be concomitant with the absence of a Soul. *sātmaka* means here the *supposed* possessor of a Soul.

[2] Lit., p. 78, sūtras 107—108. «And there is no certainty of non-existence of both concomitance and exclusion of it from the possessor of a Soul and from the non-possessor of a Soul, because the certainty of the non-existence of the one is invariably concomitant with the existence of the other».

[3] Lit., p. 78.18. «And the ablative case «from the possessor of a Soul, from the non-possessor of a Soul» must be regarded as depending on the word exclusion».

[4] *abhāva-niścaya.*

ther of the presence or of the absence — is inseparable from the affirmation[1] of the other, of the second (alternative). (Denial) necessarily implies affirmation.

(79. 1). Such is the condition. For this reason (the Buddhist's Soul-denial is here irrelevant). Since one negative certainty implies the (correlative) positive certainty, therefore both alternatives cannot be simultaneously true.

(79. 3). Why is it again that the denial of one (alternative) necessarily implies the affirmation of the other?

This question is answered —

109. The necessary presence and the necessary absence[2] (of animal functions wheresoever a Soul is absent), (these two facts) are exclusive of one another. Since neither of them can be established, (the adduced reason for proving the existence of a Soul) is uncertain, (it proves nothing).

(79. 6). The mutual exclusion of two facts means that the absence (of the one is equivalent to the presence of the other). This alone is the essence[3] of both (the facts in question). This their relation[4] constitutes their essence.[4] For this reason (the argument is uncertain).

(79. 7). The positive and the inverted connection (of the middle term are here nothing but its) presence and absence. Presence and absence (of the same thing) are by their essence mutually exclusive. (According to the Law of Contradiction) when something is delimited by its difference from something else, it takes its stand upon this contrast.[5] (79. 9). Now, presence can be defined as an absence of its own absence, (as a double negation). Thus the presence of something takes its stand upon an exclusion of its own negation. (79. 10). Negation (or non-existence) is again, (according to our theory of Negation[6]) the absence of a (definite) form[7] of it, (a form representable), con-

[1] *bhāva-niścaya.*

[2] *anvaya-vyatireka = bhāva-abhāva.*

[3] *rūpa = svarūpa.*

[4] *bhāva.*

[5] Cp. above, text p. 69. 22—70. 3, transl. p. 193.

[6] Cp. above, cp. II, sūtra 26 ff.

[7] *nirūpa-abāava*, lit. formless or illimited negation, but here the negation of a definite form must be understood, otherwise the passage would stand in glaring

structed by imagination. By contrasting (a given content) with what represents its own negation, we cognize that content as a (definite) image.

(79. 11). If that is so, the denial of the presence (of animal functions in beings having no Soul) is equivalent to their absence, and the denial of their absence is equivalent to their presence. Therefore, if we are certain that they are not present, we *(eo ipso)* are certain that they are absent, and if we are certain that they are not absent, we *(eo ipso)* are certain that they are present. (The presence and absence of animal functions in things characterized by the absence of a Soul cannot simultaneously be true).

(79. 13). Therefore, supposing (we adhere to the Buddhist view and maintain) that the existence of an (eternal) Soul is a phantom,[1] (because no creature) in reality possesses it, nevertheless this does not mean that we can, with apodictic certainty, deny both the presence and the absence of animal functions in these (soulless realities on the score that every thing is soulless). (According to the Law of Contradiction[2]) one real thing cannot simultaneously be present and absent in another one, and therefore we cannot with apodictic certainty deny them both at once, (we can only fluctuate between them).

(79. 15). Nor do we here propose to prove to our opponents[3] (the Naiyāyikas) that the (eternal) Soul does not exist at all and that real beings do not possess it, but (we propose to prove that it is incum-

---

contradiction to p. 70. 9, where a *niyata-ākāra kalpita abhāva* is layed stress on. The meaning is *rūpam paricchidyate nīrūpatām (tasya eva rūpasya abhāvam) vyavacchidya.* Such also seems to be the intention of the Tib. translators, cp. p. 180. 9—11. Jayanta speaks, p. 52. 3, of *nīrūpa-abhāva* as non-existence possessing no perceptible colour. Mallavādī, fol. 105—106, explains — *atha bhavatu yasya vyavacchedena yat paricchidyate tat tat-parihāreṇa vyavasthitam, param nābhāva-vyavacchedena bhāvasya paricchedaḥ syād ity āśankyāha svābhāvetyādi* (79. 9)... *athābhāvasya niyata-svarūpa-abhāve katham tad-vyavacchedena bhāva-vyavasthitiḥ syād ity āśankyāha (a)bhāvo hītyādi,* (79. 10). *atha bhavatu nīrūpo (a)bhāvaḥ, param na nīrūpam vyavacchi(dya rūpam ākaravat paricchidyata iti).* Kamalaśīla, p. 934. 18, uses the term *nīrūpa* in connection with *sāmānya* in the sense of *niḥsvabhāva = śūnya.*

[1] *avastu.*

[2] Cp. above, text p. 70. 12 ff.

[3] The argument here discussed is advanced by the Naiyāyika, cp. N. vārt. and Tātp. ad Nyāya-sūtra, I. 35, the opponent, *prativādin,* is the Buddhist, but Soullessness is a characteristic tenet of Buddhists against which the Naiyāyikas usually protest, both parties are mutually the opponents of one another.

bent upon them to admit that) logically[1] (the existence of a Soul remains a problem). (So far the adduced reason can prove nothing), both its presence (in living bodies) and its absence (in lifeless things) are not proved. (79.17). Just because there are no facts which could (by the methods of Agreement and Difference) establish beyond the possibilitq of doubt the presence of an (eternal) Soul (on the one side) and its absence (on the other), just therefore (the existence of animal functions can decide nothing), neither can it prove the presence nor the absence (of a Soul). (79.18). But if we had facts establishing beyond doubt the impossibility of one horn of the dilemma, these very facts would *(eo ipso)* establish the necessity of the other horn, and there could be no doubt at all (regarding the question where animal functions) are present and where they are absent. (79.20). But since this is not the case, just therefore we fluctuate between an affirmation and a denial. Doubt produces an uncertain reason. That is what (the author) has expressed (in the aphorism).[2]

---

1 *pramāṇa* here in the sense of evidence, of facts from which a valid conclusion is possible.

2 Lit., p. 79. 4—21. «Because concomitance and contraposition (or presence and absence) have the essence of mutual exclusion, just therefore, because of doubt regarding concomitance and contraposition, it is uncertain. (79. 6). Mutual exclusion is (mutual) non-existence. Just this is the essence of them both. Their relation (*bhāva*) is their essence. For this reason (the terms) concomitance and contraposition are (here used in the sence of) existence and non-existence. And existence and non-existence have both the essence of mutual exclusion. By whose exclusion what is defined, by its opposition to that is it established. Existence is defined by the exclusion of its own non-existence. Therefore existence is settled through an exclusion of its own non-existence. (79. 10). Non-existence, indeed, is formless in so far it is shown by imagination (sc. it is the absence of an imagined form). By excluding formlessness a form possessing an image is defined. If this is so, the non-existence of concomitance (presence) is contraposition (absence), and the non-existence of contraposition (absence) is concomitance (presence). Therefore, when the non-existence of concomitance (presence) is ascertained, contraposition (absence) is being ascertained, and when the non-existence of contraposition (absence) is ascertained, concomitance (presence) is being ascertained. (79. 13). Therefore if, for sure, the possessor of a Soul is no realitv and the non-possessor of a Soul is reality, nevertheless there is no certainty of the non-existence in them of both the presence and absence of breath etc., because, since the existence and non-existence at once of one thing in one thing is contradiction, the certainty of the non-existence of both is impossible. (79. 15). And the two things having and not having a Soul are not real and unreal in accordance with the opponent (the Buddhist), but in accordance with evidence, thus they are both uncertain. Therefore there is doubt of existence and non-existence concerning the possession of breath etc. in them both. Just because

(79.22). (The author once more states in what sense (the argument) is problematic.

110. Neither can we affirm (on such grounds) the necessary existence of a Soul, nor can we deny it.[1]

(80.1). Neither can we affirm (the necessary existence of a Soul on such grounds) nor can we deny it. (80.2). Because both the direct concomitance (of animal functions with a Soul) and its contraposition are uncertain, we cannot affirm neither the major term (the existence of the Soul) nor the other, the opposite fact, (its non-existence). When both the presence of the reason in similar cases and its absence in (every) contrary case is unascertainable, neither the predicate nor the reverse of it can be established. Nor is there any other (intermediate) alternative between these two. Entities either have a Soul or they have none. (80.4). We (conclude) therefore that whether in the object of the inference, in the living body, a Soul exists or not, cannot be ascertained through (the mark of) animal functions. This mark is uncertain.[2]

---

there is neither somewhere certainty of existence nor certainty of non-existence of the direct and contraposed concomitance, just therefore there is doubt of direct and contraposed concomitance (of presence and absence). (79.18). But if, albeit somewhere, there would be certainty of the non-existence of one among the positive and contraposed concomitances (of presence and absence), just this would be the certainty of the existence of the second. Thus there would be no doubt at all of the positive and contraposed concomitances. (79.20). But since there nowhere is certainty concerning existence or non-existence, just therefore there is doubt of positive and contraposed concomitance (of presence and absence). And from doubt (the reason) is uncertain, thus he says». — *anvaya* and *vyatireka* at first mean concomitance and its contraposition, cp. text p. 41. 3. Both are characterized as equipollent, cp. text p. 43. 1, as mutually implying one another, cp. text p. 52. 20. Here they are used in the sense of presence and absence, *bhāvābhāvau*, p. 79. 7, and characterized as exclusive of one another. Moreover *vyatireka* is also used in the sense of *vaidharmya* «method of Difference», cp. text 51. 5, hence *anvaya* also means the method of Agreement.

[1] Lit., p. 80. 1. «Because from this there is no certainty of the major term and of its counter part».

[2] The concluding part of the argument, beginning with p. 78. 13, is apparently directed against an opponent who had set forth an argument like the following. If the Buddhists admit the existence in some cases of animal functions and deny the existence of Souls altogether, then for them both the presence and the absence of animal functions will be concomitant with the absence of a Soul, because Soul is

(80. 6). After having explained the fallacies which are incurred when the three aspects of the logical mark are either wrong or uncertain, the author draws the conclusion,

111. Thus there are three kinds of fallacies, the Unreal, the Contrary and the Uncertain. They are respectively produced when either one aspect of the mark singly, or any pair of them, are either unreal or uncertain.

(80. 9). «Thus» means in the manner above explained. When one single aspect of them is unreal or uncertain, or when each pair of them is unreal or uncertain, we then have the fallacies of Unreal, Contrary or Uncertain reasons. «Respectively» means that the fallacy is determined by that case of unreality or of doubt which agrees with the corresponding unreality or uncertainty (of the aspects of the mark). «Respectively» means that to each object on one part there is a corresponding object (on the other).

§ 17. The Counterbalanced Reason.

112—113. One more (variety) of an uncertain reason has been established, viz., the (Counterbalanced) reason which falls in line with its own contradiction, (which is self-contradictory).—Why is it not mentioned here? Because it cannot occur in the process of (natural) ratiocination.

(80. 14). But did not our Master (Dignāga) establish one more (variety) of an uncertain logical reason, viz., (the counter-balanced reason), the reason which falls in line with its own contradiction? It falls in line with what contradicts a (principle) established on other grounds, it is contradictory. (80. 15). Or else, it is a contrary reason, because it proves the reverse of a fact established on other

---

absent everywhere. The Buddhist negation of a Soul was mentioned above, ch. III. 67, in connection with the fallacy of unreal (*assidha*) reason. There it was assumed that the minor term and minor premise in a syllogism must be something admitted as real by both parties, by the disputant and the opponent. But here the fallacies of concomitance are alone considered and the stand-point is one of formal logic, all metaphysical judgments are considered as problematic, the Buddhist denial of a Soul is not excluded.

grounds, and (in the same time) it is a right reason, since it is concomitant with its own (special) consequence. Thus it is contrary and right (at the same time).

(80.17). Quite true! Our Master has established (this variety). But I have omitted it here. Why? Because, (a reason simultaneously right and wrong), cannot occur in the process of (natural) ratioicnation.[1]

(80.21) The proper domain of inference[2] is the threefold logical tie, (sc. the necessary presence of the reason upon the subject of the conclusion, its necessary presence in similar and its absolute absence in all dissimilar cases). (This threefold logical connection), as far as it is established by positive facts,[3] (constitutes the domain of inference proper). It produces inference, therefore we call it the domain of inference. An inference (or a conclusion) is produced from such a threefold connection when proved by positive facts. Therefore this alone is the (real) domain of inference. Since (real) inference (alone) is our subject-matter, we cannot deal with a reason which is (at once) right and wrong.[4]

(81.1). Indeed, when we have proposed to deal with the threefold logical connection as far as it is established on real facts, we can introduce only such logical fallacies which are (albeit partly) established ou real facts.[5] But a (double) reason which is right and contra-

---

[1] The *viruddhāvyabhicāri* fallacy of Dignāga has survived in the Nyāya-Vaiśeṣika united system under the name of *sat-pratipakṣa*, and a corresponding aspect of the valid reason, the *asat-pratipakṣa* aspect, has been invented, in order to save the right proportion between the number of the aspects of a valid reason and the corresponding number of fallacies. Praśastapāda, p. 239. 2—3, includes it in the category called by him *anadhyavasita* reason. He admits that conflicting arguments, such as pointed out by Dignāga, occur in science (*śāstra*), but he objects to the name of a doubtful reason for it. A doubt is produced when we are not capable to decide between two aspects of the same thing, and not when an argument is counterbalanced by another one, cp. N. Kandalī, p. 241. 13 ff. It is clear that Praśastapāda's words are a reply to Dignāga's theory. Bodas thinks, Tarka-Samgraha p. 307 (Bombay, 1918), that the *satpratipakṣa* fallacy is foreshadowed by Gotama's *prakaraṇa-sama*, N. S., I. 2. 7, but this is doubtful.

[2] It is clear that this is also the only domain of logic in general; logic, inference, three-aspected reason, invariable concomitance, necessary connection, all these expressions by their implications cover the same ground.

[3] *pramāṇa-siddha*.

[4] Lit., «There is no possibility of contrary and non-discrepant».

[5] A fallacy like the one mentioned in ch. III. 60 cannot be maintained to repose, albeit partly, on positive facts. The theory of syllogism is better illustrated by fal-

dictory is not something established on real facts. Therefore, since it is impossible, it is omitted (in our system). (81.4). Why should it be impossible?

114. A (real) contradiction is indeed impossible (in the domain of the three varieties of logical dependence), as established by us, in the cases of necessary Succession, of neccessary Coexistence and of Negation.[1]

(81.7). Indeed, a (real) contradiction is an impossibility. We have already explained what we understand under a causal and under an analytical logical connection. Causality consists in the (necessary) dependence of everything upon its cause. An analytical reason consists in its being contained under the fact which is deduced from it. In order that there should be a real contradiction the effect must exist altogether without its own cause, and a property must exist somewhere beyond the concept under which it is contained.[2] (81.10). And negation should then also be something different from what has been established (by us). Negation has been established as a repelled suggestion of presence. Such negation is also unthinkable without the fact of the absence of some real object (on a definite spot). It also affords no opportunity for a (real) contradiction.

---

lacies, and the Indian and Tibetan logicians largely use quite impossible combinations, because they throw a strong light upon the canons of syllogism. What the author here wishes to express is not that contradiction cannot partly repose on facts, as every fallacy does, but that, although in our natural process of every day thinking we can draw fallacious conclusions, we cannot at once draw two diametrically opposed conclusions. This is only possible when the constructors of scientific theories depart a long way from the safe ground of realities and dwell in the sphere of metaphysics. This and the adjoining passages are very remarkable as a clear indication of the critical tendencies of Dharmakīrti's philosophy.

[1] Lit., p. 81. 5—6. «Because there is no possibility of contradiction of Effect and Own-existence whose essence has been indicated, and of Non-perception».—The author wishes to emphasize that all our thinking, or else all synthesis of thinking, consists either in the affirmation of Succession or of Coinherent Attributes, or in the affirmation of Absence of something on a bare place. There is no other general principle than these three, they control the entire domain of thought.

[2] Lit., p. 81. 9—10, «What is effect and what is own-essence, how could it exist quite forsaking its own cause and (its own) pervader, through what could it become contradictory?».

(81. 12). All right! But perhaps there is some other possible connection (between realities)?

115. There is no other inseparable connection.

(81. 14). There is no other inseparable connection than the three (above mentioned). Whatsoever logical connection exists is strictly included in these three.

(81. 15). But then, where has our Master Dignāga exposed the fallacy (of a counterbalanced reason)?

(Since two contradicting, mutually repugnant arguments cannot appear at once in the natural run of thought) —

116. Therefore Dignāga has mentioned it as a mistaken argument establishing two contradicting facts, such arguments occurring in dogmatic systems where inference concerns metaphysical problems and is founded on dogmatic (premises) and not upon an (unbiassed) observation of real facts.[1]

(81. 18). The self-contradictory reason has been established with reference to arguments founded on (blindly accepted) dogmatic theories, because it never occurs in an argument which is founded on the weight of real facts.

(81. 19). When an inference (and) the logical construction[2] on which it is founded are dogmatically believed,[3] the foundation of the argument is dogma.

(81. 19). But are dogmatical constructions[4] not also established upon some real facts?

The answer is that they are not naturally evolved out of an (unprejudiced consideration of real facts, but) they are produced under the influence of phantastical ideas.[5]

---

1 Lit., p. 81. 16—17. «Therefore the contradicting-nondiscrepant proof-fallacy has been established with reference to inference founded on dogma, not starting from observing the force of real facts in pondering over such objects».

2 *linga-trairūpyam*

3 *āgama-siddham.*

4 *trairūpyam.*

5 *avastu-darśana.*

(81.20). The contemplation of non-realities is pure imagination. Its force is its influence. When the logical foundation[1] of an inference is influenced by (such phantoms) it is not established on real facts, but on pure imagination, and imagination is not reality.[2]

(82.1). Now, what is the proper place of such dogmatic arguments?

There are subjects[3] which are the proper place for such arguments, viz., metaphysical[4] problems, problems unaccessible neither to direct observation nor to (correct) ratiocination, as, for instance, the problem of the reality of the Universals. When the investigation of these problems is tackled, dogmatical argumentation flourishes.[5] Our Master Dignāga has mentioned the counterbalanced argument (as a special fallacy) in connection with such (metaphysical problems only).

(82.5). Why again does such a fallacy occur in dogmatic argumentation only?

117. It (often) happens that promotors of systems are mistaken and ascribe (to entities) such attributes as are incompatible with their nature.[6]

(82.7). Promotors of systems ascribe, or include into entities such attributes that are incompatible with them, such as are contrary to reality. When this happens the counterbalanced reason becomes possible. This happens by mistake, through confusion. Indeed, there are such confused scientists who never stop in imagining unwarranted facts.[7]

(82.10). But if scientifical authorities can be mistaken, how can we believe ordinary men? He says —

118. When the argument is founded on the properly observed real condition of real things,

---

1 *trairūpyam.*

2 Lit., p. 81.20—82.1. «The contemplation of a non-real object is mere construction, its force is its efficiency, from it starting, not from evidence, having its stand on mere construction, the three-aspectedness of inference founded on dogma, not on evidence. — The Tib. = *āgama-siddha-trairūpya-anumānasya aprāmāṇyāt.*

3 *artha.*

4 *atīndriya.*

5 *sam-bhavati.*

6 Read *svabhāvasya* in p. 82.6.

7 Lit., p. 81.8—9. «Indeed confused makers of science (or scientific works) superimpose such and such unexisting nature».

when either a case of (necessary) Succession or of (necessary) Coexistence or of Absence[1] is thus established, there is no room for contradiction.

(82.12). (Facts) are established as logical reasons not by any (arbitrary) arrangement,[2] but by their real condition. Therefore when the facts of (necessary) Coexistence, of (necessary) Succession and of Absence are established as the real condition of real things, there is no room for (contradiction). (82.13). An established fact is an ultimately real[3] fact. Properly established is a fact established without trespassing (into the domain of fancy). Properly established real conditions of real facts are the facts which have been thus established. Such facts are not founded on imagination,[2] but they stand as stands reality (itself). Therefore they do not afford any room for illusion which could alone give an opportunity to two mutually exclusive reasons.

(82.17). Follows an example of two mutually exclusive reasonings.

119. An example of this fallacy are (the following two contradictory deductions. The first is),

> (Major premise). A (thing) which is simultaneously inherent[4] in different objects, wheresoever they be situated, (must be) ubiquitous.
>
> (Example). Just as the Cosmical Ether.
>
> (Minor premise). A Universal is simultaneously inherent in different objects which are to be found everywhere.
>
> (Conclusion). (Hence a Universal must be ubiquitous).[5]

(82.21). «An (attribute) which is simultaneously (and obviously) present in a number of objects in which it inheres, wheresoever they

---

1 *ātma-kārya-anupalambheṣu*. Lit., «in self, in effect, in non-perception».

2 *kalpanā*.

3 Ultimately real (*paramārtha-sat*) is here evidently not in the strict sense of a «thing in itself», but of something having an ultimately real substratum, cp. above trsl. p. 34, note 6.

4 *abhi-sambadhyante*= *samaveti*.

5 Lit., p. 82. 18—20. «An example for this. What is simultaneously intimately (*abhi-*) connected with those its own intimate containers which are resident in all places, that is ubiquitous, just as Ether. Intimately simultaneously connected with its own intimate containers which are resident in all places is a Universal».

be situated» — this makes up for the subject (of the general proposition). «Is ubiquitous» — is its predicate. It expresses that the fact of such simultaneous presence is invariably concomitant with omnipresence, and therefore, subaltern to the latter.

(83. 2). Now, it has been established by the great sage Kaṇāda that a Universal is motionless, is amenable to sense-perception and possesses unity. It simultaneously resides in every object with which it is connected by inherence. A pupil of Kaṇāda, named Pailuka,[1] has advanced the syllogism (in question) in order to prove that Universals are present in all particulars, and in the intervals between them, where the particulars are absent, as well. (83. 5). «Just as the Cosmical Ether» — is an example supporting the general proposition. The Cosmical Ether, indeed, is simultaneously inherent in all the objects which are contained in it, wheresoever they be situated, e. g., in trees etc. The words «a Universal is simultaneously inherent in all objects everywhere situated», contain (the minor premise establishing the fact) that the reason is present upon the subject of the conclusion.

(83. 8). The (author) understands[2] this argument as an analytical reasoning.

120. The deduction is an analytical one. The real presence of (a Universal) in a definite place is deduced merely (by analysis) of the fact that it is inherent in the objects occupying that place. Indeed, (the opposite of that is impossible), if something is absent from (a definite) place, it does not fill up that place by its own self.[3]

---

1 Pailava and Paiṭhara are evidently two invented names in connection with the theories of *pīlu-pāka-vāda* and *piṭhara-pāka-vāda*, the first was later ascribed to the Vaiśeṣikas, cp. Praśastapāda, p. 107. 5, the second to the Naiyāyikas, cp. Tarkadīpikā, p. 17 (Bombay, 1918). But no connection between these names and the doctrine of the reality of Universals has as yet been on record. Kaṇāda's sūtra I. 2. 3 is unclear. The doctrine is full blown in Praśastapāda, p. 314. 21— *antarāle ca... avyapadeśyāni*. It is one of the fundamental tenets of the united Nyāya-Vaiśesika school. From Dh.'s words it would appear that the Piṭhara-pākavādins did not share it. 2 *yojayan*, lit. «construes».

3 Lit., p. 83. 9—10. «The possession of a nature which is present in its place depends as a consequence (*anubandhinī*) upon merely the nature connected with it (i. e., inherent in it). Indeed what where is absent, it does not pervade its place by its own self. Thus a formula of the own-existence reason». — The gist of the argument seems to be that Universals cannot move, hence they must be omnipresent

(83.11). The essence of a Universal is to be inherent in the (corresponding particular) things everywhere, (wheresoever) they be situated. This property alone is sufficient to deduce from it the fact of the (real) presence (of the Universal) in these places, (i. e., everywhere).[1]

(83.14). If something possesses the essence of being inherent in a number of other things, it necessarily must be present in the places occupied by them. Therefore the fact that a Universal is present in a place is deduced from the fact of its being inherent (in the palticular things) there situated.

(83.16). It may be objected that a cow is (intimately) connected with its owner, but he does not occupy the same place[2] as the cow. How is it then that the property of occupying the same place is deduced from the fact of being in a (certain) connection with the objects occupying it? It is said in answer.

(83.17). (This connection is one of inherence). If something is not present in a place, it cannot contain in itself the objects there situated. (83.18). The connection which is here alluded to as existing between a Universal and (the corresponding particulars) possessing it, is Inherence. Such a connection is only possible between two entities occupying the same place. According to that (kind of connection, a Universal) inhering somewhere comprehends the object in which it inheres in its own essence. It thus locates its own self into the place occupied by the object in which it inheres.[3] To contain something means (here) just to occupy that very place[4] which is (also occupied by this thing). This is Inherence.

(83.21). Therefore, if something inheres in something else, it pervades that thing by its own existence and becomes itself present in the place (of that object).

(83.22). The idea (of the author) is the following one. Comprehension involves presence. If there is no presence, neither can there be

---

[1] Lit., p. 83.11—14. «The nature of a Universal is to be conjoined with those things situated in all places. This alone, the mere nature of being conjoined with it. It follows on it, it is consequent on it. What is it? He says. The fact of having the nature of being present in their place. The place of those connected is their place. Whose own-existence is present in their place, it has its own existence present in that place. Its condition is (its) essence».

[2] *sannihita* here clearly in the sense of «being present», not of being near, cp. this term in I. 13, transl. and note.

[3] Lit., p. 83.19—20. «It introduces itself into the place the object inhered in».

[4] *deša-rūpa* = *deša-svarūpa*.

comprehension, nor inherence which is equivalent to comprehension. But comprehension exists and consequently presence in the same place, (i. e., everywhere) exists as well.[1] This is an analytical deduction.[2]

(84. 3). The (contrary) syllogism advanced by Paiṭhara is now given.

121. The second, (the contra-) deduction runs thus.

(Major premise). If something perceptible is not perceived upon a place, it is absent from it.

(Example). As e. g., an absent jar.

(Minor premise). A Universal, although (supposed) to be perceptible, is not perceived in the intervals between the (corresponding) particulars.

(Conclusion). (Hence it is absent).

This negative conclusion and the former analytical deduction, since they contradict one another, produce together an uncertain (conclusion).

(84. 8). What fulfils the conditions of perception, i. e., what is a possible object of perception, what may be imagined as perceived — such is the subject of the general proposition. «It is here absent», i. e., we can take action[3] without expecting to find it there — such is the predicate. It is thus stated that the first is subordinate to the second. The example is an absent jar.

---

1 Lit., p. 83. 22. «Pervasion of real things situated in this place is subordinate to existence in that place. Because if there is no existence in its place, there is no pervasion of it, there will be no inherence-connection whose essence is pervasion. But there is pervasion, therefore (there is) presence in its place. Therefore this is an own-existence reason».

2 Since Dharmakīrti admits only two varieties of deduction, deduction of necessary Succession or Causality and deduction of necessary Coexistence or analytical deduction, he evidently could construct the conclusion about the real presence of Universals in the individual things in which they inhere as an analytical judgment or judgment of necessary coexistence. The subject of the judgment—the fact of inherence — is alone sufficient to deduce the reality or real presence of the Universal. The judgment is so constructed that its validity reposes on the law of Contradiction alone «what really inheres is really present, inherence is presence».

3 *vyavahāra.*

(84.10). The words «a Universal etc.» point to the minor premise.

(84.11). The intervals between the particulars include other particulars, as well as empty space. Although the Untversal «cow» is perceived in some particulars, it is not perceived in others, e. g., in horses etc. Neither is it perceived in empty space, where there are altogether no particulars. It follows that it is absent in these places.

(84.13). This negative conclusion and the aforesaid (analytical deduction) prove (two conclusions) which are contradictory of one another — they produce uncertainty about the subject of the inference (making the existence of Universals doubtful).

(84.14). There is no such object in existence which should (really) possess contradictory properties. One of the reasons here proves the presence of Universals in other particulars and in empty space. The other, being negative, proves their non-existence there.

(84.16). Now, one thing cannot at the same time and in the same place be existent and non-existent, because this (runs against the law of) Contradiction. Thus it is, that the (kind of) Universal which is theoretically constructed has two predicates simultaneously — omnipresence and non-omnipresence. The two reasons establishing that are in conflict with one another.

(84.18). Because it is assumed that the same Universal is simultaneously inherent in all particulars, wherever they be situated, and because it is assumed that it is visible, therefore it is concluded — from the fact of its inherence, that it is omnipresent, and from its perceptibility, since it is not visible in the intervals between the particulars, that it is not omnipresent. Thus it is that the promotor of the doctrine himself has failed to take notice of this mutual contradiction. He has constructed two conflicting attributes and has thus given a loophole for contradiction to enter.

However, in (objective) reality such contradiction is impossible.

§ 18. The import of Examples.

(84.22). Different logical reasons, since they are members of syllogisms, have been examined and, incidentally, fallacious reasons as well. Now the question is asked, whether the examples which are also members of syllogisms must not likewise be examined, and on this occasion false examples as well?

122. The exposition of the three-aspected logical reason is finished. Such a reason is quite capable alone to produce cognition of the (inferred) object. Hence the example is no separate member of the syllogism. Its definition is not given separately, because it is implied (in the definition of the reason).

(85. 3). The three-aspected reason has been expounded. What is the use of dwelling upon the examples?

However (it may be objected) that the reason alone does not, by itself, produce a cognition of the object (of inference)? The (author) answers that the reason is quite sufficient alone to produce a cognition of the deduced predicate, (he means) just the reason as he has defined it. Such a reason is capable alone to yield a result. Hence the demonstration will be complete when the reason alone has been given (full) verbal expression. The example does not really constitute a separate premise, and for this reason a definition of the example has not been given separately from the definition of the reason.

(85. 6). But it may be questioned, how is the invariable concomitance of the reason to be established, if there are no examples (to support it)? (The author answers). We do not at all maintain that there are altogether no examples (to support it), but we maintain that the example is inseparable from the reason, it is necessarily included in the reason. That is why it is said that its definition is not given separately, it is not (simply) said that its definition is not given at all.

(85. 9). Be it so! It is nevertheless a member subordinate to the reason. This should (not prevent us) from giving its definition? (This however would be useless). Since the import of such a definition is implied (in the definition of the reason), its import, its purpose, the meaning expressed by the word, are implied. For this cause (it is not given).[1] (85. 10). Indeed, when a definition of the example is given, this is done in order to produce a clear conception of what an example is. But since we already know it just from the definition of the reason, therefore the purpose of the definition is (attained), the clear concep-

---

[1] Lit., p. 85. 9. «If so, the definition also of the subservient to the reason must be just given, thus he says — because the meaning is known. The meaning, the aim, or the expressed part is known, of what the example-definition (should be). Thus its condition, essence, therefore».

tion of what an example is, is known, is realized, or the meaning of the word example, the idea (corresponding to it) is implied (in the meaning of the reason).

(85.13). How is its meaning implied?

123. The essence of a logical reason, in general, has been defined by us as consisting in its presence only in similar cases, and its absence from every dissimilar case. Further, we have specified that the causal and the analytical reasons must be shown to represent, (the first) an effect (from which the existence of a cause is inferred), (the second, a necessarily coexisting attribute) which alone is sufficient for deducing (the consequence). When the reasons are so represented, it is then shown that 1) wherever smoke exists, fire exists, like in a kitchen; if there is no fire, neither is there smoke, like in contrary cases; 2) wherever there is production there is change, like in a jar; if something is changeless, it is not a product, like Space. It is, indeed, impossible otherwise to show the existence (of the reason) in similar and its absence from (all) contrary cases with the qualification that we have introduced, viz. 1) the causal deduction (of the existence of a reason) necessarily follows from the existence of the effect, 2) the (analytically deduced) property is necessarily inherent in the fact representing the analytical reason. When this is shown, it is likewise shown what an example is, since its essence includes nothing else.

(85.22). The essence of the logical reason is (first) given in general terms, without specification. It means that the general definition, equally applies to the causal, the analytical and the negative reasons. Now, why is (this general essence which comprises) the two aspects — its presence in similar cases only, and its absence from every dissimilar case — why is it (first) generally stated? The general essence, although indicated, cannot be realized (by itself). Just the same must be represented as inherent in (every) particular case. (86.2).

Therefore it must be stated that (the logical reason), in particular, represents either the effect (from which the cause is inferred) or an (essential attribute) from whose presence alone the consequence follows (by way of analysis). These two varieties must be represented as instances possessing (the general features of a logical reason). (86. 3). Indeed, when we have clearly realized[1] (an entity as) an effect, we *(eo ipso)* have realized its presence in similar cases only, and its absence from every contrary case. (86. 4). An analytical predicate must be represented as following out of «its mere presence», i. e., (out of the presence of) the reason. The consequence (in these cases) exists wherever the reason exists. It is a consequence, i. e., it follows. Nothing but the presence of the reason, «it alone», means the reason alone, (its presence is sufficient for the consequence to follow). The «identity» of the consequence (with the reason) consists just in its being present (wheresoever the reason is present). (86. 6). When something is known to possess an inherent property,[2] it *(eo ipso)* becomes known that it is an analytical reason which is present in similar cases only and is absent from every contrary case. (86. 7). It is just this general characteristic that must be realized as inherent in the varieties (of the reason). Not otherwise. The definition of the varieties has been given for that purpose. (86. 8). What follows from this? It is (said what) follows. Namely it follows that when someone wishes to give a general defiinition, it must be done by pointing out (its application to) the particular cases. This is the general meaning.[3]

(86. 10). «Wherever there is smoke, there is fire» — this is (the general proposition) expressing the invariable concomitance of the effect (which effect represents) the logical reason. This concomitance is established by facts[4] proving the causal relation (of fire and smoke). Therefore, the example «like in the kitchen» must be given. «Where there is no fire, there never is any smoke», this is the contraposition of the major premise. It likewise must be proved (by examples), «as e. g., in the contrary cases», (namely in the pond etc.). Indeed, it

---

[1] *vijñāte.*

[2] Lit., p. 86. 6. «When the essence of the *probans* becomes known...», i. e., when one fact representing the consequence becomes known as representing an essential property of another fact which is the reason, its presence is deduced from the presence of the latter.

[3] *sambandha.*

[4] *pramāṇa.*

must be proved that the absence of fire is necessarily followed by the absence of smoke. This can be proved by pointing to instances dissimilar to the case of the kitchen fire.

(86. 13). «Wheresoever (we apprehend) the fact that a thing is produced (from causes), (we also observe that) it is impermanent», this is (the general proposition) establishing the invariable concomitance in an analytical judgment.[1] Its contraposition is exhibited by the words «wherever there is no impermanence (i. e., no change) there never is any production» (i. e., no causal relation). (86. 15). The facts[2] establishing the concomitance must be pointed to by an example of similarity When the (positive) concomitance has been established, it must be further shown that the reason is absent wheresoever the consequence is absent. Thus the examples (both positive and negative) «just as a jar» and «just as Space» must necessarily be given. (86. 17). Why is it so? Because it would be otherwise impossible to show that the presence in similar and absence in contrary cases, which constitute the general essence (of a logical connection), possess the indicated qualification, viz., that they are necessary. Necessity is the indicated qualification, it consists in the circumstance that the reason is present in similar cases *only*, and absent in *every* dissimilar case. Indeed, when the special definitions have been given, the specified character of this (necessary) presence and of this (necessary) absence of the reason has *(eo ipso)* been pointed to.

(86. 20). And it is impossible to specify the essence of the varieties (of logical dependence) without (pointing to the examples from which they are drawn). Smoke is a result (of causes and it here plays the part of a sufficient) reason. (Fire is the cause and its necessary presence) is the logical consequence. This relation, or the fact of the existence of an effect, implies logical necessity,[3] because the presence of smoke as an effect, is necessarily dependent upon the presence of fire (as its cause). This necessary dependence of an effect (upon some previous cause),[4] which is the essence (of one) of the varieties of logical dependence, cannot be shown otherwise (than by pointing to examples).[5]

---

[1] *svabhāva-hetor.*

[2] *pramāṇa.*

[3] *niyama.*

[4] *tat-kāryatā-niyama.*

[5] Lit., p. 86. 20—22. «And the essence of the particular cannot be shown otherwise. Of this *probandum* the effect, its effect, smoke. Its relation (*bhāva*), its he

(86. 22). Neither can the other relation, (the relation which constitutes the second) variety of logical dependence (namely the analytical relation) be indicated (without having in view the examples). This relation consists in the necessary concomitance of two co-inherent attributes,[1] the presence of the one being the necessary mark of the presence of the other.[2]

(86. 23). Since the relation of Causality or the relation of Co-inherence must be established (by experience) on examples like the kitchen fire (producing smoke), or the jar (being non-eternal), therefore in pointing to the facts[3] on which the general proposition[4] is based the examples by similarity must (inevitably) be quoted. (87. 1). The contrary example has the aim of pointing to the absence of the effect where the reason is absent, after their causal relation has been established (at first by positive examples). (87. 2). This is just the reason why (the contrary example) is not necessarily something real.[5] The absence of the effect when the cause is absent (since

ing an effect. Just this is necessity (*niyama*), because smoke is necessarily dependent on fire as its cause. This, the necessity (consisting in) being its effect, as having the essence (*rūpa* = *svarūpa*) of the definition of (one) variety, cannot be shown otherwise».

1 The *linga* is *svabhāva* and the *sādhya* is *svabhāva*, or else the *linga* is a *linga* for its own *svabhāva*, cp. above the sūtras III. 18—20 and the notes to the translation.

2 Lit., p. 86. 22—23. «And the pervasion of the own-existence-mark by own-existence which is the *probandum*, being the essence of the definition of (the other) variety cannot otherwise be shown».

3 *pramāṇa*. 4 *vyāpti*.

5 According to the Naiyāyiks a syllogism where the contrary example is not a reality is a syllogism without any contrary instance, a syllogism whose major premise is a generalization from positive instances alone, it is *kevala-anvayin*, *vipakṣa-hīnaḥ*, just as the Buddhist deduction of the non-eternity of the sounds of speech from the fact that they are products, *yathā sarvānityatva-vādinām, anityaḥ śabdaḥ, kṛtakatvād iti*, says Uddyotakara, p. 48. 12. The counter-example of the Buddhists is Space or the Cosmical Ether which is eternal and unproduced, but, according to Mahāyāna-Buddhists, not a reality, since all reality is non-eternal. The Buddhists retorted that if the reason is not absent in the contrary, albeit imagined, cases, it must be present, since non absent means present, and we will be landed in the absurdity of admitting the presence of a reality in an unreality. This point was then discussed with much scholastic subtlety and great animosity between the Buddhist logicians and the Naiyāyiks, cp. Tātp., p. 114. 22 ff., Pariśuddhi, p. 708—735 and the gloss of Vardhamāna-upādhyāya *ibid.* Udayana quotes the opinions of the Buddhists Jñānaśrī (p. 713) and Prajñākaragupta's Vārtikālaṃkāra (p. 730).

it is an absence) occurs in real as well as in unreal cases. Therefore we admit as negative examples real and unreal (i. e., imagined) facts. (87.3). Thus it is impossible to indicate either the positive concomitance or its contraposition without an example. (87.4). Consequently— when the essence of the logical reason has been elicited, it has been *eo ipso*[1] shown, 1) that a positive example being the fact[2] proving the concomitance of the reason (with its consequence, must be assumed) and 2) a negative example, as well, must be quoted, because it shows (subsequently), after the positive concomitance has been established— that if the consequence is absent, the reason is also absent.

(87.6). When this (relation) has been indicated the examples have been *eo ipso* indicated also. When it has been shown that such and such a fact[3] is to be taken as a fact[4] establishing concomitance from the positive side, and when (the other facts) have been shown where this concomitance is absent, the examples have been *eo ipso* given. (87.8). If it is asked, why? — we answer, because (its essence) is nothing but that. Indeed so much only is the essence of an example. For a positive example, it is to indicate the facts establishing the concomitance, and for a negative example, it is to show that the reason whose concomitance has been positively established, is absent wheresoever the consequence is absent.

(87.11). Now, all this is already clear from our explanation of the character of a logical reason. What then may be the use of giving a (separate) definition of the example?

§ 19. Fallacious positive examples.

124. Fallacious examples are also virtually rejected by this (account of the reason).

(87.13). The analysis of the essence of a logical reason discloses the (function of) examples. It virtually includes an account of wrong, i. e. fallacious, examples. When, indeed, an example has been chosen for illustrating (the general proposition), as has been explained above, if it nevertheless is not fit to fulfill its own function, it will be a

---

1 *ākhyānād eva.*

2 *pramāṇa.*

3 *so 'yam arthaḥ.*

4 *pramāṇa.*

wrong example. This is virtually implied (in our account of the logical reason).

(87.16). Some instances of wrong examples are now given.

125. (Thesis). The sounds of speech are eternal entities.

(Reason). Because they are not impenetrable bodies of limited dimensions.

(Examples). As, e. g., motion, atoms or a jar.

These examples are deficient in regard of the consequence or of the reason or of both.

(87.19). The eternal character of the sounds of speech is the consequence which must be established. The fact of not being an (impenetrable) material body (of circumscribed dimensions) is adduced as the reason. The examples of motion, of atoms, and of a jar are quoted as similar cases. They are wrong, because they are deficient either in the first attribute (the predicate eternity) or in the second (the reason — (impenetrability), or in both.

(87.21). Motion lacks the first. The atoms lack the second, since the atoms have (infinitesmal) dimension. A body is a substance which is not ubiquitous and has (limited) dimensions. Atoms are not ubiquitous and are essentially substances. That they are eternal, (i. e., unchanging), is a tenet of the Vaišeşika school. Thus they are not deficient in the predicated attribute. A jar is deficient in both. It is not eternal and is an impenetrable body of limited dimensions.

126. The same applies to cases where the presence of the predicated attribute and (of the reason) is uncertain.

1. E. g., (Thesis). This man is subject to passions.

   (Reason). Because he is endowed with the faculty of speech.

   (Example). As e. g., a man in the street.

2. (Thesis). This man is mortal.

   (Reason). Because he is subject to passions.

(Example). As e. g., a man in the street.

3. (Thesis). This man is non-omniscient.

(Reason). Because he is subject to passions.

(Example). As e. g., a man in the street.

(88. 7). The first of these (deductions) has an uncertain predicate. (All) are examples where (there is some uncertainty); either the predicated attribute is uncertain or the reason adduced is uncertain or both are uncertain.

(88. 8). (The following are) examples. In the (first example) the existence of passions is the predicate, the faculty of speech—the reason, the man in the street—the example. It is uncertain whether he really is passionless.

(88. 10). (Again in the second example) «mortal» is the predicate; «this man» is the subject; «because he has passions» is the reason. The presence of the latter in the example, a man in the street, is uncertain, but his mortality is certain.

(88. 12). (In the third example), the predicate is non-omniscience; «because he is subject to passions» is the reason. Both are uncertain in the man in the street, his not being omniscient (since this is a transcendental quality which never can be neither affirmed nor denied), and his being subject to passions.[1]

127. (Next come examples where) necessary concomitance is either absent (because of incomplete induction) or not rightly expressed (because of the carelessness of the speaker).

1. (Thesis). Whosoever speaks is subject to passions.

(Example). Like, e. g., our Mr. So and So.

2. (Thesis). The sounds of speech are impermanent.

(Reason). Because they are products,

(Example). As e. g., a jar.

---

[1] For the same reason, i. e., because an absolute freedom from passions and desires is not known from experience.

(88. 16). Deficient in regard of necessary concomitance[1] is a case where the accidental coexistence[2] of reason and consequence is alone indicated, but it is not shown that the reason is logically subordinated[3] to the consequence. An example in which the necessary concomitance of (the reason with the consequence) is not rightly expressed, is an example where the right logical concomitance (exists in the mind of the speaker), but is not put by him in the right form.

(88. 18). An example of the first kind is the following one, («whosoever speaks is subject to passions»). «Whosoever speaks», i. e., the faculty of speech, is the subject of the general proposition. «He possesses passions», i. e., the attribute of passions, is the logical consequence. Hence the existence of the faculty of speech is a fact logically subordinated[4] to the fact of having passions. The necessary concomitance (of both these attributes) is thus expressed. «Like our Mr. So and So» is the example. By the word «our»[5] the disputant and the opponent are equally included (i. e., a person is alluded to which is well known to them both) as possessing passions. (88. 21). What is really proved (by this example) is mereiy the fact of a coexistence iu M-r. So and So of the faculty of speech together with his passions. But the necessary logical subordination (of the first attribute to the second) is not proved. Therefore the example is deficient in regard of (the necessity and universality of) the concomitance.[6]

(88. 22). (In the second example) «impermanence» is the logical predicate; «because it is a product» is the reason.

(89. 1). (The example is) «like a jar». This (example) is not sufficient to express adequately the necessary concomitance (of these two attributes). Although the sounds of our speech are similar to a jar as regards production, (both are produced according to causal laws), but they cannot (on this ground) be necessarily conceived[7] as similar in regard of the attribute of impermanence. (The example, as it is expes-

---

1 *an-anvaya.*

2 *sambhava-mātram.*

3 *vyāpta.*

4 *niyama.*

5 *iṣṭa.*

6 It is clear that Dharmakīrti treats here every case of incomplete, not sufficiently warranted, induction as a fallacy of example, but the term example becomes then partly a synonym of the major premise, not only of induction, as is clearly seen in the next sūtra.

7 *pratyetum = niścetum.*

sed, proves mere coexistence, not necessary coinherence, and if deductions were allowed on the ground of mere coexistence), every thing would be deducible out of anything.[1] (89.2). But if it were clearly realized that the *essence*[2] of production implies impermanence, then we could deduce the latter from the former. (The syllogism should have been expressed thus), «whatsoever is a product is impermanent». The necessary concomitance of production with impermanence would have been clearly expressed. And then, in order to prove this concomitance, an example should be given whose object it would be to illustrate the meaning of the general sentence.[3]

(89.5). In that case the example would really serve to illustrate necessary coexistence. But in our case the example is given without at all expressing the necessary coexistence. Such an example serves only to point out some similarity. But the predicate cannot be validly deduced upon mere similarity (or incomplete induction).

(89.6). Thus the function of an example is (to prove the validity) of the invariable (and necessary) concomitance. In our case such an example is not given. The example as it is given is useless, since it proves mere similarity. It is fallacious by the fault of the speaker, (not by itself). (89.8). The speaker indeed must here convince his interlocuter. Therefore although the real stuff is not wrong, but it has been wrongly represented by the speaker. In this sense it becomes wrong nevertheless.

---

1 *atiprasangāt*, «because of an over-deduction ad absurdum; the term is used when the deduction implies giving up of every uniformity and the possibility of everything, cp. N. Kaṇikā, p. 27.11 and 28.5 *niyamaka-nimittābhāvāt sarva-sambhavaḥ-atiprasangaḥ = sarvatra-pravṛtti-prasangaḥ.*

2 *svabhāva* here in the sense of an essential attribute, implying *svabhāva-pratibandha.*

3 In the preceding syllogism the major premise which, being the result of Induction, is regarded as an inherent part of the examples, of the similar and dissimilar cases, has been given full expression, although the Induction was incomplete and the generalization unsufficiently warranted. In the present syllogism, on the contrary, the example alone is mentioned, the major premise is not expressed. Although the example of the jar is sufficient for the Bnddhist who conceives the jar, and every existent object, as a compact chain of momentary existences, it may have no sufficient proving force for his interlocutor. Therefore the speaker, for the sake of clearness, should have appended the major premise emphasizing that it is of the essence of every thing produced according to causal laws to be impermanent, i. e., discontinuant or new in every moment.

120. This also refers (to an example whose meaning has been expressed through) an inverted concomitance, e. g.,

(Thesis). (The sounds of speech are impermanent).

(Reason). (Because they are produced from causes).

(Example). (Just as a jar etc.), whatsoever is impermanent is a product.[1]

(89.11). The following is an example (which is in itself quite a right one, but the interdependence of the two attributes which it should illustrate has been expressed) in an inverted order. This is exemplified by the proposition (attached to the example of a jar etc.), « whatsoever is impermanent is a product ». The example should prove (in our syllogism) that whatsoever is produced is impermanent. Then the impermanent (or momentary) character of things could be deduced from the fact that they are produced (from causes). (The reverse has been done) in the present case, production has been represented as a consequence of impermanence and not *(vice versa)*, impermanence as a consequence of production.

(89.13). Indeed (impermanence can be deduced from production, since) production is necessarily subordinate to impermanence. But production has not been quoted (in the present syllogism) as necessarily subordinate to impermanence, therefore impermanence cannot be deduced from such production which is not quoted as subordinate to impermanence.

(89.15). Indeed, the words «whatsoever is impermanent» express the subject of the general proposition, the words «is a product»

---

[1] Lit., p. 89. 10. «Thus (the example) with inverted concomitance, what is impermanent is a product». — The formulation of this passage is very characteristic. It represents really the major premise, but is here called an example. The major premise being always a generalization drawn from particular cases or examples, these examples become virtually the equivalent of the major premise. This is why Pārthasārathi says that the Buddhist syllogism consists only of example and minor premise, cp. Šāstradīpikā, p. 239. This, of course, must not be understood as intimating that experience and induction from particular cases are the exclusive source of knowledge. On the contrary, Dharmakīrti puts great emphasis on his principle that deduction implies logical necessity (*niścaya, niyama*) which can never be found in experience alone.

express the predicate. This means that if something is produced (by its causes), it is so because it is impermanent, and not (as it should be), that if something is a product, it necessarily is impermanent.

(89.17). We cannot, indeed, conclude that something is voluntarily produced because it is impermanent, since voluntary production is not necessarily consequent on impermanence, (there are impermanent things which are not so produced). Just so would it be impossible to deduce production from impermanence, because the fact of production is not necessarily consequent on impermanence.[1]

(89.18). Although, as things stand in reality, the fact of being produced (from causes) is necessarily subordinate to the fact of being impermanent, (and this is just what the speaker means by his example; but he has failed to express himself correctly, since one must understand his words as meaning that the first attribute) is not necessarily subordinate to, (and contained under, the second). (89.19). There-

---

[1] The two concepts of «being produced by causes» and of «being an impermanent entity are really conterminous in Mahāyāna Buddhism. Existence is defined by the Sautrāntikas and Yogācāras as causal efficiency (*artha-kriyā-kāritva*). Every existence is imagined as a continual run of discrete moments of existence, the next following moment being the product of the preceding one. Thus to be a product, to be impermanent, to be momentary and to exist become conterminous expressions predicable of every empirical fact. In Hinayāna existence, or element of existence (*dharma*), was split into permanent and impermanent (*nitya* and *anitya*), uncaused and caused (*asaṃskṛta* and *saṃskṛta=kṛtaka*), *Nirvāṇa* and *Saṃsāra*. In Mahāyāna all permanent elements and Nirvāṇa itself were excluded from the sphere of existence and this term was restricted to empirical existence alone, cp. my Nirvāṇa, p. 41. It would seem that the notion of being a product or of being subject to causal laws is not contained under the concept of being impermanent. Since both concepts are conterminous and necessarily coinherent, the first may be deduced from the second just as, *vice versa*, the second from the first. The concept of voluntary production is really contained under the concept of impermanence, it is less in extension and greater in comprehension, than the latter, but not the concept of causal production in general. Nevertheless it is here stated that production cannot be deduced from impermanence and it is a *lapsus* on the part of the speaker if he has expressed himself so as to suggest the possibility of an inverted deduction, the deduction of causal origin from impermanence. The explanation of the lamas (and it is probably the right one) is that the conception of causal origin is much more familiar to us than the conception of impermanent or momentary existence which can only be established by very elaborate analysis. The *lapsus* is natural in a man profoundly versed in Buddhist philosophy, but for the sake of the listener it is more natural to start with the notion of causal origin and to deduce impermanence from it.

fore (the example «a jar etc.») is not wrong by itself, but the speaker has made a mistake (in attaching to it an interpretation carelessly expressed). It thus does not contain an inverted concomitance in reality, but owing to the carelessness of the speaker (it appears as though containing it). In a syllogism which is intended for an audience mistakes of expression must be also taken into account.

129. (Such are the fallacious examples when the syllogism is expressed) according to the method of Agreement.

(89.23). There are thus nine different species of wrong examples in the syllogism of agreement.

§ 20. Fallacious negative examples.

(90.2). In order to declare that there are likewise nine different species of wrong examples when the syllogism is expressed according to the method of Difference, (the author) says —

130. The same (applies to deductions by the method) of Difference. The examples in which either the cosequence (or the reason, or both) are not absent,[1] (as they should be in a syllogism of difference), are the following ones — atoms, motion and Space (respectively).

(90.2). When (the Mīmāṃsaka wishes to) prove that the sounds of our speech are eternal (entities inherent in the Cosmical Ether), (supposing he adduces as) a reason their quality of not being impenetrable bodies of limited dimensions, the negative example[2] of the atoms (in the contraposed major premise «whatsoever is impermanent has limited dimensions») is deficient in regard of the predicate (impermanence), since the atoms are assumed (by the Vaišeṣikas) to be eternal.[3]

---

[1] *avyatirekin.*

[2] *vaidharmya-dṛṣṭānta.*

[3] The deduction (fallacious) is here the same as in sūtra III. 125, viz.,

Thesis. The sounds of speech are eternal entities.

Reason. Because they are not impenetrable bodies of limited dimensions (*amūrta*).

(90. 3). The example «motion» is deficient in regard of the reason, because motion is not a body of limited dimensions. Space (or Cosmical Ether) is deficient in regard of both, it is eternal and illimited.

(90. 4). Thus either the predicate or the reason or both are not necessarily absent. Their «non absence» means that they are not instances of the absence (of the reason as conditioned by the absence of its consequence). In these cases, since they are not (instances of such absence), they are deficient in regard of the absence of the predicate, of (the reason, and of both together).

(90. 7). The other fallacies are next exemplified.

131. Similar are also the cases where the (necessary) absence[1] of the predicate, (of the reason and of both) is uncertain, e. g.,

(Thesis). Kapila and others are not omniscient,[2] or are not (absolutely) trustworthy.

(Reason). Because their knowledge cannot stand the special test of omniscience and (absolute) trustworthiness.

An example by contrast is the following one.

(Contraposed major premise). Omniscient or (absolutely) trustworthy is a man who teaches astronomy.

(Example). As e. g., Riṣabha, Vardhamāna and others.

The absence of the predicates «not-omniscience» and «not absolute trustworthiness» in these examples, is subject to doubt.

Major premise. Whatsoever is not an impenetrable body of limited dimensions is eternal, as motion. (But motion is momentary although not a body).

Contraposition. Whatsoever is non-eternal is a body of limited dimensions.

Example. Just as atoms etc.

But atoms are eternal, although they are impenetrable bodies of limited dimensions. Therefore the example is wrong, since in this case the example must establish the necessary concomitance of the attributes non-eternity and limited dimension. This alone would allow us then to deduce the eternity of the sounds of speech from the fact that they are not bodies of limited dimensions.

[1] *vyatireka.*

[2] Read *yathāsarvajñaḥ.*

(90.13). The absence of the predicate is uncertain in these examples.

(90.14). A negative example, in which the absence of the predicate is doubtful, is the following one. «Not omniscient» is one predicate. «Not trustworthy», i. e., not excluding the possibility of a mistake, is another one. «K a p i l a etc.» is the subject of the conclusion. The words «because of the absence (of the mark) of omniscience etc.» include the reason.[1]

(90.16). The mark of omniscience and trustworthiness, the exclusive proof (of absolute trustworthiness), is absent. This exclusive proof,[2] constituting the mark of omniscience and trustworthiness, is a science which some possess. This circumstance is the cause why (Kapila and consorts are not omniscient, because they do not possess it).

(90.19). The highest proof (which is an indication of omniscience and absolute precision is here supposed to) consist in the teaching of astronomy. If Kapila and consorts, (the brahminical sages), were really omniscient and guarantees of absolute truth, why then did they not teach astronomy? But, as a matter of fact, they did not. Therefore they neither are omniscient nor guarantees of truth.

(91.1). In the rôle of a fact[3] establishing (the rule), we have here a negative example, (an example by contrast). Every one who is omniscient or (absolutely) trustworthy has been teaching astronomy which is an indication of omniscience and a guarantee for truth, as e. g., R i ṣ a b h a, V a r d h a m ā n a and other teachers of the D i g a m b a r a s. They were omniscient and absolutely trustworthy.

(91.3). Now, it is here, on the face of these negative examples[4] of Riṣabha and Vardhamāna, uncertain, whether the predicates non-omniscience and possibility of mistakes are really contrasting, i. e., absent.[5]

Because well nigh might you teach astronomy, and nevertheless be neither omniscient nor free from mistakes! Why should these attributes be incompatible? This kind of knowledge is casual and not a necessary concomitant of omniscience. It cannot prove the existence of the latter.

---

[1] Read *ityādi hetuḥ.*

[2] *pramāṇa-atiśaya.*

[3] *pramāṇe.*

[4] *vaidharmya-udāharaṇa.*

[5] *vyatireka = vyāvṛtti.*

132. A negative example in cases where the exclusion of the reason is uncertain is as follows.

(Thesis). A Brahmin possessing the knowledge of the three Vedas should not trust M-r So and So.[1]

(Reason). Because (the man) might be subject to passions.

A contrasting example (must illustrate the rule that) whosoever is to be trusted is not subject to passions, e. g., Gautama and other promotors of legal codes. The reason, i. e., the absence of passions in Gautama and consorts, is uncertain.

(91. 10). The predicate to be deduced is the fact that a Brahmin who knows the three Vedas, the Rig, Sāma an Yajur Vedas, should not trust the words of a certain man. The subject is some definite person, M-r So and So, e. g., Kapila. «Because he is subject to passions» is the reason. Here we have in the rôle of a fact[2] establishing the rule an example by contrast.

(91. 13). An example by contrast (a negative example) is a case which proves that the absence of the predicate is necessarily concomitant with the absence of the reason. «Those whose words are to be trusted», i. e., the reverse of the predicate, is here the subject (of the contraposed general proposition). «They are free from passions», i. e., the absence of the reason is predicated.

(91. 15). Gautama, Manu and consorts are the authors of legal codes. They can be trusted by a Brahmin knowing the Veda, and they are free from passions. Thus it is that Gautama etc. are taken as contrast to the subject, (men like Kapila who, being unorthodox, cannot be trusted). But the absence of passions, i. e., of the reason, in Gautama and consorts is uncertain. Let them be trusted by the Brahmin, but whether they be subject to passions or free from them, is not certain.

133. A case where the exclusion of both is uncertain is as follows.

---

1 Insert *vivakṣita* before *puruṣa*, cp. Tib.

2 *pramāṇe*.

(Thesis). Kapila and consorts are not free from passions,

(Reason). Because they are subject to acquisitiveness and avarice.

A contrasting example should prove the rule that a person who is free from passions neither does acquire nor is subject to avarice, e. g., Riṣabha and consorts.

The absence in Riṣabha and consorts of both the predicates, i. e., freedom from passions and of acquisitiveness and avarice, is uncertain.

(91. 23). An example where the absence of both the predicate and the reason is uncertain is given. «Not free from passions», i. e., subject to passions, this is the predicate. Kapila and consorts are the subjects (of the conclusion). Acquisition is the initial appropriating of what is received. Avarice is greediness and envy which follow upon the act of initial acquisition. Kapila and consorts take possession of what is given to them and do not forsake their belongings. This proves that they have passions.

(92. 4). Here we have in the rôle of a fact[1] (establishing the general rule) an example by contrast, where the absence of the reason in all cases where the predicate is absent must be illustrated.

(92. 4). The words «every man free from passions», i. e., the negation of the predicate is made the subject (of the contraposed major premise). «Free from acquisitiveness and avarice», i. e., the absence of the reason, is predicated. The example (intended to illustrate this contrast) is Riṣabha and consorts.

(92. 6). Now, it is doubtful whether really in the case of this Riṣabha both the predicate and the reason, both the fact of being subject to passions and of having the instinct of property are absent. Indeed, it is not certain whether Riṣabha and consorts are really free from the instinct of property[2] and from passions.

(92. 8). Although in their own school they are declared to be such, but this is, nevertheless, very doubtful.[3]

---

1 *atra pramāṇe.*

2 *parigraha-āgraha-yoga*

3 *sandeha eva.*

(92.10). The last three fallacies are now exemplified.

134. An example not proving the contraposed general proposition[1] is as follows,

(Thesis). He is not free from passions.

(Reason). Because he possesses the faculty of speech.

An example by contrast (should illustrate the rule that) if something has no passions, it cannot speak,[2] as e.g., a piece of stone.[3]

Although both the attributes are absent in a piece of stone, (it neither has passions nor does it speak), nevertheless the negative proposition, that «every one who is free from passions does not speak», in its generality[4] is not proved. Therefore (the example is not a proof) for the contraposed (general proposition).[5]

(92.14). Not including the contrast is an example (not proving) the contraposed general proposition. «Not free from passions», i. e., subject to passions is the predicate. «Because he possesses the faculty of speech» is the reason.

(92.15). The contraposition will here be as follows. The words «if a person is not unfree from passions» refer to the absence of the predicate, it represents the subject (of the contraposed general proposition). «Neither is the faculty of speech present in him», i. e., the absence of the reason is the predicate. Thus it is stated that the absence of the predicate is invariably concomitant with, (and dependent on), the absence of the reason.

(92.17). The example (illustrating the rule) is a piece of stone. How is it that this example does not prove the contraposed proposi-

---

1 *avyatireka.*

2 Read p. 92. 11—12, *yatrāvītarāgatvam nāsti na sa vaktā.*

3 Lit., p. 92. 11—12. An example by contrast is «in whom there is absence of passions, he is not speaking, like a piece of stone». — Here again the major premise is regarded as inhering in the examples.

4 *vyāptyā.*

5 Lit., p. 92. 13. «Thus, since exclusion is not established pervasively, it is non-exclusive».

tion, since both attributes are (admittedly) absent in a piece of stone? Let both passions and speech be absent in it, what does it matter? A necessary absence[1] of them (inasmuch as the absence of the one necessarily entails the absence of the other) is not proved. Therefore the example is not one (which could establish) the contraposed general premise.

(92. 19). What is this necessary concomitance? The words «every one who is free from passions» indicate the negation of the consequence, this is the subject (of the contraposed general proposition). The words «does not speak» indicate the absence of the reason, this is its predicate. (92. 20). This serves to declare that the absence of the consequence is invariably concomitant with the absence of the reason. This (would really represent) a necessary concomitance.[2] (In the present case) the contrast is not established as (necesssry). The function of an example is just to prove this circumstance, (the necessity of the connection). Therefore, since this example does not fulfil its function, it is fallacious.

135. An example in which the contrast is not properly expressed is as follows.

(Thesis). The sounds of speech are not eternal.

(Reason). Because they are produced (from causes).

(Example). (In contrast with) Space (which is not produced and eternal).

(93. 2). An example not (sufficiently) disclosing the contrast is the following one. «The sounds of speech are not eternal», i. e., non-eternity is the consequence. «Because they are produced» is the reason. «Like Space» is the negative example. Here in a spoken syllogism, the meaning must be understood from the words of the speaker.

(93. 4). If it is correct in itself, but wrongly expressed by the speaker, then it becomes wrong in the form in which it is expressed, while the form in which it would be correct, is left without expression. The reason is that reason which is expressed. Thus a reason or an example may eventually be wrong in a syllogism through a mistake of the speaker's expression.

---

1 *vyāptyā vyatireka.*

2 *vyāptiḥ.*

(93.6). The cognition of the inferred fact is not based on similarity or dissimilarity, but on invariable concomitance of the reason with the consequence.[1] Therefore the general proposition, whether in its positive form, or in its contraposed form, must express that the reason is invariably concomitant with the consequence. Otherwise it would be expressed in a form which proves nothing.[2]

(93.8). The rightly expressed concomitance must be shown to be established by examples. Thus an example really is the indication of the meaning of the general proposition, positive or contraposed.[3]

(93.9). But in the present case the general proposition in the contraposed form has not been mentioned. (93.10). Therefore (it looks as if) the contrasting example has been quoted in order to prove by dint of mere similarity. In this form it has no proving force. It could have such a force if it were expressed as corresponding to a general proposition in the contraposed form.[4] But this has not been done. Therefore an example is wrong through a mistake of the speaker, when it is not expressed as illustrating a contraposed proposition (in its generality).

(93.13). A negative example containing an inverted contraposition is as follows.

136. (An example attached to an inverted) contraposition is the following one.

(Major premise). What is not subject to causal laws is eternal.

(Example). (As e.g., Space).[5]

---

[1] *sādhya-niyatād dhetoḥ*, lit. «from the reason which is necessarily dependent (*niyata*) on the consequence (*sādhya*)».

[2] *na gamaka*.

[3] Thus it is here clearly said that the weight of the major pemise depends on the examples in which it is contained.

[4] *vyatireka-viṣayatvena*.

[5] The fully expressed syllogism is here the same as in sūtra III. 128, but the positive major premise is replaced by its contraposition, viz.,

Thesis. The sounds of speech are non-eternal.

Reason. Because they are produced (according to causal laws).

Positive major premise and example. Whatsoever is produced according to causal laws is non-eternal, as a jar etc.

Contraposition and example. Whatsoever is eternal (unchanging) is not subject to causal laws, like eternal Space.

(93.15). A general proposition and its contraposition must here prove that (the fact adduced as) a reason is invariably concomitant with (the fact deduced) as its consequence. But when this relation is expressed in the contraposed form, the absence of the predicate must be proved to be invariably concomitant with the absence of the reason. Then it will be likewise shown that the reason is invariably concomitant with its consequence.

(93.17). But if it is not stated that the negation of the consequence is invariably concomitant with, (and dependent on), the negation of the reason, then the possibility of the consequence being absent when the reason is present (would not be excluded), and then the invariable concomitance of the reason with the consequence will not be established (as necessary).[1]

(93.19). Therefore it should be expressed that the absence of the consequence is invariably concomitant with the absence of the reason, but not (*vice versa*), that the absence of the reason is concomitant with the absence of the consequence.

(93.21). Indeed the words «non-subject to causal laws[2]» express the absence of the reason, (since the non-eternity of the sounds of speech is deduced from the fact that they are produced according to causal laws). This is the subject. The words «it is eternal» express the absence of the consequence. This is the predicate of (the contraposed general proposition). The meaning is thus the following one, «what is not produced from causes is necessarily eternal», (instead of saying «what is eternal is never a product»). Thus the expression means that the fact of not being a product is invariably connected with the reverse of the consequence, i. e., with eternity, but not (the contrary, not) that an eternal substance (never is a product, i. e.,) that it is invariably connected with the negation of the reason. (94.1). Thus the contraposition which should contain negation of the reason as invariably concomitant with, and dependent on) the negation of its consequence, has not been (rightly) expressed.

When the terms of the contraposition are quoted in an inverted order it is wrongly expressed. Instead of saying «whatsoever is eternal is not subject to causal laws», the speaker has said «whatsoever is not subject to causal laws is eternal». Cp. notes on sūtra III. 128. Here as elsewher «eternal» means unchanging (*nityatvam avasthāna-mātram*), «non-eternal» means momentary.

[1] *na pratīyeta = na niścīyeta.*

[2] *akṛtaka = kāraṇair na kṛtam.*

This example of inverted contraposition is likewise a mistake on the part of the speaker and wrong (in that sense).

(94. 3). After having finished with wrong examples the author points to the cause of such mistakes and says,

137. These wrong examples are not capable to demonstrate neither the general character of a valid logical reason, viz., its presence in the similar cases alone and its absence in every contrary case, nor are they capable to demonstrate the special characters (of its varieties, the uniformity of Coexistence and the uniformity of Succession).[1] Consequently it is implicitly evident that they must be rejected.

(94. 7). Examples should be given in order to demonstrate that the reason is invariably concomitant with the consequence. But these (wrong) examples cannot prove that the reason is necessarily present in similar cases *only* and absent in *every* contrary case.

(94. 9). It is now asked whether the general characteristic can be known directly by itself or it must necessarily inhere in the special cases?

Answering this question it is said that if (these fallacious examples) would have been capable of expressing the special characteristics (of the varieties of the reason), its general characteristic would have been expressed (*eo ipso*). (94. 11). But neither can the special characteristics (of the varieties) be revealed by (such wrong examples). Therefore it is evident by implication, i. e., indirectly evident,[2] that they must be considered as rejected. (Examples) are adduced in order to prove that the reason is invariably concomitant with the consequence. This they are here not able to do, therefore they are fallacious. Because they do not fulfil their function, they are wrong, such is the implication.

§ 21. Refutation.

(94. 13). So far (from the beginning of the chapter) we were dealing with demonstration. Next we will (shortly) deal with refutation.

---

[1] i. e., the *svabhāva-*, the *kārya-* and *anupalabdhi-hetu.*

[2] *arthāpattyā = sāmarthyena = paramparayā.*

139. To refute means to indicate the insufficiency and other (fallacies in an argument).

(94.16). What is to be regarded as a refutation? An indication of the insufficiency of proofs and similar (methods). Through it (the insufficiency is indicated. Thus refutation is a verbal expression (of the fact that the proofs quoted are insufficient).

(94.17). In order to explain refutation, which consists in an indication of the insufficiency of the proofs, the author says,

139. Refutation means exposing the fallacies which have been explained above, the fallacies consisting in failure to prove something. Refutation prevents the triumph of the doctrines advanced by the opponent.

(94.20). The insufficient proofs, the fallacies of Unreal, Contrary and Uncertain arguments which have been explained, their exposure, their disclosure, is refutation.

(94.21). It can be questioned whether an insufficient proof and the other (fallacies) are not (also proofs, because) they prove the contrary? Why are they then mere refutations? Because they, i. e., the disclosures of insufficiency in argument, prevent the triumph of the tenets advanced by the opponent.

(95.1). A refutation does not necessarilly require the proof of the contrary. (A reason proving the contrary is the so called) contrary reason. But if we succeed in invalidating the certainty which is the aim of the opponent, we then shall have the reverse of (that) certainty. The contrary will be established in that sense that the opposite of certainty shall be proved.

(95.3). That is all about refutation.

140. Wrong refutations are sophistry, (evasive answers).

(95.5). The word sophistry expresses similarity (to reasoning). Evasive answers are would-be answers. They resemble answers because they are expressed second in place (where an answer is expected).

(95.8). Wishing to declare that the similarity with (real) refutation consists in that they occupy the place of answers, the author says,

141. Sophistic answers are discoveries of non-existing fallacies.

(95.10). Discovery of a non-existing, an untrue, fallacy (is sophistry). It is discovered by words, hence it is a disclosure. Such are sophistic answers. They are answers by generic resemblance with answers.

§ 22. Conclusion.

If I may claim to have explained
Some words and problems in this treatise,
As pure as moon-rays is my moral merit.
If a position, prominent and lasting,
If science and religion[1] I have reached,
I wish my work will serve alone
The weal of all the living creatures.

Finished is this Comment on the «Short Treatise of Logic». It is the work of Dharmottara who has used all his skill for throwing it into the compass of one thousand four hundred and seventy seven šlokas (of 16 syllables each).

---

[1] The fact (*vastu*) described in this stanza is the conclusion of the work, the emotion (*rasa*) echoed (*anuraṇana-rūpa*) in it is either a feeling of resignation (*šānta-rasa*) or of sympathy (*karuṇā-rasa*). This expression of feeling is the principal aim (*angin*) of the author, the double meaning ot the word *dharmottara* is a subordinate (*anga*) embellishement (*alankāra*). We have here a case of *dhvani*, the *šleṣa* is suggested (*ākṣipta*), but not developed (*anirvyūḍha*), cp. Dhvanyāloka, p. II. 22 ff. The Tib. translates *jñāna* by *ye-šes*, this would mean «transcendental knowledge».

APPENDIX I.

Vācaspatimiśra on the Buddhist Theory of Perception.

Vācaspatimiśra on the Buddhist Theory of Perception.

(Nyāya-vartika-tātparya-ṭīkā, Vizian. ed., pp. 87.24—95.10. Benares ed. 1925, pp. 133. 9—144. 2).[1]

(87. 24). (The definition[2] of sense-perception in the Aphorisms of the Nyāya system includes the characteristic that) «it contains a judgment[3]». These words point directly to a fully qualified[4] (determined and complex) perception. Indeed, the terms judgment, ascer-

---

1 Vācaspatimiśra, a native of Northern India (Durbhanga), lived in the IXth century A. D. at the court of the king of Nepal. He is posterior to Dharmottara whom he quotes several times (Tātp., pp. 109, 339 and N. Kaṇikā, p. 257). About him cp. R. Garbe, Der Mondschein der Sāṅkhya Wahrheit, Introduction, and my article in Prof. H. Jacobi's Festschrift. He possessed an unrivalled mastery in the exposition of the most difficult problems, a vast knowledge in brahmanical systems and first hand information in Buddhist philosophical literature. His exposition of the Buddhist doctrine of perception is therefore of high importance. His text was commented upon by Udayana-ācārya, living in the Xth century, in a work entitled Nyāya-vārtika-tātparya-ṭīkā-pariśuddhi (quoted here as P). The latter text was again commented upon by Vardhamāna-upādhyāya, living in the XIIIth century, in a work entitled Nyāya-nibandha-prakāśa (quoted as V.). The exposition as usual is divided into two parts. In the first the Buddhist leads and makes a statement, the Realist passes remarks. In the second part they interchange their functions, the Realist answers all the arguments of the Buddhist and makes a final conclusion.

2 This definition, as interpreted by the best commentators, runs thus — «Produced by a sensory stimulus (coming from an external) object, a cognition, which is not an illusion, which is (either) an unutterable (sensation) or a perceptual judgment, this is sense-perception».

3 *vyavasāya-ātmaka*, lit. «contains a decision», it will be seen in the sequel that a perceptual judgment of the form «this is a cow» is meant.

4 *savikalpaka*.

tainment[1] and conception[2] do not mean different things. Sense perception whose essence and form consist (in a perceptual judgment) is qualified perception.

(87.26). This point, (*viz.*, that sense perception includes the affirmation of a distinct image of the object) is quite clear, the pupils will understand it (by themselves). Therefore it has not been enlarged upon by the authors of the Commentary and Subcommentary (on the Nyāya Aphorisms). But we, wishing to follow the path opened by our teacher Trilocana,[3] will give the following exposition (of the problem), according to the facts and to the arguments (adduced by both sides, the Buddhists and the Realists).

PART I.

The Buddhist makes a statement of his views. The Realist inserts suggestions.

§ 1. The parts played in perception by sensation and by imagination must be distinguished.

(88.1). (The Buddhist). It would be so, (*viz.*, the perceptual judgment of the form «this is a cow» would be included in sense perception, if it were produced by a sensory stimulus, but) this is impossible, (the definition of the Naiyāyikas is wrong), sense perception

---

1 *niścaya*, ascertainment or «necessity» in the sense in which every assertion wishing to be objectively real is a necessary assertion, as established by Sigwart *op. cit.*, I. 243. The same term is used to express the necessity of logical deductions, cp. N. b. ṭ., text, p. 19 (sūtra II. 7).

2 *vikalpa*, this term, which also means a choice, is applied to the judgment of the form «this is that», cp. Ṭipp., p. 23. 4 — *sa evāyam iti vikalpasyāvasthā ucyate.* It thus points to «the function by which we identify a numerically distinct and permanent subject of discourse» and which by W. James, Psychology, I. 461 (1890) is called «conception» or «conceiving state of mind». This same function is also called, in Europe and in India, synthesis (Ineinssetzung, *abhedādhyavasāya*, cp. N. b. ṭ., text, p. 4. 11). Thus the functions of judging, ascertaining, necessary, affirmation, conceiving and synthesis are here declared to be so many names for one and the same mental operation whose result is the perceptual judgment of the form «this is blue» or «this is a cow». It is partly Kant's «Verstand», «Vermögen der Urtheile».

3 Quoted in the Apoha-siddhi, p. 13 (B. I.).

cannot contain a decision[1] (of that form), because such a decision would include a (distint) image,[2] an image which (always) is utterable.[3]

(88. 2). However, our knowledge,[4] so far as it is due to a sensory stimulus coming from an external object, is a reflex of the object[5] (alone), (the object) does not possess the power of amalgamating (a sensation) with a name.

(88. 3). Indeed the names are not contained in the objects, (they neither are appended to them, nor inherent in them, nor produced by them[6]). Nor are the objects identical with their names. If it were so, we have had already an occasion to remark,[7] the behaviour of a man who never has learned a (given) language would be just the same as the behaviour of a man who understands it, (he could get the names by looking at the object).

(88. 4). (If the name of the object) is not to be found in the external world,[8] (neither can it be found inside us), it is not an idea.[9] It is arbitrarily applied to an object,[10] (but this does not mean that it can be got out of the object). Indeed knowledge[11]

---

1 *vyavasāya*, the decision or judgment, e. g., «this is a cow», cp. p. 89. 5.

2 *pratibhāsa*, «image» (= *aniyata-pratibhāsa*).

3 Read *abhilāpa-saṃsarga-yogya;* this is right on the assumption that knowledge contains images — *sākāra-pakṣe* (V).

4 *vijñānam* refers here to sensation.

5 *arthāvabhāsa*, viz. *niyata-avabhāsa.*

6 *na santi, saṃyogena, samavāyena, kāryatayā vā* (P).

7 Tātp., p. 82. 5 ff. There was a school of Grammarians who maintained that names were identical with things (*nāmadheya-tādātmyam arthānām*), that even new-born children and deaf-dumb persons had their ideas from a congenital Name-forming Force (*śabda-bhāvanā* = *śabda-vāsanā*), since naming is primary in our knowledge, ibid. p. 83. 11 ff. To a certain extent they held just as Dr. John B. Watson, although on other grounds, that «we do not think, but only talk». To this Force as manifested in the eternal words of the Scripture, the school of Mīmāṃsakas ascribed the origin of our religious and moral duties.

8 *artha-asaṃsparśī; arthāsaṃsparśaś ca atadvṛttitvād a'adutpatteś ca* (P.).

9 *saṃvedana-dharmo jñatṛtvādiḥ* (P), although there may be a *śabdākāra* as *grāhyākāra*, it is *arthāsaṃsparśī*, i. e., *arthākārāsaṃsparśī.*

10 *niyojanāt* = *niyogato yojanāt* = *bāhya-sāmānādhikaraṇyena pratīteḥ* (P.); *niyoga* = *svecchayā niyoga*, cp. Kamalaśīla, p. 88.

11 *jñānam* here refers to the qualified percept corresponding to the object as the real possessor of all its attributes, *arthāt sarūpakād upajāyamānam jñānam vikalpa-rūpam* (P.). Dignāga has established that this object is a spontaneous construction of our mind according to the exigencies of our language, or just of its syntax, it is a *nāma-kalpanā.* The names are divided in class-names, adjectives,

produced by an external object can point[1] only to that object and not to its name.

(88. 6). The colour of an object may be associated with a certain flavour, but the visual sensation perceives the colour and not the flavour. (Similarly our sense perception apprehends the object and not the name. If therefore the Realist admits no other origin of our knowledge than the external world, he ought to conclude that all our ideas are unutterable, since there are no names in the external things).[2]

(88. 6). Therefore the cognizing individual[3] (really apprehends by his senses just a simple reflex, but he) thinks that (his imagined mental construction with all its general features also) is present in his ken.[4] This mental construction[5] converts[6] an object which is quite independent from any association with a name into an object containing (the connotation of its) name. (The cognizing individual possesses indeed a faculty of sense-perception and a faculty of imagination). When he thinks that he perceives a constructed image by his senses, he simply

---

verbs and substantives, all constituting together the *pañcavidha-kalpanā*, cp. Tātp, p. 82. 6 ff. and 102. 2 ff. Since the Realist contends that all these categories are objective realities, but not mnemo-verbal constructions, the Buddhist deduces this view *ad absurdum* (*prasanga*). He says that from the standpoint of the Realist the qualified percept should only point to the qualified object, but not to its grammatically arranged structure—*yato asya pratyakṣasysa nābhilāpa-saṃsarga-yogyatā-sambhavas tasmād.... vikalpa-rūpam artham eva ādarśayed iti prasangaḥ, nābhilāpa-saṃsargitayā.* If that structure were borrowed from external reality it ought to exist there. Just as in European philosophy there was a struggle between the advocates of an *intellectus archetypus* and an *intellectus ectypus*, so in India the Vaiyāyikaraṇas and Mīmāṃsakas favoured, so to say, a *vox archetypa*, the Naiyāyikas — a *vox ectypa*. The Buddhists maintained, as against this, that if the categories were borrowed from the external world, they must have pre-existed in that world. If they did not, the objects would be unutterable, like sensations are. The Buddhists then replaced the *anādi-śabda-bhāvanā* of the Mimāmsakas by an *anādi-vikalpa-vāsanā* conceived as a Biotic Force responsible for the logico-grammatical structure of the empirical world. Cp. B. Russel, Outline, p. 254 and 174—5, on the connection between syntax and physics.

1 *ādarśayet, na cārtham upadarśayti, abhilāpa-saṃsargitvād, arthasya ca tadabhāvāt* (V).

2 Here ends the *prasanga*, follows the *viparyaya*.

3 *pratipattāraḥ*.

4 Construct *vikalpa-vijñānam... vartamānam abhimanyante.*

5 *vikalpa-vijñānam.*

6 *ādarśayat.*

conceals,[1] as it were, his imaginative faculty and puts to the front his perceptive faculty. This imaginative faculty[2] is the mind's own characteristic,[3] (its spontaneity), it has its source in a natural constructive capacity[4] by which the general features[5] of the object are apprehended. Since the image is called forth by a reflex,[6] (we naturally) think that we perceive the image as present in our ken,[7] (but it is really constructed by productive imagination).[8]

(88.10). Thus (there are two conflicting deductions that can) be established.

I. *(First syllogism).*

(Major premise). Knowledge originating in a sensory stimulus is unutterable.

(Example). Just as a simple reflex.[9]

(Minor premise). But (our ideas), the constructed images,[10] the subject of discourse, are called forth by stimuli coming from (external) objects.[11]

(Conclusion). (Therefore they cannot be designated by a name).

(88.11). This is a *deductio ad absurdum.*[12] It is a negative argument according to the sixth figure of Negation.[13]

---

[1] *tiraskurvat* = *adhyavasyat* (P).

[2] *utprekṣā-vyāpāra.* Read *utprekṣā* p. 88.8 instead of *upekṣā.*

[3] *mānasam ātmīyam.*

[4] *vikalpa-vāsanā*, on *vāsanā* cp. notes in the sequel.

[5] *aniyatārtha* in the seuse of *aniyata-pratibhāsa*, cp. N. b. ṭ., p. 8.8, 8.15—16.

[6] *anubhava-prabhavatayā.*

[7] *vartamānam.*

[8] Lit., p. 88.6—10. «Therefore the cognizers falsely impute as a present experience a constructed idea (*vikalpa-vijñānam... vartamānam*) which points to a thing (by itself) not connected with a word as connected with a word, by concealing its own mental function consisting in imagination, arisen from a natural capacity (*vāsanā*) of differentiating arrangement (*vikalpa*), apprehending a non-limited (*aniyata*) object, and putting in front sensation (*darśana*), which is a (passive) faculty of direct experience (*anubhava-vyāpāram*), because it, (i. e., the differentiating arrangement) is called forth by a direct experience». — The emendation in the Benares ed. is wrong.

[9] *nirvikalpakam.*

[10] *vikalpāḥ.*

[11] They are the constructions of productive imagination, but imagination is stirred up by a simple reflex, therefore they are *indirectly* also products of external reality.

[12] *prasanga-sādhana.*

[13] Cp. above, N. b. ṭ., p. 33.6 ff., transl. p. 91.

(88. 12). The denied fact is the possibility of verbal designation. It is the contrary of the impossibility of such verbal designation. Subordinate to the latter is the fact of being produced by the object (directly, as a simple reflex).[1] This fact is established[2] (by the preceding argument). It proves the impossibility of giving names (to our ideas) and disproves the possibility of doing it. (But this is absurd). (88. 14). Because, indeed, (no one) can deny the obvious fact that these (perceived) images[3] are associated with their names. For sure, it is therefore clear that they are not (mere reflexes), they are not produced by the (genuine) efficiency of the objects (alone).[4]

(88. 15). Indeed, (we can also draw the following conclusion which destroys the foregoing one).

II. *(Second syllogism).*

(Major premise). Whatsoever represents an idea associated with a name is not (a simple reflex) produced by a sensory stimulus (alone).

(Example). Just as the ideas of God, of Matter etc.

(Minor premise). And all our ideas, the subject of our discourse, are such (constructions).[5]

(Conclusion). (They are not simple reflexes produced by the object).

(88. 17). This is a negative deduction according to the eighth figure of Negation.[6] What is denied is the fact of being produced by a sensory stimuls coming from the object. This fact is subordinate to the fact of

---

1 viz., «whatsoever is a simple reflex cannot associate with a connotative name».

2 *upalabdhiḥ.*

3 *pratyaya.*

4 We would throw this counter-argument in the form of a Mixed Hypothetical syllogism thus,

Major premise. Whatsoever is produced by an object (directly as a simple reflex) cannot receive a connotative name.

Minor premise. But our ideas have names.

Conclusion. Therefore they are not simple reflexes.

5 It will be noticed that all our ideas as constructions of our faculty of productive imagination are here contrasted with pure sensation, the limit of all constructions. The ideas of God, of Matter and other most abstract ideas are, in this respect, not different from the idea of «blue» which is constructed by a contrast with non-blue and other colours.

6 Cp. above, N. b. ṭ., p. 34. 13 ff., transl. p. 96.

not being susceptible to receive a name.[1] Its opposite is the fact of being susceptible of receiving a name. (Therefore this incompatible fact being established, it excludes the possibility of utterable ideas being reflexes).

(88.18). Nor (can it be maintained that simple reflexes may sometimes receive a name, and) that the contraposition (of the major premise in the above syllogism, *viz.*, «whatsoever is a simple reflex does not represent an idea associated with a name») is uncertain.[2] Indeed what is produced by the object must conform to the real content[3] of the object, not to the (different) content of the name, and we have already stated[4] that names are not contained in the object nor are they identical with them. If our ideas could reflect something which is not included in their object,[5] they then could reflect anything, and (we would arrive a the absurd conclusion) that everybody must be omniscient,[6] (his ideas being capable of reflecting anything you like).

§ 2. The contention of the Realist that names correspond to realities rejected.

(88.21). (The Realist). Names are associated with things as a consequence of an arbitrary agreement.[7] When a thing is perceived, the name given to it is remembered. Thus it is that a thing is apprehended as associated with a name.

(88.22). (The Buddhist). But then, let a name evoke the memory of just the thing about which[8] the agreement has been concluded. (Humanity) have concluded an agreement exclusively concerning Universals which pervade[9] (an indefinite number of particulars). But a (Uni-

[1] i. e., whatsoever is a sense datum is unutterable».

[2] *sandigdha-vyatirekitā*, means that the rule has exceptions, as assumed by the Naiyāyiks, since they maintain that the qualified percept is also produced by the sensory stimulus.

[3] *artha-rūpa* = *artha-svarūpa*.

[4] Cp. above, Tātp. p. 88.3 and 82.13. 83.13 ff.

[5] *asambaddha*.

[6] Like the Mahāyānistic Buddha possessing «mirror-like» omniscience.

[7] *sanketa*. — The Buddhist admits only two relations, Identity and Causation (*tādātmya*, *tadutputti*). Names are neither identical with external objects nor are they their products. But the Realist remarks that there are other relations, e. g., association by an arbitrary convention (P).

[8] Read *yatraiva tarhi*.

[9] *anugata* = *deśa-kāla-anugata* (P).

versal) has never been (really) perceived (by the senses). On the contrary, the thing (really) perceived is the particular,[1] the (extreme concrete and) particular witch is alone the ultimate reality,[2] (it is the thing in itself shorn of all its extensions). Therefore it (alone) is the efficient cause of sensation,[3] but not the Universal.[4] The (Universal) is bare of any kind of efficiency, it is a spurious (reality).

(88. 25). Thus it is that what is really perceived (by the senses) is not the meaning[5] of a name, and what is meant by[6] a name is not what is really perceived (by the senses).

(88. 26). Moreover,[7] (that names are given not to reality, but to logical constructions, not to sense-data, but to Universals, appears clearly from the fact that sensations are unutterable), if sensation[8] were utterable[9] we would know what heat[10] is from its name, just as we know it by actual experience, and if we could feel it from its name, cold would disappear (as soon as the word heat would be pronounced).[11]

§ 3. The Realist contends that the Universals are inherent in Particulars. The answer of the Buddhist.

(89. 1). (The Realist). (We agree) that names, just as logical marks, refer to Universals, but the Particular *possesses* the Universal

---

1 *svalakṣaṇa*.

2 Read *paramārtha-sad ataḥ*...

3 *vijñānasya*. The *vijñāna* is produced by *svalakṣaṇa* which is *trailokya-vilakṣaṇa*, but nevertheless *darśana-gocaraḥ sarūpa-katvāt* (P), *svasadṛśa-ākāra-ādhāyakatvāt* (V), it is not *ākāra-kadācitkatva-anumeya* (V).

4 *sāmānyam artha-kriyāyām aśaktatvāt tan na paramārtha-sat, asattvān na tad vijñāna-janakam, ajanakatvān na sarūpakam, asarūpakatvān na darśana-gocaraḥ* (P).

5 *sambandha*.

6 *anugata* = *deśa-kāla-anugata* (P).

7 This argument is answered below in the II[d] part, text p. 93. 24—26.

8 *dṛṣṭa* = *pratyakṣa*, cp. p. 93. 24.

9 *śabda-vācya* = *abhilāpya*.

10 *na hy auṣṇyād atirikto vahnir nāma asti bauddhamate* (P).

11 The usual example is the impossibility to convey by words the knowledge of colours to the blind. Cp. B. Russel, Outline, p. 12, «in each case what is really a datum is unutterable». P. remarks that heat, although a datum, is not unutterable, people understand what the word means, *sanketo' pi tatra* (V.-*svalakṣaṇe*) *kenacid upāyena* (V.-*atad-vyāvṛttyā*) *bhaviṣyati*. But what the word expresses is not «really a datum», *na ca vahni-śabdāt sarvathā vahner apratītiḥ, tasmāc śabda-kalpanā-ullikhitam avastv eva vastvābhāsam* (P).

(which is inherent in it), the Universal is *also a reality* [1] and it is in this (united form, together with the Universal) that the Particular produces perception (of both).

(89. 2). Thus a simple reflex [2] (or pure sensation) is produced in the first (moment) of the sensory stimulus [3] coming from the object). But the real object [4] which is apprehended [5] by it, is endowed with class character. When this (double reality) is thus apprehended, its name, whose connotation [6] has been previously established, is brought to memory and then a qualified perception,[7] (or a perceptual judgment) of the form «this is a cow» arises. It is produced (initially) by a contact [8] between the organ and the object, (but) it apprehends [9] (ultimately) a thing which is endowed with class-characters and is designated by a (connotative) name.

(89. 5). (Kumārila)[10] the author of the Digest puts it thus,

> The thing perceived is double,[11]
> Although [12] evoked by a reflex.

And further,[13]

> And then a judgment [14] is produced.
> In our mind [15] the thing appears
> With Qualities and Universals.
> This also is a sense percept.

---

1 *vastu-bhūta.*

2 *nirvikalpakena.*

3 *akṣa-sannipāta.*

4 *vastu.*

5 *vedanāt.*

6 Read *upalabdhacara-sambandhasya.*

7 *vikalpa-pratyayaḥ.*

8 *sannikarṣa.*

9 *avagāhin* = *viṣayī-karoti.*

10 Śloka-vārtika, pratyakṣa-sūtra, 118. Nirukta is here the name given to Ślokavārtika.

11 Kumārila, kār. 118—119, admits that what is perceived in the first moment is the «pure» object (*śuddham vastu* = das «reine» Object), the object shorn of all its extensions and distinctions (*anuvṛtti-vyāvṛtti-rahitam*), but it nevertheless contains them.

12 Read *bodhe'pi.*

13 *Ibid.*, 120.

14 *avasīyate.*

15 *buddhi.*

(89.8). (The Buddhist). No! (we do not admit the existence of a double reality apprehended by the senses), because the (Universals), class-character and other properties, do not exist as separate bodies [1] (united with the particulars) and are not apprehended (separately) by pure sensation.[2]

(89.9). Indeed, Class and its possessor, Motion and the moving thing, Substance and Quality, or the Inherence (of the latter) in the former — are not present to our mind [3] as separate things. And things which never have produced separately a reflex [4] in our mind, (which possess no separate efficiency by themselves), cannot be mixed as milk with water, by the man who cognizes them.[5]

(89.11). Therefore we think that the right view is the following one. The particular [6] is a unity and has no parts,[7] but it is differentiated by class character and other properties superimposed upon it by our primeval faculty [8] of productive imagination.[9] (This undifferentiated transcendental unity) is thus differentiated and imagined as possessing such and such (qualities and actions).[10]

---

1 *piṇḍa.*

2 *avikalpakena.*

3 *cakāsati = pratibhāsante.*

4 *apratibhāsamāna.*

5 Read *tad-vedinā*; it is a *vaidharmya-dṛṣṭānta*, milk and water have been perceived separately and can be mixed. Pure substance is supposed to be perceived in a momentary sensation, but the Categories have no reality besides application to sense data, therefore a mixture in a realistic sense is impossible. The example can also be understood as a *sādharmya-dṛṣṭānta*, milk and water are not mixed for the swan who is credited with the capacity to drink the milk out of the mixtnre and leave the water behind, just as the Sānkhya Saint intuits the conscious Soul as separated from Matter. The irreducible character of pure sensation and pure thought are usually illustrated by pointing to the irreducible Indian solid and liquid atoms, which nevertheless *de facto* (*pratipattitaḥ*) are mixed in the milk, cp. N. Kaṇikā, p. 258. 1—2. (translated below).

6 i. e., the extreme concrete and particular, the «thing in itself».

7 *avibhāga = niravayava = niraṃśa (vastu).*

8 *anādi-vāsanā.*

9 *vikalpa.*

10 *tathā tatheti guṇa-karma-gatena sādhāraṇatvena vikalpyate* (P), *vyāvṛttyā bhāsate, na dṛśyate* (V).

§ 4. The absurdity of putting Universals and Particulars on the same line as realities.

(89. 12). (The B u d d h i s t). And further. Supposing we (really) apprehend by sense-perception [1] (at once) two [2] kinds of ultimate realities [3] (the bare particular and the Universal), how is it then to be explained that there is between them a (possessive) relation as between a characterized point and its characteristics. (We apprehend them simultaneously, but) when we simultaneously apprehend two of our fingers, they do not become (possessively) related so as to be the one a substance and the other its quality. (89. 14). Indeed, (if substance and quality are a combination of two things, these things must interact, we would then conceive) the characteristic as the active [4] term of the relation and the characterized as its passive term. Otherwise they could not be what they are. But they are both contained [5] in the same presentation, [6] they cannot (consequently) be related (neither logically) as the one intimating the existence of the other, nor (causally) as the one producing the other. Since they are simultaneous, this would be against the rule that the cause necessarily precedes the effect. [7]

(89. 17). And further, (let us admit simultaneous causation as between a supported thing and its supporter). Supposing class-character and other properties are (really) placed upon a real thing (which supports them, [8] what will be the consequence?). A single thing, (say, a tree), will then have to support (the Universals) Existence, Substantiality, Solidity, Arboreity and Ašoka-ness. (Why is it then), that at a distance we do not perceive all these characteristics (at once)? (Why is it that at a distance we perceive the Universal Existence alone? If all the others are put on the same footing as Existence), then in per-

---

1 *vedanam* = *anubhava* = *grahana*.

2 Benares ed. *vastu-traya*, viz. *vyakti*, *ākṛti* and *jāti*, P. and V. read *dvaya*.

3 *paramārtha-sat*.

4 *upakāraṇa*.

5 *samārūḍha*.

6 *vijñāna*.

7 Read *paurvāparya-aniyamāt* = *aniyama-prasangāt*. Since they are simultaneous and apprehended in the same cognition, there is between them neither real (*svarūpataḥ*) causality, nor logical (*jñaptitaḥ*) connection.

8 The Buddhist begins by imputing a mechanical union (*saṃyoga*), and then deduces an absurdity by interpreting it as a natural relation (*svabhāva-sambandha*), cp. the refutation in the II[d] part.

ceiving one of them we ought to perceive them all.[1] (89. 19). The fact of «supporting»[2] something is, indeed, pregnant[3] with efficiency. A plate situated just under an apple which would otherwise fall to the ground is a «support»[4] (of that apple), it (affects it and) produces an apple which does not fall to the ground.[5]

(89. 21). The same must happen here (to the Universals if they are situated upon the substance), the substance will support them (and will not allow them to fall away).

(89. 22). Now the following question arises: When the substance supports its attribute, is there or not between the two terms of this relation a third unity, the relation itself, in the form of a force uniting the related terms? Indeed such a unity is impossible, because this would envolve us into a hopeless process, we would be obliged to imagine a new link connecting the force with each of the terms and so on *ad infinitum.*[6]

(89. 23). Therefore we must conclude that the relation of a substance to its qualities is a natural one.[7] Every substance, as soon as it springs up into being from the causes producing it, is such. It supports a great number of Universals (by the fact of its existence alone, without special forces or processes).

(89. 24). Acordingly, when nothing but the bare presence of something has been discerned (at a great distance, the object is supposed to

---

[1] Lit., 89. 19. «When from a remote place there is perception conditioned by one attribute (*upādhi*), a perception must follow as characterized by all attributes».— But at a distance we can discern the mere presence of something indefinite, we neither can see a trea nor an Aśoka tree. Cp. N. b. ṭ., text, p. 48. 8, transl. p. 134.

[2] *ādhāra-ādheya-bhāva.*

[3] *upakāra-garbha.*

[4] *ādhāra.*

[5] According to the Buddhists the apple is a «string of events» (*kṣaṇika*), the apple in the basket is an altogether different event (*kṣaṇa*) produced by different causes. The realist, although believing in the stability of the apple, admits causation of the basket which stops its downward movenent and counteracts gravitation (*gati-nivṛttim gurutva-pratibandham ca . . . vidadhat.* P.).

[6] Lit., p. 89. 22—23. «And not does it help by other forces, because, if it would help by an other force, there would be also falling into infinity by imagining (ever) other forces». — This is exactly Bradley's (Logic, p. 96) argument against the reality of relations. The Realists assume here Inherence as an Ens (*padārtha*).

[7] *svabhāva-sambandha* is, e. g., the connection between fire and heat, for the Buddhists they are one, for the Naiyāyiks two unities connected by *svabhāva-sambandha*, cp. below note on the passage text p. 93. 26 where the argument is refuted.

have exhibited) its capacity of supporting the Universal «Existence». But just the same essence of the object is supporting all the other Universals, Substantiality etc., (since all are supported at once). (89. 25). Thus it is that all of them, Substantiality, Solidity, Arboreity, Ašoka-ness etc., become quite useless, since when the Universal «Existence» is cognized, they ought to be cognized *eo ipso*, they are included in the same essence. (In our opinion), the Universal «Existence» is nothing but an indication of the ultimately real (element in our knowledge, all its distinctness is brought in by productive imagination).[1]

(89. 29). Accordingly it has been said (by, Dharmakīrti), «If a philosopher admits that in perceiving one thing with many attributes, we really perceive many things, then, in perceiving one attribute, we *eo ipso* ought to perceive them all, since all are produced at once, by the same force».[2]

(90. 2). «If one is perceived the others become irrelevant. Is it possible (under these conditions) that the one should be perceived and the others not? Surely when one is perceived all are perceived».[3]

«If an object with different (real) attributes is apprehended,[4] «it is then split[5] (in a number of realities). But if it is a unity[6]

---

[1] Lit., p. 89. 25—27. «Thus just all Substantiality, Solidity, Arboreity, Ašoka-ness etc., determined by its essence, are objectivized by the idea of Existence (*sattva-vikalpena*) which is merged in the absolutely existing thing».

[2] Lit., p. 89. 28—90. 2. «For whom (= *yasya daršane*) the intellect = *vikalpa-dhīr*) apprehends an object possessing (*bhedino* = *višiṣṭasya*) different additions (*upādhi*), (for him), if the characterized thing (*upakāryasya* = *višeṣyasya*) being the same (*ekātmanas*) as the force serving to help (*upakāra-angam yā šaktiḥ*) the different additions, is apprehended at once (*sarvātmanā* = *sarvair upādhibhis eka-svabhāva*), what differentiation there will be, is uncertain?» (P — *apitu sarvo-pādhibhir višiṣṭo niščita eva syāt*). These stanzas are found in Dharmakīrti's Pramāṇa-vārtika in the *apoha*-section, ch. I, kārikā 54 and first half of 55 (fol. 12a. 2 of the Sholutai monastery edition). (A. Vostrikoff).

[3] Lit., p. 90. 2—3. «If one helper has been apprehended, the others do not help (*nopakārās* = *nopakārakāḥ svabhāvāḥ*), therefore (*tato*) the others are they not perceived while this one is perceived? (read *adṛṣṭā ye*, acc. to Tib. and Tātp., 339. 5, P. adds *kim nāma?*). If this one is perceived, all are perceived». Ibid., I. 579. It is interesting to compare what W. James Psychology II. 8, says about the first sensation of an infaut, «in a mere «this», or «something there»... it has Objectivity, Unity, Substantiality, Causality, in the full sense in which any later object... has these things». For the Buddhists the «this» is the ultimate element.

[4] *dhīr*.

[5] *bhedin*.

[6] *abhinnātman*.

which is not split in a number of partial forces,[1] each supporting a different attribute, how can there be any clear cut difference[2] among the «supported» (attributes), if they are supported all at once.[3] If the apprehended object[4] is the supporter of one attribute, it (*eo ipso* supports all the others), the others are not supported[5] (separately). Whether (every single) attribute has been perceived or not, (does not matter). If the one is perceived, all the others also ought to be perceived».

(90. 3). Now, according to our oppinion, the distinct perceptions[6] (or perceived images) are produced[7] (by our Reason's spontaneity), by an innate[8] natural constructive capacity.[9] What they apprehend and what they affirm[10] (in a perceptual judgment) are both mere relations,[11] not (independent) reality.[12] They do not in the least touch[13] the ultimate reality. But indirectly they are however connected with real things, (the efficient point-instants). They therefore guide the purposive[14] (efficient actions) of men, they help them to reach[15] their aims, they lead to successful[16] activity, and this is the reason why, although they do not penetrate to reality itself,[17] they nevertheless are not quite identical with one another, (each construction represents another relation).

(90. 7). And further, (let us concede that our conceptions do not apprehend the ultimately real, they nevertheless may be caused by

---

1 *anga-śakti.*

2 *bhedo niścitaḥ.*

3 *sarvātmanā*, lit. «by one essence», = *ekena svabhāvena.*

4 *grāhya.*

5 *nopakārāḥ = nopakārakāḥ.*

6 *vikalpāḥ.*

7 *-upādānāḥ.*

8 *anādi.*

9 *vikalpa-vāsanā.*

10 *gṛhṇanti sāmānya-mātram, adhyavasyanti santānam* (P). Cp. Tātp., p. 342. 3.

11 *anya-vyāvṛtti-rūpa.*

12 *avastu alīkatvat* (P).

13 *gāhate.*

14 *pravartayanti.*

15 *prāpayanti.*

16 *avisaṃvādayanti.*

17 *vastu-svabhāva.*

reality? No! If it be manitained that) the object and the senses (after having been stimulated and) after having produced a simple reflex,[1] subsequently produce, in collaboration with memory, also the distinct image,[2] (we answer) that this is impossible, because (the two different acts of the senses) will be separated by the intercalation of an act of memory, *viz.*, the recollection of the name of the object.[3] (90. 9). This has been put (by Dharmakīrti) thus,

«If a (reflex) of the object has been produced[4] and afterwards the recollection of the name appended,[5] and if we consider (the resulting distinct image) as a sense-perception,[6] (it is clear that) this object (the object corresponding to the image) will be separated (from the first)».[7]

(90. 10). Neither can it be maintained that just the same act of the senses which has produced the simple reflex, itself produces, with the collaboration of memory, the distinct image.[8] For it cannot be maintained that an act of memory does not separate (the process of sense-perception in two parts), because of the rule, that not separating is (only) the thing itself,[9] (nothing can be regarded as separated by its own self). (90. 12). (It has been said by Dharmakīrti),[10]

---

7 *ālocita*. 8 *savikalpikām api dhiyam.*

9 Lit., p. 90. 7—9. «And further. When the real object has been indistinctly felt (*ālocita*) by the senses, then the senses (*indriyam*), possessing a function separated by the immediately produced recollection of the name and the object, cannot produce (together) also the distinct thought (*savikalpikām api ahiyam*)». Read *tadanantarotpannašabda*...

10 *arthopayogaḥ = sannikarṣaḥ* (P).

11 *anu-yojanam.*

12 *akṣa-dhīr.*

13 Lit., p. 90. 9—10. «If the object has been efficient and again there is the mnemic subsequent efficiency of the word, if that is referred to sense-knowledge, this object will be separated». — This stanza is found in Dharmakīrti's Pramāṇa-vinišcaya, fol. 154[b]. 6, Bstan-hgyur, v. 95, Choni ed. — The problem whether sensation (*nirvikalpaka*), being quite heterogeneous from conception (*vikalpa*), can nevertheless *produce* the latter, has raised a long controversy. Šāntirakṣita, Kamalašīla and others answer in the affirmative, cp. Tattvs., 1306, they admit heterogeneous causation, *ibid.* 1310, but Bhāvivikta(?) and others object, because of *bhinna-viṣayatva, ibid.* 1307. As a consequence of this there was also a divergence between the two parties on the character of *samanantara-pratyaya* and *mānasa-pratyakṣa.*

1 *vikalpa-pratyaya.*

2 *svānga.*

3 This is the first part of the stanza, it is continuaed on p. 90. 16.

«If the senses have not produced a cognition[1] at first, because they do not possess the special faculty[2] of doing it, they neither will be able to do it afterwards».

(90. 13). Indeed, what is gone by, (what has vanished, will never be apprehended by the senses), it is not their field of action,[3] and you may employ thousands of devices, you will never induce them to do what is not their own special job.[4] (90. 14). Nor can memory whose domain is the past ever cognize[5] the present which, has not been apprehended before.[6] If that were possible, the blind would be able to perceive colours by memory. This has been said by (Dharmakīrti), —

(90. 16). «Then a visual sense perception[7] would be possible even when the faculty of vision would be lost».[8]

§ 5. The Buddhist concludes.

(90. 17). Thus it is that the judgmants[9] (which apply to existence the Categories of) Names, of Class, of Quality, of Motion (or Causation) are excluded (from having their origin) in sensuous[10]

---

1 *buddher.*

2 *upayoga-aviśeṣataḥ = viśiṣṭa-upayoga-abhāvāt.*

3 Cp. N. Kaṇikā, p. 258. 1—2 — *anubhava - samāropayor vikalpa - avikalpa-rūpatayā drava-kaṭhinavd tādātmya-anupapatteḥ,* i. e., perception and imagination (or experience and imputation), being by their essence non-constructive and constructive (or passivity and activity) are as opposed as the hard and the liquid stuffs are, they cannot be the same thing». — The Indian atoms are physical, the solid and the liquid are ultimate elements.

4 Lit., p. 90. 14. «And not even by thousand contrivances this can be induced to act upon the non-domain (of its activity)».

5 *gocarayitum.*

6 *an-anubhūta-pūrvam.*

7 *netra-dhīr.*

8 This is the continuation of the stanza whose first part is quoted above, p. 90. 9. It is found in Dharmakīrti's Pramāṇaviniścaya, fol. 155ᵃ. 1, Bstan-ḥgyur, Mdo, vol. 95. Choni ed. It is there separated into two halves with the authors own comment between them, just as it is done by Vācaspati. The Tib. has *arthāpāye.*

9 *kalpanā.* This refers to the five Categories established by Dignāga (*pañca-vidha-kalpanā*) as exemplified in the judgments, «this is M-r SO and SO», «this is a cow», «this is white», «this is the possessor of a jug» and «this is moving», cp. Tātp., p. 82. 6 and 102. 2 ff.

10 *pratyakṣatvena.*

(experience). And also, (first of all), the judgments (applying the Category) of Substance[1] of the form («this is a brahmin) carrying a stick», (i. e., «this is a sticky thing»). (Dharmakīrti has said on this occasion),

> «The relation of characterizing Quality to a characterized Substance, this foundation of our empirical knowledge, is created (by our Reason), it is not (cognized by the Senses)».[2]

(90.19). Indeed this complicated function[3] (of a synthesis of apprehension) could never be discharged by (passive) sensitivity, it can be done only by (spontaneous) Thought, because the senses apprehend only the present moment. They do not think!

(90.21). (What Dharmakīrti here says with reference to the Category of Substance equally refers to the Categories) of Quality and Motion, they also are not (ultimately real). It has been said above,[4] (with respect to the Categories of Substance and Quality, that things which have not produced reflexes separately) can not be put together like milk and water. Analysis and synthesis are not reflexes.[5]

(90.22). It follows that the qualified percept is not a sense perception.

PART II.
The Realist takes up every Buddhist argument and answers. The Buddhist passes remarks.

(90.23). (The Realist). We answer as follows.

§ 1. The simple reflex and the qualified reflex are both produced by a sensory stimulus.

(90.23). (The Realist). First of all (we must consider the Buddhist) view that there is an incompatibility between (a simple reflex)

---

[1] *dravya-kalpanā.*

[2] Lit., p. 90. 18—19. «Having grasped the common-sense standing, the characteristic, the characterized and the relation, this is understood (by the Reason) in putting them together, not otherwise».—This stanza also is found in the Pramāṇaviniścaya, ibid., fol. 155ᵃ. 3.—Usually the words of Dignāga *sarvo'yam anumāna-anumeya-bhāvo* etc. are quoted on this occasion, cp. Tātp., p. 39. 13, 127. 2 etc.

[3] *vyāpāra-kalāpa.*

[4] Tātp., p. 89. 10.

[5] *viveka-sambandhayor*... On the analogy of 89. 10 we would expect *rūpa-vivekena apratibhāsane.*

produced by a stimulus (coming directly) from the object[1] and a (composite) reflex[2] capable of being covered by the connotation of a name, (the latter is a creation of productive imagination). We maintain, as against this, that there would be incompatibility, if it were true that (every object is but a string of events and the only real object is a point-instant of efficiency), the extreme particular,[3] (the thing in itself). But that is not so! (90. 25). (The author) will establish in the sequel[4] that the objects (of the external world are not momentary events, but) possess stability, and that they (really possess all their attributes), class-characteristics and other (real Universals). (He will establish that these enduring and composite objects) are ultimately real, (that their content) can be covered by a connotative name. Therefore the object itself produces the simple reflex[5] and the conditioned reflex[6] as well. Consequently there is between them no incompatibility.

(90. 27). It follows also that the above[7] *deductio ad absurdum* (which was founded on the supposition that a reflex is always unutterable) is wrong, since there are reflexes[8] which are utterable.[9]

---

1 *artha-sāmarthya.*

2 *pratibhāsa = pratibimba ādarśavat.*

3 *svalakṣaṇa = kṣaṇa = artha-kriyā-kārin = paramārthasat = vastu.*

4 Cp. comments on N. S., II, 2. 58 ff.

5 *artha-sāmarthyajaḥ (pratibhāsaḥ = niyata-pratibhāsaḥ).*

6 *abhilāpa-saṃsarga-yogyaḥ pratibhāsaḥ = aniyata-pratibhāsaḥ.* as in N. b. ṭ., p. 8.

7 The deduction against the Realist is the one mentioned on p. 88. 10, «what is produced immediately by the external stimulus, is not accompanied by the connotation of the name». The contraposition will be, «what is accompanied by the name, is not produced by the object». This major premise is not warranted (*saṃdigdha*) by facts, according to the Realist, since according to him, the distinct perception is also produced by the senses.

8 *abhilāpa-saṃsarga-yogya-pratibhāsaḥ=niyatā buddhiḥ*, cp. Tātp., p. 13. 5.

9 Lit., p. 90. 23—28. «First of all, as to what has been said, that there is a contradiction between being born from the efficiency of the object and being a reflex capable of coalescing with a name, to this we will say, that there would be a contradiction, if the own-essence were the only object, but it is not so. And he will teach (read *upapādayiṣyati*) an ultimately real object possessing class-characteristics etc., possessing stability, fit to coalesce with a name. Therefore cognition produced by it is produced by the efficiency of the object and contains a reflex (*pratibhāsa*) capable of coalescing with a word. Thus no contradiction. And thus a doubtful contraposition (*vyatirekitā*) of the *deductio ad absurdum*». — It is clear from this that according to the Realist the logical and grammatical, or syntactical, structure of the world preexists, and is borrowed by our understanding from objective reality.

§ 2. The attributes of external objects, but not their names, are external realities.

(90.28). (The Buddhist's view is that) the attributes[1] are not something apart from the substance of the thing,[2] but productive imagination[3] constructs[4] them as something different. Thus (the synthetic images[5]) are not due to a stimulus[6] coming from the object, (but to imagination).[7]

(91.1). (The Realist). (This view) is not to the point. We shall prove in the sequel[8] that (the attributes and the Universals) are separate[9] (realities connected with the substance of a thing by Inherence[10]). (91.2). As to the names of the things we admit that they do not inhere[11] in them. This does not prevent the names and the attributes (to refer to the same things[12]), there is a conformity of external reality (with the structure of language). This we have explained above.[13]

(91.3). (The Buddhist's view, indeed, is that if) we have (a judgment of naming of the form) «this is M-r So and So», the name,

---

1 *jātyādi.*

2 *dravyādi*, the «real» thing has no parts (*niraṃša*).

3 *vikalpāḥ.*

4 *kalpayantaḥ.*

5 *vikalpāḥ*, this term here refers to both the act and the content of productive imagination.

6 *artha-sāmarthya.*

7 Lit., p. 90.28—91.2. «And it is not to the point, that the synthetic images (*vikalpāḥ*), which arrange (*kalpayantaḥ*) as different the class-characteristics etc. which are not different from the things etc., are not born from the efficiency of the object».

8 Cp. comments upon N. S., II. 2.58 ff.

9 *bhedaḥ.*

10 Inherence (*samavāya*) is imagined in the kindred Vaišeṣika system as a kind of omnipresent Universal (*padārtha*), a kind of semisubstantial force which connects the result with its material cause. The result is declared to be something quite different (*atyanta-bhinna*) from the material out of which it is created (*ārabdha*), but nevertheless connected with it by Inherence. The attributes or Universals are likewise imagined as separate entities, but connected with their respective substances by Inherence.

11 *bhede 'pi.*

12 *sāmānādhikaraṇyam.*

13 Lit., p. 91.2—3. «And how, although there is difference of them, their designations possess co-substrateness, that has been taught below». Cp. Tātp., p. 84.8 ff.

although designating the person, does not inhere[1] in it, and the personal identity[2] indicated by the name is but a logical construction[3] (covering a series of events). This construction[4] is not (a simple reflex, it is not due entirely to the stimulus) coming[5] from the object,[6] (but to a mental synthesis).

(91.4). (The Realist). However, this again is wrong! We have already had occasion[7] to discuss this point when commenting upon the term «Unutterable»[8] (introduced by the Naiyāyiks into their definition of sense perception as against a school of Grammarians[9] which pretended that the names were inherent in the things[10]). (We have maintained there[11]) that our conceptive thinking does not represent (external) objects as identical with their names. The name is arbitrarily given. It (*means* the object and) is connected with it by a special relation of naming. (91.5). Nor is the name apprehended by the same sense-organ by which the corresponding object is perceived. On the contrary (what really happens is this). At first the object, although it possesses all its general and special features, produces a simple reflex,[12]

---

1 *bhinnena śabdena.*

2 *abheda.*

3 *kalpanam*, cp. B. Russel, Outline, p. 56. «Peter really covers a number of different occurrences and is in a sense general», cp. Tātp. p. 84. 8, *ḍittho nānā-deśa-kāla-avasthā-saṃsṛṣṭaḥ piṇḍa-bhedaḥ.*

4 *vikalpānam.*

5 *anarthajatvam.*

6 Lit., p. 91. 3—4. «And it is not right that by arranging non-difference *abheda-kalpanāt*) of the object through a separate name «this is Ḍittha», the arrangements (or synthetic images-*vikalpānām*) are not born from the object, (*viz.*, are not reflexes)».

7 Cp. Tātp., p. 84. 8 ff.

8 *avyapadeśya.*

9 The school of Vaiyākaraṇa's, cp. above p. 259.

10 Read with the Benares ed., ...*yathā na śabhābdedena artho vikalpair upadarśyate, kiṃtu taṭastha eva śabdaḥ svavācyatayā saṃsargeṇa saṃjñinam upalakṣayati, na ca śabdārthayor*... Lit, (it has been said) that non-sensuous thoughts (*vikalpa*) do not point to the object as non-different from the name, but the name is standing quite aside, it points to the possessor of the name by a relation consisting in being named». — Thus the relation of the name to the thing is neither Identity (*tādātmya*), nor Causality (*tadutpatti*), nor attribution (*viśeṇa-viśeṣya-bhāva*), but a special relation (*vācya-vācaka-saṃsarga*) arbitrarily established (by *sanketa*). The name is not a *viseśaṇa*, but an *upalakṣaṇa* (P).

11 Cp. Tātp., p. 85. 9 ff.

12 *ālocite*, cp. Tātp., 84. 16, *prathamam indriyārtha-sannikarṣād ālocite... artha-mātre* («das reine Object»).

(it is but very imperfectly discerned). Its name is then remembered. The name is connected with name-giving, and (indirectly) with that condition of the thing which it had at the time when it first, by convention, received its name. The name is thus necessarily brought to memory, but it does not in the least help to create the perceptual image.[1] Orelse new-born children aud dumb-deaf persons would be deprived of percepts arising from their sensations, because they could not remember names.

(91. 9). However, that former condition of the object, the condition it had at the time of name-giving does participate (indirectly) in the formation of the concept, because the object represents, (not a string of events, but) a unity[2] comprising both its present condition and (all its) former conditions, they are united in a synthesis produced by the senses.[3] But the name is something accidental, it does not penetrate, (so to say, into the interior) of the sense produced image.[4]

(91. 11). This (idea) has been expressed thus,

If I remember Devadatta
His name is in my heart.
But that does not prevent my eyes
To see his frame at present.

(91. 13). By these words (the author) does not mean that the proper name enters into (the composition of the mnemic image), but he points to the unity of the body in its present and its former conditions, (this unity) being apprehended in an image called forth by a visual sensation.[5]

(91. 14). This also has been expressed (in the following dictum),

The recollection of the name
Does not adulterate perception.
From the thing named it stands apart,
It cannot hide its sensible aspect.

---

1 Lit., p. 91. 5—8. «Nor are the object and the word apprehended by the same sense organ, but at first the object with its general and special features is glanced at; in reminding of its condition which existed at the time of agreement, it necessarily reminds also of the word which existed at that time; but the recollection of the name is of no use for the production of the synthetic image (*vikalpa*) born from sensation (*indriyaja*)».

2 *ekasya.*

3 *indriyajena vikalpena.*

4 *indriyaja-vikalpa-utpādam prati* (*nāsti upoyogaḥ smaraṇasya*), *vyavahāram prati tu asyaiva upayogaḥ* (P).

5 *indriyaja-vikalpa.*

This means that (the recollection of the name of the object) does not produce a break in the operation[1] of the senses and of the external object,[2] (they create both the primitive sensation and the subsequent synthetic conception).[3]

§ 3. Answer to the Buddhist theory that every moment is an object apart.

(91.16). (The Buddhist). The sensible stimulus[4] calls forth (the simple sensation, but) not the complex percept,[5] because the latter depends upon a recollection of former experiences.[6]

(The Realist). This is not to the point! (The causes of a phenomenon are always complex). You yourself (are responsible) for the dictum,[7]

> From a unique cause nothing is produced.
> From some totality of causes (and conditions)
> Does every (single) thing arise.

(91.18). If that were not so, the object and the senses could not even produce a simple sensation, because they depend on light and aroused attention. If the (fully qualified percept) has not been produced in the first moment, that comes because memory has not yet cooperated. But if the seed in the granary has not yet produced the sprout, it will not be prevented to produce it (later on), in cooperation with soil, (light, moisture) and all the totality of causes (and conditions).

(91.22). (Of course you, the Buddhist, will maintain that the seed producing the sprout and the seed not producing it are two different

---

1 *arthendriya* = *artha-sahitendriya* (P).

2 As assumed by the Buddhist, cp. above, p. 271, text, p. 90. 7 ff.

3 This only means that the sensory stimulus is «lodged in the centre of all the factors» (*madhyam adhyāsīnam indriyam*) which participate in the production of a full percept, memory plays an important part among them (P). This the Buddhist also admits, because he admits that the synthetic image is *indirectly* (*pāramparyeṇa*) produced by the senses and the object. Nevertheless, since the external object for the Buddhist is a string of events, the synthetic image would have no corresponding object at all, because it corresponds to an enduring object. Therefore the Realist brings forth the next argument based on the stability of the external things (P).

4 *indriyārtha-sannikarṣaḥ*.

5 *vikalpasya* = *savikalpaka-pratyakṣasya*.

6 *prāg-avasthā*, cp. 91. 9.

7 Most probably by Dignāga, not yet identified.

objects, the seed is a string of events), according to the Law of Contradiction the same thing cannot be producing and not producing (the sprout [1])! But this is wrong! We will establish that in the chapter devoted to the repudiation of the Buddhist theory of a Universal Flux.[2]

(91.23). (The Buddhist). There could be (cooperation between the senses and memory, if their respective fields of action were not quite different). However, (you must admit) that the previous condition of the object is not amenable to the senses. The field of action of the senses is limited to the present. Neither is the present amenable to memory. The field of action of memory is limited to the past.[3] A recollection is produced when the former impresions[4] (which lay dormant in our consciousness) are stirred up to activity. (91.25). Therefore the senses can never cooperate with memory. They both have different fields of action. Indeed, even if you take a thousand eyes and (a thousand) lamps, they will not help your ears in the perception of a sound, (because) their proper field of action (is limited), it is only a coloured (surface)!

(91.27). (The Realist). However, do you not yourself (admit heterogeneous causation). When a visual sensation of colour follows immediately upon an olfactory one, (do you not admit) that the latter, (as a preceding moment), is one of the causes of the former.[5] But the sense of vision[6] perceives only colours, it cannot cooperate with a perception[7] which is bent upon odour. If you retort that causation is

---

1 Lit., p. 91. 22—23. «And not is it that the mixture of contradictory attributes, consisting in producive and non-producive, is a cause of a break. This will be taught in the Break of the Breaking into moments». — An allusion to the Buddhist theory of Causation which admits only causation as coordination of events and transforms every object into a string of events. According to this theory the seed in the granary is «other» than the seed in the soil.

2 Cp. Tātp., p. 379. 25 ff.

3 *pūrvānubhava.*

4 *saṃskāra.*

5 An allusion to the Buddhist theory of causation. Every object being resolved into a string of events the foregoing moment is always the cause of the following one (*samanantara-pratyaya*). The visual sensation is produced by the sense of vision (*adhipati-pratyaya*), the object (*ālambana-pratyaya*), light (*sahakāri-pratyaya*) andaroused consciousness, i. e., the preceding moment of consciousness which may be an olfactory sensation. Cp. however Tattvas., p. 13. 10 and Kamalašīla's comment.

6 Read *cakṣū rūpa-viṣayam.*

7 *jñānam.*

proved by the joint Method of Agreement and Difference,[1] not by the homogeneousness[2] of the objects, (we will not object), it is also our opinion.[3]

(92.3). (The Buddhist). But (a qualified percept) refers (also) to that condition of the object which belongs to a past time, this previous condition of the object cannot produce a stimulus[4] on our sensitivity, how then could it be a *sense* perception?

(92.4). (The Realist). The Cosmic Aether, the atoms etc. are in a (perpetual) contact with the senses, does it follow that they are perceived? Do you (really think[5]) that whatsoever is in a contact with the senses ought to produce sense-perception?

(92.6). Not[6] every contact with the senses produces, indeed, sense-perception, but whatsoever (possesses the nature of belonging to) the special domain of sense cognition is perceived through it,[7] (and the qualified object belongs to this domain of perception).

(92.7). (The Buddhist). But really, how can the senses without being stimulated by a contact[8] produce that kind of knowledge? Or we may ask, this knowledge, (the qualified percept, if it exists) why should it be sense-knowledge? And if it is sense knowledge, does your characteristic «born from a stimulation of the senses by the object» apply to it? because just that kind of knowledge, (*viz.*, the synthetic perceptual image), will not be comprised in the definition. (Real sense-perception, in the strict meaning of the term, is only pure sensation).

---

1 *anvaya-vyatireka*.

2 *samāna-viṣayatā*.

3 Udayana remarks that, as a matter of fact, both parties, the Realist and the Buddhist, admit heterogeneous causation, for instance, when an olfactory sensation is immediately followed by a visual one. This fact is known from experience, *phala-darśanāt* (V). But the function (*vyāpāra*) is determined by induction (*kāryeṇa anuvidhīyamānatā-mātra-unneya*) which proves that a visual sensation is never produced by the olfactory sense, but only by the sense of vision. But the Realist thinks that although the sense of vision by itself (*kevala*) apprehends only the present, in cooperating with memory this function can be altered, it will apprehend the present combined with the past. The Realist thinks that such a combination is objectively possible, the Buddhist denies it.

4 *sannikṛṣṭa*.

5 Read *tat kim yad...*

6 Drop one *na*.

7 Here the Realist frames his definition so as to include in it a sense-perception of the Universals inhering in particulars.

8 Read *asambaddham*.

(92.9). (The Realist). We concede the point![1] The previous condition of the object is not amenable to the senses, (it is the domain of memory)! It is nevertheless apprehended[2] by that our cognition which is the outcome of our sensitivity with the collaboration of memory, or with the collaboration of learned reflexes.[3] (92.11). You cannot indeed maintain that what is produced by our sensitivity[4] with the collaboration of memory is *not* produced by our sensitivity. Thus it is wrong to maintain that our definition of sense perception does not comprise (the fully qualified percept or the perceptual judgment).[5]

§ 4. THE PERCEPTION OF STABILITY NOT AN ILLUSION.

(92.13). (The Buddhist). However, how can a gliding cognition,[6] a cognition that apprehends (two) consecutive (momentary) events in the object, represent one cognition? The objects are different. They are even incompatible, since the one is present in the ken, the other absent.[7] Indeed, (if we take the perceptual judgment of the form «this is that», e. g., «this is a cow»), we have in it the element «that» which refers to (a Universal, and a Universal is always) beyond the ken.

---

1 *mā bhūt.*

2 *viṣayī-kriyate.*

3 *saṃskāra = pūrva-saṃskāra-pāṭava,* traces of former experiences.

4 *indriyārtha-sannikarṣeṇa.*

5 The real intention (*āśaya*) which the Realist has here at heart is the following one. The past condition of the object is not totally absent, it is also present, since it resides in the object as its characteristic (*viśeṣaṇatayā*). The present is related to the past, and this relation (*sambandha*) is a reality, hence the past must be a reality (P). The definition of the Naiyāyiks mentions a contact between the senses and the object. But the object, according to them, contains its characteristics, hence there is also a contact with these characteristics, and with the past of the object. This relation is called conjunct inherence (*saṃyakta-samavāya*). The Nyāyakaṇikā, p. 256, records the Buddhist argument against the reality of relations which is very similar to the one used by Bradley and repudiated by B. Russsel, Outline, p. 263. Whether M-r Russel would endorse the Naiyāyika view I do not venture to decide. In any case it would be wrong to maintain that the Naiyāyiks «conceive a relation as something just as substantial as its terms». They establish very subtle differences between various kinds of relations.

6 *parāmarṣa,* Udayana, p. 587, accuses the Buddhist of *atiparāmarśa-kuśalatā deśya-atitucchatā ca.*

7 Lit., p. 92. 14. «And because of coalescence of the incompatible attributes of transcendency and non-transcendency of the ken».

The element «this» is alone (really) present.[1] When incompatible, mutually exclusive, attributes are assigned[2] (to things) they cannot represent a unity, otherwise (there would be a unity of contradictories and) the whole universe would be a Unity.[3]

(92.16). And the objects are different,[4] because it would be a contradiction to admit that the same single object resides in a former and in a following space-time.[5] (A difference in space-time is a diffe-

---

1 That the element «this» refers to a datum and is «unutterable» (*anabhilāpya*) has been noticed by several European philosophers of different tendencies, lately by B. Russel, Outline p. 12, «what is really a datum is unutterable and what can be put into words involves inferences which may be mistaken», the Buddhist would say «which are always mistaken» (*bhrāntam anumānam*), since they lack the immediate evidence of a datum. As to the element «that» which is utterable and corresponds to a Universal, Udayana makes the following remarkable comment on this passage,—«Although the compass of the element «that» (in the judgment of the pattern «this here is that») is not totally covered by constructive thought, (V. — some constructions are sense — perceived), nevertheless there is a construction in the synthesis (of the elements «this here» and «that»). The Realist, the advocate of enduring objects possessing stability, should at any price vindicate the reliability of our knowledge concerning the element «that». Otherwise the whole Universe will be cut to pieces and torn asunder. And the opponent likewise should assail that reliability with all his might. Indeed, only by repudiating it, will he disprove the reality of Universals, and thus it will become an easy task for him to repudiate the reliability of that thought-construction which establishes a link (between the elements «this» and «that»). This is the idea (expressed in this passage)».

2 *viruddha-dharma-syṃsarge.*

3 Lit., «because of the deduction (*prasangāt*) of the Unity of the three worlds». Thus Vācaspati anticipates the path of those European philosophers who established their Monism upon a unity between contradictories.

4 Udayana thus expresses the general meaning of this passage—«Although, for the Omniscient, cognition is one and eternal, notwithstanding that his objects are (infinitely) manifold, (and in this point there is agreement with the Naiyāyika), nevertheless, if the latter (*paro*) would also admit that the unity of our conceptions corresponds only to momentary patches of colour, blue etc., he would never establish his (realistic) views, nor would we in this case succeed to explain how a (synthetic) unity suddenly appears in our cognition, (when the corresponding objects are infinitely manifold). Therefore the unity (— *viṣayatvam asya*) of the synthesis of our thought is either nothing but imagination or it must be ultimately real. If the Naiyāyika (*paro*) admits the first, he will fall in line with us, (but he will never do it). Therefore the unity which he aims at is an ultimate unity in the object, (a unity of substance) through a variety of changing states. This theory we (Buddhists) combate by proving that the object is a manifold (string of events)».

5 Lit., p. 92.16—17. «And a break in the object, because of the contradiction, of two conjunctions with a former space-time and a following space-time».

rence in substance). Indeed it is just as when a precious ruby is perceived, its non-existence, (i. e. all non-rubies) are excepted, if they were not excepted, neither would the presence[1] (of the ruby) be determined, because the one term is the complete negative of the other.[2] The topazes and other precious stones are also *eo ipso* negatived (when a ruby is determined). If they were not negatived, we would be landed in an absurdity; the same thing could at the same time be a ruby and a non-ruby, because the ruby could then be identical with a topaz or some other precious stone and consequently it would be necessarily identical with the non-ruby.

(92. 22). Just so when the same thing is located in a former space-time the negation of this space-time is excluded, and in this way[3] any subsequent space-time is also excluded, since it is necessarily covered by the negation of this space-time. Thus it cannot possess the essence of being located in a subsequent space-time. Consequently if a thing would possess another substance than that which is located in a given space-time, we would be landed in the incongruity of it being identical and non-identical (with itself).

(92. 26). Thus it is proved that the objects (of the simple sensation and of the qualified percept) are different, since location in one space-time makes the thing materially different from the thing located in another space-time.[4]

(92. 27). (The Realist). To this (argument) we answer as follows. If (in the perceptual judgment of the pattern «this is that») there is a break in the gliding cognition referring to (two) consecutive conditions of the object, the one of which is absent and the other present, well then! there will also be a break in the (single element) «this» which is also a construction. It is also partly absent and partly present, partly a construction and partly a non-constructed (datum)

---

[1] Read *bhāvo*.

[2] Lit., «because its essense (*rūpa*) is the exclusion of its own non-existence».

[3] *kramena*.

[4] «The notion of substance, in the sense of a permanent entity with changing states, is no longer applicable to the world» says a modern philosopher. (B. Russel, Outline, p. 309). Here we have one of the Buddhist arguments. There are many others. The one derived from the analysis of causation, as existing only between moments, is favoured by Dharmakīrti. The Buddhists began by denying the Ego at a very early date, they then denied every essence (*svabhāva*), or substance, in the external world. The existence of a thing was by them converted in a string of events or in a staccato movement of discrete moments (*kṣaṇa*).

As regards its location in the external world it is (an inference[1] and) a construction, as regards its subjective side, the sensation, it is present and it is a datum.[2]

(93.2). Therefore ought you not to admit that there may exist one cognition notwithstanding some complexity in the object?[3] But then, in the present case, what contradiction can there be, if the same cognition transcends the ken regarding the object at the previous space-time and does not transcend the ken regarding just the same object at the following space-time?[4]

(93.2). As to the question that (every point) of space-time makes a different object, (thus converting the existence of the object into a string of events), this is also wrong!

(93.3). Right it is that when we perceive the real[5] ruby we (at the same time) negative the opposite, (the non-rubies). If we would not exclude the negative, we would not have the other, (the positive), because all entities contain the negation of their opposites by implication.

(93.5). But why are topazes and all other precious stones negatived (when a ruby is ascertained)?

(Buddhist). Is it not because they are necessarily included in the non-rubies?

(Realist). But wherefrom comes this necessary inclusion in the non-rubies?

(Buddhist). From the fact that their identity with the rubies has never been apprehended.[6]

---

1 That the external object is inferred is now generally admitted. In India it was a special tenet of the Sautrāntikas.

2 Lit., p. 92.27—93.2. «It also, indeed, transcends the ken and does not transcend, it is an arrangement (*vikalpa* = *kalpanā*) and a non-arrangement. Regarding the object it is transcending and it is an arrangement, regarding the self it is non-transcending and a non-arrangement (*avikalpaḥ*)».

3 Lit., p. 93.2. «Therefore through a break in the object no contradiction, if so?».

4 Read with the Benares ed. «*nanv ihāpi tad evaikam vijñānam tasyaivaikasya vastunaḥ pūrva-deśa-kāla-sambandhe parokṣam aparokṣam cāpara-deśa-kāla-sambandha iti ko virodhaḥ*».

5 *svarūpa* refers to the realist view that the ruby is a positive thing and its negation a real absence, while for the Buddhist the ruby is what A. Bain calls a positive-and-negative name, since «the negative of a real quality is as much real as the positive». According to Buddhists all names are in this sense relative (*apoha*).

6 Read with the Benares ed., *kadācid api tādātmyen-ānupalambhād iti cet, yatra tarhi tādātmyam upalabhyate na tatra...*

(Realist). Well then, (it will follow that), if identity is apprehended, there will be no necessary exclusion. (93. 8). And thus the ruby which is apprehended as identical through different space-times in a synthetic presentation called forth by a sensation,[1] (such a ruby) cannot be divided (in itself in a string of events). (93. 9). Therefore let there be two different space-times, or two different locations[2] (of the object in them), they are (really) mutually exclusive of one another, never have they been reflected[3] (in our knowledge) as being one and the same. But not so the ruby, the precious stone whose substance is embraced by these (different situations). The ruby is a thing apart from the two (points in time-space in which it alternately is located). (93. 12). If one thing is different, this does not mean that the other thing is different too. This would lead to the over-absurdity[4] that there would be altogether nothing identical (or similar in the Universe).

(93. 13). (The Buddhist). A constructed image which embraces different conditions of the object (sometimes) arises independently from any stimulus exercised by the object upon our sensitivity. Therefore (it is clear that the images in general) do not originate in our sensitivity.

(The Realist). This is not to the point[5]! Because, (it is true), we know from experence[6] that a man fallen desperately in love can evoke the image of his beloved and his perception will be as direct[7] (as a sensation), although there will be no stimulation of his senses (by the object). However, it does not mean that all our images are such, (*viz.*, that they are independent from our sensitivity), and that our sense data consisting in a feeling of awareness of a pattern of colour, blue or other, will also be independent from our sensitivity.[8]

---

1 *indriyajena vikalpena*. 2 *sambandhau*. 3 *apratibhāsanāt*.

4 *ati-prasangāt*. 5 *na sāmpratam*. 6 *dṛṣṭam*. 7 *avikalpakam*.

8 Lit., p. 93. 13—16. «And not correct is it that also in the absence of a contact between the sense organ and the object, because a concept (*vikalpasya*) exists consisting in touching (*parāmarṣa*) the former and following condition, there will be a non-sense-origination. If that were so, it has been observed, that even without any interaction between sense-organ and object there is also a direct perception (*avikalpakam*) regarding this object, of the love-sick man imagining his beloved, therefore it would follow that also direct perceptions (*avikalpakāḥ*) consisting in experiencing (*anubhava*) blue etc. will be not sense-originated». — It must be remembered that according to Buddhist philosophers even the image of a blue patch is already a construction or a real concept, since it includes the opposition with the non-blue or the other colours of the spectre, it is as A. Bain puts it, a positive and negative name. Pure sensation, the quite indefinite moment, is alone absolutely free from any mental construction.

(93.16). And if (the Buddhist) answers that he makes some difference between (a datum), the perception (of a pattern of colour), blue or other, and the perception (of the mental image) of the beloved woman, (we will retort that) from our standpoint there is likewise a difference between images originating in sensation and not so originating. (The latter are produced) by onr faculty of imagination, (the former) by the faculty of perception.[1]

(93.19). (The Buddhist). (The difference is the following one). When we in the image (we are contemplating) feel the action of our perceptive faculty, (when the image is a percept), (we conclude) that it contains a layer[2] of pure sensation, provided there is no evidence to the contrary.[3]

(93.20). (The Realist). The right view,[4] (on the contrary, is the following one). All the functions[5] (of which our cognition consists), without any exception,[6] have their origin in our sensitivity. They are either (direct), non-constructive[7] or (indirect), constructing and contrasting.[8] They all rush upon the same object in an uninterrupted stream, every one concerned only with itself[9] and disregarding all the others. They come up and down, (appear and disappear), it is impossible to discern (any fixed order between them), so that the one would necessarily follow the other. Therefore[10] those our images (or concepts) which have their origin in sensation (are percepts), produced by our faculty of sense perception, they are nothing else.[11]

§ 5. Answer to the Buddhist argument of the unutterable character of sensation.

(93.24). (The Realist). (The Buddhist argues[12] that sensation is unutterable, if it were utterable we would know what heat is from its name, just as we know it from actual experience, and if we could really feel it from its name, cold would be removed as soon as the word heat would be prononced. To this we answer), the sensation[13]

---

[1] Cp. the same phrasing in the closing word of the first chapter of N. b. ṭ., text p. 16. [2] *upādhi.* [3] *sati sambhave.*
[4] *yuktam utpaśyāmaḥ*, p. 93. 23—24. [5] *vṛttayaḥ.* [6] *sarvā eva.*
[7] *avikalpakāḥ.* [8] *vikalpakāḥ = anuvṛtti-vyāvṛtti-kalpakāḥ.*
[9] *aham-ahamikayā.* [10] Read *tasmāt.* [11] Read *nānye.*
[12] The argument is found in the first part, text p. 88. 26—28.
[13] *pratyakṣa.*

of heat and its name refer to the same real fact, however the reaction[1] is different, and this finds its explanation in the fact that the causation is different, the sensation is direct, the name an indirect suggestion. Therefore the sensation of cold ought not to disappear from the mere idea of heat (when suggested by its name), since an (actual) connection with some heat is indispensable. (Consequently the universal quality denoted by the name is not a reality *per se*).[2]

§ 6. Answer to the argument of the unreality of Universals.

(93.26). (The Realist[3]). (We will now examine the Buddhist

---

[1] *pratyaya*, here a term embracing both sensation and conception.

[2] Lit., p. 93.24—26. «And although word and sensation are intent upon reality (*vastu*), there is not non-difference of cognition, because through a difference of causes the difference of transcendency of the ken and non-transcendency is possible. Nor ought the removal of cold which originates from a conjunction with heat arise from knowledge of heat».

[3] In order to understand here the argument of the Naiyāyiks we must keep in mind that they admitted the reality of relations, *viz.*, they admitted that between the two terms related (*sambandhin*) there was a third unity in the shape of the relation itself (*sambandha*). The relation of this third unity with the related, terms was a so called «simple relation» (*svabhāva-sambandha* = *viśeṣaṇa-viśeṣya-bhāva*), i. e., a relation without a third relating unity. In this way the Indian realists escaped from the danger of an infinite process which obliged Bradley to deny the reality of all relations as well as of separate unities and to merge them all in One Whole. The Indian Realists assumed thus three kinds of relations, mechanical or separable conjunction (*saṃyoga*) between substances, inherence or inseparable conjunction (*samavāya*) between substance and attribute — these both relations real unities — and simple relation (*svabhāva-sambandha*) without the reality of the link. The absent jar, which was for them a reality, resided, they declared, upon the empty place, by a simple relation (*viśeṣaṇa-viśeṣya-bhāva* or *svabhāva - sambandha*) and was perceived by the senses. The subject - object relation (*viṣaya-viṣayi-bhāva*) was also a simple relation. The reality of relations required as a corollary the stability (*sthāyitva*) of enduring objects. The Buddhist who denied this stability and converted the existence of every object into a stream of momentary events (*kṣaṇikatva*) divided all relations into real (*vāstava*) — that was the relation of Causality between the consecutive moments (cp. above, Short Treatise, p. 69), and logical (*kalpita*) — these were the relations of the thing with its attributes and motions superimposed (*āropita*) upon it by productive imagination (*kalpanā* = *vikalpa-vāsanā*). The first relations can also be called external or causal (*tadutpatti*), the second internal or relations of existential Identity (*tādātmya*). The subject-object relation was thus a simple relation for the Realist,

argument[1] that if the bare presence of something is discerned at a great distance and if this fact is interpreted as) the perception of a substance supporting[2] the Universal[3] «Existence»,[4] why then are all the other attributes of the thing, (if they are on the same footing as the Universal Existence), not equally perceived all at once? (We answer, — because the thing and its attributes are not a unity). Indeed the substance of the thing is characterized by, (i. e. related to), its attributes, but neither the attributes nor their relation[5] to the substance are identical with the substance itself,[6] (all are different unities).[7]

(93. 28). If what is related to the substance (were nothing over and above the substance), if it were the substance itself, there would be (in the world) no relations altogether, because the same thing cannot be related with its own self[8]!

---

and a causal relation for the Buddhist. It is clear that the Buddhist never could accept the perceptibility of relations through the senses. Even causality as a relation was for him a construction of the mind. Only its members, the moments, were real.

1 Cp. above, in the first part, text p. 89. 17—90. 7. P. says that this is an answer to Dharmakīrti's vārtika *yasyāpi* etc, cp. p. 89. 28 ff.

2 *viśiṣṭe* = *upakārye*, cp. p. 89. 24.

3 *upādhi* = *jāti* (P).

4 For the Buddhist this is the only really perceived element and its perception the only real sense-perception, all the other elements of the subsequent distinct image are constructions of imagination.

5 *viśiṣṭatvam* = *sambandha* (P) = *samavāya*.

6 Every attribute is cognized according to the special conditions of its perceptibility (V). The Realists have never admitted that the attributes and the relations (*avaccheda* = *upakāra*) are supported by the substance in its one supporting essence (*upakāraka-eka-svabhāvatayā*), so as to be included in one unity (P). This means that the Realist has never admitted a mechanical separable relation (*saṃyoga*) between substance and attribute, comparable to apples in a basket. This is imputed by the Buddhist for the sake of argument (*upagama-vādo 'yam saugatasya*). The Buddhist is therefore accused of great skill in extraordinary combinations (*ati-parāmarśa*) with utter inaneness of real argument and receives at the end the advice of sticking to sound realism, p. 94. 15.

7 Lit., p. 93. 26—28. «And not, if this one is characterized by one characteristic, the consequence of it's being perceived as characterized by other characteristics. Indeed, the substance of the thing is characterized by the characteristics, but neither the characteristics nor the fact of being characterized by them are the substance».

8 Lit., 93. 28—94. 1. «And what is substance-joined is not substance, it it were so, no conjointness at all, indeed just this does not join with this». — Cp. Bradley, Logic, p. 254—«the terms of a relation must always be more than the relation between them, and, if it were not so, the relation would vanish».

§ 6. The substance-attribute relation is as real as the subject-object relation.

(94. 1). Moreover, (if you contend that the substance-attribute relation is contained in a single entity, you may extend [1] the argument to the subject-object relation.[2] Supposing) we perceive a coloured surface. It is a subject-object relation.[3] The object is a system of atoms (characterized by the fact of their cognition). But they do not constitute a single entity (with this cognition).[4] If they did, (this would involve you in a series of absurdities,[5] e. g., the following one). Since all cognitions by all observers would be on the same footing (as included in the atoms themselves), all the atoms would be (always) cognized by everybody.

(94. 4). (If you retort that the subject-object relation is distinguished from the substance-attribute relation in that) the atoms of the coloured surface remain as external objects (even if they are not perceived), i. e., even if their relation to their cognition (by an observer) does not exist, we will answer no! (the thing cannot be related as an object, if the relation does not exist), or else, if a thing could

---

[1] *na kevalam kālpanike vyavahāre tavaivam samarthanam, api tu pāramārthike' pi* (P). According to the Sautrāntikas the relation between *svalakṣaṇa* and *jñānākāra* is *pāramārthika.* — Cp. with this Bradley's difficulties in considering the subject-predicate relation, when a character is assigned to Reality, Logic, p. 484.

[2] *viṣaya-viṣayiṇoḥ parasparam viśeṣaṇa-viśeṣya-bhāvaḥ* (V).

[3] *viṣaya-grahaṇa-dharmam;* acc. to V. we must read — *dharma,* cp. Siddhānta-kaumudī, § 863.

[4] Lit., p. 94. 1—2. «Moreover the cognition of colour is an attribute of apprehending an object, intent upon a multitude of atoms, it is not the essence of the atoms (or, the atoms are not its essence)». — P. says that *paramāṇu-svabhāvaḥ* is a *ṣaṣṭhī-tatpuruṣa,* but he admits also the interprefation *paramāṇavo jñānasya svabhāvāḥ.* V. explains this remark by the fact that on the analogy of *viṣaya-grahaṇa-dharma* which is a *bahuvrīhi,* we would expect — *svabhāvam.*

[5] Other absurdities could be deduced, if cognition were included in the object, 1) if the cognition included in the atoms were one cognition, the atoms would be known only to one person, a second person would never know them, since his cognition would not be included, or else 2) there would be as many cognitions as there are atoms, 3) if the cognition were one, the atoms would be one atom and the thing would be invisible; the Buddhist would be bereft even of the constructed unity of the thing which would become imperceptible, 4) if the atoms became identical with their cognition, there would be only one atom and again an invisible thing, 5) the thing would be immaterial. Since these absurdities are too obvious, the author has neglected them (P).

remain an object of cognition (naturally), without entering into a special relation to an observer, every one would be omniscient,[1] (since every thing would be his object).

(94. 5). (The Buddhist remarks),—"Is not the subject-object relation[2] and ultimate fact[3]? The (essence of the external) thing is to be an object, and (the essence of) cognition is to be the subject, (there is no third reality between them in the shape of a relation).

(94. 6). (The Realist). Well then, (let us admit for the sake of argument) that the relation of substance and quality[4] is also, just as the subject-object relation, quite an ultimate fact; it will then be nothing over and above the terms related.[5] However, in the chapter devoted to the repudiation of the Buddhist theory of a Universal Flux,[6] we will prove (the contrary, i. e., we will prove) that the relations are (something real, something) over and above the things related.[7]

(94. 8). Thus, (the above Buddhist argument against the reality of the Universals, *viz.*), if one Universal, (say simple Existence) is perceived (at a great distance), all other attributes (if they are on the same footing as realities) ought to be equally perceived, (this argument) is wrong.[8]

§ 7. Is it possible that two separate realities should be cognized in one presentation?

(94. 9). (The Realist). (As to the other Buddhist argument[9] against the reliability of our qualified percepts and the reality of the

---

1 This over-absurdity (*atiprasanga*) is already mentioned above, text p. 88. 20. The Yogācāras, falling in line with some modern philosophers, have deduced from this consideration that the objects do not exist when we do not look at them; and the real world of the Realist is nothing but a dream.

2 *artha-jñānayoḥ.*

3 *svabhāva eva*, i. e., *svabhāva-sambandha*, cp. p. 287 n. 3.

4 *upādhi-upādhimator api.*

5 *svarūpa-abhedaḥ = svabhāva-anatirikta = svabhāva-sambandha.*

6 *kṣaṇikatva*, this theory transforms the world-process into strings of events developing in a staccato movement, cp. Tātp., p. 379. 27 ff.

7 In the Nyāya-kaṇikā, p. 256. 3, Vācaspati also records a Buddhist argument against the reality of relations which is just the one used by Bradley (Logic, p. 96, Appearance, p. 32).

8 For the Buddhist *jñānārthayor sambandha* is *kārya-kāraṇa-bhāva* and *svabhāva-sambandha*; for the Realist there is *svabhāva-sambandha* in the cases of *bhāva-abhāvayoḥ, samavāya-tadvatoḥ, viṣaya-viṣayinoḥ*, but a real link (*anubhūyamāna-sambandha=vigrahavān sambandhaḥ*) in *dravya-guṇa-karma-jāti-tadvatām* (P).

9 This argument appears in the first part, text p. 89. 12—17.

Universals which are reflected in them, the argument, namely that, if substance and attribute are two realities), the one characterized by the other,[1] they cannot be included into the compass of one presentation,[2] (since two separate things are always perceived in two separate presentations, this argument is also wrong). We answer as follows.[3]

(94.10). Neither would such a relation be possible, if substance and attribute were perceived in two separate (independent) presentations. Indeed, an (independent) cognition of the characterizing attribute, if it at the same time knows nothing about the characterized substance, will never be fit to determine this substance, and (*vice versa*, an independent) cognition of the characterized substance, if it knows nothing about the characterizing attribute, will not be able to determine its own object, because *(ex hypothesi)* they know nothing about one another.[4] (Consequently there must be one qualified percept corresponding to a characterized substance).

(Buddhist. The substance and quality relation is logical, it is not ultimately real, the ultimate reality is something unique, undivided, but) a congenital capacity[5] (of constructive imagination, our Reason, imputes upon it a double aspect as substance and quality. It is to this

---

[1] *viśeṣaṇa-viśeṣya-bhāva.*

[2] *eka-vijñāna-gocaratvepi* (read thus with the Benares ed).

[3] Lit., p. 94. 9—10. «And that between two objects of one cognition there is no relation of characteristic to characterized, to this we say».

[4] This is not a *bona fide* positive argument, but a dialectical retort called *pratibanda* = *pratibandī-karaṇa* = *deśya-*(or *codya-*)*-ābhāsa* = *tulyatā* = *tulyatā-āpādana.*

[5] «We do not deny the empirical usage of those Categories, but we explain it, to a certain extent (*yathā-kathamcit*), by assuming a special creative Force (*vāsanā*) of our reason. Those for whom their empirical use is founded on objective reality must explain it by its correspondence to that reality (*artha-dvāreṇa*)» (P). — *tābhyām vāsanā* = *viśeṣya-viśeṣaṇābhyām vāsanā*, the same idea as in the text p. 89. 11—12 is here laconically expressed. Thus the difference between the realistic and nominalistic view-points reduces to a shade — *viśiṣṭa-vyavahāram upapādayan saugato naiyāyikam eva āśrayate.* (V). The Realist finds the origin of our knowledge in the objective world (*artha*) and passed experience (*saṃskāra* = *vāsanā*), the Buddhist finds it also in the same two places, but the objective world for him are only the momentary things, the point-instants of efficiency (*sva-lakṣaṇa* = *kṣaṇa*), and past experience (*vāsanā*), replacing the Soul, assumes the role of a transcendental Force of Illusion (*avidyā-vāsanā* = *māyā*) creating the categories as «fictions of the mind... which a common delusion erroneously takes for independent facts» (Bradley, Logic, p. 96)

capacity of our Reason) that the logical relation of substance and quality is due.

§ 8. The Realist concludes.

(94.14). (The Realist). Let us for the present leave off considering the reality and the ideality[1] (of the Universals and their relation[2] to particulars)! We will take up this subject later on.[3] However, (let me tell you) that it would be better for you if all the efforts you are making to prove their[4] ideality[5] were bestowed on the proof of their (reality and) amenability to the senses.[6] If you would have done it, you would have (certainly) succeeded in establishing with clear evidence[7] that (substances and their qualities really exist and are picked up) by our faculty of perception,[8] (they are not constructed by our faculty of imagination[9]). (94.16). Otherwise, (if you are not willing to do this, there is nothing left for you than) to imagine[10] an under-stratum[11] of pure sensation[12] (corresponding to a thing in itself[13] upon which these categories have been erected by our Reason).

(94.16). (The Buddhist). (You maintain that these categories are produced from sensation). However, the senses do not think,[14] (they only react)! How could they put together[15] all (the complicated edifice of the categories), Substance, Quality and others?[16]

---

1 *avāstava* = *mānasatva*.

2 viz., *viśeṣana-viśeṣya-bhāva*.

3 N. S., II. 2. 58 ff.

4 *asya* = *viśeṣaṇa-viśeṣya-bhāvasya*.

5 *mānasatva*.

6 *indriya-jatva*.

7 *sākṣāt*, but P. has — *asya indriyārthasannikarṣajatve svābhāvikam sakṣātkāritvam eva pramāṇam ity arthaḥ*.

8 *darṣana-vyāpāratva* (from *darśana-vyāpāra* as *bahuvr.*) = *indriyajatva*.

9 *darśana-vyāpāra* is here evidently contrasted with *utprekṣā-vyāpāra*, cp. above text p. 88. 8—9 and the concluding passage of the first chapter of N. b. ṭ.

10 *kalpyeta* (sc. *bhavatā*), i. e., *vinā pramāṇena* (P).

11 *upadhānam*.

12 *nirvikalpaka*.

13 *svalakṣaṇa* = *paramārthasat* is evidently understood, cp. N. b. ṭ., I. 14.

14 *avicāraka*.

15 *samākalayet* = *vikalpayet* = *utprekṣeta* etc.

16 *viśeṣaṇa-viśeṣya-ādi*.

(94.18). (The Realist). Well then! do you really think that your Reason[1] can construct them?

(94.19). (The Buddhist). Yes, it does! because the Reason (is not limited in its objects as the senses are), it apprehends every object.

(94.19). (The Realist). (If you confine the function) of the Intellect to (the cognition) of the past,[2] how can you tell that) it can

---

1 *mānasam jñānam = vicārakam, saṃkalanakam jñānam*, i. e. Reason as constructive, logical, even mathematical (*saṃkalana = gaṇana-rūpa*) thought, thought integrational of diferentials (*kṣaṇa*). It is a spontaneous capacity of our Reason to create the Categories under which reality is subsumed by cognition.

2 *Manas* as *vikalpa-vāsanā* may be assimilated to Kant's Reason (*sarvārthān kalpayiṣyati*). Here perhaps the rôle assigned to the Intellect (*manas*) in early Buddhism, which is quite different, is alluded to. There it is a synonym of *vijñāna* and *citta*, they all mean pure sensation (*vijñānam prativijñaptiḥ*). It is classified as the sixth sense, the inner sense (*āyatana* № 6). The qualified percept, termed *saṃjñā*, is a special faculty (one of the *saṃskāras*) which is classified under *āyatana* № 12, (not among the *indriya*'s, but among the *viṣaya*'s), and under *saṃskāra-skandha*. As to the combining, creative force of the Reason it is rather to be found in the element (*dharma*) called *cetanā* «Will» which, besides its function as the personal will of individuals, has a cosmical function and is a synonym of *karma*. This meaning the term *cetanā* has only in Buddhism. When all the elements (*dharmas*) are classified in 18 *dhātus*, the intellect (*manas*), for the sake of symmetry, as is expressly stated, occupies two items, the *dhātu* № 6 (*mano-dhātu*) and the *dhātu* № 18 (*mano-vijñāna-dhātu*), they represent the same element of pure sensation (the same *dharma*), but they are distinguished in that the first is the preceding moment of consciousness, the moment preceding actual sensation (*sparša*), after sensation comes feeling (*vedanā*) and after feeling the image or qualified percept (*saṃjñā*). All these three mental phenomena are again classified under *āyatana* № 12. In this arrangement *manas*, although participating in the cognition of every object, fulfills the very modest part of a preceding moment of consciousness, it cannot be charged with the burden of constructing the Categories, Substance, Quality and others. The Sautrāntika-Yogācāra school has brushed this whole construction of the Vaibhāṣikas aside, and replaced it by two faculties, sensation and conception, also called direct and indirect cognition, or sense-perception and inference (*pratyakṣa-anumāna*). The *ālaya-vijñāna* of the old Yogācāras has been rejected. The functions of our Reason belong to indirect cognition; it is variously determined as arrangement (*kalpanā*), imagination (*utprekṣā = āropa*), dialectical arrangement (*vikalpa=atad-vyāvṛtti*), judgment (*adhyavasāya*) etc. Imagination is helped by memory and memory is founded on impressions (*saṃskāra*) left by past experience. For the Realist who admits a Soul, these impressions are residing in the Soul as qualities belonging to a spiritual substance. For the Buddhist, for whom there is no Soul and no substance altogether, the impressions become autonomous, they then receive the name of *vāsanā* (probably borrowed from the Sānkhyas) which is sometimes explained as *pūrvam jñānam*, sometimes as *sāmarthyam*, i. e., a

apprehend every object, (since it does not apprehend the present)? According to our system the Intellect[1] (or inner sense), although not limited in its objects (like the other senses), is nevertheless by itself just as unconscious (as all senses are). It does not think.[2] Conscious is the Soul alone. The Soul is the receptacle of all cognitions and of all the traces[3] which are left behind by them (in our experience). The Soul puts on record every sensation and arranges (past experience in suitable combinations).

(94. 22). (Kumārila[4]) has expressed this idea in the following words,

> The Soul alone contains all knowledge,[5]
> The Soul is known as the cognizing Ego,
> It has indeed[6] the force of recollection,
> It has the force of combination.

(94. 23). It is, indeed, the Soul that (at first) in a sensation[7] throws a glance[8] at an indistinct[9] object, the (actual) possessor (of those general attributes which are not noticed in the first moment). It then awakens the dormant traces[10] (of former experience and) cre-

---

force, or *the* Force, the Force *par excellence,* which creates the world as it appears to naive realism; *vikalpa-vāsanā* can thus be compared with Reason when it is charged with the task of an autonomous creation of the Categories of our Understanding. It is clear from the context that much of the business which in realistic systems devolves upon the Soul, is in Buddhism entrusted to *vāsanā* or *vikalpa-vāsanā.* We may accordingly translate it in this context as Reason. On the theory of cognition in Early Buddhism, cp. my Central Conception, p. 54. P. and V. explain — *yadi pūrvakam vijñānam manaḥ pratipatty-anubandhitayā na sarva-viṣayam,* and the following *acetanatayā* as *sakala-saṃskāra-anādhāratayā,* i. e., *na ālaya-vijñānatayā.*

1 *manas.* In the Nyāya-Vaiśeṣika realistic systems all consciousness is an appurtenance of an omnipresent substantial and eternal individual Soul. The senses are physical (*bhautika*). There is an inner sense, or Intellect (*manas*) which is also imagined as physical, having the dimension of an atom. It is swiftly moving between the senses so as to establish their connection with the Soul. It may be, to a certain extent, likened to a nervous current.

2 *na vicārakam.*

3 *saṃskāra.*

4 Ślokavārt., pratyakṣa, 122.

5 *sthitam jñānam* = *jñāna-vāsanā* (P).

6 *co hetau* (P).

7 *indriya-artha-sannikarṣāt.*

8 *ālocya.*

9 *sammugdha.*

10 *saṃskāra,* in Buddhism replaced by *vāsanā* which discharges the same function without a Soul.

ates a recollection of formerly experienced things.[1] Armed with this recollection, it creates, but again necessarily[2] through the medium of the senses, the judgment[3] «this is a cow!».

(94. 25). This idea has been expressed in the following (stanza[4]),

The senses are the instrument of knowledge,
The conscious Agent is the Soul alone,
And since it has the faculty of recollection
It will arrange[5] all things in combinations.

(94. 27). Therefore, although we agree that it is impossible to distinguish in a single presentation two different parts, the one causing the other, in as much as the one suggests the existence of the other,[6] nevertheless (a single cognition of a substance with its attributes is possible). There is in every percept an element of sensation[7] and an element of former experience.[8] They are (as though) the one characterized by the other. Both these elements together produce the qualified percept. This is the sort of efficient production

---

1 *pūrva-piṇḍa-anusmṛti.*

2 *prāg eva,* P. refers *prāg* to *ālocya.*

3 *vikalpayati*; *vikalpa* = *adhyavasāya* = *niścaya.* Thus, in order to save the qualified percept (*savikalpaka*), the senses activated by the Soul are credited not only with the faculty passively to react (*grahaṇa*), but also actively to construct (*kalpanā*) the object as substance and qualities. The senses think and judge, because the Soul thinks and judges through the senses (!).

4 The first part of it is found in Ślokavārt., pratyakṣa, 121.

5 *kalpayiṣyati,* the same function which p. 94. 23 is called *saṃdhāna* «synthesis».

6 *upakārya-upakāraka-bhāva* is a term which embraces both logical suggestion (*jñāpya-jñāpaka-bhāva*) and real causation (*kārya-kāraṇa-bhāva*). Here only the first is mentioned, but it is an *upalakṣaṇa,* both are meant (P). *nāsti* is explained as *na sarvatra asti, kvacit tu dravya-guṇa-karmaṇām asti,* because according to the Naiyāyiks there is a special quality or force (*sambandha*) uniting the substance with its qualities. P. remarks that there is no *upakāra* in the *viśeṣaṇa-viśeṣya-bhāva,* since it is *svābhāvika,* i. e., *svabhāva-sambandha,* cp. above notes on text p. 93. 26 and 89. 22. The *upakāra* is therefore limited to *atad-adhikaraṇa-vyavaccheda-pratīti-jananam eva,* what seems to be nothing but our old friend *apoha.* Udayana adds that since no *upakāra* is needed in a *svābhāvika* relation, we must understand the term to be used according to the majority of cases (*sambhava-prācuryeṇa*), i. e., according to the substance-quality relation where a *sambandha* = *upakāra* is needed. Evidently the problem of the relation of sensation to a perceptual concept is insoluble on realistic lines and Udayana rightly points to the contradictions in Vācaspati's expressions.

7 *arthālocana.*

8 *anugata-smaraṇa.*

which we here admit, (but not the causation between two parts of an indivisible presentation).[1]

(95. 1). Indeed, (in the external world) we see colours and things which possess them. Both these parts are real separate entities. Reality as it stands consists always of these two things.[2] It is wrong to maintain[3] that reality only appears in our knowledge in this (double aspect of Substance and Attribute), and that our Reason is autonomous[4] in creating them. On the contrary, they are reality itself,[5] (they appear as they exist).

(95. 3). (The circumstance that both parts are not grasped in full at the first moment of cognition is irrelevant. Nothing warrants us to expect) that whatever exists must be apprehended (in full at the first moment). If only one part of the reality is seized at first, this does not mean that the cognition is wrong. (95.4). The full complex percept[6] is produced by (two) causes,[7] (sensation and memory), as has been stated. It may very well be a constructed image[8] in which the colour will be assigned the rôle of an attribute, and the possessor of the colour the rôle of a substance. It will be a sense-perception[9] nevertheless, since, although representing a later stage, it is also produced by a sensory stimulus.[10] (95. 5). (In our opinion the circumstance that a part is later produced does not make it an «other» thing).

---

1 Lit., p. 94. 27—95. 1. «Therefore, although there is no relation (*bhāva*) of producing and being produced as a relation of intimating and being intimated, when something is apprehended in a single presentation, nevertheless efficient production (*upakārakatvam*) consists in being the efficient cause (*utpādakatvam*) in regard of a cognition which apprehends (*avagāhi*) the relation of characterizing attribute to characterized substance (*viśeṣaṇa-viśeṣya-bhāva*), between a glance at the object (*arthālocana*) and a recollection of its extensions (*anugata-smaraṇa*)».

2 *arthau.*

3 as the Buddhist have done in India and Kant in Europe.

4 *āpāta-janman* «born nobody knows where»; since in this context this characteristic is understood as the opposite of *artha-svarūpa-janman,* it is clear that an autonomous intellect is meant, an *intellectus archetypus* as contrasted with an empirical knowledge, an *intellectus ectypus.*

5 *svarūpa-mātreṇa.*

6 *savikalpakam.*

7 *sāmagrī,* «totality of causes and conditions» = *hetu-kāraṇa-sāmagrī;* here two causes are meant.

8 *kalpayet.*

9 *pratyakṣa.*

10 *indriya-artha-sannikarṣa-prabhavatayā.*

Things possess duration,[1] and (during the time their existence lasts) they gradually produce their results, by successively combining with the totality of causes and conditions [2] which create together a (stable) result. This our Theory of Causation will be established later on[3] (as against the Buddhists who admit causation only between moments and no duration at all).[4]

(95. 7). Thus (we can throw our conclusion in the form of the following syllogism [5] which can be considered) as proved.

1. (Thesis). The qualified percepts,[6] (the minor term), the subject of our discourse, are sense perceptions with respect to (all facts constituting) the proper domain [7] (of perception).

2. (Reason). Because they are produced by a sensory stimulus [8] with which they are invariably concomitant.

3. (Major premise and example). Whatsoever is thus (invariably concomitant with a sensory stimulus) is a sense-perception, just as a bare sensation.[9]

4. (Minor premise). The (qualified percepts) are such, *viz.*, (invariably concomitant with a sensory stimulus).

5. (Conclusion). Therefore they are such (sense-perceptions).

---

1 *akramasya.*

2 *sahakāri-bheda* = *hetu-kāraṇa-sāmagrī.*

3 In the chapter on the theory of Universal Flux (*kṣaṇikatva*), Tātp., p. 379. 27 ff.

4 Lit., p. 95. 1—6. «Indeed two things are also standing in a relation of colour and the possessor of colour, they are not thus apprehended by knowledge which is born adventitiously, (i. e., nobody knows wherefrom), but (they are both so apprehended) in their bare essence. Indeed, not is it that whatsoever exists, so much must be apprehended, therefore if one part is apprehended there is no want of reliability (*apramāṇatā*). But qualified (complex) perception born from the mentioned complex may (nevertheless) arrange (*kalpayet*) class-character etc. as the colour, the thing as the possessor of colour. It will be taught that also a non-gradual (thing) does its effect by degrees, owing to the gradual taking up of the co-factors».

5 The syllogism is here inductive-deductive, 5 membered, the form admitted in the Nyāya-Vaišeṣika school.

6 *vikalpāḥ* = *savikalpakam pratyakṣam.*

7 *svagocare;* the proper domain of sense perception is thus, for the Realist — the thing together with its qualities, for the Buddhist the bare thing without any qualities or relations.

8 *indriyārtha-sannikarṣa-ja.*

9 *ālocanam.*

(95.9). Thus it is established that the words «containing a perceptual judgment[1]» (have been inserted into the definition of sense perception in the aphorisms of the Nyāya system) in order to include among sense perceptions, (not only pure sensations, as the Buddhists contend, but) also the qualified percepts, (or perceptual judgments of the form «this is a cow»).

---

1 *vyavasāyātmaka.*

APPENDIX II.

Vācaspatimiśra on the Buddhist Theory of a radical distinction between sensation and conception (pramṇāa-vyavasthā *versus* pramāṇa-samplava).

Vācaspatimiśra on the Buddhist theory of a radical distinction between sensation and conception. (pramāṇa-vyavasthā *versus* pramāṇa-samplava).

§ 1. Preliminary.

The Indian realists, Naiyāyikas, Mīmāṃsakas etc., admitted two kinds of sense-perception, a primitive, simple sensation without participation of conception (*nirvikalpaka*), and a more determinate, complex perception with participation of conception or construction (*savikalpaka*). The difference between the two kinds of perception was for them one of degree, of distinctness and clearness. Dignāga starts, Pramāṇa-samuccaya, I. 2, by establishing a radical, essential and even, as will be seen, transcendental, difference between pure sensation and conception. The latter in his system includes judgment and inference. What the realists call perception and inference is by Dignāga replaced by sensation and conception; although he retained the terms, but gave them another interpretation and scope. We have thus in his system pure sensation and pure conception and the corresponding distinctions of pure object, which is identified with reality itself, or the thing in itself, and pure Universals. According to the realists the Universe contains particulars, universals and mixed things (*vyakti-jāti-ākṛti*). They are apprehended by different sense faculties and by ratiocination. The same thing may be cognized in many ways. There are no strict distinct limits for each source of knowledge. Dignāga opposed to this a sharp distinction between two sources corresponding to two kinds of objectivity. The objects are either Particulars or Universals and the sources of knowledge are, accordingly, either Sensation or Conception. Particular and Universal are empirically (*sāṃvyavahārika*) conceived by the realists, transcendentally (*paramārthataḥ*) understood by Dignāga. His Particular is the point instant, the thing in itself, absolutely undifferentiated and radically different from all constructions of the conceptive faculty of our mind. The concrete individual thing (*svabhāva-viśeṣa*), being a meeting point of several Universals, is nevertheless treated as a particular in European logic, for the Buddhists it is a construction and therefore treated as a Universal cognized by inference. The presence of fire is perceived, according to the Realists, by two sense-faculties, the visual sense and the tactile sense, or it may also be inferred from the presence of smoke. This fire is the concrete, empirical, physical object fire. For the Buddhists the sense of vision apprehends only colour, the tactile sense only heat, and the distinct image of fire is a construction of productive imagination (*kalpanā*), a Universal, a conception by dint of its sameness with similar points of reality and its contrast with every thing dissimilar. Such construction by similarity and contrast is the essence of indirect, conceptual or inferential knowledge. It will be seen from the examples given by Vācaspati that even the perceptual cognitions of the form «this is blue», «this is a jar», «this is a cow» are treated as perceptual judgments, as conceptions, i. e., conceiving states of mind and, therefore, inferences, cp. Tātp., p. 338. 0, *sa ca vikalpānām gocaro yo vikalpyate, deśa-kāla-avasthā-bhedena eka-tvena anusandhīyate* and Udayana adds *anumānātmakatvād vikalpasya.*—According to Sigwart, Logik, II p. 395, the perceptual judgment «this is gold» is an inference, — «sobald ich sage «es ist Gold», interpretire ich das Phämonen durch einen allgemeinen Begriff, und vollziehe einen Subsumtions-schluss». By a broader definition of inference all conceiving activity, all comparing knowledge (*sārūpya-pramāṇa*) is called indirect, i. e., non-sensuous cognition or inference. The Buddhist view receives the name of a «radical distinction» between the sources of our knowledge (*pramāṇa-vyavasthā*), the Realist maintains the view which is called their «coalescence» (*pramāṇa-samplava*).

§ 2. A PASSAGE OF UDDYOTAKĀRA'S NYĀYA-VĀRTIKA,

ed. Calcutta, 1897 (B. I), pp. 5. 5—5. 12.

(5. 5). (The Buddhist) objects and maintains that the cooperation[1] (of the different sources of our knowledge in the cognition of one and the same object) is impossible, since each of them has its own special field of action. This we (Naiyāyiks) deny, because we do not admit that (each has its own special object). There is indeed such a theory. Every source of our knowledge is supposed to have a special object. Sensation[2] apprehends particulars (only), inference[3] apprehends universals (exclusively). That alone is an object of our knowledge which is either a universal or a particular. Sensation is not intent upon a universal, and never is inference[4] intent upon a particular.[5] (5. 9). This we, (Naiyāyiks), deny, because we do not agree (with the reason). We neither admit that there are only two sources of knowledge, (sensation and conception[6]), nor that there are only two (quite distinct) objects of knowledge, (the particular[7] and the univer-

---

[1] Or mixture — *samplava = sankara = ekasmin viṣaye sarveṣām pramāṇā-nām pravṛttiḥ.*

[2] *pratyakṣa*, sense-perception according to the realists.

[3] *anumāna*, according to the Buddhists it includes conception.

[4] The Buddhist understands «conception».

[5] The Buddhist understands «the ultimate particular, the point-instant», the Naiyāyik understands the empirical concrete thing.

[6] The Naiyāyik understands «sense-perception and inference».

[7] i. e., the ultimate particular. This fundamental feature of the Buddhist system has been noticed and very well expressed by the learned editor of the Tattva-sangraha, Introduction p. 43, — *svalakṣaṇasya avācyatvam..., atyantika-*

sal), nor do we maintain that they cannot coalesce. Why? The sources are four in number, (perception, inference, analogy and testimony). The objects are of three kinds, the universal, the particular and the individual thing as possessor[1] of Universals, (concrete universals).

§ 3. The Comment of Vācaspatimiśra.

Nyāya-vārtika-tātparya-ṭīkā, Vizian. ed. pp. 12. 16 ff., Benares ed. (1925), pp. 17. 16 ff.

(12. 16). There is a theory (of the Buddhists according to which Perception is Sensation, and Inference is nothing but Conception, they represent two originally independent sources of our knowledge), each apprehends a special, originally independent[2] (element) in the cognized object. When a reference to them is made in the plural (and not in the dual), their subdivisions are meant. (12. 17). Sense-perception, being produced by a stimulus coming from an object, is intent upon that object, (because it is produced[3] by it. But moreover) only that thing is an object of perception whose presence invariably calls forth its image.[4] (12. 18). A Universal cannot produce the same (results, it neither can exercise a stimulus, nor can it call forth an image of the

---

vibhedaś cej jāter iṣṭaḥ svalakṣaṇāt, the particular is conceived as something unique and inexpressible, because possessing no connotation.

1 *tadvat* = *sāmānyavad-viśeṣaḥ*, it is really a «particular universal», a *contradictio in adjecto*, just as sensation-imagination.

2 It is not enough to state that perception and inference have special (*viśiṣṭa*) objects of cognition, these objects represent originally independent (*bhinna*) elements, since empirically there is an element of sense perception when we infer the presence of fire on the hill, and there is an element of constructive thought in every percept, thus *pratyakṣayor anumānayor vā samplave na bādhakam uktam* (*viśiṣṭa-śabdena*), *tathāpi vijātīya-pramāṇa-samplava-nirākaraṇa-paro' yam granthaḥ* (V).

3 It is not enough to mention that cognition is intent on the object (*artha-gocaras*) in order to imply that it is produced (*artha-sāmarthya-samuttha*) by it. This would be the standpoint of the Naiyāyiks and the Universals would be included among the causes of perception. Therefore emphasis is put upon *artha-sāmarthya.* Only an efficient object, only a particular is a cause (*hetu*) producing perception. This again is not enough, because there is always a plurality of causes. Therefore that cause alone is the object which calls forth in our cognition its own image (*ākāra-ādhāyaka*) (V).

4 Lit., p. 12. 17—18. «That object alone is the field of perception which obliges its own knowledge-reflex to conform with a positive concomitance and its contraposition». — *jñana-pratibhāsa* = *jñāna-ākāra* (V); *aniyata-pratibhāsa* is meant in the sense of N. b. ṭ., p. 8. 8.

object), since it is altogether devoid of any kind of (direct) causal efficiency.[1] (12.19). (Nor can the empirical[2] Particular, which is the meeting point of several Universals, do it. But the transcendental) Particular can. This alone is (pure reality), reality in the ultimate sense, (the thing in itself), because the essence of reality (according to the Buddhists) is just the faculty of being causally efficient. (12.20). It is a point-instant (in time-space, it transcends empirical space and empirical time[3]), it is just the thing in itself shorn of all its extensions.[4] It is not an extended body.[5] The ultimate reality is not a thing which is one and the same in different points of space.[6] Nor has it duration through different instants of time. Therefore sense cognition,[7] (sensation) apprehends the point-instant of reality,[8] (the efficiency moment, the thing in itself, which alone[9] possesses the faculty of affecting our sensitivity).[10]

(12.22). That a Particular (of this kind) should also be cognized (by the conceiving, synthetic, faculty of our mind, or) by inference, is impossible. (The sphere of absolute particulars is not the sphere of inference). The latter cognizes relations,[11] and relations are of two kinds only, (either logical or real), either Identity or Causation.[12] In an absolute particular no relation can be found. (Uniformally) related[13]

---

1 This is against the Naiyāyiks who admit that sense perception apprehends the particular and the Universals inhering in it as well, thus admitting a complex (*samplava*), qualified perception which the Buddhist denies as sense-perception; *viśiṣṭa-viṣayatvam abhipretya sāmānyasya pratyakṣa-aviṣayatvam uktam* (V).

2 *sāṃvyavahārikam svalakṣaṇam* (P), = *vyavahāra-mātra-viṣayaḥ=avāstavam* (V). *sāṃvyavahārikaḥ = anādi-vāsanā-vāsitaḥ* (N. Kandalī, p. 279. 15).

3 *artha-kriyā-sāmarthyena eva vastutva-vyāvasthāpanāt, kimartham tasya deśādy-ananugamaḥ?* (V). — *deśa-kāla-ananugatam vicāra-saham ity arthaḥ* (P).

4 *asādhāraṇa.*

5 *adeśātmaka.*

6 *deśato 'nanugamena.*

7 *pratyakṣam.*

8 *svalakṣaṇa = kṣana.*

9 *artha-kriyā-siddhy-artham tad-abhidhānam* (V).

10 Lit., p. 12. 20—22. «This alone is its own non-shared (read *asādhāraṇam*) essence, that there is ultimate reality of the one which possesses an un-spatial Ego by not being extended (*ananugama*) in space (or by not being repeated in space), and there is momentariness by not running through (*ananugama*) time».

11 *gṛhīta-pratibandha-hetukam.*

12 Causation between «strings of events» (*santāna*) is also constructed, cp. N. b. ṭ., p. 69.

13 *pratibandhaḥ sāmānya-dharmāv āśrayate.*

are always two Universals. (12. 24). (But a real Universal is an impossibility).[1] A thing cannot represent a unity and reside in different places, at different times and in different conditions. (12. 25). (Since Universals are thus illusory realities, and inferential knowledge has to deal with Universals only, does this mean that their knowledge is altogether objectless? [2]). The Universals are indeed (not realities [3]), they are logical constructions produced by a congenital capacity (of our Reason [4]); we must admit that their objective existence in the external world, belongs (only) to the domain of our inferential knowledge, it is either a dialectical (superstructure upon reality) or an objectivized image.[5]

(12. 26). Their essence,[6] indeed, (is not positive, but relative, since they always contain) a correlative negation.[7] (This is proved by three [8] facts), 1) (reality is not their essential attribute), they are positive and negative,[9] 2) (although internal mental constructions they have) resemblance with external reality, and 3) they are *distinct* [10]

---

1 *paramārthasat sāmānyam vicāra-asaham* (P), *kārtsnya-ekadeśa-vṛtti-nirāsāt* (V); the Buddhists admit a *vyāvṛtti-rūpam, alīkam, anādi-vikalpa-vāsanā-vāsitam sāmānyam.*

2 *tat kim, sāmānyasya asattvāt, svalakṣaṇe ca pratibandha-graha-asambhavād anumānam nirviṣayam eva?* (P).

3 *vikalpādhiṣṭhānam* = (*vikalpa*)-*viṣayo 'līkam iti yāvat* (V).

4 ......*adhiṣṭhānam vikalpākārasya vā alīkasya bāhyatvam anumāna-gocaro*... V. thinks that *alīkabāhyatvam* and *vikalpākāratvam* refer to two different ideas (*matāntaram*), the first refers to an objectivized image, the second, as is seen from the sequel, — to a dialectical superstructure, having *indirect* reality.

5 Lit., p. 12. 23—26. «That indeed is caused by the apprehended mark of a (uniform) tie. And the tie consisting in identity-with-that and origination-from-that cannot be grasped in a particular as its object, it thus reposes on two Universals. And the one Universal cannot reside in different places, times and conditions. Therefore it is the place of construction originating from a beginningless Force, it must be assumed that the sphere of inference is the externality of a (dialectically) constructed form or an objectivized image (*alīkasya*)».

6 *niṣṭhā* = *svarūpam.*

7 *anya-vyāvṛtti*=*apoha, anya-vyāvṛtti-niṣṭham*=*pratiyogi-niṣedha-svarūpam.*

8 Cp. the somewhat different formulation of the three points Tātp., p. 340. 6 ff., translated in Appendix V.

9 Cp. Bain, Logic, I. 54 ff. — Existence, is not their essence, their *asādhāraṇa-dharma*, in contradistinction from an ultimate particular (*svalakṣaṇa*) in which existence is inherent, which is only positive, since we cannot say «something is not», because this «something» is nothing but mere existence, pure reality. Cp. Tātp., p. 338. 1 and F. Brentano, Psychologie, II, p. 49 ff.

10 *niyata-pratibhāsa* = *niyata-ākāra* as in N. b. ṭ., p. 70. 6, = *anya-vyāvṛttyā;* it is exactly the opposite of *niyata-pratibhāsa* in N. b. ṭ., p. 8—9, where it is = *arthena, indriyeṇa vā, niyamita.*

images, (i. e., they contain a sharp distinction from, or negation of, all other things).

(As regards the first point the argument can be thrown into the form of the following syllogism).

(Major premise). Whatsoever can alternately be affirmed and denied (has no existence in itself, but becomes existent relatively), as distinguished from something else.

(Example). As, e. g., the fact of not being a body of limited dimensions.[1] It is found in consciousness (which is not impenetrable and) exists, and in the horns on the head of a hare which do not exist (and therefore are also not a body).

(Minor premise). A (Universal, being) a mental construction,[2] can be alternately affirmed and denied, «there is a jar», «there is no jar».

(Conclusion). («Jar» is not existence «in itself», it exists relatively to other things).

(Verification). If «jar» were existence in itself,[3] the words «it is» would never be used, being superfluous; nor would the words «it is not» be possible, because they would contradict (the existence which would then be included in the thing «jar»). If it were non-existence in itself, the same consequence would follow.[4]

(13. 4). (As to the second point, it should be noticed that the Universal) is devoid of every direct efficiency, it is an (imagined) illusive Ens. There is no sameness between it and the point of absolute reality (represented by the element «this», so as to produce the perceptual judgment «*this* is a cow»), except the fact that both exclude[5] the negation («non-cow»).[6]

(13. 5). (As to the third point, it must be noticed that) the distinct image of «a cow», and the definite connotative designation «a cow», would never be possible without (having present in the mind its) distinctions[7] from horses or other (animals).[8]

---

1 *amūrta*. 2 *vikalpa-gocaro*. 3 *asādhāraṇo-bhāvo*.

4 Cp. Bradley, Logic, p. 121, «It may be, after all, that everything «is» just so far as «it is not», and again «is not» just so far as it «is».

5 Instead of *manyate' nya-vyāvṛtteḥ* read *anyato' nya-vyāvṛtteḥ* or *anyatra vyāvṛtteḥ*.

6 Cp. Bradley, *ibid.* «If everything thus has its discrepant in itself, then every thing in a sense must be its own discrepancy».

7 Cp. Bradley, *ibid.* «Everything is determined by all negation».

8 Lit., p. 13. 5. «And the definite idea and designation «cow» not without the exclusion of horse etc.». — What is here called *niyatā buddhiḥ* refers to the same

(13.6). Therefore the Universal is nothing but the Negation of the Correlative,[1] it is (therefore) an internal[2] (mental construction, but related to external reality, since in our behaviour) we do not notice the difference,[3] it is quasi-included in external reality[4] and thus gives reality[5] to our (conceptual, or) inferential knowledge. (13. 7). Being thus indirectly connected with external reality, it has efficacy,[6] it becomes consistent experience.[7] Although it is an illusion of reality, it is nevertheless a source of right knowledge, in so far it belongs to a man who thinks (and acts) consistently.[8]

(13. 9). Thus it is that the particular (as the ultimate reality) is not the object on which inference (or conception) is intent. That sensation, on the other hand, is not intent on Universals, has already been pointed out. Nor is there any other source of knowledge (except these two, sensation and conception). Whatsoever (has a claim to be) a source of right cognition is included in these two, or, if it is not included in them, it is not a source of right knowledge. Nor is there any other object of cognition different from the particular, (*viz.* the ultimately particular) and the Universal, (there is no mixed entity in the cognition of which) both sources of our knowledge could participate.

---

thing which above p. 12. 27 was designated as *niyata-pratibhāsa*. It is evident that *niyata* is here used in the sense of «distinct», *niyata-pratibhāsa* = *niyatā buddhiḥ* = *niyata-ākāra*, not in the sense of «limited» *niyata* = *arthena indriyeṇa vā niyamita* as in N. b. ṭ., p. 8. 9 and 8. 20, cp. above, p. 305 n. 10.

1 *anya-vyāvṛtti-rūpam.*

2 *abāhyam.*

3 *bāhya-bheda-agrahāt*, i. e, we do not think that «a cow» is not an external object.

4 *bāhyatvena avasīyamānam.*

5 *pravartayati.*

6 *prāpayat.*

7 *saṃvādakam sat.*

8 Our conceptual knowledge is thus a dream accompanying real facts. This theory will be expounded with more detail in Appendix V. — Lit.. p. 13. 6—8. «Therefore the Universal whose essence is distinction from the different (*anya-vyāvṛtti*), being non-external, being plunged in the external through non-perception of the difference from the external, directs inference towards the external; and by being indirectly tied up to the external, it makes us reach the external; being consistent, although wrong, it is, by being located in the cognizer, a means of right knowledge».

§ 4. The answer of Uddyotakāra.

Nyāya-vārt., pp. 5. 9—14.

(5.9). This is wrong! We do not admit it. We, first of all, do not admit (the limitation) of two sources of knowledge, nor of two kinds of object, nor of the impossibility of their mixture. Why? The sources of our knowledge are, indeed, four in number, (perception, inference, analogy and testimony). The objects are of three kinds, the particulars, the universals and their mixture. (5.11). A mixt (knowledge) is possible in that sense that the same object can be apprehended by any source of knowledge, as e. g., by the senses (etc.). (5.12). A sense faculty is a source of knowledge, it illumines, (as it were), the objects. Sometimes it is limited, sometimes mixed. It is limited, e. g., in the cognition of odours (which can be apprehended by one sense faculty only). It is not limited in the cognition of solid bodies which are cognized by two senses, (by vision and touch). As regards the perception of Existence or of the fact of possessing attributes, (i. e., the Categories of Substance and Quality), this is cognized by every sense.

§ 5. Comment of Vācaspatimiśra.

Tātp., p. 13. 12—13.

(13.12). In saying «this is wrong!» (the author of the Vārtika) rejects (the Buddhist theory) and explains (the reasons for doing it). That the theory is really such, (i. e., wrong), will be (repeatedly) stated here, (in the course of this our work).

(Remark of Udayana, p. 114). If the Universal is unreal and the Absolute Particular alone ultimately real, the latter cannot be mixed with the former, because a combination of the real with the unreal is impossible. (The empirical individual thing is thus founded on an absurdity). The author says, «that this theory is wrong, (will be proved later on)». He wishes to say that the path (of Buddhist philosophy) leads into great depths (and cannot be lightly dealt with at present).

(Remark of Vardhamāna, *ibid.*). Since the (Buddhist) onslaught leads into great depths, if the author would undertake to refute it here, it would make his text very heavy (reading [1])!

[1] This is the first short statement of Buddhist Idealism in the Tātparyaṭīkā. Its different phases will be repeatedly expounded and refuted in detail in the course of the work wheresoever the opportunity of doing it will present itself, cp. pp. 88 ff., 100 ff., 127 ff., 144 ff., 182 ff., 268 ff., 338 ff., 379.25 ff., 463 ff. etc. etc. These subtlest Naiyāyiks, Udayana and Vardhamāna, deemed Buddhist philosophy an «impervious path», *gahanaḥ panthāḥ*.

APPENDIX III.

The Theory of Mental Sensation (mānasa-pratyakṣa).

The theory of Mental Sensation.

I.

Preliminary.

The genesis of sensation according to the Abhidharma can be represented thus (cp. my Central Conception, p. 54 ff.), —

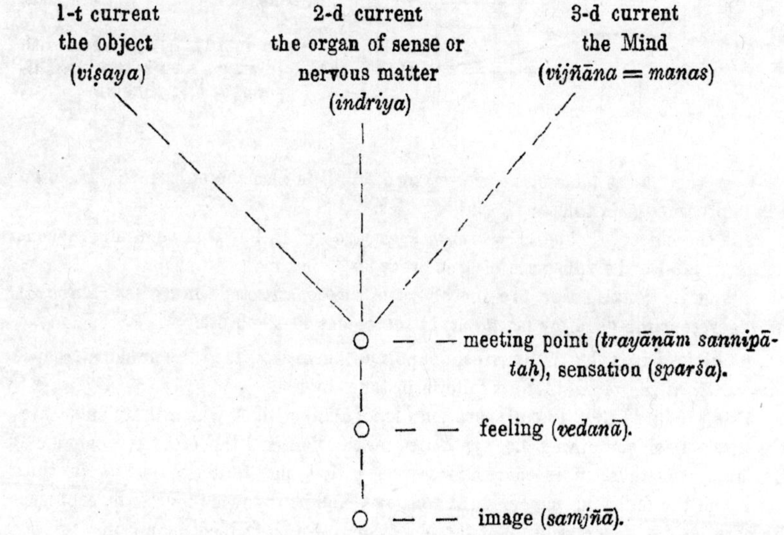

The moment of sensation (*sparśa*) has 1) a homogeneous cause (*causa materialis* = *samanantara-pratyaya*) in the preceding moment of the Mind, or of consciousness in general, including latent consciousness, 2) a predominant cause (*causa efficiens* = *adhipati-pratyaya*), in the special sense-organ (*indriya*), and 3) an object-cause (*ālambana-pratyaya*), say, in a patch of colour for the sense of vision. The interconnection of these cooperating elements is imagined in early Buddhism according to the prevailing view of causality (*pratītya-samutpāda*) as functions of one another, as cooperators or cooperating forces (*saṃskāra* = *sambhūya kāriṇaḥ*), because a cause never works alone (*na kiṃcid ekam ekasmāt*). The elements are not pulling one another, but appearing contiguously (*nirantara-utpanna*) as functions of one another. In Mahāyāna the conception is radically changed. All elements of existence have only *relative* (*śūnya*) reality, as «the long and the short» (*dīrgha-hrasva-vat*), cp. my Nirvāṇa, p. 30 ff. The separation of the unique current of consciousness into subject and object is already an impntation (*āropa* = *kalpanā* = *grāhya-grāhaka-kalpanā*). Instead of the three real currents producing together sensation in early Buddhism, we now have in the Sautrāntika-Yogācāra school only two constructed ones. Their cooperation can be represented in the following table, —

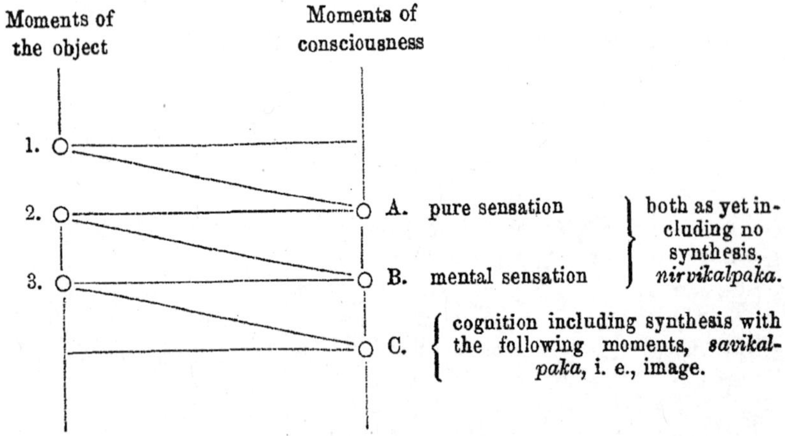

1 is the object (*ālambana-pratyaya*) of A; it is also the substrate (*upādāna*) of 2; it precedes A in time.

2 is the object (*ālambana* = *viṣaya* = *gocara*) of B, but it is contemporaneous with A; it is also the substrate of 3, it precedes B in time.

3 and its continuation are the object of the constructed image (*savikalpaka*), they represent the duration (*santāna*) of the object 1—2—3 etc.

A is produced by 1; it is contemporaneous with 2; it is the substrate-cause (*samanantara-pratyaya*) of B, it follows in time upon 1.

B is produced by 2 in collaboration (*sahakārin*) with A which is its substrate; it is also a flash containing no synthetic imagination and therefore not capable of illusion or mistake; it is contemporaneons with 3 and follows upon 2 in time.

3 and the following moments, as well as C and its following moments, represent the parallel duration (*santāna*) of the object and of its qualified cognition.

1 = *svalakṣaṇam* = *prathama-kṣaṇaḥ* = *rūpa-kṣaṇāntarasya upādānam* = *indriya-vijñāna-viṣayaḥ* = *tasya ca ālambanam* = *nirvikalpaka-janakam*.

2 = *rūpa-kṣaṇāntaram* = *prathama-kṣaṇasya upādeyam* = *uttara-kṣaṇaḥ* = *nirvikalpaka-jñāna-samāna-kālaḥ* = *nirvikalpaka-indriya-vijñāsyasya sahakāri* (*mānasa pratyakṣa-utpāda-kriyām prati*) = *mānasa-pratyakṣa-viṣayaḥ* = *tasya ca ālambanam* = *mānasa-pratyakṣa-janakam*.

3 etc. = *santāna*.

A = *indriyaja-vijñānam* = *svalakṣaṇa-ālambitam* = *samanantara-pratyayaḥ* (*mānasa-pratyakṣam prati*) = *rūpa-kṣaṇāntarasya sahakāri* = *viśadābham* = *nirvikalpaka-pratyakṣam*.

B = *mano-vijñānam* = *manasi-kāraḥ* = *rūpa-kṣaṇāntara-ālambitam* = *rūpa-kṣaṇāntara-sahakāriṇā indriya-vijñānena janitam* = *nirvikalpakam* = *viśadābham* = *mānasa-pratyakṣam*.

would it be right to assume that the mentioning of consciousness[1] (in the above aphorism of Dharmakīrti) refers to something mental,[2] (not to pure sensitivity), since the point at issue[3] (in this passage) is whether pure passive sensitivity[4] (without any mental spontaneity) can guide our purposive actions,[5] and whether it can be reckoned as a source of right knowledge. (31. 10). Indeed, how is it possible to consider a simple passive reflex[6] to be a source of right cognition? (O, yes!). It is (a source of right knowledge), if it accomplishes its own function. And its function is just the function of evoking a mental image of its own object.[7]

Consequently this (argument of Jñānagarbha and consorts) is negligible,[8] because a mental construction can be evoked from a heterogeneous source, (from a simple reflex).

III.

The Nyāya-kaṇikā of Vācaspatimiśra on the theory of Mental Sensation.

(Reprint from the Pandit, p. 120. 7—120. 17).

(120. 7). We (Buddhists[9]) do not favour (the theory according to which) the Mind is a special organ[10] (of sense), an organ to be put on the same line as the organ of vision etc.[11] But we maintain (that the Mind is a stream of thought, and in that stream) every preceding mo-

---

[1] *saṃvit.*

[2] *mānasam.*

[3] *cintyatvāt.*

[4] *indriya-vijñānasya.*

[5] *vyavahāreṇa.*

[6] *indriya-vijñānasya.*

[7] *svaviṣaye vikalpa-janakatvam.*

[8] *yat kiṃcit.*

[9] I. e., the Yogācāra-Sautrāntika school, cp. Tātp., p. 97. 1. The other Hīnayānists reckon 6 organs of sense, 5 of the outer senses and one of the inner sense. They also have a series of 22 *indriyas*, but then these organs have quite a different function, cp. Abh. Kośa, I. 48. The realists, Nyāya, Vaišeṣika, Mīmāṃsaka, and the Sāṅkhyas characterize *manas*, the Mind, as a sixth organ. The Mādhyamika-Buddhists and the Vedāntins, very characteristically, fall in line with the realists. According to W. Ruben, Die Nyāyasūtras, An. 55, 56, the author of these sūtras did not regard *manas* as an *indriya*, but according to the Bhāṣya, he admitted 5 outer and one inner sense, jus as the other realists.

[10] *kiṃcid indriyāntaram* cp. Tātp., p. 97. 28 ff.

[11] *cakṣurādivat.*

positive and negative examples.[1] Nor is the origination of a mental element possible as long as (the stream of consciousness) is engaged in a visual reflex. Indeed, we never have experienced the simultaneous appearauco of two simple reflexes,[2] two bare sensations, of the same patch of blue colour at once. This has never been witnessed.

(31.1). Therefore a constrncted image[3] can be called forth by a simple reflex[4] (or pure sensation), not withstanding it is heterogeneous. Consequently the production of a mental image does not prove the existence of a mental (element in the form of a mental sensation). (31.2). Nor is it right to maintain that a simple reflex and a mental image[5] belong to two different streams of existence,[6] just as the two (personal) streams called Devadatta and Yajñadatta are. (If that were the case), it would make[7] the origination (of the mental image) from the quite heterogeneous simple reflex impossible. (31.4). Both (phenomena, the bare sensation and the constructed image), belong to the same stream of consciousness; we must therefore necessarily admit the (partially) heterogeneous origin of the mental image, because (Dharmakīrti), the author of the Vārtika,[8] has stated,

«When the one, (the simple reflex), is apprehended, (the other features) also will apprehended, they be appear by the force of a conscious (germ),[9] and by the force of memory which has ist own function to achieve».

Here in the words «a conscious (germ)» just a simple reflex[10] is referred to, not something mental.[11] (31.8). And therefore if it is asked how can a constructed mental image, (i. e.), something remembered, be called forth by a simple (passive) reflex, (we answer, that this is possible), because heterogeneous origin (is also possible). (31.9). Nor

---

1 N. Kaṇikā, p. 121.11, gives the example of the cognition of something refreshing which follows in the track of a sensation of white colour produced by a piece of camphor, white colour and refreshment are heterogenous.

2 *nirvikalpakayor.*

3 *vikalpakasya.*

4 *indriya-vijñānād eva.*

5 *savikalpaka-nirvikalpakayor.*

6 *bhinna-santāna-vartitvam.*

7 The *cheda* before *yena* must be dropped, and one after *na syāt* inserted.

8 Not found in Pr.-vārt., but Pr.-viniścaya (Co-ni, f. 158a. 3) has — *don mthoñ-ba-ñid mthoñ-ba-la, myoñ-bai-mthu-las byuñ-ba-yi, dran-pasmthoñ-bar ḥdod-pa-yis, tha-sñad rab-tu ḥjug-pa-yin.* (A. Vostrikoff).

9 *samvit-sāmarthya.*

10 *indriya-vijñānam eva.*

11 *mānasam.*

sations (of different origin), of different senses, should arise simultaneously.

(30.12). Nor is it right to maintain that mental sensation, since it is not apprehended as existing separately, does not exist at all. (Its existence is proved by the fact that) in the next moment something homogeneous with it, *viz.*, the image of the blue patch of colour,[2] is present to the mind. If there were (nothing intermediate), no mental sentation, then the constructed image of the blue [1] patch, which immediately follows in its track,[2] could not arise. A mental construction can arise out of something homogeneous with it, out of something mental,[3] not out of a quite heterogeneous simple reflex.[4] (30.15). Just as when a patch of blue is apprehended[5] (by the senses in the stream of thought called) Devadatta, the judgment[6] «this is blue» is produced (in the same person), not in the (different) stream called Yajñadatta. The difference between mental sensation[7] and the enduring phenomenon of a mental image[8] is not the same, (not so radical), as between the two streams of (passive) pure sensitivity and of the stream of a (spontaneous) mentality.[9] Indeed, both (the mental sensation and the mental image) do not represent (passive pure) sensitivity, both are called *mental*.

(30.17). Our reply to the upholders of this theory is as follows. You maintain that a mental construction[10] must arise out of something homogeneous with it, and you deduce from that the necessary existence of a mental (element, although unobservable directly). This deduction is unwarranted, because experience proves[11] that things can (also) originate out of elements heterogeneous from them. This can be established by

---

1 *nīla-vikalpa;* thus the perception of a definite colour is considered to be a mental construction by way of contrasting the blue with the non-blue; it is also a perceptual judgment «this is blue».

2 *tat-pṛṣṭha-bhāvī.*

3 *mānasātmano.*

4 *indriya-vijñānāt.*

5 *gṛhīte.*

6 *niścayo.*

7 *mānasa- viz. pratyakṣa.*

8 *mano-vikalpa-santāna.*

9 *mano-vijñāna-santāna,* in the opinion of Jñānagarbha it is a *santāna,* in the opinion of Dharmottara it is a *kṣaṇa.* Instead of *tathendriyā...... bhinnatvāt* read *yathendriya... bhinnatvam na tathā...*

10 *vikalpa.*

11 *darśanāt.*

pudiates the argument adduced by Jñānagarbha[1] and others for the sake of establishing its existence, (viz., the argument that) mental constructions spring up[2] (from mental sensation which is something intermediate between pure sensation and conception). (He repudiates this argument) indirectly,[3] (without mentioning it), simply by emphasizing[4] (that no direct proof is needed).

(30. 9). They, indeed, give the following explanation. Both the pure sensation and the mental one arise while the sense of vision is operating. It is not right to maintain that two sensations cannot exist at the same time, because two sensations of the same sense really cannot, but not two sensations of two different senses. It has been established (in the Abhidharma) that six (different sensations) can exist simultaneously.[5] Therefore (there is no impossibility that) two sen-

---

[1] Ācārya Jñānagarbha is the author of a short treatise Satya-dvaya-vibhanga-kārikā and its vṛtti. A block print of its Tibetan translation, printed at the monastery of Bde-chen-lhun-grub-gliṅ (Aga in Transbaikalia) is in my posession. There is in the Bstan-ḥgyur, Mdo v. 28, only a commentary on it, the Satya-dvaya-vibhanga-pañjikā, by Šāntirakṣita. Whether it is the same person as the celebrated ācārya Bodhisattva is doubted by Tāranātha, cp. his text p. 163. Tsoṅ-kha-pa denies it, cp. Legs-bšad-sñiṅbo, f. 70^{b}. 2. Kārikā 14 (mūla f. 2, vṛtti f. 7) deals with causality in the usual Mādhyamika style—«a manifold Ens is neither produced from a manifold, nor from a unity, nothing is produced from a unity, nor a unity from a manifold». The *vṛtti* explains, that if many causes did not produce many things, they would cease to be causes, since every cause, in order to be a cause, must produce something. The perception of colour, being produced by a double cause, the sense of vision and the intellect (*samanantara-pratyaya* = *manas*), the result is also double, as containing a sensation and a conception. On the other hand, the percept of a colour is a unity (*ekam vijñānam*). As a Mādhyamika the author evidently rejects the momentarines of being (*kṣaṇikatva* and *svalakṣaṇa*), he conditionally may admit the parallel run of sensation and thought. It seems that some of those logicians who were Mādhyamikas at heart admitted the possibility of a parallel similtaneous run of sensation and thought, but not Haribhadra, cp. below, p. 339 n., and this has given rise to much controversy in India and Tibet, as will be seen from the Blo-rigs of Jamyaṅ-shadba, translated below. In the Tattvas., p. 391, Šāntirakṣita and Kamalašīla admit heterogeneous causation, cp. also Parišuddhi, p. 609 ff.

[2] *vikalpodayāt* are evidently the first words of a kārikā by Jñānagarbha or some of his followers, it is repeated below, p. 30. 17, in the words *samāna-jatīya-vikalpodayāt*.

[3] *bhangyā*. [4] *avadhāraṇād eva*.

[5] According Abh. Koša-bh., I. 28, a great number of mental *dharmas* can arise simultaneously. The idea of the Sāṅkhyas is also that different sensations o different senses may be present to the mind simultaneously, the idea of the Naiyāyiks is that this is quite impossible.

will make the object present in our ken; why indeed should then pure sensation not arise in the second moment also, why should not both moments receive the same name of a sensation of the outer sense (or of pure sensation)?[1]

(30.5). Another question is then asked. If mental sensation[2] is really something different from pure sensation,[3] this must be established by positive facts, by observation, (experiment[4] or other proofs). (If that cannot be done), then its definition, so far it is not at all founded on facts,[5] will be (useless, it will be as though) non existent. (Dharmottara) answers,[6] «the existence of snch mental sensation is a postulate of our system, there are no facts to prove its existence».[7] In describing the character of this (mental sensation) as something similar to sensation in general[8] and in stating that its existence is assumed as a postulate of the (whole) systeme, Dharmottara re-

---

1 Lit., p. 30. 3—5. «When the eye is engaged, why, for sure, should cognition by the outer sense not arise, (a cognition) homogeneous, since the second moment would (also) be making amenable to sense? therefore why should not both be called sensations of the outer sense?».—We would expect *yogyī-karaṇe* instead of *yogya-karaṇe* = *sākṣāt-kāriṇi*, cp. above p. 8. 10. Dharmottara says, p. 10. 22 ff., that if we do not admit, or postulate, a difference in kind between the first and the second moment of sensation, there will be no pure sensation of the outer sense altogether. The Ṭipp. explains this as meaning that either both moments will equally be pure sensation or none. Dh. insists that we have no empirical proof of the existence of mental sensation in the second moment of perception, because we cannot isolate it and observe it, but if we will not assume its existence, the whole system falls asunder, since the system requires a radical difference between the world of pure sense and the constructions of imagination. The arguments in favour of the existence of mental sensation imagined by Jñānagarbha and others Dharmottara does not admit as valid, cp. below.

2 *mānasam pratyakṣam.*

3 *indriya-jñānāt.*

4 As has been pointed out in the Introduction Dharmakīrti establishes the existence of pure sensation by what may be called a real experiment (*pratyakṣa*) in introspection, *pratyakṣam kalpanāpoḍham pratyakṣeṇaiva sidhyati.*

5 *yāvatā pramāṇāsiddham eva.*

6 N. b. ṭ., p. 11. 1.

7 Mallavādī, f. 31, introduces this passage thus, *nanu indriya-vijñāna-vyatirikta-lakṣaṇakasya adarśanāt lakṣaṇam ayuktam evety āśankyāha etac cetyādi* (p. 11. 1). The existence of a mental sensation following immediately on the sensation of the outer sense is thus regarded as something transcendental (*śin-tu lkog-pa* = *atyanta-parokṣa*).

8 *indriya-vijñāna-sadṛśa.*

C = *savikalpakam jñānam = santānālambitam = adhyavasāyātmakam = sārūpyātmakam = anya-vyāvṛtti-rūpam = anumānātmakam = nirvikalpaka-jñāna-utpannatvāt pratyakṣam api.*

In the now following translations from the Ṭippaṇī, from Vācaspatimiśra's Nyāya-kaṇikā, and from Jamyañ-shadba's Blo-rigs a vivid pincture can be gathered of the controversies that raged in India and Tibet on this interesting problem of a gap between a simple reflex and a constructed mental image, a problem not yet solved by modern epistemology.

II.

The Nyāya-bindu-ṭīkā-ṭippaṇī on the Theory of Mental Sensation.

(N. b. ṭ.-ṭippaṇī, ed. B. B., pp. 29. 15—31. 11).

(29. 15). Further, is it sure that as long as the outer sense faculty[1] is engaged, the existence of a mental feeling (concerning the same object) is excluded? Answering this question (Dharmottara) says, «as long as the sense of vision is engaged whatever (bit) of cognition (of the presence) of a patch of colour (in our ken) we may have, necessarily depends on that sense (alone)».[2]

(30. 1). The following question is then raised. Although two homogeneous cognitions cannot exist at the same moment, (two heterogeneous ones can). Therefore a sensation of the outer sense[3] may exist at the first moment (and continue to exist) in the second moment when a mental feeling will (also) arise, notwithstanding the fact that the organ of vision will continue to be engaged?[4] To this (Dharmottara's) answer is as follows. «(This is impossible, since) otherwise, says he, no such sensation as depends (exclusively) on the sense of vision would at all exist»,[5] (i. e., there will be no pure sensation, no simple reflex althogether, there will always be a germ of mental synthesis present).

(30. 3). What he means is this. If we assume that in the second moment (the outer sense, e. g.), the sense of vision, is engaged just as it is engaged in the first moment, its function will also be the same, it

---

[1] *cakṣuṣi.*

[2] *sarvendriyāśritam* in 29. 16 is meant for *sarvam indryāśritam jñānam.*

[3] *indriya-vijñānam.*

[4] *vyāpāravati cakṣuṣi.*

[5] Cp. N. b. ṭ., p. 10. 21.

ment is (the cause, viz.), the substrate-cause,[1] of the next following one. This preceding moment, indeed, is called (by us) the «homogeneously immediate cause». It is homogeneous as a (moment in the same stream) of consciousness, and it is immediate, since it is separated by nothing. (120.10). This (second moment of cognition) is created,[2] (not alone by a stimulus coming from the object upon the senses, as the first moment of sensation is, but) it is created by the next following moment of the object,[3] in collaboration[4] with the Mind, (i. e., according to our theory) with the preceding moment of consciousness, the moment of pure sensation.[5] This second moment of the *object* is contemporaneous[6] with the first moment of *sensation*, or with the simple reflex, produced by the first moment of the object. The first moment of the object is (also) the substrate-cause (or *causa materialis*)[7] of the second moment of the same object.[8] (Thus there are two consecutive moments of the object producing two consecutive moments of cognition; the latter are, a simple reflex, and a flash of mental feeling). This (mental flash) comes after the moment of pure sensation has passed.[9] It is (not an abstract mental cognition, it is) vivid[10] (as a sense-cognition). It has its own external object, namely the second moment of the object, the moment which collaborates in producing it. Such is mental sensation. It is not pure sensation[11] (which is a simple reflex upon the outer sense), because it springs up when the simple reflex[12] is over.

(120.14). Neither (can it be characterized) as an intention upon something internal,[13] because the object upon which it is intent is the

---

1 *upādānena.*

2 *janitam*, p. 120.12.

3 *rūpa-kṣaṇa-antareṇa*, p. 120.11 to be corrected from *rūpekṣaṇa-.*

4 *sahakāriṇā*, p. 120.11.

5 *indriyaja-vijñāna* (p. 120.10) = *nirvikalpaka-pratyakṣa.*

6 *samāna-kālena*, p. 120.12.

7 It is clear that the *samanantara-pratyaya*, also called *upasarpaṇa-pratyaya* is the counterpart of the *samavāyi-kāraṇa* of the Naiyāyiks.

8 *indriyaja-(vijñānasya)-viṣaya-kṣaṇa-upādānena* = *prathama-viṣaya-kṣaṇa-upādānena*, viz., *rūpa-kṣana-antareṇa*, i. e., *dvitīyena kṣaṇena prathama-kṣaṇa-upādānavatā.*

9 *uparata-indriya-vyāpārasya* (sc. *puruṣasya*), cp. lit. transl. below.

10 *viśadābha* = *viśadābhāsa.*

11 *indriyajam.*

12 *tad-(-indriya-)-vyāpāra-.*

13 *āntara.*

second moment of the external object, this second moment of the object being a product of its preceding, first, moment and the first moment, (as has been just mentioned), is the object grasped by pure sensation, (the object which has produced the simple reflex).[1]

(120. 15). And it is not true that there would be no blind and no deaf persons, (if they could perceive external objects by a reaction upon their inner sense).[2] The sense faculty,[3] (the organs of the outer sense), are absent with them, hence they have no pure sensation,[4] (no simple reflex) produced upon the senses.[5] They, consequently, (will have no mental sensation, since) the latter is a product[6] of the former. Nor can it be objected that (such a secondary mental flash) is not a sensation. It is a sensation, because it is vivid, (it is not an abstract thought).[7]

---

1 The compound *indriyaja-viṣaya....* must be analysed thus — *indriya-jasya* (= *nirvikalpakasya*) *yo viṣayaḥ* (= *svalakṣaṇam*), *tasya yad vijñānam* (*nirvikalpakam*), *tasya* (*nirvikalpakasya*) *yo viṣaya-kṣaṇaḥ* (= *svalakṣaṇam* = *prathamo viṣaya-kṣaṇaḥ*), *tena yaj janitam kṣaṇāntaram* (= *rūpa-kṣaṇāntaram* = *dvitīyo viṣaya-kṣaṇaḥ*), *tasya gocaratvam*, *tasmāt*. The upshot is very simple, the second moment of cognition apprehends the second moment of the object. But they are not contemporaneous, since the moment of the apprehended object precedes the moment of consciousness which apprehends it.

2 Cp. N. b. ṭ., p. 10. 20.

3 *indriya*.

4 *-vijñāna*.

5 *taj-ja-*.

6 Lit. «because there is no substrate».

7 Lit., p. 120. 7—17. «We do not favour (the thing) called the Mind as some other organ, the eye etc. But we say that it is just the preceding (pure) consciousness, the substrate of the following one. Just this, indeed, is similar as sensation and immediate as non-separated, it is called a homogeneonsly immediate cause. Here it is created (*janita*) by another moment of colour (*rūpa*) having as its substrate (*upādānena*) the object-moment of that-sense-produced (*tad-indrya-ja*), with whose sense-produced consciousness (*vijñāna*) as a homogeneous precedent it is working together, having as object the moment which is its own producer, a vividly shining cognition (of the man) whose sense-function is over, this is mental sensation. It is not sense-produced, since it appears when the function of the latter is passed. An it has no object in the internal, (it is not intent upon internal facts), because it is intent (*gocara*) upon another moment, produced by the object-moment of the consciousness of the object of the sense-produced, (cp. above the analysis of the compound). Nor is there absence of the blind and deaf, because of the circumstance (*-tayā*) that they have no organs, (and) because through not having consciousness by it produced, a substrate is lacking. Nor is it non-sense-perception, since it shines vividly».

In the sequel, pp. 120. 21—124. 6, Vācaspatimiśra, commenting upon the corresponding passage of Maṇḍanamiśra's Vidhiviveka, ibid, pp. 120. 3—122. 6, sets forth a series of arguments against the theory of a momentary mental sensation. They all centre in the realistic view that the object of cognition has *duration*, that it is a real unity which cannot be split into moments. This unity of the object, as Vācaspati puts it, «is consecrated by Recognition»,[1] in the perceptual judgment «this is the same crystal (which I have seen before)». Maṇḍanamiśra says,[2] «the object is not present to the senses as split into moments, it appears to the senses as a unity; moreover we repudiate your theory of momentariness, (or universal flow of all existence)».[3] And Vācaspati winds up[4] the discussion by stating, «thus it is established that the senses do not reflect separate moments, therefore it is not possible that the intellect should grasp the moment following upon the moment which has produced the simple reflex, but, on the contrary,[5] the intellect grasps just the same object as has been grasped by the senses».

On these grounds the Realists establish the theory of what they call the «duplication» of the sources of our knowledge *(pramāṇa-samplava)*.[6] The same object is apprehended twice, at first by the senses dimly, and then a second time, by the intellect with more clarity and distinction.

IV

The Grand Lama Jam-yañ-shadpa on the theory of Mental Sensation.

Blo-rigs,[7] f. 28ᵃ. 3—31ᵇ. 4 (Tsu-gol).

The second (variety of direct cognition) is mental sensation (or 28ᵃ. 3
non-sensuous feeling of the presence of an object in our ken). Its definition, its own varieties, and the peculiarity of its genesis, these three points, (will be examined).

---

1 *Ibid.*, p. 126. 9, *pratyabhijñā bhagavatī sthāpayiṣyati (abhedam).*

2 Ibid., p. 122. 5—6.

3 *kṣaṇikatva-pratikṣepāt.*

4 *Ibid.*, p. 126. 4—6.

5 Read *kiṃ ca* instead of *kiṃcid.*

6 Cp. above, Appendix II.

7 The Grand Lama Jam-yañ-shad-pa (Ḥjam-dbyañ-bšad-pa Ṅag-dbañ-brtson-grus) lived in the XVIIth century (1648-1722). He is the founder

§ 1. Definition.

28a. 5 By a mental sensation (or non-sensuous feeling) we understand a (peculiar) sensation of the presence of an external object, a sensation following upon the sensation of the outer sense which itself evokes it; it apprehends the second moment of the object seized by the (outer) sense, and (it is also) characterized as excluding all constructive imagination and (hence) incapable of illusion. This is its definition. The fact falling under this definition[1] is, (e. g.), the mental feeling[2] of something blue evoked by the outer sense (of vision) when the latter contains the reflex[3] of a patch of blue colour. Incidentally the words of the definition «it is a sensation apprehending the second moment of the object seized by the outer sense which itself evokes it» do away with the query, whether (it is not a recollection, whether) it apprehends its own object, an object present to it,[4] or whether it is not
28a. 6 (already) a clear and distinct cognition.[5] Indeed, «The Language of Dialectics[6]» says, «it is excluded that it apprehends the already apprehended, because it seizes the second moment». Since it is (also) defined as a moment of consciousness immediately following the preceding moment (in the same stream of thought), it is distinguished from the direct perception of the Mystic, (whose direct perception of the Absolute is also an intelligible intuition, but not at all homogeneous with the moment which precedes the moment of illumination). In telling that mental sensation is produced by, (and follows on), the sensation of the outer sense, an objection urged (upon this theory) by non-Buddhists is answered, (the objection namely) that there would be no blind and no

---

of the monastery La-brang, a very celebrated seat of learning in Amdo (Eastern Tibet), and the author of an enormous amount of scholastic literature very much studied in Mongolia and Tibet.

1 *mtshan-gzhi.*

2 *sñon-ḥdzin yid-mṅon.*

3 *sṅor-snaṅ dbaṅ-mṅon.*

4 it really apprehends the moment of the object which immediately precedes in time the moment of mental sensation, cp. above table on p. 312.

5 *bcad-śes* = *paricchinnam jñānam;* the definition of clear and distinct cognition is given in the Blo-rigs, 10a. 2. On f. 6b. 1 This kind of cognition is mentioned as one of the seven different kinds of mental processes (*blo-rigs*).

6 Btog-ge-skad = Tarka-bhāṣā, a work by Mahāpaṇḍita Bhikṣu Mokṣākaragupta (Cordier has Ghābriyākaragupta du grand Vihāra de Jagattala) = Thar-pai-ḥbyuṅ-gnas-kyi-spas-pa; it is incorporated into the Bstan-ḥgyur, Mdo, vol. 112 (ze), the passage quoted is found f. 380b. 6 (Narthang).

deaf persons, if they could perceive external objects by a mental sensation.[1] The (same) «Language of Dialectics» has it, «since it is said that 28b. 2
it is a intellectual fact, (but) produced by sense-cognition...» beginning with this passage up to the words — «...by telling that it is exclusively produced by a homogeneous preceding moment, the confusion of an (ordinary) mental feeling with the intuition of the Buddhist Saint, (the Mystic), is excluded[2]». Thus it is that the fact of being a mental sensation is necessarily subordinated to the fact of being produced by a sensation of the outer sense. This is (also confirmed) by the «Language of Dialectics», where it is said that «mental sensation is produced immediately after the sensation of the outer sense[3]».

§ 2. The varieties of mental sensation.

There are five varieties of mental sensation, viz., mental sensation 28b. 3
grasping colour (and lines), mental sensation grasping sounds, olfactory mental sensation, flavorous mental sensation and tactile mental sensation.

§ 3. The peculiarity of the genesis of mental sensation. Three theories.

The (author) of the «Mine of Logic»[4] (Saskya-paṇḍita) 28b. 4
and his followers maintain that (there are three different solutions of this problem, viz.) —

1. (First theory). At first one moment of pure sensation, (a simple reflex produced by a stimulus sent out by the object) arises. After it one moment of mental sensation is produced. After it, one moment of

1 Cp. N. b. ṭ., p. 10. 20.

2 *Ibid.*, f. 380b. 6 — 381a. 1.

3 This quotation is probably an abridgement of the passage — *rañ-gi yul-gyis de-ma-thag lhan-cig-byed-pa-can-gyi dbañ-poi šes-pa mtshañs-pa-de-ma-thag-pai rkyen-gyis bskyed-pa yid-gyi rnam-par-šes-pai zhes pao, ibid.*

4 Rigs-gter = Nyāya-nidhi, a concise treatise in mnemonic verses by Saskya-paṇḍita Kun-dgaḥ-rgyal-mtshan, held in high esteem by the Tibetans as their oldest original exposition of Buddhist Epistemology. Copies of the Lhasa block print are very rare, no one is available at Leningrad, but a commentary by Rgyal-tshab is found in the Mus. As. Petr. The author lived in the XIIth century (1182—1251) A. D. in the celebrated Sa-skya monastery, south-east of Lhasa. He is also the founder of a sect which had many votaries and monasteries, at present either in decay or turned over to the dominant Ge-lugs-pa sect. According to tradition his work was originally written in sanscrit.

pure sensation (again) arises, and so on, pure sensation and mental sensation (of the object) are alternately[1] produced. This is, (they maintain), the opinion of the author of the Alaṃkāra, (i. e., of Prajñākaragupta).

28b. 5 2. (Second theory). At first one moment of pure sensation arises. In the next moment there is a double sensation, a pure one and a mental one, it is the second moment of (outer) sensation, together with the first moment of (internal) mental feeling. They are conditioned by the immediately preceding moment of consciousness, playing the part of a *causa materialis*, and the sense-faculty, playing the part of a *causa efficiens*. In accordance with these conditions, (both sensations) run simultaneously (making two parallel streams of sensation), beginning from the second moment of pure sensation up to the end (of the perceptual process). During it (we must distinguish) three elements, a double element of sensation of the external object and one element of internal self-consciousness. This three-partite sense-perception is advocated, (they maintain), by the brahmin Śankarānanda.[3]

29a. 2 3. (Third theory). Finally, Master Dharmottara maintains that (a mental sensation) necessarily arises just when pure sensation is at an end.[4]

From among these three theories the first and the last, (says the author of the «Mine of Logic»), are wrong. That one in the middle is alone the right one. It is there stated,[5]

---

1 *spel-mar*, lit. «mixed up».

2 Pramāṇa-vārtika-alaṃkāra, a work by Prajñākaragupta usually quoted as Rgyan-khan-po = Alaṃkāropadhyāya. The work contains a commentary on books II—IV of Dharmakīrti's Pramāṇa-vārtika and fills up the vols 99 and 100 of the Bstan-ḥgyur Mdo. The author lived presumably in the IXth century and initiated a new school in the interpretation of Dharmakīrti's philosophy.

3 Bram-ze Bde-byed-dgaḥ-pa, author of an independent commentary on the Pramāṇa-vārtika of Dharmakīrti called Pramāṇa-vārtika-ṭīkā. The work was planned on a very large scale and has been left unfinished. The extant part covers only the first book of Dharmakīrti and fills up vols 103 and 104 of the Bstan-ḥgyur, Mdo. The author was a Kashmir brahmin, he is usually quoted as the Great Brahmin, Bram-ze chen-po.

4 *dbaṅ-mṅon-gyi rgyun-mthaḥ-kho-nar*; *rgyun* usually means duration, but here it is apparently used in the sense of no-duration or duration of a moment. It is just the opinion mentioned N. b. ṭ., p. 11. 1.

5 Since no copy of the Rigs-gter is available, this quotation could be identified only in Rgyal-tshab's commentary, where it is found f. 91a. 1. The

«Both the alternation (theory of Prajnākaragupta), and the substitution (theory of Dharmottara) contain contradictions».

(Such is the view of Saskya-paṇḍita and his followers)

§ 4. Examination of the theory ascribed to Prajñākaragupta.

Now, it is wrong to impute to (the author) of the Alaṃkāra, 29^{a}.4
(Prajñākaragupta), the alternation theory. Not in a single Tibetan translation of the commentary and sub-commentary on this work can it be found.

(Khai-ḍub)[1] in his «Elucidation of the seven Treatises» says, «That the author of the Aḷaṃkāra favoured the alternation theory, (according to which the moments of pure and of mental sensation follow one another in turns), this is founded exclusively upon a tradition current among scholars. Not in a single work, as far as they are translated in Tibetan, does it appear, neither in the text of the Alaṃkāra itself nor in the literature following it».

And (Rgyal-tshab) in his Comment upon the «Mine of 29^{a}.5
Logic»[2] says, «the alternation theory is not to be found in the translations of the Alaṃkāra existing at present». It seems that the alternation theory is a great mystification,[3] because it is pregnant of

---

full title of this commentary is Tshad-ma-rigs-gter-gyi rnam-bšad legs-par-bšad-pai sñiṅ-po, but it is also known under the abridged title of Rigs-gter-dar-ṭik; we read there — *Rgyan-gyi bzhed-pai spel-ma-dañ-ni Chos-mchog-gis bzhed-pai rgyun-gyi mthaḥ-mar gcig-kho-nar skye-ba gñis-ka-la-yañ gnod-byed yod-par thal*, etc. The words marked by o will make up together the verse quoted.

[1] Mkhas-grub, a pupil of Tsoṅ-kha-pa; the work quoted is a commentary upon the seven logical treatises of Dharmakīrti, its full title is Tshad-ma-sde-bdun-gyi rgyan yid-kyi mun-sel, the passage is found on f. 117^{a}.4 of the block print made in the Aga monastery, Bde-chen-lhun-grub-gliṅ. Tsoṅ-kha-pa (1357—1419), the founder of the now dominant sect, had three celebrated pupils, Gyal-tshab (Rgyal-tshab, 1364—1462), Khai-ḍub (Mkhas-grub, 1385—1438) and Gendunḍub (Dge-ḥdun-grub, 1391—1474). The latter was the first Dalai Lama. All have written logical works. The Commentaries of Rgyal-tshab are renouned for original and deep thought, they are usually called dar-ṭik=vistara-ṭīkā's, those of Khai-ḍub are distinguished by detailed discussion, they are called ṭik-chen = mahāṭīkā's.

[2] Rigs-gter-dar-ṭik, f. 91^{b}. 6 (Aga).

[3] *tha-chad.*

many mistakes and it contradicts the standpoint of Pramāṇa-
29b. 1 vārtika, (although everyone pretends) to speak from this very standpoint. (If it be objected that) this is not clear,[1] (that the Pramāṇa-vārtika is not explicit enough, we will answer that), (on the alternation theory) the alternately arising sensations (of the outer sense) will not be able to apprehend the object continually, just because the moments of the outer and the inner sense will be mixed up. And it is also impossible to admit (that there will be a continuous apprehension also on the alternation hypothesis), because it is stated in the Pramāṇa-vārtika,[2] «if a thing would be apprehended in turns, we would not have the experience of its continuous contemplation».

(Moreover the contention) that the Alaṃkāra favours the alternation theory cannot be correct, because (we know that) it assumes simultaneity of the sensations of the outer and inner senses, (their pa-
29b. 2 rallel run). That this is really so,[3] (follows out of the circumstance that) this Master did admit in mental sensation a germ of constructive thonght,[4] and he did not deem it a contradiction to admit the simultaneous existence of pure sensation[5] with constructive thought. Indeed,
29b. 3 he delivers himself as follows, «the element[6] «this» (of the judgment «this is that») which arises in us with regard to something lying in our ken before we have recognized[7] in it (an habitual object), we reckon as a mental sensation, since its (function) is to make the thing present to our senses[8]». It is also true that Dharmottara has a quarrel[9] with him (on this point), as will be detailed later on.

29b. 4 If we compute the elements present in such sense-perception (as ascribed to the author of the Alaṃkāra), we will really find that they are three, (viz. an element of pure sensation or simple reflex, an element of mental feeling including some imagination, and the element

---

1 *ma-grub-na.*

2 Pr. vārt., ch. III (on sense-perception), *kārikā* 256, f. 183b. 2 in the Aga block-print.

3 *der-thal.*

4 *rtog-pa gcig = kalpanā kācid.*

5 *dbaṅ-mṅon dus-su*, lit., «that at the time of sensation of the (outer) sense construction is produced».

6 *śes-pa = jñānam* in the sense of *idaṃtā-jñānam.*

7 *goms-las mdun-na gnas-pa-las = abhyāsāt prāg avasthānāt*, this evidently refers to *anabhyāsa-daśā-āpannam jñānam*, cp. Tātp., p. 8—9.

8 This quotation could not yet be identified.

9 Cp. N. b. ṭ., p. 11. 1 and the Ṭipp. translated here.

of self-consciousness). (However) this theory (of the author) of the Alaṃkāra cannot be accepted (as a correct account of the part) of the senses (in perception), because, as a consequence[1] of it, we will be obliged to admit the presence of (a germ) of constructive imagination in direct cognition,[2] (i. e., in a simple reflex), whereas (our best authorities), the Sūtra[3] and the Vārtika, establish that sensation, (i. e., the part of the senses in cognition, or the simple reflex) does not contain any mental construction. This and other objections (can be made against this theory). However, from the stand-point of the Extreme Relativists, (the Prāsangika-Mādhyamikas), it will be quite acceptable.[4]

§ 5. Examination of the theory ascribed to Šankarānanda.

Further, it is not true that the (Great) Brahmin favoured the theory imputed to him (by Saskya-paṇḍita), because neither the translation of his works nor the authorities of the Holy Land[5] point to it as favoured by him. It is a bare affirmation (on his part). (Khai-ḍub) in his «Elucidation of the Seven Treatises» says,[6] «It is a mere tradition among the ancient (teachers) that the Great Brahmin favoured such a view. Not in any of the Tibetan translations of his works is the source (of this mistake) to be found». Moreover, you (Saskya-paṇḍita) assume that this (sensuous part of cognition which you imagine as having been analyzed by Šankarānanda) necessarily always contains three elements.[7] We object that the precision

29b. 5 29b. 6

---

1 *thal-ba dañ.*

2 *sgrub-ḥjug-pai rtog-pa*; the realistic Vaibhāṣikas admit a germ of imagination, called by them *svabhāva-vitarka* in every sense-cognition, cp. Abh. Koša, I. 33. The Mādhyamikas would probably fall in line with the realists.

3 Sūtra, in this context, refers to Dignāga's Pramāṇa-samuccaya.

4 The Mādhyamikas cannot admit the absolute reality of the «thing in itself» (*svalakṣaṇa*), because this would mean a deadly blow to their Universal Relativism. As a consequence of this they cannot accept neither the theory of sense-perception, nor the separateness of the two sources of cognition (*pramāṇa-vyavasthā*), nor self-perception (*svasaṃvedana*) ect., cp. my Nirvāṇa, p. 135 ff. They are obliged to accept the realistic logic of the Naiyāyikas with a proviso concerning its relativity and worthlessness for the cognition of the Absolute.

5 *ḥphags-yul* = *ārya-deša*, India, *ārya* means here a Buddhist Saint.

6 *Op. cit.*, f. 123b. 6.

7 viz., sensation of the outer sense, mental sensation and self-consciousness.

of these mathematics[1] is questionable. You may, if you like to, reckon seven elements, it will even be more accurate. Really it is so,[2] because on the side of the object there are five elements, (its five sensible qualities), with the element of sensation and the element of attention,[3]
30a. 2 this will really make seven elements. (Rgyal-tshab) in his Commentary upon the «Mine of Logic» says,[4] «if we reckon the elements in the object, they will be five, and if we add the elements of sense and of the intellect, it will make seven». And (Khai-ḍub) in his «Elucidation of the Seven Treatises» also says,[5] «there is no great ntility in computing how many elements there are in this genesis (of mental sensation), therefore there can be no precision in the work of computing them».

30a. 4 And further. It is a very great mistake to imagine that in the stream of thought which constitutes the ordinary man,[6] at the time when his sensitivity is engaged in apprehending an external patch of colour, there is (simultaneously with it) an intelligible feeling clearly apprehending this same patch. This is in glaring contradiction with all the passages of the Seven Treatises and their commentaries where the definition of mental sensation is taught. Not enough of that, it is directly denied in passages like the following ones,

30a. 5 1. «Allthoug heterogeneous (sensations) may arise simultaneously, but one of them will be (always) predominant in clarity. It will then weaken the force of the others and will not allow any other to appear over the threshold of consciousness».[7]

---

1 *rtsi-dgos-pa*.

2 *der thal*.

3 *yid-byed* = *manasikāra*, here mental sensation (*mānasa-pratyakṣa*) is simply called attention, which is one of the *citta-mahā-bhūmika-dharmas*.

4 Rigs-gter-dar-ṭik, f. 91b. 5.

5 *Op. cit.*, f. 124a. 2.

6 *pṛthag-jana*. The holy man (*ārya*) is credited with exceptional intuition.

7 Pr. vārt., III ch., *kārikā* 521, f. 230a. 5 of the Aga block-print. Only the first part of the *kārikā* is quoted by Jam-yaṅ, the second part is,

nus-pa ñams-par byas-pai-phyir,
kun-gzhi-las gzhan ḥbyuṅ-ba min.

The term *kun-gzhi* = *ālaya* in this place has given rise to a great deal of controversy among Tibetan commentators. The majority are not inclined to interpret it as meaning *ālaya-vijñāna* in the sense in which that term is used by Asanga and Vasubandhu, i. e., as implying the doctrine of a «store-honse-consciousness» where all the traces of former impressions and all the germs of the futnre ones are stored up. They therefore interpret here *ālaya* as meaning only *mano-vijñāna*, and

2. «When consciousness is engaged in cognizing one object, it is incapable of cognizing (at the same time) another one», etc. etc.[1]

The first[2] (circumstance, *viz.*, the circumstance that the theory of 30ª. 6
the simultaneous presence of two different sensations is in glaring

---

the passage as meaning «there is thus (in that moment) no other consciousness than mental sensation». It seems however possible to assign to *ālaya* here the meaning of consciousness in general without referring it to a special theory. As a matter of fact the Pramāṇa-vārtika never mentions the *ālaya-vijñāna* doctrine and there is evidence enough to maintain that Dharmakīrti rejected it as a Soul in disguise. Jam-yañ-shadpa says, Phar-phyin-mthaḥ-dpyod, vol. *ña.* (rnam-rdzogs), f. 61 ᵇ³—62 ᵃ³ (Aga) — *yañ kha-cig, kun-gzhii sten-du tshogs-drug ḥkhor-bcas-pa gag-pa-la ḥdod-pa mi-ḥthad-par-thal, skabs-ḥdir kun-zhi mi ḥdod-pai-phyir. ḥgrel-chen-du, lañ-gšegs-kyi luñ, rnam-par-thar-pa* (read *šes-pa*) *bryad-ñid dañ zhes drañs tsam ma-gtogs kun-zhi dañ ñon-yid-kyi bšad-pa med-pai-phyir. khyab-ste,* Ḥphags-Señ *dañ sde-bdun skabs-su kun-zhi ḥdod-pa mun-mdaḥ yin-pai-phyir.* Zhi-ḥtshos *kyañ, dbu-ma-rgyan dañ rañ-ḥgrel las, de dag-gis ni gañ sña-phyi med-par sems-gñis ḥbyuñ-ba ḥdi-ni gnas·med-do nas, luñ dañ ḥgal-ba bzlog dkao, zhes dañ. rnam-ḥgrel-las, rtog-gñis cig-car mthoñ-ba med, ces gsuñs-pai phyir. sde-bdun-rgyan-las, sde-bdun-gyi skabs-su kun-gzhi khas-len-par ḥdod-pa de-dag-ni rañ-ñid ma-rig-pai dmus loñ zhes-so.* This means—Further, some maintain, that it is wrong to hold that all six kinds of consciousness with the accompanying mental phenomena (*citta-caitta*) are locked up in a store-house-consciousness, because in this case, (i. e. from the standpoint of the Svātantrikas) the «store-house» doctrine is not accepted. With the exception of the Lankāvatāra-sūtra and some purely metaphorical (*drañs* = *neyya*) expressions neither the «store house» nor the *kliṣṭa-manas* are ever mentioned. This is right, because both Ārya (Vimuktasena) and Haribhadra, and also (Dharmakīrti) in his Seven Treatises hold that the theory of a «stored consciousness» is an arrow shot into darkness. Moreover, Šāntirakṣita in his Mādhyamikālaṃkāra with his own comment, says, «a double sensation (*sems-gñis*) which appears (at once) without succession from two (different sources *de-dag-gis*) cannot exist», and he continues up to the passage «it is difficult to deny that this runs against Scripture». And again Pramāṇa-vārtika says «two ideas (*kalpanā-dvayam* = *rtog-gñis*) cannot exist simultaneously». «The ornament of the Seven Treatises» (by Gendunḍub) says, «those who maintain that in the system of the Seven Treatises the «store-consciousness» doctrine is admitted are blind men (living) in the darkess of their own ignorance!». — The passage quoted from Šāntirakṣita's Madhyamikālamkāra is found f. 15ᵇ. 1—16ᵃ. 2 of the blockprint (Aga), and the passage from Gendunḍub (the real title of the work is Tshad-ma-rigs-rgyan) is found f. 96ᵇ. 3—97ᵃ. 2 of the block-print (Aga). (A. Vostrikoff).

[1] *Ibid.*, II ch., *kārikā* 113, f. 98ᵇ. 5 of the Aga block-print; the second quarter of this *kārikā* is,

nus-med don-can mi-ḥdzin-phyir.

The block-print of the Sholutai monastery reads *don-gzhan.*

[2] The words *dañ-po grub-ste* usually point to a dilemma mentioned precedently, viz. to the first part of the dilemma with the closing words *gañ-zhig.*

contradiction with all the passages where the definition of mental sensation is taught), is quite right, because (this theory) contradicts all the characteristics of that (mental sensation), viz., 1) that (mental sensation) is called forth by the sensation (of the outer sense), 2) that it apprehends the second moment of the object which has been (in the preceding moment) cognized by the outer sense, etc. With all these characteristics the theory of the simultaneous presence of two different (currents of) sensation is in contradiction. This is quite clear.

30b.1 And further. You, (Saskya-paṇḍita) maintain that from the standpoint of the Brahmin (Šankarānanda) there is at first a moment of sensation by the outer sense and, after it, a double sensation arises, an outer one and a mental, inner one. (And you also maintain) that, according to his standpoint, sensation always necessarily consists of three elements. This is not right, because (the supposed theory of the Great Brahmin) requires us to admit that there is a double kind of sensation, the one consists of two elements, the other includes
30b.2 three. It is really so,[1] because the one kind of sensation, (the first moment) which[2] must be characterized as consisting (only) of two elements, is endowed by you with three parts. That the first circumstance is right,[3] (viz. that the first) moment (is dipartite), must be admitted, because in the first (moment), when the single moment of sensation (by the outer sense) is produced, it consists only of two elements. It is really so,[4] since at that time there is no other sensation than 1) this sensation (of the outer sense) and 2) self-consciousness. If you do not admit that,[5] (and insist that sensation is always three-partite), then you will have to assume the double sensation, (outer and mental, already) in this (first) moment, and many other incongruities will ensue, (you will be obliged to admit the collapse of the whole theory).

§ 6. Vindication of Dharmottara's theory.

30b.4 Therefore, in our opinion, the view of the great scholar Dharmottara is the only right one. He has the proper view of the genesis of intelligible sensation as established (by Dharmakīrti) in his

---

1 *der thal.*

2 *yañ-zhig* here also points to the first part of a dilemma which in the sequel will be alluded to by the words *dañ-po grub-ste.*

3 *dañ-po grub-ste.*

4 *der thal.*

5 *ma grub na.*

Seven Treatises, (viz., that mental sensation) arises immediately after pure sensation, when the run of (pure sensation) has vanished. (Pure sensation is one moment). This is (the only plausible way to realize) its procedure,[1] since (all other attemps to describe it) are proved to lack logical consistency, viz., 1) the theory according to which mental sensation continues to exist after the moment following on pure sensation,[2] 2) the alternation theory, 3) the theory that pure sensation consists of three elements, 4) the theory of the Alaṃkāra, that (every) sensation includes (a germ) of constructive imagination. These last, four theories evidently have (no great importance), authoritative[3] is only the first one, (that one of Dharmottara), because that cognition of an external object, where the predominant part[4] is played by the intellect, is not reckoned as sense-perception, (i. e., it is not a sensation). Indeed, the (Abhidharma)-sūtra says, «the appre- 30b. 6
hension of colour (and lines) is double, as conditioned by the sense (of sight), and as conditioned by the intellect[5]», and the Pramāṇa-samuccaya[6] (confirms this) in stating that the intellect also when it apprehends an object (in a mental sensation, does not possess the character of constructive imagination). Thus, in the moment of pure sensation (by the outer sense), intelligible sensation is not yet present, but when the first has vanished, the second immediately arises. It is immaterial whether at the time of both these sensations the totality of causes producing the pure sensation is complete or not, because, (albeit they be complete), the change is produced by the efficiency of a conflicting factor (the intellect, or attention), which may be present

1 The construction of this sentence is worthy to be noticed, *gan-zhig* here also points to the first part of a dilemma of five parts, it will be in the sequel indicated by the words *dañ-po grub-ste.* Lit. «...because just such is its genesis on the one hand (*de skye-ba gañ zhig*) and because (on the other hand) the existence of mental sensation after the second moment of (outer) sensation, and the alternate origin, and... ...are proved to be wrong. The last arguments are easy (to understand as wrong). The first is right».

2 Mental sensation lasts only one moment, the moment of aroused attention, and this moment is the moment following the outer sensation, its continuation is constructive imagination, the real function of the intellect.

3 *grub-ste.*

4 *dban-rkyen = adhipati-pratyaya.*

5 According to the Abhidharma sensation (*sparśa*) arises at the meeting point of three things, the object, the sense-organ and consciousness (sc. bare consciousness-*vijñāna*). The next step is a feeling and a distinct cognition (*vedanā-saṃjñā*).

6 Cp. Pr. samucc., I. 6.

31[a] 2 or absent. We read[1] in the «Elucidation of the Seven Treatises» (by Khai-ḍub), —

«It does not matter much for the continuity of pure sensation, (without any participation of mind or attention), and for its discontinuity, whether all causes (and conditions) producing it are completely present or not, but it is not indifferent whether some counter-acting agency has appeared or not, because as long as there is nothing to stop the run of (the moments of) pure sensation, it will go on enduring without interruption, and the entrance-door for intelligible sensation will be closed».

31[a].3 Mental sensation appears for not more than a single moment, because if it were a lasting phenomenon (it would apprehend a distinct image in a perceptual judgment), and we would have clear and distinct cognitions produced straight off by the force of a simple reflex, (we never would have illusions), and the constructed judgment «this is not right» would never arise.[2] This is quite right, (i. e., it is quite right that, if mental, direct sensation could last more than a single moment, an error would be impossible, since truth would arise automatically). Therefore, since the matter is quite transcendental,[3] (the existence of this moment of mental sensation) is assumed (more or less) dogmatically.[4] We read in the «Commentary upon the Short Treatise[5]» (by Dharmottara), «This mental sensation is merely a postulate of our system. There are no facts which could establish its existence
31[a].5 (directly)». And (Rgyal-tshab) in his «Commentary upon the Short Treatise of Logic[6]» delivers himself as follows, «Now, this

---

[1] *Op. cit.*, f. 121[a]. 3.

[2] Lit., «Mental sensation does not appear after one moment, because, if a duration (*rgyun* = *santāna*) did appear, certainty (*ñes-pa* = *niścaya*) would appear by the force of a simple reflex (*myoṅ-ba* = *anubhava* = *pratibhāsa*) and the imputation (*sgro-ḥdogs* = *āropa*) «this is not right» would not be produced». Cp. Dharmakīrti's words quoted Anekāntajaya-patāka, p. 177, — *na pratyakṣam kasyacid niścāyakam, tad yad api gṛhṇāti tan na niścayena, kim tarhi tat-pratibhāsena.*

[3] *śin-tu-lkog-ḥgyur.*

[4] The Nyāya-bindu-ṭīkā is evidently quoted under the name of Ḥthad-ldan-chuṅ-ṅu «The Small Commentary», since the passage is found on p. 25. 9—11 of our edition of its Tib. translation (B. B. VIII). The «Great Commentary» would then be the same author's comment, Ramaṇī, on Pramāṇa-viniścaya.

[5] *luṅ-gi tshad-mas* = *āgama-pramāṇena.*

[6] Rigs-thigs-dar-ṭīk. The full title of this work is — Tshad-ma-rigs-thigs-kyi ḥgrel-ba legs-bšad-sñiṅ-poi gter, the passage is found f. 14[a] 6 of the block-print of the La-brang monastery.

(theory) of mental sensation must be accepted as founded on dogmatic assertions, although subjected to a threefold critical[1] purification; there is no other (direct) evidence (establishing it empirically)».

To this (contention, that mental sensation is something transendental), some (philosophers take exception). They maintain, that mental sensation is present in every ordinary[2] man. It cannot be transcendental[3] (or occult) in these ordinary men, because its existence is proved by their own direct perception.[4] And the fact that it really is so[5] is established by introspection which exists in their personality and which apprehends this (their own mental sensation). This (again) is really so,[6] (simply) because they are conscious beings.[7] 31ᵃ. 6

This is not right![8] 31ᵇ. 1

It really is right,[9] because every consciousness is self-consciousness.[10]

Nevertheless (your argument) is not right,[11] because, although we really can by introspection establish (as a rule) that knowledge having duration and (every case) of right cognition[12] (in general) is 31ᵇ. 2

---

1 The threefold scrutiny (*dpyod = vicāra = mīmāṃsā*) which every sacred text or trustworthy testimony must undergo is 1) the test of experience (*pratyakṣa*), 2) of inference (*anumāna*) and 3) of non-contradiction (*avirodha*). Accodingly the objects are divided into 1) evident facts (*pratyakṣa*), 2) inferred facts (*parokṣa*) of whom we have formerly had some experience, 3) very much concealed facts (*atyanta-parokṣa = śin-tu-lkog-pa*) which are either transcendental, unimaginbble entities, orelse facts never experienced, but nevertheless not unimaginable.

2 *so-so-skye-bo = pṛthag-jana*, i. e., not a Saint, not the man who possesses direct intuition of the Absolute, something like Kant's «intelligible Anshauung» as contrasted with «sinnliche Anshaung» of ordinary men.

3 *śin-tu-lkog-gyur = atyanta-parokṣa*.

4 This argument is here thrown in the usual Tibetan form, viz.,

Minor term — mental sensation in the run of consciousness of every ordinary man.

Major term and Example — it is not at all quite so transcendental in an ordinary man.

Middle term — because its presence is established by your direct perception, (i. e., introspection).

5 *der thal.* 6 *der thal.*

7 Lit., «because there is knowledge in his continuity, (stream of thought—*santāna*)».

8 *ma-khyab*, lit. there is no invariable concomitance (between the middle and the major terms).

9 *khyab-par-thal.*

10 Lit. «if it is knowledge it is pervaded by self-grasping self-knowledge».

11 *yañ ma-khyab-ste*, «no concomitance again».

12 i. e., every *santāna* and every *pramāṇa*.

accompanied by self-perception, we (by no means) can maintain that every cognitive phenomenon (without exception) is susceptible of being grasped by introspection.[1] And even that is a concession made[2] (by us to the advocates of introspection).

31[b]. 2 Moreover, if we take our stand upon (the ideas of these advocates of introspection, we will be landed in the following absurd consequence). (Let us take as subject, or) minor term, the fact that the consciousness of an ordinary man contains (nevertheless a feeling of) its own ultimate unreality[3]; (we then must take as predicate, or) major term, the fact that this feeling must be cognized directly in the consciousness of this ordinary man, because he has introspection, for we have admitted an invariable concomitance (between introspection and cognition of external objects).[4] It is really so, because this feeling is nothing

---

[1] Jam-yañ establishes in the Bro-rigs seven varieties of meaning for the term «thought» (*blo-rigs-bdun*). Prof. B. Erdmann, in the Ch. Sigwart memorial Philos. Abhandlungen (Tübingen, 1900), has endeavoured to determine the various meanings of the German term «das Denken». The historian of philosophy will perhaps be tempted to make a curious comparison

[2] The comment adds that the if introspection were not fallible, the Cārvāka would know that he makes inferences; he nevertheless denies it, hence his introspection is not sufficient to establish even the presence of a *pramāṇa*.

[3] In the Abhisamayālaṃkāra I, this germ of the idea of *śūnyatā* is called *prakṛti-stham gotram*. Jo-nañ-pa, the predecessor of Tsoñ-kha-pa, went all the length of maintaining, in his Ri-chos-ñes-don-rgya-mtsho, that every man is a real Buddha, and therefore the teaching of the Path is useless.

[4] Lit. (the text p. 339. 5: *de-la kho* ff.). «On this they say, mental sensation in the consciousness (*rgyud*) of an ordinary man being the subject (*chos-can*), it will follow (*yin-par-thal*) that it (= *khyod*) is not very occult in the ordinary man, because it (= *khyod*) is established by a perception in his consciousness. (31[b]. 1). (Again) this follows (*der thal*), because this is established by introspection grasping it in his consciousness. This (again) follows, because in his consciousness there is knowledge. No concomitance! Concomitance follows, because wheresoever there is knowledge, it is invariably concomitant with the presence of self-grasping introspection (31[b]. 2); if (this is maintained), again no concomitance because, albeit in the (cases) of continuous knowledge and of right cognition (*santāna* and *pramāṇa*) there is concomitance with (the fact) of being established by introspection, but there is no (such) concomitance with being cognized by introspection in every case of knowledge. And even this is a concession (*go-thob*) made. Moreover, for them (31[b]. 3) the subject being the knowledge characterized by personal unreality in the consciousness of an ordinary man (*thsur-mthoñ-gi rgyud*), it will follow that it (= *khyod*) is cognized by the perception of the ordinary man, because it is cognized by his introspection. This concomitance (they) admit. (And) this follows (*der*

but a case of cognition of external objects, and it is maintained[1] that 31ᵇ. 3
every cognition is also self-cognition (of whatsoever may be found in it).
If (the argument) is admitted,[2] we will have the absurd consequence[3]
that (every ordinary man) mnst be a Saint![4] They have accepted it!

All other points are easy to understand. 31ᵇ. 4

V

The text of the translated part of the Blo-rigs

Tsu-gol block-print, Blo-rigs, f. 28ᵃ. 3—31ᵇ. 5.

gñis-pa, yid-(kyi) mṅon-(sum) la mtshan-ñid, dbye-ba, skye-tshul-gsum. daṅ-po ni. raṅ-ḥdren-byed-kyi dbaṅ-mṅon-las byuṅ zhiṅ, dei bzuṅ-don skad-cig gñis-pa ḥdzin-pai, raṅ-ñid rtog-bral ma ḥkhrul-bai cha-nas bzhag-pai gzhan-rig mṅon-sum-de (28ᵃ. 5) dei mtshan-ñid. sṅor snaṅ dbaṅ-mṅon-gyis draṅs-pai sṅon-ḥdzin yid-mṅon lta-bu dei mtshan gzhi. dei mtshan-ñid-kyi zur-du raṅ-ḥdren-byed-kyi dbaṅ-mṅon-gyi bzuṅ-yul skad-cig gñis-pa ḥdzin zhes smos-pas (28ᵃ. 6) raṅ yul da-ltar-ba ḥdzin nam sñam-pa daṅ, de bcad-šes yin nam sñam-pai log-rtog sel-te, Rtog-ge-skad-las, skad-cig gñis-pa ḥdzin-pai-phyir bzuṅ-zin-pa ḥdzin-pa-ñid bsal-lo, zhes gsuṅs-pai-phyir. (28ᵇ. 1) mtshuṅs-pa de-ma-thag smos-pas rnal-ḥbyor mṅon-sum bsal-zhiṅ; dbaṅ-poi mṅon-sum-las byuṅ zhes-pas phyi-rol-pas loṅ-ba daṅ ḥon-pa-sogs med-par thal-bai log-rtog bsal te. Rtog-gei-skad-las, dbaṅ-(28ᵇ. 2)-pai šes-pa-las skyes-pai yid yin-pas, zhes-pa-nas, mtshuṅs-pa-de-ma-thag--pai rkyen-gyi khyad-par-gyis kyaṅ rnal-ḥbyor-pai šes-pa yid-kyi mṅon-sum-ñid-du thal-ba bsal-te zhes-pai bar gsuṅs-pai-phyir. des-(28ᵇ. 3)--na yid-mṅon yin-na dbaṅ-mṅon-gyi rjes-su byuṅ-bas khyab-ste, Rtog-gei-skad-las, dbaṅ-mṅon ḥdas-ma-thag-tu yid mṅon skye-bao, zhes gsuṅs-pai-phyir.

---

thal), because it is (nothing but) his knowledge of the external world. (31ᵇ. 4). This concomitance (they) admit. If they admit (the argument), it will follow that (the ordinary man) is a Saint, since they have accepted it. The remaining is easy to understand ».

[1] *khyab-pa-khas.* [2] *ḥdod-na.* [3] *thal* = *prasanga.*

[4] In order to have a direct intuition of the irreality of the phenomenal world and of the non-existence of an Ego, an educated man must have undergone a long course of philosophic studies and after that practice concentrated meditation. If illumination comes, he will contemplate the absolute truth directly and become a Saint (*ārya*). cp. my Nirvāna, p. 16 ff.

gñis-pa. de-la dbye-ba-na. gzugs-ḥdzin yid-mñon, sgra-(28b.4) ḥdzin yid-mñon, dri-ḥdzin yid-mñon, ro-ḥdzin yid-mñon, reg-bya-ḥdzin-pai yid-mñon dan lña yod.

gsum-pa. skye-tshul-la. Rigs-gter rjes-ḥbrañs-dañ-bcas-pa na re, dañ-por dbañ-mñon skad-cig-ma (28b.5) gcig skye, de rjes-su yid-mñon skad-cig-ma gcig skye, de rjes dbañ-mñon skad-cig ma gcig skye-ba--sogs dbañ-yid spel-mar-skye-ba Rgyan-mkhan-poi lugs-su byas-pa dañ. yañ dañ-por dbañ-mñon skad-cig-ma (28b.6) gcig skye, dei rjes des de-ma-thag-rkyen dañ dbañ-pos bdag-rkyen byas-nas, dbañ--mñon skad-cig-ma gñis-pa dañ yid-mñon skad-cig dañ-po gñis, rkyen, mtshuñs-pas skyed la, dbañ mñon skad-cig gñis-pa-(29a.1)-nas mthar ḥgags-pai-bar dus-mñam yin-pa, ḥdi-la phyir-ltai mñon-sum gñis dañ, nañ-ltai rañ-rig-gi ḥgros-gcig dañ gsum ste. mñon-sum ḥgros gsum-po ḥdi bram-ze (29a.2) Bde-byed-dgaḥ-ba-am Šaṃ-ākara-nandai lugs-su byas-pa. yañ dbañ-mñon-gyi rgyun mthaḥ kho-nar skye-ba slob-dpon Chos-mchog-gi lugs. gsum gyi sña-phyi gñis mi-ḥthad-la, bar-ma ḥthad zer-te. Rigs-gter-las (29a.3),

spel-ma dañ ni rgyun-gyi mthaḥ
gñis-ka-la yañ gnod-byed-yod,

ces-so.

Rgyan-gyi lugs spel-mar ḥdod-pa mi-ḥthad-par-thal, de Rgyan-gyi ḥgrel-pa ḥgrel-bšad bod-du ḥgyur-ba gcig-las-kyañ mi ḥbyuñ-(29a.4)-pai-phyir-te. Sde-bdun-yid-kyi-mun-sel-las, dbañ-yid spel-nas skye-bar Rgyan-mkhan-pos bzhed-do, zhes mkhas-pa-rnams la grags-pa tsam-du zad-kyi, bod-du ḥgyur-bai Rgyan rjes-ḥbrañs-dañ-bcas-pai gzhuñ-(29a.5)-lugs gañ-na-añ mi gsal-lo, zhes dañ; Rigs-gter-dar-ṭīk-las kyañ, spel-mar skye-ba da-lta ḥgyur-bai Rgyan-gyi ḥgrel-pa-na mi snañ-ño, zhes gsuñs-pai-phyir. spel-mar skye-ba tha-chad yin-par-thal, gnod-byed mañ-(29a.6)-la, Rnam-ḥgrel lugs-las phyir ḥgyur kyañ, de lugs-su smra-bai-phyir; ma grub-na, dbañ-mñon rim-gyis skye thse-bar-ma-chad-par yul mi ḥdzin-par thal, dbañ-yid skad-cig-ma spel-ma dei phyir. ḥdod-mi-nus-te Rnam-ḥgrel-(29b.1)-las,

rim-gyis ḥdzin-na de myoñ-ba,
rnam-chad med-par snañ mi-ḥgyur,

zhes gsuñs-pai-phyir. des-na Rgyan-gyi lugs-la dbañ-yid spel-mar ḥdod-pa mi-ḥthad-par-thal, Rgyan-gyi lugs-la dbañ-mñon yid-mñon dus-(29b.2)-mñam-pa bzhed-pai-phyir. der thal, slob-dpon des yid-mñon-la rtog-pa gcig ḥdod-pas, dbañ-mñon dus-su yañ rtog-pa skyed-pa mi-ḥgal-pai-phyir-te; R g y a n - l a s,

goms-las mdun-na gnas-pa-la
«ḥdio», zhes-(29b. 3)-ni šes-pa-gañ,
mñon-sum byed-phyir de-la ni
yid-kyi mñon-sum yin-par-ḥdod,

ces gsuñs-pai-phyir dañ, C h o s - m c h o g dañ rtsod-tshul-yañ yod-mod-kyañ, gzhan-du spro-o. ḥdir ḥgros brtsi-na ḥgros gsum-par (29b. 4) bya-o. R g y a n - g y i lugs de mñon-sum-du mi ruñ-bar-thal, de-la sgrub-ḥjug-gi rtog-pa yod-par thal-ba-dañ, mñon-sum rtog-bral-du M d o dañ S d e - b d u n - gyis bšad-pa mi ḥthad-par thal-ba sogs-kyi skyon yod--pai-phyir. thal-(29b. 5)-ḥgyur-bai phyogs yin-na ruñ-bar--ḥgyur-ro.

yañ B r a m - z e i bzhed-par ḥdod-tshul de yañ mi ḥthad-par-thal. de B r a m - z e i gzhuñ-ḥgyur-ba-dañ, ḥphags-yul-gyi mkhas-pas dei bzhed-par ston-byed med-pas, dam-bcaḥ (29b. 6) tsam-du ḥgyur--bai-phyir-te. S d e - b d u n - y i d - k y i - m u n - s e l - las, B r a m - z e - - c h e n - p o i bzhed-pa-yin zhes sña-ma-dag-la grags-pa tsam ma-togs, B r a m - z e i bod-du ḥgyur-bai gzhuñ-lugs gañ-na-añ khuñs-med-ciñ, zhes gsuñs-(30a. 1)-pai-phyir.

gzhan-yañ. khyod-kyis de la ḥgros-gsum ñes-can byas-nas, rtsi--dgos-par ḥdod-pa mi-ḥthad-par-thal, ḥgros-bdun-kyañ rtsi-ḥdod-na, brtsis chog-pai-phyir. der thal, yul-gyi sgo-(30a. 2)-nas ḥgros lña dañ dbañ-po dañ yid-byed-kyi ḥgros gñis dañ bdun yod-pai-phyir-te. R i g s - g t e r - d a r - ṭ ī k - las, yul-gyi ḥgros sbyar-na lñar ḥgyur-la, dbañ-po dañ yid-kyi ḥgros bsnan-na, bdun-du-ḥgyur-ro, zhes (30a. 3) dañ, S d e - b d u n - y i d - k y i - m u n - s e l - las, skye-tshul ḥdi-la ḥgros-du yod brtsis-pa-la dgos-pa-chen-po yod-par ma-go-bas, ḥgros-du-rtsi-dgos-pai ñes-pa-med-la, zhes gsuñs-pai phyir.

gzhan yañ. mig-gi (30a. 4) dbañ-mñon yul-gzugs-la ḥjug-bzhin-pai dus-su so-skye-dei rgyud-la gzugs gsal-bar mthoñ-bai yid-mñon ḥdod-pa šin-tu tha-chad yin-par-thal. de-ni S d e - b d u n rtsa-ḥgrel-gyi yid-mñon-gyi mtshan-ñid ston-(30a. 5)-pai gzhuñ thams-cad dañ ḥgal-ba gañ-zhig der ma zad; R n a m - ḥ g r e l - las,

cig-car rigs-mi-mthun skye yañ,
šin-tu gsal-bai sems gcig gis,

zhes sogs dañ,

rnam-šes dañ gzhan zhugs-pa-yi,

zhes-(30a. 6)-sogs du-ma daṅ dṅos-su ḥgal-bai-phyir. daṅ-po grub-ste, dbaṅ-poi rgyu byas-pa-dan, dbaṅ-mṅon-gyi bzuṅ don skad cig gñis-pa bzuṅ-bar bšad-pai rgyu-mtshan thams-cad daṅ ḥgal-bai-phyir šin-tu rtogs sla.

(30b. 1) gzhan-yaṅ. B r a m - z e i lugs-la khyod-kyis daṅ-por dbaṅ-mṅon skad-cig-ma gcig kho-na daṅ, de rjes dbaṅ-mṅon daṅ yid-mṅon gñis skye-bar ḥdod-pa daṅ, dei lugs-la mṅon-sum ḥgros gsum-pa-kho-nar byed-pa mi-(30b. 2)-ḥthad-par-thal, de-ltar-na mṅon-sum ḥgros-gñis-pa daṅ ḥgros-gsum-pa gñis-kar ḥdod dgos-pai-phyir. der thal, mṅon-sum ḥgros gñis-pa gcig dgos-pa gaṅ zhig-ḥgros gsum-pa khyod-kyis khas-blaṅs-(30b. 3)-zin-pai-phyir. daṅ-po grub-ste, daṅ-por dbaṅ-mṅon skad-cig-ma gcig kho-na skye-dus mṅon-sum ḥgros gñis-pa yin-pai-phyir; der thal, de dus dbaṅ-mṅon daṅ raṅ-rig gñis-las mṅon-sum gzhan med-pai-phyir. (30b. 4). ma grub na, mṅon-sum ḥgros gñis-par dei-tshe ḥgyur-ro sogs skyon-du-ma ḥphen šes-par bya.

des-na raṅ-lugs-la S d e - b d u n - gyi yid-mṅon skye-tshul paṇ-chen C h o s - m c h o g - ltar dbaṅ-mṅon-gyi rgyun-mthar skye-ba yin-te; de skye-(30b. 5)-pa gaṅ-zhig, dban-mṅon skad-cig gñis-pa phan-chad yid-mṅon yin-pa-daṅ, spel-mar skye-ba daṅ, rtog-bral-gyi mṅon-sum ḥgros-gsum-du skye-ba-daṅ, mṅon-sum rtog-bcas R g y a n lta-bu--rnams mi-ḥthad-par bsgrubs zin-pai-(30b. 6)-phyir. rtags-phyi-ma-rnams sla, daṅ-po grub-ste, yid-dbaṅ-gis bdag-rkyen byas-pai gzhan-rig mṅon-sum mi bzhed-pai-phyir-te; M d o-las,

gzugs šes-pa-ni rnam-gñis te,
mig daṅ yid-la brten-pa-o,

zhes daṅ. T s h a d - m a-(31a. 1) - k u n - b t u s - l a s, yid kyaṅ don daṅ, zhes gsuṅs-pai-phyir, dbaṅ-mṅon dus-su yid-mṅon mi-skye-la, de rdzogs rjes de-ma-thag-tu skye-ste, de-dag-gi dus-su dbaṅ-mṅon skye-bai rgyu-tshogs tshaṅ-ma-(31a. 2)-tshaṅ mtshuṅs kyaṅ ḥgal-rkyen yod-med dbaṅ--gis yin-pai-phyir-te. S d e - b d u n - y i d - k y i - m u n - s e l-las, ḥdi rgyun daṅ rgyun ma rdzogs goṅ la rgyu-tshogs thsaṅ-ma-thsaṅ mtshuṅs-kyaṅ, ḥgal rkyen yod med mi-mtshuṅs te, rgyun ma-(31a. 3)-rdzogs goṅ-du dbaṅ-šes bar-ma-chad-par ḥbyuṅ-bas, yid-mṅon skye-bai sgo bkag-pai-phyir-ro, zhes gsuṅs-pai-phyir. yid-mṅon skad-cig-ma gcig-las mi-skye-ste, rgyun skye-na myoṅ-stobs-kyis ṅes-par ḥgyur-bas, mi-ḥthad-(31a. 4)-do, zhes sgro-ḥdogs mi-byed-pai-phyir. khyab-ste, des-na de šin-tu lkog-gyur yin-pas luṅ-gi tshad-mas grub-pai-phyir-te. Ḥ t h a d-l d a n - c h u ṅ - ṅ u - las, yid-kyi mṅon-sum de-ṅi grub-pai-mthaḥ-la grags-pa tsam yin-kyi, ḥdi grub-par-(31a. 5)-byed-pai tshad-ma-ni yod-pa-ma-yin-no, zhes dañ. R i g s - t h i g s - d a r - ṭ ī k - l e g s - b š a d - r i n - p o - c h e i - g t e r - las, yid-kyi mñon-sum de-yañ bdag-cag-rnams-kyis dpyad-pa-gsum-gyis dag-pai luñ-la brten-nas rtogs-par-bya-(31a. 6)-ba-yin-gyi, tshad-ma gzhan-gyis rtogs-par mi-nus-so, zhes gsuñs-pai-phyir.

de-la kho na re. so-skyei rgyud-kyi yid-mñon chos-can, khyod so--skye-la šin-tu lkog-gyur ma-yin-par-thal, khyod dei rgyud-kyi mñon-sum-gyis grub-(31b. 1)-pai-phyir. der thal, dei rgyud-kyi de-ḥdzin-pai rañ-rig-mñon-sum-gyis grub-pai-phyir. der thal, dei rgyud-kyi šes-pa-yin-pai-phyir-na. ma-khyab. khyab-par-thal, šes-pa yin-na rañ-ḥdzin-pai rañ-rig yod-pas khyab-pai-phyir-(31b. 2)-na, yañ ma-khyab--ste, rgyun-ldan-gyi šes-pa dañ tshad-ma-la rañ-rig mñon-sum-gyis grub-pas khyab-kyañ, šes-pa-tsam-la rañ-rig-gis gzhal-bas ma-khyab-pai-phyir. ḥdi-yañ go-thob byas-so.

kho-rañ-la ḥo-na, tshur-mthoñ-gi rgyud-gyi gañ-(31b. 3)-zag-gi-bdag-med-kyis khyad-par-du-byas-pai šes-pa chos-can, khyod tshur-mthoñ-gi rgyud-kyi mñon-sum-gyis rtogs-par-thal, dei rgyud-kyi rañ-rig-mñon-sum-gyis rtogs-pai-phyir. khyab-pa-khas. der-thal, dei rgyud-kyi gzhan-(31b. 4)-rig-gi šes-pa yin-pai-phyir. khyab-pa khas. ḥdod-na, ḥphags-par-thal, ḥdod-pai-phyir. des lhag-ma-rnams rtogs sla-o.

APPENDIX IV.

Vasubandhu, Vinitadeva, Vācaspatimiśra, Udayana, Dignāga, and Jinendrabuddhi on the act and the content of knowledge, on the coordination (sārūpya) of percepts with their objects and our knowledge of the external world.

Vasubandhu, Vinitadeva, Vācaspatimiśra, Udayana, Dignāga and Jinendrabuddhi on the act and the content of knowledge, on the coordination (sārūpya) of percepts with their objects and our knowledge of the external world.

I

Vasubandhu on Coordination (sārūpya) between images and their objects.

Abhidharma-Koša, book IX, Bstan-ḥgyur, Mdo, vol. 63, ff. $103^{b}.7$—$105^{b}.1$, transl. by L. de la Vallée-Poussin, Abh. koša, IV, p. 273 ff., and by me in the Bulletin de l'Academie des sciences de Russie, 1919, p. 852 ff.

(Vatsīputrīya). Now, if there absolutely is no (permanent) Soul, how is it then, that the detached moments of consciousness can remember or recognize things which have been experienced a long time ago?

(Sautrāntika). Consciousness, being in a special condition and connected with a (previous) knowledge of the remembered object, produces its recollection.

(Vatsīputrīya). What is this special condition of consciousness which is immediately followed by remembrance?

(Sautrāntika). It is a condition which includes 1) attention directed towards this object, 2) an idea either similar or otherwise connected with it and 3) absence of bodily pain, grief or distraction etc., impairing its capacity. But supposing all these conditions are realized, consciousness nevertheless is not able to produce remembrance, if it is not connected with a previous experience of the remembered object. If on the other hand it is so connected, but the above conditions are absent, it likewise is not able to produce it. Both factors are necessary — (a previous cognition and a suitable state of mind). Then only memory appears. Experience shows that no other forces are capable (of evoking it).

(Vatsīputrīya). But (if there were absolutely nothing permanent, it would mean that) one consciousness has perceived the object and an-

other one remembers it. How is this possible? In this case things experienced by Devadatta's consciousness would be remembered by the consciousness of Yajñadatta.

(Sautrāntika). No! because there is no connection between them. They are not mutually related as cause and effect, as is the case between moments belonging to the same stream of thought. Indeed we do not at all maintain that one consciousness perceives and another one remembers. (The stream of thought is the same). On a previous occasion[1] we have explained the manner in which a complete change is gradually taking place in a chain of consecutive moments. Thus it is that a consciousness which did perceive an object formerly, is (gradually) producing a consciousness which remembers it now. What fault can you find with this argument?

As to recognition it is simply the consequence of a recollection, (and requires no further explanation).

(Vatsīputrīya). If there is no Soul, who is it that remembers?

(Sautrāntika). What is the meaning of the word «to remember»?

(Vatsīputrīya). It means to grasp an object by memory.

(Sautrāntika). Is this «grasping by memory» something different from memory?

(Vatsīputrīya). It is an agent who acts through memory.

(Sautrāntika). The agency by which memory is produced we have just explained. The cause producive of a recollection is a suitable state of mind (and nothing else)!

(Vatsīputrīya). But when (in comomn life) we are using the expression «Caitra remembers» what does it mean?

(Sautrāntika). In the current (of phenomena), which is designated by the name Caitra a recollection appears. We notice the fact and express it. It is no more!

(Vatsīputrīya). But if there is no Soul, whose is the recollection, (whom does it belong to)?

(Sautrāntika). What is here the meaning of the Genitive «whose»?

(Vatsīputrīya). It denotes proprietorship.

(Sautrāntika). Is it the same as when somebody enquires, of what objects who is the proprietor?

(Vatsīputrīya). It is just as when we say «Caitra is the owner of a cow».

(Sautrāntika). What does it mean to be the owner of a cow?

---

[1] Abh. Koša, II. 36. c.

(Vatsīputrīya). It means that it depends on him to employ her for milking or driving purposes etc.

(Sautrāntika). Now, I should like to know to what place must I dispatch my memory, since it is supposed that I am the master of it.

(Vatsīputrīya). You must direct it towards the remembered object.

(Sautrāntika). What for shall I direct my memory?

(Vatsīputrīya). In order to remember.

(Sautrāntika). Hallo! I must employ the very thing I already possess in order to get it! Indeed that is well spoken! Great is the merit (of such discoveries)! And then I should like to know, in what sense memory is to be influenced: in the sense of its being produced, or in the sense of its being dispatched, (like a servant)?

(Vatsīputrīya). In the sense of production, since memory cannot move (like a servant).

(Sautrāntika). In that case the proprietor is simply the cause and the property will simply be its effect. The cause has a rule over the effect, and this rule belongs to the cause (only in the sense of its producing) a result. Memory is the property of something which is its own cause. As to the name of an owner given to the united elements of Caitra with respect to those of the cow, this name has been given only because it has been observed that there exists a relation of cause to effect between him and the movements and other changes in the cow, but there is no real unity whatsoever neither in Caitra nor in the cow. Consequently there is in this case no other proprietorship than a relation of cause to effect. The same argument may be applied to the questions «who is it that perceives?», «whom does perception belong to?» and other similar questions: (who feels, who has notions, who acts etc.?). The difference consists in the fact that (instead of the described state of mind producing memory), the corresponding conditions for a perception are: activity of the senses, presence of the object and aroused attention.

(Vatsīputrīya). There are others who argue as follows: (a Soul must exist), because wherever there is an activity it depends on an agent. Every action depends on an agent as, e. g., in the example «Devadatta walks» there is an action of walking which depends on Devadatta, the agent. To be conscious is likewise an action, hence the agent who cognizes must also exist.[1]

---

[1] **Yaśomitra** supposes that the view of the grammarians is here alluded to: *bhāvasya bhavitr-apekṣatvād iti vaiyākaraṇāh.* But **Hiuen Thsang** thinks that

(Sautrāntika). It must be explained what this Devadatta is.

(Vatsīputrīya). It is an Ego.

(Sautrāntika). That is begging the question!

(Vatsīputrīya). It is what in common life we call a man.

(Sautrāntika). This does not represent any unity whatsoever. It is a name given to such elemests (of which a man is composed). The elements are meant when we say «Devadatta walks». When we say that «consciousness cognizes», it is just the same.

(Vatsīputrīya). And what is the meaning of the expression «Devadatta walks», (if there is no individuality whatsoever)?

(Sautrāntika). It is an unbroken continuity of momentary forces (flashing into existence), which simple people believe to be a unity, and to which they give the name of Devadatta. Their belief that Devadatta moves is conditioned (by an analogy with their own experience, because) their own continuity of life consists in constantly moving from one place to an other. But this movement is but a (series of new) productions in different places, just as the expressions «fire moves», «sound spreads» have the meaning of continuities (of new productions in new places). They likewise use the words «Devadatta cognizes» in order to express the fact that a cognition (takes place in the present moment) which has a cause (in the former moments, these former moments being called Devadatta). (But is it simple people alone whose language is so inadequate?). Great men have likewise condescended to denote the (mentioned facts) by such (inadequate) expressions, when they were pleased to use the language of common life.

(Vatsīputrīya). But we read in Scripture: «consciousness apprehends». What is consciousness here meant to do?

(Sautrāntika). Nothing at all! (It simply appears in coordination with its objective elements, like a result which is homogeneous with its cause). When a result appears in conformity with its own cause it is doing nothing at all, nevertheless we say that it *does* conform with it. Consciousness likewise appears in coordination with its objective

---

this controversy about the reality of a subject is directed against a Sāṃkhya philosopher. The aim of Vasubandhu is to establish that there are cognitions, but no real cognizer. This may be directed against the Sāṃkhya system where *ātman* is the cognizing principle, but it does not agree with it inasmuch as the ātman is passive, not an agent. We retain the designation of Vatsīputrīya as adversary, because, as usual, he may start questions not only in accordance with his own views (*svamatena*), but also from the stadpoint of an other system (*paramatam āśritya*).

elements. It is (properly speaking) *doing* nothing. Nevertheless we say that consciousness *does* cognize its object.

(Vatsīputrīya). What is meant by coordination[1] (between consciousness and its objective element)?

(Sautrāntika). A conformity between them, the fact owing to which cognition, although caused (also) by the activity of the senses, is not something homogeneous with them. It is said to cognize the object and not the senses. (It bears the reflection of the objective element, which is its corollary). And again the expression «consciousness apprehends» is not inadequate, inasmuch as here also a continuity of conscious moments is the cause of every cognition. («Consciousness apprehends» means that the previous moment is the cause of the following one). The agent here also denotes simply the cause, just as in the current expression «the bell resounds» (the bell is doing nothing, but every following moment of sound is produced by the previous one). (We can give) an other (illustration): consciousness apprehends similarly to the way in which a light moves.

(Vatsīputrīya). And how does a light move?

(Sautrāntika). The light of a lamp is a common metaphorical designation for an uniterrupted production of a series of flashing flames. When this production changes its place, we say that the light has moved, (but in reality other flames have appeared in another place). Similarly consciousness is a conventional name for a chain of conscious moments. When it changes its place (i. e. appears in coordination with another objective element) we say that it apprehends that object. And in the same way we are speaking about the existence of material elements. We say matter «is produced», «it exists», but there is no difference between existence and the element which does

[1] *Sādṛśya*(= *sārūpya* = *tad-ākāratā* = *viṣayatā*) is here not simple similarity, but a Buddhistic technical term, «coordination» which is here meant to explain the connexion between consciousness and its object. It is clear that there is no «grasping» or «apprehending» of the object by knowledge according to Vasubandhu. The objective element is appearing simultaneously with the flashing of consciousness, both are independent, but there is a mutual correspondence between them; cp. my Central Conception, pp. 55—56, and Prašastapāda, p. 112. 20. The latter explains *sārūpyāt* by *viśeṣaṇa-sambandham* (= *samavāyam*) *antareṇa* and contrasts Vaiš. S. VIII. 1. 9 which implies that the attribute, e. g., colour inheres in external reality and is the cause producing our cognition of it. Thus the term *sārūpya* implies an indealistic view of attributes, or of Universals, and iscontrasted with the term *samavāya* which implies a realistic one, Cp. below, p. 355 n. 2.

exist. The same applies to consciousness, (there is nothing that d o e s cognize, apart from the evanescent flashings of consciousness itself).

(Sāṃkhya).[1] If consciousness is not a product of a Soul, (if it has no other cause than consciousness itself, if it is only a string of conscious moments), the following moment springing up from the preceding one, then how is it to be explained 1) that it does not remain perpetually just the same, and 2) (if there be a change), why not in a fixed order of succession, like a sprout, a stem, leaves etc. (produced from a seed)?

(Sautrāntika). (As regards the first point, we answer that) all elements which partake in the process of life are characterized by a constant change, (they have no duration). They constitute a stream in which the next moment is necessarily different from the preceding one. Such is the inmost nature of every thing living!

(Sāṃkhya). (There are exceptions! e. g. in cataleptic states neither body nor mind undergo any change).

(Sautrāntika). If there really were exceptions (to the principle of Universal Change), and if the ascetics after being merged in transic medidation and having reached the climax of it would really appear in a state of perfect identity of body and mind, (without absolutely any change in them), then there could be no difference between the last and the first moment of such a state of medidation, and there could be no spontaneous awakening from the trance in the last moment. (Therefore there is an imperceptible constant change going on even in such states as catalepsy).

(As regards the second point we maintain that in the continuous stream of ideas) there positively is a fixed order of succession: if one idea springs up from another one, it does so with necessity. There is a certain affinity (between ideas), in virtue of which there are ideas somehow related to others and having the power of evoking them. As for instance, when the idea of a woman is immediateiy associated (in the mind of an ascetic) with the idea of an impure body, or (in the mind of a married man) with the idea of husband, son etc., and if later on, in the changing stream of thought, the same idea of a woman reappears, it has the power of evoking these ideas of an im-

---

1 According to Yaśomitra the opponent is here a Sānkhya philosopher. That system admits the existence of two substances only, the one spiritual (*puruṣa*) representing the Individual's Soul which is an eternal light of pure consciousness, unchanging and motionless, and the other material (*pradhāna*), perpetually changing (*nitya-pariṇāmin*) according to causal laws. The question would then mean: «yonr «consciousnes» (*vijñāna*) must be either *puruṣa* or *pradhāna*?»

pure body or of a husband, son etc., because they are associated with it, but it has not the power of evoking other (ideas, not so associated). Again the idea of a female may be followed by various ideas arising one after another, (but if we examine them, we shall find) that only such ideas really appear which are either very common (in the corresponding stream of thought), or most intensely felt in it, or (at last) have been experienced at a very recent date. The reason for this is that the Vital Energy[1] of such ideas has more power (to the exclusion of other influences), except (of course) the influence of the present state of one's body and the immediate objects of cognition.

(Sāṃkhya). If this Vital Energy (inherent in ideas) has so powerful an influence, why does it not produce perpetually (its own, one and the same) result?

(Sautrāntika). Because, (as we have said above), the elements partaking in the process of life are characterized by a perpetual change. In conformity with this principle of Universal Change the Vital Energy itself is perpetually changing and so does its result (the idea). This is only an abridged account of all the modes (of association) between ideas. A thorough going and full knowledge of them belongs to Buddha. This has been stated (by Rāhula, the Elder) in the following stanza:

Every variety of cause
Which brings about the glittering shine
In a single eye of a peacocks tail
Is not accessible to limited understanding.
The Omniscient knows them all!

(It this is true in respect of complicated material phenomena), how much more is it with respect of immaterial, mental phenomena!

II

Vinītadeva's Comment on the sūtras I. 18—21 of the Nyāyabindu.

(Tibetan text ed in the Bibl. Ind., Calcutta, 1913, pp. 52. 1—54. 10).

(52. 1). In order to repudiate the (current) misconception of a (separate) result (in the shape of a *content* cognized by the *act* of sense-perception, the author says),

I. 18. This direct cognition is itself the result of (this) way of cognition.

---

[1] *bhāvanā* = *vāsanā* = *karma* = *cetanā* = *saṃskāra.*

The meaning[1] of this is the following one. If you adhere to the view that sense-perception is an instrument of cognition, then there should be a result of (the act of cognizing by this instrument, a result) in the shape of a definitely circumscribed[2] patch of colour or some other (sense-datum), just as an axe (being an instrument through which the act of cutting wood is carried into effect) must have, as experience shows,[3] a (separate) effect in the fact that the piece of wood which is being cut becomes separated into two pieces. (Every action has its instrument and its result). (52. 7). Therefore, (in opposition to this view), it is said that «this perceptive cognition is itself the result of (this) instrument of cognition». This perceptive cognition, (the instrument), is just itself (also) the result produced by the instrument, there is no other separate result, (the *act* of cognition and its *content* are the same).

(52. 10). It is now asked, how is it (to be understood) that (the act) possesses the essence of a result of sense-perception? To this it is said,

I. 19. Because it has the essence of a distinct cognition of the object.

A distinct cognition is (here a perceptual) judgment.[4] When sense-perception possesses this essence, or this nature, (it is said) that it has the essence of a distinct cognition. This condition[5] is just the fact that sense-perception receives a definite form. Therefore, because (the act of) sense perception appears in the form of a distinct cognition, (there is no difference between the act of being *intent* upon an object and the resulting *content* of the cognition of that object). (52. 15). This (should be understood) in the following manner. If we artificially construct a relation[6] between the cognizing (act of cognition) and the cognized (content of cognition), then we (really) shall have a result in the shape of a perceptual judgment on that object. Knowledge is indeed of the essence of a judgment[7] regarding its object, and sense perception *also* is regarded as being of the essence of knowledge (52 19). Therefore, sense perception, so far as it possesses

---

[1] *ḥbrel-ba = sambandha.*

[2] Read *yoṅs-su-bcad-pai* instead of *yoṅs-su-dpyod-pai.*

[3] *mthoṅ-ba-bzhin-no.* [4] *gtan-la phebs-pa = niścaya.*

[5] *dei dṅos-po-ni = tasya bhāvaḥ.*

[6] *tshad-ma dan gzhal-byar tha-sñad btags-pa = pramāṇa-prameya-vyavahāra-āropa.*

[7] *= jñānam artha-niścayana-svabhāvam, pratyakṣam api jñana-svabhāvam iṣṭam.* Cp. Bosanquet maintaining, Logic p. 32 ff., that cognition is a perpetual judgment.

the essence of a (perceptual) judgment regarding its object, receives the character of a result, (of a distinct image, the presence of which is called forth by the senses). So is this to be understood, this is established (by the author).

(53. 3). (Now, from this point of view), if we consider the phenomenon of sense-perception [1] in its resulting phase,[2] what shall we then regard as the instrument, (through which the act of cognition arrives at this result)? To this it is said,

I. 20. (The instrument) of cognizing consists in coordination (between the image) and its (real) object.

Coordination is similarity.[3] «Its (instrument)» means the instrument of perception. That sense perception which is a perception of an object representing a distinct image, this its (coordinated image) is the (real) instrument of cognition.[4] (53. 8).

What is the meaning (of the assertion) that coordination (of the image) with the object, (or the sense of sameness) is the (real) source of (all) our knowledge? To this it is said,

I. 21. By the way of it a distinct cognition of the object is established.

Since by the way of a coordination of the object, its distinct cognition is ascertained (in a judgment), this coordination, (or this sense of sameness), is the (real) source of (all) our knowledge.

(53. 11). Indeed we then have (the judgments) «this is distinctly blue», «it is not yellow». The source of this definiteness (is the sense of sameness) and we can maintain that this is the (real) source of our knowledge, (when we make an imputed distinction between the act and the content of knowledge).

(53. 15). Indeed the senses cannot produce this definiteness (by themselves), because the (pure element of) sensation, although it is the cause (of our cognitions) is the same in all cognitions. How could it then (by itself) possess the force of distinguishing every separate cognition (from all the others)? (54. 1). If a given (pure) sen-

---

[1] *mñon-sum-ñid* = *pratyakṣa-bhāva.*

[2] *ḥbras-bui rañ-bzhin* = *phala-svabhāva.*

[3] Coordination (*sārūpya*) first of all means the connection between the object and its image, but it implies the difference of the image from all dissimilar ones and its connection, owing to the sense of sameness, with all the similar ones.

[4] *tshad-ma* = *pramāṇa* in the sense of *sādhakatama-kāraṇa* = *pramā-karaṇa* (cp. Tarka-bhāṣā, p. 10, Poona ed.), = *prakṣṛtopakāraka* (cp. N. b. ṭ. Ṭipp., p. 42. 3), the nearest psychological antecedent, the *causa efficiens par excellence.*

sation could produce a cognition (of the presense) of a blue patch, and could not produce a cognition of a yellow or of some other patch of colour, then it would possess the force of producing distinctness. But since as (pure) sensation it is (everywhere) present[1] and (always) the same, it is not the cause producing distinctness. On the other hand coordination is not always the same, it is therefore the cause producing the distinctness (and clearness) of every single cognition. (54. 6). Indeed, when we cognize something as being blue, it is then the image of blue, (its sameness with other blue objects), which produces (clearness and) distinctness, because (we then are aware) that it is not yellow or of another (colour).

(54. 8). Because, when we have (constructed) the image[2] of the blue, we can judge[3] «this is a cognition of blue and not of yellow», therefore this coordination (or coordinated image is the real) source of (all) our knowledge.[4]

III

Vācaspatimiśra on the Buddhist theory of identity between the act and the content of knowledge, and on coordination between our images and external reality.

Nyāyakaṇikā, pp. 254. 12—260. 22.

§ 1. Repudiation of the Mīmāṃsaka theory of a pure, imageless Consciousness.

(254. 13). The opponent, (viz., the Buddhist), now raises another problem.[5] It is impossible, (says he), that our cognitions should (exactly) correspond to external objects,[6] because of the following (inso-

---

[1] *ñe-ba* = *sannihita*. [2] *rnam-pa* = *ākāra*. [3] *sñam-pa* = *mati*.

[4] By pure sensation we have knowledge of the presence of a blue patch, but we do not yet know that it is blue, it is *nīlasya jñānam*, but not *nīlam iti jñānam*.

[5] In the preceding passage the theory of the origin of our knowledge through direct intuition (*nirviṣaya-pratibhā-vāda*) was discussed. Although on this theory knowledge is autonomous, independent from experience, nevertheless for the sake of argnment (*dūṣaṇābhidhitsayā*), the problem was divided, and it was asked whether these direct intuitions correspond to external reality or not, cp. p. 254. 8 ff. Mandanamiśra and his commentator Vācaspatimiśra seize this opportunity to discuss the various phases of Buddhist Idealism, pp. 254. 13—268. 15.

[6] Read *bāhya-viṣayam*.

luble) dilemma. Is the cognized object[1] apprehended by pure consciousness or is it apprehended by a consciousness which includes the image of the object[2]? The first is impossible, because (really, what does it mean to be an object?). None of its definitions will apply to such an object (of pure consciousness)! (254. 16). Indeed, (we have the definition that to be an object means simply to exist, whatsoever exists is an object). This means that every thing becomes an object (automatically), because it exists.[3] But (on this theory), since all things (of the universe) exist equally, all will equally be objects of our knowledge, (all will be cognized because they exist), and every body will be omniscient!

(254. 17). Now, (take another definition), a thing which *produces* knowledge is its object. We thus evade the absurd consequence (just mentioned), because (a cognized object) will be only a definite thing, for a definite person and for one definite[4] cognition only. (254. 19). But another absurdity arises, (viz.), the organ of vision and all other sense-organs are also factors producing cognition, they (will fall under the definition and thus become, not organs, but) objects of cognition. (254. 20). A further absurd consequence will ensue, viz., that (by this flash of pure consciousness) we will never be able to cognize something present, since at the time of (this flash) the thing which has produced it will be just gone by; (according to our system, all efficient things) are moments,[5] and (the moment of) the effect can never be simultaneous with (the moment of) the cause. (254. 21). The simultaneousness of the object (and of its cognition can be saved, if we assume that the object) is contained in the one totality[6] (of causes and con-

---

1 *tad-viṣayaḥ*, viz. *artho vijñāna-viṣayaḥ.*

2 Lit., p. 254. 13—15. «The opponent takes up the second part. Is it not that consciousness (*vijñāna*) possessing (*bahuvr.*) an external object (read *bāhya-viṣayam*) is impossible, because it cannot stand before the dilemma, whether its object is of the non-shaped (*nirākārasya*) consciousness or of (consciousness) possessing shape?».

3 Read *sattayā.*

4 Read *kaṃ cid eva.*

5 Drop the *cheda* before *kṣaṇikatvena.*

6 The Buddhist assails the Mimāṃsaka in urging upon him the fact that since his pure consciousness will be posterior to the object that called it forth, it will illumine nothing, the momentary object will be gone. The Mimāṃsaka in defence appeals to the Sautrāntika theory of cognition (*para-matam āśritya*). The cognized object is not the preceding moment (*pūrva-kṣaṇa*), but the next following one contained in the same «totality» of factors which are simultaneous with cognition (*eka-sāmagrī-vartamāna-jñāna-samāna-kālīna-viṣaya-kṣaṇa*). The four factors (*pra-

ditions producing together the act of cognition), but then (the former objection remains, viz.), the organ of vision and the other organs, since they also are contained in the same totality, will be simultaneous with cognition and will be, (according to the definition, not the organs producing cognition, but the objects) apprehended (in that cognition).

(54. 24). (M ī m ā ṃ s a k a). Be that as the case may be! Knowledge (is knowledge)! It is a special faculty which is produced by its own causes, (and obeys to its own laws). It throws light upon some objects only, not upon every object, and only upon an object present (in its ken). Such is its sovereign power (that cannot be questioned)! (This is enough to explain why) the senses are not objects, (but organs), of cognition! Accordingly it has been stated that «the essence of cognition is to cognize its object».

(255. 2). (The B u d d h i s t). Now, let us consider the following point. (You maintain that) cognition is a certain (mental) activity whose existence is conditioned by its own laws. (We will then ask) what is the object upon which this activity is intent?

(M ī m ā ṃ s a k a). The object which this activity is intent upon is the cognized thing.

(The B u d d h i s t). And how is this thing affected by that activity? Is it «turned out», as a figure shaped by the sculptor, or is it modified as rice corns are when they are crushed in a mortar, or is it consecrated as the pestle and other sacrificial implements are when they are sprinkled with holy water, or is it acquired as milk is by milking (the cows)?[1]

(255. 6). (M ī m ā ṃ s a k a). What is the use of these imputations which are out of question! I maintain that cognition has the power to reach the object.

(T h e B u d d h i s t). And what is this «reaching» (of the object)?

---

tyaya), the object (*ālambana-*), preceding consciousness (*samanantara-*), the predominant factor or the sense faculty (*indrya=adhipati-*) and light (*sahakāri-pratyaya*), unite accidentally in one totality (*sāmagrī*) and become cooperating forces (*sahakārin* = *eka-kārya-kārin*). Nobody knows who produces whom, but when they meet cognition is produced, cognition is their function, it is a case of *pratītya-samutpāda*, *asmin sati idam bhavati*, cp. my N i r v ā ṇ a, p. 86. The Buddhist idealist answers that if the object is defined as the cause producing cognition all the four members of the «totality» being equally causes, they all will fall under the definition and, according to it, all will become objects.

[1] An allusion to the old scholastic division of the objects into objects produced, modified, consecrated and reached, (*utpādya*, *vikārya*, *saṃskārya*, *prāpya*).

(Mīmāṃsaka). It is the fact of being rightly cognized, it is an attribute of the thing cognized, (its illumination).[1] It exists (nevertheless) only in regard of a definite cognizer, just as the numbers, two (three) etc., are qualities (residing in the object), but they exist only relatively to the individual mind who counts them. (This attribute of being illuminated by knowledge) ceases to exist as soon as cognition is over, just as the numbers, two, (three) etc., exist no more (apart from the separate unities) when the cognition which has counted them is over.[2]

---

[1] The Indian Realists, Mīmāṃsakas and Naiyāyikas, held a kind of anti-conceptualist doctrine of knowledge. They denied the existence of concepts, or images, altogether and imagined cognition as a pure light of consciousness which is not in itself affected by the form of the object cognized, just as the light of a lamp is always the same and does not change according to the object illuminated. According to the Mimāṃsakas knowledge produces in the external object a new quality called «cognizedness» (*jñātatā*) or «illumination» (= *artha-prakāśa*), which disappears as soon as cognition is over. The realists devised this theory probably wishing to escape all the consequences of the fact of coextensiveness of existence and knowledge (*sahopalambha-niyama*), urged upon them by the idealists. They also denied selfconsciousness (*sva-saṃvedana*) and direct introspection, and maintained that we have no direct experience of our knowledge at all (*vijñānam atyanta-parokṣam*), but when the quality of «cognizedeness» is produced in an object, we by an inference conclude of the presence in us of knowledge, cp. Ślokavārt. śūnyavāda, 76 — *śuddham eva nirākāram grāhakam saṃvid asti hi.*

[2] The idea that number (*dvitvādi-sankhyā*) as well as position in time and space (*paratva-aparatva*) are relative, and hence subjective and notional, seems to be an early concession of Indian Realists to Buddhist criticism. These notions are said by them to owe their origin to the Principle of Relativity (*apekṣā-buddhi-janya*), cp. Praśastapāda, p. 111 ff. and 164 ff. But for the Buddhists relative means unreal (*āpekṣiko'yam viśeṣana-viśeṣya-bhāvo, na vāstavaḥ*), for the Realists, all Universals being realities, relations are also real in spite of being relative (*āpekṣiko vāstavaś ca*, cp. N. Kandalī p. 117. 25). Number two is imagined as a full blown reality comfortably residing in two things, in two different places. The Buddhist contention that they are purely notional, merely signs of reality (*jñāpaka, laingika, jñānamātram*), is rejected by Praśastapāda on the score that all attributes, or all Universals, are real, cp. ibid. p. 112. 16. He says that the characteristics (*viśeṣaṇa*) of an object cannot owe their origin to mere «coordination» (*sārūpyāt*), but to «characterization» (*viśesana-viśeṣya-sambandha*). Both terms, although they gramatically mean the same, are used, the one as connoting an idealistic interpretation, the other—as an extremely realistic one. The Indian realists have gone in their tendency to infer realities from mere names a considerable bit further than their European matches. The Mīmāṃsakas follow the same tradition when they assert the real production by the pure light of knowledge of a real quality in the shape of the «cognizedness» (*jñātatā*) of the object. This theory is

(255. 9). (The Buddhist). I may open my eyes (as wide as possible), I do not arrive at perceiving this attribute of «cognizedness» in the same manner as I perceive the attributes «blue» etc. Moreover it will follow (from your theory) that objects past and future will never be cognized, because it is unthinkable that a thing should be absent, while its attribute (its «cognizedness») should be present.[1]

(255. 13). (Mīmāṃsaka). But if I maintain that this attribute of illumination by cognition is nothing different from cognition itself! On the contrary, it is just the light of cognition! And the light of cognition is but cognition itself!

(The Buddhist). How is it that the illumination of one thing becomes the illumination of another one, (the luminosity of knowledge becomes the illumination of its object)?

(Mīmāṃsaka). (255. 15). Because such is the specific character of their nature. Indeed, physical objects like colours etc. (have their own laws), as they spring up from the causes producing them, they do not throw any light (of cognition), neither upon themselves nor upon others. But knowledge, as it springs up from its (specific) causes,[2] has the power[3] to throw light upon its own self and upon others. Knowledge cannot begin its existence without an object, and then unite with an object at a later date. An axe, (e. g., obeys to other laws), it springs up from its causes and exists (at first) alone, it then combines with a fissure (by it produced) at a later date.[4] But (knowledge) is always combined with an object, this fact cannot be questioned (or explained). Indeed the axe also, according to the causes which have produced it, consists of iron. There is no special reason for this fact and its explanation is never asked.

(255. 20). And although the (double faculty) of throwing some light on its own self and on others is the quintessence of our knowledge, (this does not mean that the object is immanent to knowledge and that this double) faculty is objectless. When we contrast it with other things, (with inanimate things which are unconscious, we say) it

---

here compared with the Vaiśeṣika theory of number and Śrīdhara accordingly deals with the whole Buddhist theory of cognition in his section on Number, cp. N. Kandalī, p. 122. 33—130. 19.

1 Read *apratyutpanno dharmī dharmaś ca*...

2 Read *sva-pratyaya-samāsādita* —

3 Read *prakāśana-samartham.*

4 This is according to the Realist, but not according to the Buddhist, cp. below, the translation from Udayana.

is *a light* which illumines itself and others. When we contrast it with other faculties (we say it is) a *power* of throwing light upon itself and upon others. (In the first case) we more or less imagine it as a result, (as a content). (In the second case we, on the contrary), imagine it as an instrument (or as an action produced by) cognition. The differentiation is more or less imputed, (the fact is the same, but in this way) there is a faculty of cognition and there is an object of it.[1]

(The Buddhist). (255.24). To this we reply as follows. What meaning do you attach to the assertion that knowledge posseses the power[2] of throwing light upon itself and upon others? If you mean that such is its own nature,[3] we agree! But if you mean that there is a real mutual relation (between the object and the subject), we will ask, of what kind is this relation?

(Mīmāṃsaka). It is a subject-object relation.

(The Buddhist). (256.3). The consequence will be that this relation, (if it is something real) must inhere in the object as well as

---

1 Lit. 255. 20—23. «And illumination of self and other (read *sva-para-prakāśanam*) having its own nature by a contrast (*nivṛttyā*) with non-illumination, in some way or other (*katham cit*) receives (*bahuvr.*) an imagined differentiation as «a result»; the power of illuminating self and other, by a contrast with non-power in some way or other becomes through an imagined exclusion «an instrument of knowledge», thus the power is not without an object».

The Mīmāṃsaka is here represented as compelled to admit that his light of pure consciousness and the illumination of the object by it are not two facts, but one, because knowledge is never without an object, such is its nature that can neither be questioned nor explained. The Buddhist avails himself of the opportunity to bring home to the Mīmāṃsaka his favorite idea of the identity of image and object. The light of knowledge, if it is the same thing as the illumination of the object, is in danger of having no object at all, since the object will be immanent to knowledge. It is just what the Buddhist wants, and he represents the Mīmāṃsaka as admitting self-consciousness (*sva-para-prakāśa = sva-saṃvedana*) and an imagined difference (*kalpita-bheda*) betweeen the act and the content, the instrument and the result, or between the object and subject, of cognition cp. below the translation from Jinendrabuddhi.

2 Read *sva-para-prakāśana-samartham.*

3 Both the Mimāṃsaka (cp. above, p. 254. 15) and the Buddhist admit that the essence of cognition is to include an object and to be self-conscious, but the Buddhist explaines it as the same fact which in different contexts can be differently characterized, according to the view we take of it. The Mimāṃsaka, although very near to that view (cp. above, p. 255. 20—24), nevertheless, as a realist, admits a real relation, a real tie (*sambandha*) between object and subject, something like a chain which resides at once in both the related things and unites them. On relations and their reality cp. above p. 287 n. 3.

in its cognition, (i. e., in two different places), and then it will be itself different, just because it resides in different places. (There will be no union at all, object and subject would be separated as before). Therefore only these two different entities will remain, (their supposed uniting tie is itself disunited).[1] Moreover, as already mentioned, the past and the future (could never be cognized on this hypothesis, since) how could this one uniting tie reside in objects (separated by time). (256. 5). But if you admit, (as you are now bound to do), that the subject-object relation is immanent to our knowledge alone, how can it then be connected with external objects? Thus it is that while you are expatiating on the capacity of our knowledge to throw a light upon itself and upon others, you are driven against your will to admit the identity of (the exeternal objects), the patches of blue etc., with their cognition. (256.7). And thus it is that if you maintain that knowledge contains no images, we will never arrive to know what it means to be an object of this pure imageless consciousness,[2] (i. e., what union there can be between this internal light and an external object).

(256.8). We must conclude that the external object corresponds to a cognition which includes its image.

(256.9). Moreover, (the theory of an imageless consciousness leads to an absurdity). If, (as you maintain), the illumination of the object (by knowledge) is nothing but the fact of the self- luminosity of knowledge, the difference among the objects must be then determined according to a difference between their cognitions. But cognition (according to this theory) contains no differences, since it contains no images, (it is always the same). (Neither will the objects contain any differences). We then will not be able to distingnish, «this is our consciousness of something blue», «that one, of something yellow». People wanting to take action (in pursuit of their special aims will not know how to do it, and) will commit no purposive actions at all.

---

[1] Cp. Bradley, Appearance, p. 33. «The links are united by a link, and this bond of union is a link which also has two ends... this problem is insoluble».

[2] Lit., p. 256. 7—8. «And thus, since the essence of an object of knowledge is averse (*ayogāt*) to imageless consciousness, the (external) thing is an object of image-containing consciousness».

§ 2. Consciousness contains images coordinated with external objects.

(256.12). On the other hand, if we admit that our cognitions contain definite images, then the coordination of the blue patch[1] (with its image), being the cause which imparts definiteness to it, will be the source of our right cognition, and its aspect of being a content of our consciousness which receives, (as it were), definiteness in the shape of a patch of blue colour will be the result (of that act of cognition).[2] (256.14). And although (on this theory) coordination (of our knowledge) and that knowledge itself are just one and the same reality, nevertheless they can be differentiated (in imagination), by imagining a double aspect of the same thing, the aspect of an act of cognition and the aspect of its content. The essence of cognition is settled by one principle contrast (of cognition to non cognition). But many other differentiations may be imagined which are all included in it, and thus an imagined differentiation is created, according to different standpoints, so far the fact of cognition is differently viewed and differently contrasted, (as an action when it is contrasted with other actions, or as a content when it is contrasted with other contents).[3] (256.16). It has been said (by Dignāga)[4] «the mere existence of pure consciousness is not yet the definite consciousness of an object, because it is always the same, and (if there were no images), we would arrive at the consequence that all our cognitions must be undifferentiated. But the sense of sameness introducing itself into our consciousness, brings in coordination».

(256.18) (We now have a good definition of what an object of cognition is). An object is the cause which produces cognition and

---

[1] i. e., the indefinite point of external reality will become a definite patch of blue only for us, only owing to the existence in us of an image corresponding to it

[2] Here apparently Vācaspatimiśra borrows his expressions from Dharmottara, cp. N. b. t., p. 15. 20 ff.

[3] Lit., p. 256. 14—16. «Although coordination and cognition is (here) just the same thing, nevertheless through constructions (*vikalpair*) whose essence is an intention (*avagāhana*) of the shape contained in one contrast, (i. e., many secondary differentiations can be evolved from one chief differentiation, or chief feature), it reaches the condition of sources and result of cognition, (this condition) being an imagined difference, produced by a difference of things to be excluded, (or to be contrasted with)». Cp. *ibid.*, p. 262. 2.

[4] Quoted also in the N. Kandalī, p. 123. 24.

corresponds to its image.[1] Thus the senses, (although also being producers of cognition), are not its objects.[2] (As to the simultaneousness of cognition and object, they are also explained on this theory). To be conscious of an object[3] means to be conscious of its image which has been evoked by the object. The images are present at the time of cognition, thus their simutaneousness is explained. It has been said (by Dharmakīrti) —

«If it is asked, how can an (absent) object, separated from us in time, be perceived, we will answer, to be perceived rightly, means only to be the cause of the (corresponding) image, to be the moment (capable of) evoking the mental image».[4]

(256.23). And thus, in this sense it is right to maintain that the (external) object is *felt*, (i. e., cognized). For this reason the Sautrāntikas teach that the (external) things are the objects of our cognition, but their (definite, constructed) form is immanent to knowledge.

§ 3. Contest with extreme Idealism. Sense perception does not warrant the existence of an external world.

(256.25). (The Yogācāra). All this is wrong! Because, indeed, if you maintain that images are inherent in our knowledge and they refer to (external) reality, we shall ask, (how do you come to know this?) Do you know it by direct evidence or by inference?

(257.1). First of all, you cannot invoke direct awareness,[5] because your awareness testifies to the presence in you of the image of something blue, this image is locked up[6] in its own self, (it cannot make a step beyond, in order) to grasp another blue thing, (the blue object). Indeed the reflected image is one blue thing, not two blue things, (the image and the object)?[7] And we have already called

---

[1] Cp. N. Kandalī, p. 124.9.

[2] Lit., p. 256.18—19. «And owing to an objectivity through coordination-with-it and origination-from it there is no deduction-of-it upon the senses etc.».

[3] *artha-vedanam.*

[4] Quoted Tātp., p. 101.14 with the reading — *kṣamam* instead of — *kṣaṇam.*

[5] The discussion of the first part of this dilemma is finished below p. 258.15.

[6] Lit. «is quite finished in its own image merely».

[7] Among modern Europeans B. Russel is, e. g., is opposed to «the intrusion of the idea between the mind and the object», cp. Mysticism, pp. 133 and 222, Analysis of Mind, p. 180. He will consequently be a *nirākāra-vādin,* just as a Mīmāmsaka.

attention [1] to the fact that it is impossible to be at once (out of the cognition and in the cognition), to be a separate thing (from knowledge and to be cognized by it as) its object.

(Sautrāntika). (257.4). Let it be so! However the object of cognition is double,[2] the *prima facie* apprehended (in sensation), and the distinctly settled (in a perceptual judgment). (257.5). Now, in respect to sense-perception, what is immediately seized (in a sensation) is only one single moment, but what is distinctly settled (in a perceptual judgment) is a compact chain of moments, (the constructed thing), the object of our purposive action. (257.6). If that were not so, cognition could not guide the actions of those who act in pnrsuit of definite aims.[3] (When we speak of) knowledge guiding [4] our actions and leading to successful attainment [5] of aims, we only mean that knowledge points [6] to an object of a possible (successful) action.[7] Now, the moment of sensation is not the moment of action,[8] since the latter does not exist any more when the action takes place. But the chain of moments, (the continuity of the object) can be (the aim of purposive action). (257.9). However, (a chain of moments) cannot be grasped directly (in sensation), and therefore we must admit (the importance and conditioned reality) of the constructed [9] (chains of moments).

(257.9). The same applies to an inferential judgment.[10] The object it is *prima facie* intent upon is a Universal, (an absent thing constructed in imagination), whose essence is to represent a contrast with some other things.[11] But the (corresponding) judgment [12] refers that Universal to (some particutar point of reality [13]), which becomes the object of our purposive action and is capable of being successfully attained. (257.11). Both these ways of cognition, (direct perception proceding from the

---

1 Cp. above, p. 255. 14 ff.

2 Here again Vācaspati's phrasing seems to be influenced by Dharmottara, cp. NBT, p. 12. 16 ff.

3 Read *artha-kriyārthinaḥ*.

4 *pravartaka*.

5 *prāpaka*.

6 *upadarśaka*.

7 *pravṛtti-viṣaya*. With this passage cp. NBT, p. 3. 6 ff.

8 Lit. «not the object of action».

9 *adhyavaseyatvam* = *vikalpitatvam*.

10 *anumāna-vikalpa* = *anumita-adhyavasāya*.

11 Read *anya-vyāvṛtti-rūpam*.

12 *adhyavaseyas*.

13 i. e., *svalakṣaṇa*, cp. NBT, p. 12. 20—21.

particular to the general and inference proceding from the general to the particular), are right means of cognition only in respect of successful purposive action, as has been stated (by Dignāga[1]), «a man who has distinctly delineated his object by these two modes of cognition in a judgment,[2] takes action, and is not lead astray». Thus it is that the external (real object) is not accessible to our direct knowledge, but being indirectly ascertained (in a judgment) it is an object (of cognition nevertheless).

(Yogācāra). (257.14). All this is wrong![3] You do not know at all what a judgment is!

(Sautrāntika). A judgment is a mental construction[4] (of the form «this is blue»).[5] Indirect cognition (or inference), because in its essence it is nothing but constructive thought, is conterminous with (judgment).[6] Direct cognition (or sense-perception) is also a judgment because it calls forth a thought-construction.[7]

(Yogācāra). (257.16). But a construction also, since it is intent upon the image (produced by it and cannot make a step beyond it), how can it judge, (or execute constructions regarding external reality)?

(Sautrāntika). (257.17). (This is however possible), if you accept (the following explanation). The image (which a man feels inwardly present in his mind) is his own. It is not something (artificially) constructed[8] (by combining in thought). On the contrary, it is something intimately and directly felt.[9] Indeed, a mental construction is something arranged (by our mind's initiative). The true essence of a thing is never an arrangement. It is always (something unique), something not standing in any relation to whatsoever,[10] (something unutterable), something that cannot be designated by a (connotative) name. It is (also something concrete and vivid), a gla-

---

1 This quotation has not yet been identified.

2 *adhyavasāya.*

3 Read *tan na.*

4 *vikalpa,* cp. Tātp., p. 87.25, 338.15 and Ṭipp., p. 23.4—5.

5 A fuller befinition of a perceptual judgment (*vikalpa* = *adhyavasāya*) is found Tātp., p. 338.15, translated below in Appendix V.

6 *vikalpa-rūpatvāt tad-viṣayam,* cp. Udayana, Pariśuddhi ad Tātp., p. 338.15.

7 *vikalpa-jananāt.*

8 Lit. «the domain of choice or arrangement».

9 *saṃvedanam.*

10 *sarvato bhinna* cp. Tattvas., p. 390.25, *trailokya-vilakṣaṇa,* cp. Tātp., p. 338.17.

ring reflex,[1] (non-operated upon by the mind). (257.20). Thus it is that images are not mental arrangements (for a consciousness which feels their immediate presence) in itself. But the mind projects the inward reflex[2] into the external world and guides the purposive actions of those who are desirous of dealing with these external objects, in directing them towards this or towards that thing. Nor are the people (who are thus guided by images projected into the external, world) deceived (in their aims, since experience does not contradict them), because indirectly (these images, although themselves subjective and notional), are produced by external (reality); and since they are related to reality, the real aims are successfully reached. Accordingly, it has been stated (by Dharmottara[3]), (judgment or inference guides the purposive actions of men), because «the course it takes consists in having *prima facie* to deal with mental contents of a (genenal) unreal character and in ascertaining through them some real fact».[4]

(257.24). (Yogācāra). Please explain what is meant by the words «(knowledge) constructs (in a perceptual judgment a kind) of reality out of that unreality which is the image present to it[5]».

---

1 Cp. N. b. ṭ, p. 12.3 (= *sputābha*), and N. Kaṇikā, p. 281.6 — *sākṣātkāro viśadatā*. — *viśada-pratibhāsa* refers to the same thing as *niyata pratibhāsa* in N. b. ṭ., p. 8. 10.

2 *svābhāsam vikalpayantaḥ*.

3 Cp. N. b. ṭ., p. 7. 13.

4 Lit. 257. 17—23. «If it is opined that one's own shape is not the object (or the domain) of constructions, (of choice, of combinations), but of intimate feeling (*saṃvedanasya*) which is immediate (direct), (drop the *cheda* before *pratyakṣasya*, and put it after that word, and insert *sa* before *hi*). An object of mental construction is something that is being arranged combined and contrasted), but the essence of something is not being constructed, because it, being excluded from everything, cannot be (combined with a name, and because it is a vivid reflex. Therefore, not being in themselves constructions, they arrange their own shape as being external and direct, here and there those who wish to deal with them. And since mediately they are produced from the external, because they are connected with it, because they reach it, they do not deceive the people. As has been said «because it operates (read *pravṛtter*) in ascertaining an object in a non-object which is its own (immediate) reflex».

5 When the cognition of a blue patch arises we experience internally a modification of our feeling and project it into the external world in an internal judgment «this is the blue». The words of Dharmottara quoted by Vācaspati refer in NBT, p. 7. 13, to inference, but p. 18. 9 ff. he also maintains that there is in the resulting aspect of inference no difference between perception and inference, since both are judgments asserting a coordination (*sārūpya*) between an image and a point of reality.

(Sautrāntika). Does it not mean that it imagines a real object, (i. e., some efficient point-instant producing a possible sensation)?

(Yogācāra). What is the essence of constructive thought? Is it an imagined sensation[2] or some other function? The first is impossibile! (An imagined sensation is indeed a *contradictio in adjecto*). Sensation and imagination being the one passive and the other active,[3] (the one non-constructive and the other constructive, imaginative sensation) would be as it were a liquid solid stuff.[4] (Constructive thought or imagination) is a function different (from sensation). The question is whether it operates after (sensation) or simultaneously with it? The first is impossible, because cognition[5] being a momentary[6] flash) cannot operate by degrees. Even those schools who deny Universal Momentariness,[7] even they maintain that thought, as well as motion, cannot operate intermittently[8] and therefore (sensation

---

1 Read p. 257. 25 – 258. 1, *kim vikalpasya svarūpam, anubhavāropa uta vyāpārāntaram*, and drop the following *svarūpānubhavaḥ*.

2 *anubhava-āropa* = *pratyakṣa-āropa* = *pratyakṣa-vikalpa*, this would involve a *samplava* between the two quite different sources of knowledge in contradiction to the Buddhist principle of *pramāṇa-vyavasthā*, cp. App. II.

3 *vikalpa-avikalpa*, the order of these two terms is here inverted in keeping with Pāṇini, II. 2. 34.

4 Lit. p. 258. 1—2. «Because of the impossibility of identity between actual experience (*anubhava*) and construction (*samāropa*) whose essence is non-differentiation and differentiation, just as between the solid (read *kaṭhina*) and the liquid».— The solid and the liquid elements are, according to Indian conceptions, ultimate elements, not two different conditions of the same stuff. When milk coagulates into curds this is explained in assuming that the solid element which was always present in milk becomes prominent (*utkṛṣṭa*). Only the Sāṅkhya would explain it as a *pariṇāma*. In the eyes of the Buddhist as well as of the Naiyāyik the simile means that sensation and thought are different in principle and cannot be mixed up.

5 *vijñānasya*.

6 For the Buddhist every existence is motion, and motion consists of a chain of absolute infinitesimal moments (*pūrva-apara-kāla-kalā-vikala-kṣaṇa*), for the realists the things are either moving or stationary and every unit of motion, as well as of thought, consists of three moments, the moments of its production, its existence and its extinction.

7 The Mīmāṃsaka and Nyāya-Vaiśeṣika schools are first of all meant. They deny that the existence of every object is split into point-instants. In fact all schools except the Buddhists deny the Universal Flux, and among the Buddhists the Mādhyamikas also deny it, on the same grounds as the Vedāntins. The Sāṅkhyas with their *pariṇāma-nityatva* of *pradhāna* come very near the Buddhist *kṣaṇikatva*. cp. Central Conception, p. 80 and Introduction.

8 *viramya-vyāpāra*.

and imagination), cannot operate alternately, (when something is felt and imagined at the same time). (258. 5). But if you assume that sensation and imagination work simultaneously, we can admit this, with the proviso[1] that the object[2] is immanent[3] in cognition; because if we suppose that what we feel is (not in us), but out of us,[4] the term «feeling» will loose itself every intelligible meaning.[5]

(258. 7). And thus, what is really immediately felt in us is the (double) subject-object aspect of our knowledge,[6] and what is constructed in imagination is the (external) object. (258. 8). Our own self, what we internally feel in us, is not something constructed in imagination,[7] (on the other hand the external) object, since it is constructed in imagination, is not the thing actually felt in sensation.[8] (258. 9). (We cannot know) whether the (external) object exists or does not exist, but (what we call) construction (of an object) is nothing but the (imagined) «grasping» (aspect of its idea).[9] It has been already mentioned that to «grasp» something external to our knowledge is impossible.[10]

(258. 11). (Sautrāntika). (We also assume a kind of) imputed externality,[11] (viz.), our images (coalesce with external objects in that sense) that we are not conscious of the difference,[12] aud that is why our purposive actions, (when guided by our judgments), are directed towards external objects (and are successful).

(258. 12). (Yogācāra). But (when they coalesce), is the external object also cognized at that time or not? The first is excluded, according to what we have just said, viz., that (real) «grasping» is an impossibility. But if no external object is really apprehended and we simply dont feel the difference (between the external thing and an imagined idea), this undiscrimination alone could not guide our purpo

---

1 *kevalam.*

2 *vedyaḥ.*

3 *ātma-bhāva-avasthita.*

4 *para-bhāva-vedane.*

5 *svarūpa-vedana-anupapattiḥ = svarūpeṇa vedanasya anupapattiḥ.*

6 Read *grāhya-grāhaka-ākāro 'nubhūto.*

7 Lit., p. 258. 8—9. «But the self is not superimposed upon the non-felt».

8 *pratyakṣa-vedyaḥ.*

9 Lit., p. 258. 9—10. «And this superimposition is nothing but (*eva*) the grasping of something either existing or not existing».

10 Cp. above, p. 256. 1—6.

11 *bāhya-samāropas.*

12 *bhedāgraha = akhyāti,* this celebrated principle has been also adopted by Prabhākara for the explanation of illusions, cp. Tātp., p. 56 ff.

sive actions towards a definite aim, since (undiscriminated from our image will be not exclusively one definite object, but all) others will be also undiscriminated at that time, and the consequence will be that (our image) could direct us not towards the definite object to which it corresponds, but) to another one.[1]

(258. 11). Thus it is that our immediate feeling cannot be relied upon as a proof of the reality of an external world.

§ 4. IMPOSSIBILITY TO PROVE THE REALITY OF AN EXTERNAL WORLD BY RATIOCINATION.

(258. 16). (Yogācāra). Neither can (the reality of the external world) be established by inference. It has been, indeed, sufficiently explained that, just as simple awareness, inference cannot seize the external object neither directly, nor indirectly.[2] There is no fact from which its existence could be deduced with logical necessity.[3] (If such a fact exists), it must be either an effect (of external reality from which the existence of the cause could be necessarily deduced) or a fact possessing externality as its inherent property, (the existence of this property could then be deduced analytically). There are no such facts.[4]

---

1 Lit., p. 258. 14—15. «But if it is not grasped, there will be no definiteness of action by not grasping the difference, because, since other ones are at that time not grasped, towards another one also activity will be consequent». — For a more detailed explanation of the principle of *bhedāgraha* or Neglected Difference and the use which is made of it in order to make intelligible our perception of the external world cp. preliminary note to Appendix V, on *apoha*.

2 According to the Sautrāntikas the direct function of sense perception is the awareness of the presence of something in one's ken (*grahaṇa*), its indirect function — the evoking of its general image in a perceptual judgment (*pratyakṣa-balād utpannena vikalpena adhyavasāyaḥ*). The direct function of inference, on the other hand, is the construction of a general image, its indirect function is the ascertainement of the presence of something in our ken, cp. above p. 257. 4 ff. and N. b. ṭ., p. 7. 13, 11. 12 and 12. 16 ff. The Yogācāra of the old school and the Mādhyamika-Yogācāras reject this theory.

3 Since there are only two kinds on Uniformity in nature, Uniformity of Succession or Uniformity of Coexistence, a neccessary deduction is only possible either from a following effect or from a subaltern quality, but no such successive facts or coexisting facts can be found from which the externality of our objects could be deduced. The Sautrāntika will presently apeal to Solipsism as a fact inherent in the denial of an external world.

4 Lit., p. 258. 17—18. «And there is no such *probans* dependent (read *pratibaddhas*) upon the external, neither its identity nor its result».

(258. 18). (Sautrāntika). However there is one! Yourself, you the Yogācāra, deny Solipsism, and you admit the influence of a foreign stream of thought upon my stream of thought. When the perceptions of walking and speaking arise in my mind (and they do not refer to my own walking and speaking because they) are not preceded by my own will to walk and to speak, (we assume the existence of another person who walks and speaks). We then can throw the argument in the following syllogistic form),

(Major premise). If something appears accidentally in a combination otherwise constant, it must depend upon a special cause.

(Example). Just as my perceptions of external purposive movements and of (foreign) speech, which depend upon the presence of another personality.

(Minor premise). Such are the perceptions of external objects, the subject of our controversy.

(Conclusion). (They are due to a special cause).

This is an analytical judgment,[1] (since the predicate, the necessary existence of a special cause, is an inherent property of the subject, the occasional change in our stream of thought). And this special cause lying outside our subjective stream of thought is the external object.

(258. 23). (Yogācāra).[2] (The external object is superfluous, there is an internal) Biotic Force[3] which accidentally becomes mature and

---

[1] Lit., p. 258. 18—22. «Does not the following (proof) exist? All things that are accidental, if something exists, depend upon a cause additional to it, just as the ideas reflecting cut-off-walking-and-speech (read *vicchinna-gamana-vacana-*) depend upon another stream, and such are also the subject of controversy (= the minor term), the six (kinds) of outwards turned ideas (*pravṛtti-vijñāna*), while the stream of the store of inwardly turned ideas (*ālaya-vijñāna*) exists. Thus a reason of own existence». — Cp. the same argument as quoted by Vācaspati in Tātp. p. 464. 12 ff., and by Jinendrabuddhi, in an abridged form, in the following translation in this Appendix. The *pravṛtti-* and *ālaya-vijñāna* are thus defined in Tātp., p. 145. 17—*pūrva-cittam pravṛtti-vijñānam yat tat ṣaḍ-vidham, pañca rūpadi-jñānāny avikalpakāni, ṣaṣṭham ca vikalpa-vijñānam, tena saha jātaḥ samāna-kālaḥ cetanā-viśeṣas tad ālaya-vijñānam ity ucyate.*

[2] Beginning with 258. 23 the Yogācāra assumes the rôle of a *pūrvapakṣin.*

[3] *vāsāna*, often *anādi-vāsanā*, sometimes explained as = *pūrvam jñānam*, cp. Santānāntara-siddhi, sūtra 65, sometimes as = *sāmarthyam*, cp. Kamalaśīla, p. 367. 21. It performs in the Buddhist system of Idealistic Monism the function of explaining the origin of phenomenal plurality out of transcendental unity and is in many respects similar to the *karma* = *cetanā* of the early Buddhists, the *māyā* of the Mādhyamikas and Vedāntins, the *vāsanā* of the Sānkhyas, the *bhā*

evokes an idea; this idea is also accidental (and changing concomitantly with a change in its cause).

(258. 24). (Sautrāntika). But is not your Biotic Force (in this case simply) the force of subjective thought, contained in one continuous stream, the force to produce out of itself corresponding objective thoughts. Its (so called) maturity is its (perfect development and) readiness immediately to produce its effect. Its cause is the preceding moment of the same stream, because you (the Yogācāra) do not admit (in this case) causality between different streams.[1] (259. 3). But then, either

---

vanā of the Mīmāṃsakas, the *adṛṣṭa, apūrva, abhyāsa* and *saṃskāra* of all shools. The Sānkhyas derive it from the root *vās* «to perfume», the Buddhists from the root *vas* «to live». In the Abh. Koša, IX, it is nsed identically with *bhāvanā* as a designation of the universal force which propels life. We have accordingly tried to render it by the Bergsonian élan vital, since it seems to possess some of its connotations. *Vāsanā* is sometimes divided into *anubhava-vāsanā* and *avidyā-vāsanā* or *anādi-(avidyā)-vāsanā*. The first = *saṃskāra* = *smṛti-janaka-sāmagrī*, means the influence of former experience, habit, habitual way of thought and life in general. On the difference between *vāsanā* and *saṃskāra* cp. S. N. Dasgupta. The Study of Pātañjali, p. 111. (Calcutta, 1920). This notion implies the reality of the external world. The term *avidyā-vāsanā* oı *anādi-vāsanā*, on the other hand, implies an idealistic view of the Universe, different in the old Yogācāra and the new Yogācāra-Sautrāntika schools. The importance of former experience is by no means denied (*vāsanā* = *pūrvam jñānam*), but the existence of a duplicate world beyond the world of our sensations and ideas is deemed problematic and metaphysical. It is thus an internal, spiritual force creating the illusion of this external world and might also be called the Force of Transcendental Illusion, similar to the *māyā* of the Vedāntins. Every idea is impregnated or perfumed by that force (*vastrāder mṛga-madādinā vāsyatvam yathā*). The extreme Yogācāras apparently denied the doctrine of *svalakṣaṇa-sārūpyam*, they maintained that (*na*) *dṛṣṭa-arthakriyā-svalakṣaṇa-sālakṣaṇyena* (= *sārūpyeṇa*), (*api tu*) *anādi-vāsanā-vaśāt* (*alīkasyaiva dāha-pākādika-sāmarthya-āropaḥ*), cp. Tātp., pp, 145. 9 ff., 464. 11 ff; N. vārt., p. 69 — *śakti-viśiṣṭaḥ cittotpādo vāsanā*. We have seen above, p. 296, that when the origin of the the Categories of our understanding is found in former experience, the force prodncing them is called *anubhava-vāsanā*, and when it is ascribed to a spontaneous faculty of our Reason, it is called *vikalpa-vāsanā*. Thns Empiricism may be called *anubhava-vāsanā-vāda*, and Rationalism — *vikalpa-vāsanā-vāda*. The extrem Idealism of the Yogācāras may then be called *atyanta-* or *ekānta-vikalpa-vāsanā-vāda*. Our Reason in the role of the creator of the illusion of an external empirical world would be then called *avidyā-vāsanā*, our Reason as containing innate ideas — *anādi-vikalpa-vāsanā*, the empirical world as contrasted with transcedental reality — is then *anādi-vāsanā-vāsitaḥ sāṃvyavahārikaḥ pratyayaḥ* cp. N. Kandalī, p. 279. 15.

[1] Dharmakīrti admits that the presence of another personality is the predominant cause (*bdag-rkyen* = *adhipati-pratyaya*) or *causa efficiens* of our presentations of external purposive movements and speech, cp. Santānāntarasiddhi, p. 63.

every (moment) in the subjective stream of thought will be a «cause of maturity», or not a single one, because (as moments of subjective thought all are in this respect) equal. They are equal, because if you, according to your intention, chose in the subjective stream one moment as ready (to produce out of itself a given objective thought), all other moments will be just in the same position!

(259.5). (Y o g ā c ā r a). (No!), because every new moment has a different force. Since the moments change, their effects are also changing.

(259.6). (S a u t r ā n t i k a). But then, (if every moment is different), there will be only one moment capable of producing the image of a blue patch or [1] capable of arousing it from (its dormant condition in the store-consciousness). No other moment will be able to do it, (the image of the blue patch will then never recur in the same individual). Or, if (other moments) will also be (able to do it), how is it that every moment (is supposed) to have a different efficiency? (If it is not different), then all the moments of the stored up subjective stream of consciousness [2] (uninfluenced by external objects, being in the same position), will have the same capacity; and, since an efficient cause being present, cannot postpone [3] its action, (all the moments will then produce just the same image of a blue patch).[4]

(259.10). If all our ideas have the same origin in the subjective stream of thought, they must be always the same, (since their cause is always the same). But this (constancy) is incompatible with the (actual) changing character of our ideas.

(259.11). (If there were no external cause), there would be unchanging constancy of thought, which excludes change. (But change exists and) is thus proved to depend upon an external cause.[5] Thus it is tha an invariable concomitance (between the change of thought and it external cause) is established. (259.12). Neither do you, Idealists, admit all our knowledge of the external world [7] to be produced b the influence on us of other minds,[8] you admit it only (in order t

---

1 Read *veti*. 2 *ālaya-santāna*. 3 Read *ca...anupapatti*

4 Cp. the same argument developed in Šāstra-dīpikā, p. 180 ff.,— *sarva daiva nīla-vijñānam syāt*; and SDS., p. 26.

5 This would be a negative deduction according to the 4th figure, *nātra kādā cittvam, sadātanatvasya prasangāt*, or according to the 6th figure, *nātra sadāta natvam, hetvantarāpekṣatvāt, sadātanatvasya yad viruddham kadācitkatvam, ten yad vyāpyam (vyāpakam?) hetvantarāpekṣatvam, tasya upalabdhiḥ*; cp. NB, 35 and 37.

6 *vijñānavādin*. 7 *pravṛtti-vijñāna*. 8 *santānāntara-nimittatvam*.

avoid Solipsism) in regard of some of our (external) perceptions, (viz.), the perceptions of external purposive movements and of (another man's) speech.[1] (259. 14). Moreover, even assuming, (for the sake of argument, that every occasional external perception) is produced by the influence of a foreign personality, the effect cannot be changing, since such a personality is constantly present. (259. 15). (You cannot maintain that the other personality is sometimes present and sometimes absent), because the chain of moments constituting the personality is quite compact[2] and cannot be occasionally relegated to a remote place, since according to (your) Idealism,[3] space as an external entity does not exist. And because thought is not physical, (the foreign personality which is only) thought, never does occupy a definite place. (259. 18). (Nor can a stream of thought be occasionally present) in respect of the time (of its appearence), since you do not admit the appearence of something (new, of something) that did not previously exist. Therefore our syllogism proves the existence of external (physical) objects.[3]

(259. 19). (Yogācāra). This is wrong! Although (in our opinion) the origin of all our external perceptions is exclusively to be found in our internal stream of thought,[4] there is nevertheless an occasional variety of perceptions. The reason (in your syllogism) is fallacious, it

---

1 Read *gamana-vacana-pratibhāsasya vijñānasya.*

2 *sāndratara.*

3 The solution of the problem of Solipsism by Dharmakīrti in his Santānāntarsiddhi is that, from the point of view of absolute reality, there is only one spiritual principle undivided into subject and object and, therefore, no plurality of individual existences. But from the empirical point of view there are necessarily other personalities existing in the external world, just as there are external objects existing and cognized by the two sources of our knowledge, sense-perception and inference, as they are characterized in Dignāga's and his own epistemological system. Nevertheless he himself calls his view idealism (*vijñānavādi* and *yogācāra*) and maintains that an idealist can speak about other personalities and an external world just as a realist does, but for the sake of precision he ought to speak not about other personalities, but about «his representations» of other minds, to speak of other minds is only an abbreviation Our ideas, in this system, are not cognitions of reality, but constructions or dreams about reality. They are indirect cognitions just as dreams are, since dreams are also conditioned by former real experiences, but feebly recollected in a morbid state of mind. Hence Dharmakīrti and Dignāga are represented here as Sautrāntikas, although in their own opinion they are Yogācāras. They are therefore called Sautrāntika-Yogācāras. Their opponents are the old Yogācāras of Asanga's school and the later Mādhyamika-Yogācāras.

4 *sva-santāna-mātra-prabhave'pi = ālaya-vijñāna-prabhave 'pi.*

is uncertain,[1] its absence in contrary cases is uncertain,[2] (since the change of our perceptions can be explained from within).......... (260. 11). Moreover, when you maintain that to be an object of knowledge means to be, 1) (a point of reality) producing cognition, and 2) to be coordinated with the respective image (by the sense of sameness),[3] (we will object that all the other causes and conditions of our knowledge are also to a certain extent coordinated with it through a sense of sameness, viz.) when a perception of colour is produced the sense of vision produces the limitation[4] (of it to the visual sphere), light produces the distinctness[5] (of the image), the previous moment of consciousness[6] produces the following[7] one. Since all these causes are coordinated with their respective results by (special kinds of) coordinations,[8] and since they are the causes (of our perception of a blue patch of colour), they (according to your definition) must be also objects, (not only causes), just as the blue patch (is an object, because it is a cause). (260. 18). And if you maintain that the object is absolutely the same[9] (as its image), and that that is it what makes it an object, then (we will answer) that the preceding conscious moment,[10] the moment preceding our perception of the blue, possesses still more sameness than the (external) blue object, and that it consequently (will fall under your definition and) constitute an object of our image of the blue patch! (Hence your «coordination» explains nothing!).[11]

(260. 20). (S a u t r ā n t i k a). To be an object of our knowledge does not only mean to be (a point of reality) producing it and coordinated with its image, but it also means to be established as such by a perceptual judgment,[12] («this is the blue»). This judgment refers just to an external thing, not to something else. (The sensation or feeling is

---

1 *anaikāntika.*

2 *sandigdha-vipakṣa-vyāvṛttika.*

3 *utpatti-sārūpyābhyām viṣayatve (sati)*, cp. Tātp., p. 463. 25 — *na sārūpya-samutpattī api viṣaya-lakṣaṇam.*

4 *niyama.*

5 Read *spaṣṭatā.*

6 *saṃskāra* here evidently in the sense of *samanantara-pratyaya.*

7 *jñāna.* 8 *sārūpyaiḥ.* 9 *atyanta-sārūpyāt.*

10 *nīla-vijñāna-samanantara-pratyayasya.*

11 Lit., p. 260. 15—18. «Moreover, if objectness comes from origin and coordination, eye, light and *saṃskāra* also respectively, through the coordinations of limitation, clearness (read *spaṣṭatā*) and consciousness, and through origin from them, must be grasped just as the blue».

12 *adhyavasāyāt.*

purely internal, but in the following moment we have constructed an image, projected in into the external world and identified it with a point of external reality, i. e., we have judged).

(Y o g ā c ā r a). No! We have already answered this. We have proved above [1] (that neither by immediate awareness nor by inference can the reality of the external world be established).

IV

Udayana-ācārya on the Buddhist theory of an identity between the act of cognizing and the content of a cognition.

Nyāya-vārtika-tātparya-ṭīkā-Pariśuddhi, ed. Calcutta 1911, pp. 152—155.

(152. 1). A source of knowledge [2] (is compared by the Realists with) an instrument. It is the special cause (of a mode of cognition), its predominant cause,[3] (such as the senses in sense perception). When the result is achieved there is no need of such an (instrument) to produce (the result a new),[4] just as, when (the tree) has been cut down, there is no need of an axe (in order to cut it down anew). Therefore, just as the function of an axe consists in cutting down the tree which is not yet cut down, just so does the function of our sensitivity and of the other (sources of our knowledge) consist in cognizing an object which is not yet cognized. This is the opinion of the M i m ā ṃ s a k a s.

(152. 6). However, there is another theory, (the Buddhist one). (The ultimate cause producing cognition is the fact of) a coordination [7]

---

[1] Cp. above, p. 257. 4 ff. [2] *pramāṇa.*

[3] *karaṇa* = *sādhakatama-kāraṇa* = *prakṛṣṭa-upakāraka*=*adhipati-pratyaya.*

[4] Lit. «And when the thing to be produced is produced, there is no producing for its like». *karaṇa-jatīyasya indriyādeḥ* (V).

[5] Lit. «Therefore, just as the axe becomes functioning with respect to cutting, because of the fact that its object is the non-cut, just so...».

[6] The definition of *pramāṇa* as *anadhigata-artha-adhigantṛ* is accepted by both the Buddhists and the Mīmāṃsakas, but the latter understand under object the empirical object which has stability and, in the continuous run of its perception, receives in every moment a new time-characteristic. The Buddhists understand the transcendental object which has no duration, which is «other» in every moment.

[7] *sārūpyam,* cp. Tātp., p. 14. 13, the fact that a constructed mental image with all its inhering attributes corresponds to the utterly heterogeneous (*atyanta-vilakṣaṇa*) point-instant of efficient reality, the transcendental object. In Appendix V, on *apoha,* it will be explained that this coordination is founded on relativity (*anya-vyāvṛtti*).

(between a mental image and the real) object (corresponding to it). What indeed is the result produced from a source of knowledge? It is (knowledge itself), a distinct cognition of the object. Nothing else is meant by the content of right knowledge.[1] A source of knowledge has, indeed, nothing else to do with respect to its object than to cognize it. (To attend to the object and to «fetch» it are the same). The «fetching»[2] of the object by our knowledge is nothing but the focussing[3] of our attention on it, and the latter is nothing but the cognition of an aim of our possible purposive action.[4]

(152.10). Therefore a source of knowledge has no result over and above the distinct cognition of its object, (the result of cognition is cognition, the act and the content of cognition are undistinguishable). This has been expressed by Dharmakīrti (with respect to sense-perception) in the following words,[5]

«Just this direct cognition is itself the result of (the act) of cognizing, as far as it has the form of a distinct cognition».

(153.1). That alone is a source of right knowledge what determines the object (in distinguishing it from all similar and all dissimilar ones). And that alone determines the object what restricts its image as belonging just to this object. If it is not restricted to the right object, it will belong neither to that object nor to any object, and thus the

---

1 *pramā = pramiti-kriyā = artha-pratīti-rūpā,* evidently here refers to the «content». *kriyā,* when distinguished from *karaṇa,* will be its result. If the senses are compared with an instrument, sense-cognition will be the result. The Mīmāṃsakas assume three consecutive steps in cognition, the following being the result of its predecessor, sensation, attention and «fetching» or conception (*dṛṣṭi-pravṛtti-prāpti*). The ultimate result (*prāpti = pratīti*) is evidently the «content» of cognition, it is called here *pramiti-kriyā = pramā = pratīti-rūpā* only with the respect to the simile of the axe — the instrument, and its result the act of cutting (*chedana*). If the senses are the instrument, sensation is the result; if sensation is the instrument, attention is the result, and if attention plays the part of an instrument, conception will be the result. That these three steps exist empirically the Buddhist would not deny, but cognition is for him the correspondence of an image constructed by our productive imagination according to the forms, or categories, of our understanding with a point-instant of external reality. This is *sārūpya,* conformity *of* the image (*ākāra*), and this is also the image itself, there being no real distictnion between the image and the fact of its coordination with the object, cp. NBT ad I. 20—21.

2 *prāpti = adhigati = pratīti = bodha,* the ultimate result, the «content».

3 *pravṛtti,* the «act» proper, *viz. jñānasya pravṛttiḥ,* cp. NBT, text, p. 3. 5 ff.

4 *pravṛtti-yogya-artha = artha-kriyā-samartha-artha.* — *pravṛtti* here in the sense of a purposive action, not of an act of objective cognition.

5 Cp. NB, I. 18.

distinct image will not be coordinated with the object. (153. 5). If it did produce a cognition of some indefinite object, how could it be called a means of right knowledge?

Now, such (passive sources of our knowledge as our) senses are, although they belong to the causes producing knowledge,[1] cannot (alone, by themselves impart distinctness and) determine our cognition as referring just to the right object.[2]

(153. 7). Indeed, a sensory stimulus produced on the visual sense by a patch of blue colour, is not yet a cognition of the blue as blue, because pure sensation produced by a patch of yellow colour (so far it is only pure sensation) is just the same. It is the concept (or the image) of the blue alone which makes the stimulus produced on the sense of vision a real cognition of the blue patch.[3]

(153. 9). Therefore it is the image[4] of the object alone, the image contained in our understanding,[5] which determines our cognition as a cognition of a definite object.[6] It also determines the (cognized external) object. Therefore it (can be compared with) an instrument, (with the ultimate cause) of Cognition, since it determines (and distinguishes) the objects of our knowledge (between themselves).

(153. 12). This has been expressed by Dharmakīrti in the following words,[7]

«The source of cognizing consists in coordination (between the constructed image and its real) object. Owing to this a distinct cognition of the object is produced».

(153. 14). The words «a distinct cognition of the object is produced» mean that a distinct cognition of the object is determined, and

---

[1] Read *jñāna-karaṇair.*

[2] *tadīyatayā = niyata-viṣaya-sambandhitayā* (V).

[3] Lit., p. 153. 7—9. «Indeed, the blue-knowledge of the blue is not simply because produced by the eye, because of the consequence of suchness of the yellow-knowledge, but only from being the form of the blue there is blue-knowledge of the blue». — The difference between a pure sensation produced by something blue (*nīlasya jñānam*) and the definite cognition or judgment «this is blue» (*nīlam-iti jñānam*) is found already in the Abhidharma-sūtra, it is quoted by Dignāga in his bhāṣya on Pr. samucc., I. 4, by Kamalaśīla in TSP, p. 12 and his NB.--pūrva-pakṣa-saṅkṣipti and in other texts.

[4] *artha-ākāra = artha-sārūpya.*

[5] *buddhi-gata = mānasa = kālpanika.*

[6] *tadīyatayā = niyata-viṣaya-sambandhitayā.*

[7] NB, I. 20—21.

thus it also means so much that the (external) objects of our knowledge are being distinguished (between one another).

(154. 1). (It could be objected that one and the same thing), a thing undivided in itself, cannot represent (at once) the instrument and its result, (i. e., the instrument and the action which is expedited by the instrument. This would be a contradiction [1]). However it is not a contradiction. (There are cases when this is possible). The relation between an instrument and the work produced by it [2] is, indeed, either (real) as between the possessor of a function and that function itself,[3] or (logical) as between a logical antecedent and its consequence.[4]

(154. 3). The axe, e. g., is a (real) instrument (only at the moment of its) contact with the tree (which is to be cut). It is called an «instrument» in common life because of this (future) contact which is its function. (154. 5). But the contact itself is not really a unity [5] different from the axe at the moment of contact.[6] (The instrument and its working are at this moment just the same event).

(154. 6). On the other hand, we surely know [7] cases when the logical antecedent and its consequence are included in the same concrete entity. Such is, (in the mental field, the subject-object relation inclu-

---

1 Cp. NBT, text, p. 15. 11, transl. p. 41.

2 *karaṇa-phala-bhāva.*

3 *vyāpāra-vyāpāri-bhāva.*

4 *gamya-gamaka-bhāva.*

5 *vigrahavān = pramāṇa-siddhaḥ* (V) = *na tucchaḥ,* just as the *abhāva* according to the Realists is *vigrahavān = na tucchaḥ.* According to the Buddhists the utmost that can be said is that it is a name — *api tu vyavahartavyaḥ param,* Tātp., p. 389. 23.

6 *saṃyujyamāna eva.* For the Realists the axe is an object possessing stability, a substance (*sthāyi-dravya*). The operation of the axe must be, therefore, something real, in order that the operating axe be distinguished from the non-operating one. As Bradley, Logic p. 254, puts it, «the terms of a relation must always be more than the relation between them, and, if it were not so, the relation would vanish». The Indian Realists, therefore, boldly assume a real relation (*vigrahavān sambandhaḥ*) as a third unity between the two unities related. Cp. above p. 287 n. 5. But for the Buddhist the axe is a string of events, the axe at the moment of contact is another entity than the axe outside that moment. The axe is a construction of our mind, real is alone the string of contacts, i. e., the string of efficiencies, of which the axe is an integration. For the same reason there is no difference between the «content» and the «intent» of every cognition.

7 *dṛṣṭa eva.*

ded in every) self-conscious idea[1] and (such is) in the external field, (the relation of some logical marks to the fact deduced from them, e. g., when) we deduce that whatsoever is an Ašoka is also a tree. (154. 8). The tree is, indeed, not something different from the Ašoka, nor the Ašoka different from the tree. Their difference lies in the logical field, (the conceptions are alone different). (The same thing can be differently conceived from different standpoints). It is then differently contrasted,[2] (as contrasted with other trees it is an Ašoka, and as contrasted with other plants it is a tree). The same applies to the difference between (an instrument, or) a factor[3] (in general and the function) produced by it. There is no difference at all, (it is absolutely one and the same thing). This is the theory of the Sautrāntikas.[4]

(155. 1). The author[5] quotes another (Buddhist) theory: pure[6] knowledge containing in itself no image at all has the capacity (like a lamp) to shed light both on its own self and on the non-self, (i. e., on the external object. This capacity) is the source of our knowledge. That, indeed, is the source of right knowledge whose function it is to throw light upon the objects (of our cognition). By light-throwing we understand the essence of consciousness, it is the attribute of those (beings) who are conscious. (155. 3). But such sources of our knowledge

---

[1] *sva-prakāše vijñāne*. V. remarks *gamya-gamakayor yadi viṣaya-viṣayi-bhāvas tatrāha, sva-prakāša iti, atha jñāpya-jñāpaka-bhāvas, tatrāha, bāhye ceti.*

[2] *vyāvṛtti-bhedas*.

[3] *kāraka* is more general than *karaṇa*, the latter is the «instrumental factor», all cases, except the Genitive, express some «factors».

[4] Lit., p. 155. 1—11. «And there is no contradiction of instrument and result being found) in an undivided self. This, indeed, is either the relation of a function to the possessor of the function or of the conveyed to the conveyor. Indeed, only the axe which is conjoined with trees etc. by conjunction, by function, is called in common life an instrument. And there is, for sure, no conjunction possessing a body, (a thing) different from the conjoined axe. The relation of conveyed to conveyor also has been surely (*eva*) experienced in a self-luminous cognition and in an external tree suggested by šiṃšapā. Indeed the tree, for sure, is not something other than the šiṃsapā, nor the šiṃšapā (other) than the tree. But in imaginative dealing, just as there is a difference of exclusion, just so between a factor and its possessor, thus no difference whatever, thus the Sautrāntikās». — The Sautrantika-Yogācāras are meant, since Dharmakīrti is quoted. But in the 9th Koša-sthāna Vasubandhu speaking from the standpoint of the Sautrāntikas emits similar views, cp. my Soul Theory of the Buddhists, p. 854.

[5] Tātp., p. 14. 14.

[6] *eva*.

as the senses are,[1] are different, because they (by themselves) are unconscious. Now there is no other conscious (substance) besides (the flow) of consciousness itself. Therefore this consciousness itself being the (only) conscious (element)[2] and exercizing the function of apprehension, is the source of (all) our knowledge. As to the difference between a function and (something stable) possessing that function, there is none at all, just as in the case of the axe at the moment of its contact with the tree.[3] This is the opinion of the Vaibhāṣikas and of other (sects) who deny the presence of images in our cognition.[4]

V

Dignāga and Jinendrabuddhi on the act and the content of knowledge, upon the coordination of ideas with their objects and our knowledge of the external world.

§ 1. Pramāṇa-samuccaya, I. 9, and the author's explanation.

Bstan-ḥgyur, Mdo, vol. 95, f. 95[b]. 5 ff.

Here also,[6] the process of cognition is supposed to have a resulting (content), because it is imagined[7] as being an act.

---

[1] *indriyādīni.*

[2] i. e., no Soul being admitted.

[3] i. e., there is no substantial axe different from the flow of efficient moments imagined by our Reason as being a stable thing. The non existence of a Soul is deduced from the general principle of the non-existence of anything stable, is existent what is efficient and efficient is only the moment. V. remarks — *tasya* (*cetanasya*) *sthiratve artha-kriyāyā abhāvāt.*

[4] The Vaibhāṣikas even denied the existence of images in dreams. They tried to prove that even in dreams we somehow perceive real external objects. This their theory is ridiculed by Dharmakīrti in his Santānāntarasiddhi. The *saṃjñā* was considered by them as external (*viṣaya*) to pure consciousness (*vijñāna*), cp. my Central Conception, p. 97 and 100.

[5] Denying the presence of images in our cognition, *anākāra-vādinas,* are among the Brahmanical systems chiefly the Mīmāṃsakas, and among the Buddhists — the Vaibhāsikas, i. e., the early 18 sects.

[6] The *kārikā* must have been something like this, *pramāṇa-phalatvam iṣṭam kriyayā saha kalpanāt, pramāṇatvena cāropaḥ, kriyām vinā ca nāsti tat.*

[7] Read *rtog-pai-phyir* instead of *rtogs-pai-phyir.*

We do not follow here the realistic (philosophers) in assuming that the result of cognition differs from the act, because the supposed result is only the image of the cognized object and (this image) is wrongly imagined as separated into an act (and a content).[1]

It is a metaphor, when we assume that our ideas are instruments of knowledge, and (when we assume) that they cannot exist without exhibiting an activity.

As for instance, when corn is produced, it agrees (in kind) with its cause (the seed), and people say that it has «taken» the shape of its cause. The same thing has happened also here, (when people think that cognition) is also not debarred of activity, (they think it «takes» or «grasps» the form of its object).

§ 2. Comment of Jinendrabuddhi on this aphorism.

Bstan-ḥgyur, Mdo, vol. 115, ff. 34ᵇ. 6—36ᵃ. 7 (Pekin).[2]

(34ᵇ. 6). The words «here also» mean «according to our opinion». The words «because it is imagined as possessing activity» mean «because it is imagined[3] (as a thing) together with its activity». This is the cause why the rôle of an instrument of knowledge is metaphorically imputed[4] (to cognition). The (supposed) instrument of cognition exists only as a result, i. e., the cognizing activity of this instrument of knowledge[5] is (its own) result, and it is (the result) just itself, in its own identity. Therefore there is here no difference (between the act of cognition and its resulting content). Here, (in this system), there is no result of cognition separately from the instrument (or the act) of cognizing, as this is the case in the realistic[6] (systems). In this (system) no such fault as they alone have committed! The words «only

---

1 *ḥbras-bur gyur-pai šes-pa* = *phala-bhūta-jñāna*, lit. «because this cognition has arisen as possessing the form of the object».

2 Jinendrabuddhi is the author of a very thoroughgoing and detailed commentary on Pramāṇa-samuccaya which fills the whole of vol. 115 of the Bstan-ḥgyur, Mdo. He is presumably the same person as the author of the great grammatical work Kāšikā-vivaraṇa-pañjikā, also called Nyāsa, and lived, according to the editor of that work, S. C. Chakravarti, in the middle of the VIIIᵗʰ century A. D.

3 Read *rtog-pai-phyir* instead of *rtogs-pat-phyir*.

4 *ñe-bar-ḥdogs-pai rgyu* = *upacārasya kāraṇam*.

5 *tshad-mai rtogs-pa ni*.

6 *phyi-rol-pa-rnams* = *bāhyāḥ*, non-Buddhists.

as a result» etc. lay stress upon this meaning. There is (immanent in cognition) not the slightest bit of the distinct nature of a thing produced and of its producer. Indeed our ordinary idea (of causation), of «producer» and «produced», is in any case not far away from having the nature of an imputation.[1] (35a. 1). And this is really also the case here! Cognition, so far it possesses the character of something attained,[2] evokes the idea of a thing produced, and thus it may be imagined[3] as (a kind of) result. (But the same fact is also) imagined, and spoken[4] of, as an instrument of knowledge, because it (as it were) also «grasps» the image of the (object) and appears thus (in the rôle) of something exhibiting activity. (35a. 3). Thus it is that this cognition, so far it «grasps» the image of its object, although it (really) has no activity, receives the name of an action, consisting in cognizing its own object, but not otherwise. And thus the image of the object, since it is identical with the (supposed instrument), is itself called an instrument of cognition.

(35a. 4). And this is right! because, when we say «an action is being produced», we do not at all refer (to the universal interconnection[5] of all elements of existence according to which) every thing is the producer of every action and every action is being produced by all (the elements of the Universe), because (from this point of view) there would be no definiteness,[6] (we would never know who is whose producer). But if one thing springs up without an interval, immediately after another one, then we say that the former is the producer[7] and the following is alone the action produced by it. (35a. 6). Now, (supposing) we have a patch of colour and a stimulus[8] produced (by it on our senses), we then (immediately) have a feeling of its presence in

---

[1] Read *rtog-pai ño-bo-las;* cp. NBT, text p. 69.

[2] *lhag-par rtogs-pai ño-bo = adhigama-rūpa.*

[3] *ñe-bar gdags-par-bya-o.*

[4] *ñe-bar-gdags-te, tha-sñad-du byao*, i. e., a metaphor is constructed by our imagination, and this metaphor is the foundation of our usual way of thinking and speaking (*vyavahāra*, cp. NBT, p. 29. 22).

[5] The *kāraṇa-hetu,* causal connection, is probably here referred to, according to it all elements of the Universe are the causes of a given phenomenon with the exception of its own self, because nothing can be its own cause, but every thing else can, cp. Abh. Koša, II. 50, *svato'nye kāraṇa-hetuḥ.*

[6] *thug-pa-med-par thal-ba = anavasthā-prasanga.*

[7] Read *yin-te,* instead of *yin zhe-na,* the latter reading is repeated in the Narthang edition f. 37a. 7.

[8] *las-la,* in the sence of *don-byed nus-pa-la.*

our ken and a consciousness of its *coordination* with some external object, (a sense of sameness) according to which we can distinguish and determine «this is a cognition of blue», «that one is of yellow». (Our cognitions) then receive these (definite) shapes.[1] If this were not the case, any cognition would refer to any object and no cognition would refer to a (definite) object, because there would be no differentiation.[2]

(35a. 7). All determination (maintains the Sānkhya) is evolved from an undifferentiated[3] (primitive) condition of all things and (qualities as having their root in primitive Matter). But this we cannot admit, because 1) (primitive Matter) is inanimate,[4] 2) all cognitions as having the same cause (would not be differentiated). Moreover there is (according to the Sānkhya system) no interaction[5] (at all between Matter and Consciousness). This alone would be sufficient to make any perception of objects[6] impossible.[7] (35b. 1). Without (assuming) a «coordination» (of the image) with its object no perception of objects is at all possible, since definite knowledge consists just in this (coordination). Therefore, the definiteness of (our judgments) «this is my cognition of blue», «this one is of yellow» is due to the fact of a coordination (between our image) and its object, it is (immediately produced) by the latter, and there is nothing else that could create it.

(35b. 2). Therefore just this (coordination through the sense of sameness) is (predominantly) the producer[8] of a distinct cognition of

---

1 Lit., f. 35a. 6—7. «There, by what cognition (*šes-pa gañ-gis*) having the essence of coordination (*hdra-ba* = *sārūpya*) with the essence of immediate feeling (*ñams-su myoñ-ba* = *anubhava*) concerning the action (*las-la* in both ed.) of colour etc., (by what cognition) the distinctness «this is a cognition of blue», «this one is of yellow» is produced, by that (its) essence of a producer of what is being definitely settled, is this being made to appear».

2 Coordination through our sense of sameness is thus the real source of cognition, if we at all are to distinguish between cognition as a source of knowledge and cognition as its result. This (inexplicable) sense of sameness is thus much more the cause of cognition than the coarse concept of a supposed «grasping» of the object through the instrumentality of the senses, because it appears as the most efficient feature, the *sādhakatama-kāraṇa* = *prakṛṣṭopakāraka* = *adhipati-pratyaya*.

3 *mi-gsal-ba* = *avyakta*.

4 *šes-pa ma-yin-pa-*.

5 *phrad-pa* = *sannikarṣa*, *saṃyoga*, *saṃsarga*.

6 *don-la lta-ba*.

7 The reason why Sānkhya views are mentioned in this context is perhaps that this school also constructs a kind of *sārūpya*, cp. my Central Conception, p. 64.

8 Cp. the definition of *adhipati-pratyaya* Ab. Koša, II, and Mādh. vṛtti, I. p. 86, cp. my Nirvāṇa, p. 17. 6.

the object, because when all the causes (and conditions) of a cognition have united and (the sense of sameness) has arisen it immediately is followed by the coordination «this object — that cognition». (35b. 3). And further, (when we maintain that this coordination) «produces» (cognition), we mean that it produces it so far it is the foundation of distinctness, we dont mean that it really creates it (in a realistic sense), because (it represents the essence of cognition itself), it does not differ (from cognition).

(35b. 3). Let it be so! But is it not a contradiction to assume in one undivided reality, in the same fact of knowledge, two sides, of which the one produces the other? No, there is no contradiction! Because we just maintain that in reality there are here no (two) different things, (there is but one thing differently viewed), two (imagined) different aspects have been superimposed on it, the aspect of something cognized and the aspect of an agency cognizing it.

(35b. 5). And because (the same thing) can indirectly appear as different, if it is differently contrasted (either with one thing or with another). Although there be no difference in the (underlying) reality, the conception[1] of it may be different, it can then appear either in the rôle of a «produced» thing or of its «producer».[2] (35b. 6). For example (we say) «that honey which makes you drink it, is being drunk by you», «I myself oblige myself to grasp my own self», «my mind grasps (its own self)». In all these cases there is in reality no (two) different things of which the one would be definitely only «the agent» and the other only «the thing produced». (This is clear), in such cases there is no quarrel (on that question).

(35b. 7). But how is it that (in this other case, viz. in the case of cognition)? Although there (also) is no act (of cognition different from its content) it seems as though there were (an action)? The author says, «for instance etc.». What is immediately felt (in the case of perception) is just one thing, the image, blue or other. We must necessarily admit that this represents the essence of our knowledge, that otherwise it could not be connected with an object (which transcends it). (35b. 8). No external reality different from it, whether

---

1 *vijñāna-pratibhāsa*.

2 Lit., p. 35b. 5—6. «And because of an imputation of different exclusions (*ldog-pa* = *vyāvṛtti*), albeit there is no difference in reality, by a difference of the reflected idea (*rnam-par-šes-pai snañ-ba* = *vijñāna-pratibhāsa*) it is shown as distinguished in the produced and the producer».

having the same form or not, can at all be found. (35a. 1). Neither is an external support for it logically admissible.[1] Why? This question we will discuss in the sequel, on the occasion of an examination of the opinion of (Vasubandhu) the author of the «Vāda-vidhāna».[2]

(36a. 1). As to the (usual) argument[3] (of the Sautrāntikas in favour of the existence of an external world), it is the following one.

(If an instance in which a visual) perception is the result, (and an instance in which) it does not occur,[4] have every circumstance in common save one,[5] (that one occuring only in the former; the circumstance in which alone the two instances differ) is clearly the cause of our perception. And such is the external object, (since an intact faculty of vision, the presence of light and aroused attention[6] do not produce perception in the absence of a patch of colour, but they do produce it as soon as a coloured surface is present). Thus it is that by the Method of Difference[7] the existence of an external world is proved.[8] This (argument) is not well-grounded, because the absence of the effect in the shape of a perception (in the second instance) can be also explained (without imagining an external reality), by the circumstance, (namely, that at the given moment), the Biotic Force[9] (which controls

---

1 *dmigs-pa ḥthad-pa yaṅ ma-yin-te* = *ālambanam api na ghaṭate*, i. e., *vicāryamānam buddhau na ārohati.*

2 Pr. samucc., I. 14 ff.

3 Lit., «construction», *rtog-pa* = *kalpanā*. It is, in an abridged form, the same argument as the one mentioned in the N. Kaṇikā, 258. 18 ff. and the Tātp., p. 464. 8 ff.

4 *ḥbras-bu śes-pa mi-skye-bas ni.*

5 *rgyu-gzhan-rnams yod-pa-yaṅ* = *kāraṇāntarāṇi santy api.*

6 The *karaṇāntarāṇi* «every circumstance in common save one» are 1) *adhipati-pratyaya* = *cakṣuḥ*, 2) *sahakāri-pratyaya* = *āloka* and 3) *samanantara-pratyaya* = *manasikāra* or *saṃskāra*, the one additional and decisive is 4) *ālambana-pratyaya* = *artha.*

7 *vaidharmya* = *ldog-pa.*

8 Lit., f. 36a. 1—2. «Albeit the other causes be present, since the result, the cognition is not produced, another cause is elicited. That is the external object».— It will be scarcely doubted that, leaving alone the extreme laconicity of the Indian author, his argument as formulated according to the Method of Difference agrees exactly with J. S. Mill's method of that name, cp. Logic I, p. 452 (1872). This is also a glaring example of how misleading literal translations are, if it is desired to have an idea of the full connotation present to the mind of the Indian thinker.

9 *bag-chags* = *vāsanā*, cp. above, p. 368; *avidyā-vāsanā* is here meant.

the evolution of life) was not ripe to produce (the perception in question).

(36a. 3). Therefore, what we really experience are only our own (sensations and) ideas,[1] except them nothing at all (can be really experienced). But just these (our sensations and) ideas are self-conscious. Self-consciousness, therefore, (can be regarded as a kind) of result.

(36a. 4). Now, let there exist an external object! (Whether it exists or not is irrelevant), because even in that case, (even if it really exists), it is (for us really) a definite object only as far as we have had an internal experience of it. Therefore this alone, (i. e., the self-consciousness of our ideas alone, not the cognition of an external object) can be rightly deemed to represent the result of our cognition, since it can be distinctly cognized in that form only which is its own, definitely settled, (internal) form. To experience (internally) an (external) object according to its own (external) essence is impossible. (Otherwise, if our perceptions were passive, if they did represent the external object as it is), they always would have (exactly) the same form. But (we know that) our sensations[2] (of the same object) have different degrees (of intensity). (36a. 5). We observe, indeed, that different persons, can have respecting the same object various sensations, either acute or feeble or otherwise shaped. But the same real object cannot appear in different forms, because it would then be different in itself, (it would not be the same object).[3]

(36a. 6). However,[4] although convinced that there is no possibility of cognizing the (external) object in its real essence, (the author) is desirous so to formulate his view of the problem of the resulting phase (in the process of cognition) that it should satisfy both the Realists who maintain the existence of an external world and their opponents who deny it.[5] He says,

---

1 *rnam-par-šes-pa* = *vijñāna*, the term evidently embraces here sensations as well as conceptions.

2 *rnam-par-rig-pa-rnams ni* = *saṃvedanāni*.

3 Cp. N. Kaṇikā, p. 265. 13—14.

4 *dei-phyir*, lit. «therefore».

5 *phyi-rol-dañ-cig-šos-kyi phyogs-dag-la mod-cig kho-nas ḥbras-bui khyad-par rnam-par-bzhag-pa byed-par bzhed-pas* = *bāhyetara-pakṣau bhavatām eva iti phala-višeṣa-vyavasthām cikīrṣur āha*, «He says with the desire to determine the special result from whatsoever of the both standpoints, the external and the other».

§ 3. Dignāga's aphorism, Pramāṇa-samuccaya, I. 10 and his own comment.

(Bstan-ḥgyur, vol. 95, f. 95b. 7 ff.).

We can also envisage the internal feeling (of something either desirable or not) as a kind of resulting content in the process of cognition, since the object (and the consequent purposive action) are determined[1] by it. The image of the object will in any case assume the rôle of the source of cognizing it. Through it alone something is cognized.[2]

(95b. 7). The self-feeling[3] can be also[4] (constructed as a kind) of resulting content (as against *the act* of cognizing). Every cognizing (mental state) is here (from one side) the reflex[5] of an object, (from another side) it is a reflex of the (cognizing) self. From among these both reflexes, the second, that one which represents self-feeling, (can be regarded as a kind) of result. Why? Because the object (and the

---

1 The aphorism is quoted by Pārthasārathimiśra in his comment on Ślokavārtika, p. 158, but the order of the pādas is inverted and *tādrūpyāt* = *de-yi ño-bo-las* must be read instead of *tad-dvaye*, (which is probably due to a desire of contrast with the *trayam* of I. 11).

sva-saṃvittiḥ phalam cāsya, tādrūpyād artha-niścayaḥ,
viṣayākāra evāsya pramāṇam, tena mīyate.

Lit., «Its result is also self-feeling, according to its form the object is determined, just the image is the source of knowledge, through it it is cognized». — The words *tādrūpyād artha-niścayaḥ* are reminiscent of *artha-sārūpyam asya pramāṇam*, N. b., I. 20, cp. Tātp., p. 34. 7 and Kamalaśīla, p. 560. 18, *tādrūpyād iti sārūpyāt*. But here the term refers to a coordination between feeling and the ascertainment (*niścaya*) of the object, and evidently also to the subsequent purposive action, not between the point instant of reality and the image as in the NB. Pārthasārathi thinks that the opinion of the Sautrāntikas is here expressed, *jñānasya viṣayākāro nīla-pītādi-rūpo* (instead of-*rūpā*) *arthena jñāne āhitaḥ sa pramāṇam*, cp. Tātp., p. 14. 12, where the same theory is alluded to — *viṣaya-sārūpyam sākārasya vijñānasya pramāṇam*, and N. Kaṇikā, p. 256. 14 (translated above).

2 *don-ñes* = *artha-niścaya* is explained as *don rtogs-par-byed* = *artha-adhigama*, and *artha-adhigama* is explained in NBT, pp. 8. 9 and 15. 4 as the attitude of the cognizer, his possible purposive action.

3 *rañ-rig-pa* = *sva-saṃvedana.*

4 «also» (*ca*) points to a possible arrangement, *rnam-par-rtog-pa.*

5 *snañ-ba* = *pratibhāsa.*

consequent purposive action) are determined by it. When (we attribute the rôle of) the object of cognition to its idea together with the cognized object as immanent in it,[1] then a self-feeling corresponding to it arises, a feeling which determines the object either as something desirable or undesirable. But if we (attribute the rôle) of the object of cognition[2] to the external thing alone, then (we must attribute the rôle) of the source of this cognition just to the image (we have of it). Although the self-feeling still exists in our cognition, but this its feature is then disregarded, and the image of the object (plays the part) of the source of its cognition, because this object is its (corresponding) cognized part. Whatsoever be the image reflected by our cognition,[3] whether it be the image of something white or non-white or of any other colour, this image together with the object possessing this shape will have the function of producing[4] the cognition. Thus a variety of functions is attributed metaphorically to (what essentially is but the same fact of) cognition. They can be differently arranged (either as a content or as an act), either as a cognizing agency or as its object, (but merely) in imagination, because (in absolute reality) all elements of existence[5] are devoid of any causal efficiency.[6]

---

1 Lit. «If the object (*don = artha*) is the knowledge (*śes-pa = jñāna*) together with the object (*yul = viṣaya*)».

2 *gzhal-bya = prameya.*

3 *śes-pa-la snañ-ba = jñāna-pratibhāsa.*

4 *ḥjal-bar-byed-do = pramāpayati.*

5 *chos-thams-cad ni bya-ba dañ bral-ba = nirvyāpārāḥ sarve dharmāḥ, (pratītya-samutpannatvāt).* The old Buddhist formula of causation as «dependently-together-origination» is here alluded to by Dignāga, this fuudamental idea of causation from which the whole millenial later developement of Buddhist philosophy started. The elements of existence are coordinated (*asmin sati idam bhavati*), they cannot encroach or obtrude upon one another, cp. my Central Conception, p. 28 and my Nirvāṇa, p. 39 ff.

6 *Saṃvedana = saṃvit = saṃvitti = rig-pa = rnam-par-rig-pa* is usually defined as one of the synonyms of *jñāna,* cp. Kamalaśīla, p. 563. 11, but the subjective side of knowledge, its immediate data as revealed in introspection are more especially meant, hence it is often used as a synonym of *anubhava = myoñ-ba.* It is evidently closely related to *vedanā = vedanā-skandha = tshor-ba* in the sense of the feelings of pleasure and pain. According to the Abhidharma these feelings are external (*viṣaya*) with respect to consciousness (*citta*). In Nyāya they are external (*viṣaya*) with respect to cognition (*buddhi*), although inhering in the Soul. The Sānkhyas went the length of declaring them objects of the external world, against which theory both the Naiyāyiks and the Buddhists protested, cp. NBT, p. 11. 9 ff. The later Buddhists, on the contrary, identified them with the Ego. They admitted no other Ego than the feelings of desirability or non-desirability. They insisted on

§ 5—12. COMMENT OF JINENDRABUDDHI.

(Bstan ḥgyur, v. 115, ff. 30a. 8. ff.).

(36a. 8). At first the rôle of the resulting content of cognition was attributed to the cognition[1] of the objective (part). (Now it is attributed to the subjective part), therefore the word «also», pointing to an alternative arrangement,[2] has been inserted. The word «here» points to sense-perception (which is the subject matter) of the preceding passage. (36a. 8). (The author) mentions a subjective part, (the self-feeling of either desire or aversion) and an objective part, (the object-feeling of something either white or of another colour). «Its

---

this double division, abandoning thus the third item, the indifferent feeling admitted in Abhidharma, cp. Abh. Koša, I. 14, evidently because the indifferent state, the state without any feeling, would be nobody's state, the substitute for the Ego being absent. Although the NBṬ, p. 11. 6 ff., defines *svasaṃvedana* as *jñānasya anubhava*, it clearly defines it as *sukhādy-ākāraḥ* and insists that there is absolutely no such conscious state from which every feeling would be absent. The «feeling» of the presence in us of a perception is evidently conceived as belonging to the emotional sphere and is put on the same line as the feeling of pleasure or ease. Jinendrabuddhi explains it also as *śes-pa-yi ni śes-pa* = *jñānasya jñānam* (cp. Mdo, vol. 115, f. 37b. 1), with reference to Dignāga's words that the result of cognition is self-consciousness (*svasaṃvitti*), as a feeling of something either desirable or undersirable. But he seemingly makes some distinction between the sensation of ease and the «sense of sameness» -*sārūpya-vedana*, cp. below p. 394. Pārthasārathimiśra pregnantly remarks, *loco cit.* p. 158, *viṣayākāro viṣaya-viṣayaḥ, svasaṃvittis tu vijñāna-viṣayā*. Thus cognition is cut off by *sva-saṃvitti* from its owner, the cognizing Ego, but at the same time it is also cut off from the external world. For the Realist the result of cognition is the full perception of an external object; the object, for the Buddhist, being immanent, the result is also immanent. This has been expressed as essential identity of cognition and its result, of the cause and the result of knowledge (*pramāṇa* and *pramāṇa-phalam*). This celebrated Buddhist theory evoked a unanimous protest of all other schools and was very often misunderstood. There being only one fact of cognition, there is no separate cognizer and no cognized object, no object external with respect to cognition. What the other schools conceive as cognizer and cognized become all merged in cognition. Keeping this in our mind we may arbitrarily differentiate this one fact of cognition by diverse analogies and metaphors as an agent, an act, an instrument and an object. Previously «coordination» *artha-sārūpyam* was established as the source of knowledge and *artha-pratīti* as its result, although both are the same. But other arrangements are also possible, e. g., *sva-saṃvitti* may also be constructed as a kind of result. The Realists have inherited this theory of a double result which according to them is either *pramā* or *hānopadāna-buddhi*, cp Ślokavārt., pratyakṣa, Kār. 68 ff., and Tarkabhāṣā, p. 28.

[1] Lit., «a feeling of the object», *yul-rig-pa* = *viṣaya-vedanam*.

[2] *rnam-par-brtag-pai don* = *vikalpitārthaḥ*.

reflex itself[1]» means its own reflex, itself, the real reflex itself,[2] also (appearing) as «grasping» aspect. (36b. 1). It is the reflex of this cognition as cognizing just its own self. This means that this aspect of our cognition is a reflex from within,[3] which has the form of the cognition of a cognition, i. e., (of self-cognition), the cognition of its own self. (36b. 2). As to the expression («the object-feeling»), «the reflex of the object», it admits of a (double) interpretation. (If we, siding with the Realists), take our stand on the existence of an external world, it will mean an image[4] corresponding to an (external) object. If not, (i. e., if the existence of an external world is denied), it will (simply) mean the representation,[5] (the idea), of that object. Indeed, the object is then the «grasped» part (immanent) in cognition, since that is what in common life is called[6] an object, (and both the realist and the idealist likewise call it an object).

§ 6. The result of our cognition from the standpoint of the Idealist.

(36b. 3). The words «in that case[7] (the result will be an image corresponding to an external object)» contain the following (implication). The question whether an external world exists or not is otiose.[8] In either case what we really have an experience[9] of, are (sensations and) images.[10] (Its subjective part), the self-feeling, the experiencing of the Ego,[11] (may be regarded) as a result.[12] (36b. 4). The (author) asks, why? i. e., for what reason? It would not be right to attribute to this

1 *ḥdii snañ-ba rañ ñid-do* = *asya pratibhāsaḥ svayam eva.*

2 *rañ-gi ño-boi snañ-ba* = *svarūpa-pratibhāsa.*

3 *rañ-ñid-kho-nas snañ-ño* = *svasminn eva bhāsate.*

4 *yul lta-bur snañ-ba* = *viṣayavad bhāsate.*

5 *yul ḥdii snañ-bao* = *asya viṣayasya pratibhāsaḥ.*

6 *tha-sñad-byas-pa* = *vyavahriyate.*

7 *dei zhes pa* evidently refer to *dei tshe*...

8 Lit. «whether the external object exists or also not, whatsoever (the case may be)...».

9 *ñams-su myoñ-la* = *anubhūyate* = *vedyate.*

10 *snañ-ba-can-gyi śes-pa* = *ākāravaj-jñānam*, sensations are of course also meant.

11 *rañ ñams-su myoñ-ba.*

12 The Realist and the Idealist can agree in visualizing this fact as a kind of relative result, they will disagree, if the cognition of an external object is supposed to be the result. We must understand that the feeling evoked by the idea with the object included in it will be the result.

internal aspect of our cognition the rôle of a result for the simple reason that self-consciousness exists.[1] The Realist will not admit it, because (he has an other result in view, viz.), the function of our sense-faculties, (according to him), is to cognize the external objects, and not (mere) ideas.[2] (36b. 5). And (from his standpoint) it would not be right to maintain that the cognition of an object is nothing but the cognition of its idea, since (for him) the object is different from the idea. Therefore he will never admit that the self-consciousness of the idea is the result (arrived at in cognition). This is the meaning of the question. (The author) answers: (for the Idealist it is a result nevertheless, because our behaviour) towards the object is determined[3] by it. Such is the reason; the following words (of the author) are only an explanation on that meaning. The word «indeed»[4] means «because». Because, when the cognized object is immanent[5] in cognition, the cognizing individual cognizes something either desirable for him or not, according to what he internally feels.[6] Therefore it is right to attribute the rôle of a result to this internal feeling.

(36b. 7). The object immanent (in cognition) means cognition together with the object. «Together with the object» here means an object whose essence is equivalent to the «grasped» aspect of the idea,[7] it refers to the standpoint (of the Idealists), of those for whom (cognizability is cogitability), every thing cognizable is internal, since this alone is the ascertainable object.

(36b. 8). Because, even from the standpoint of the Realist, even if we admit the existence of an external world, since every thing here is nothing but sensation (and image),[8] there is nothing real beyond our ideas,[9] therefore, if we only have a mental state in which a desire

---

1 because everything is the result of something.

2 *rnam-par-šes-pa* = *vijñāna*.

3 *ñes-pa* = *niyata*.

4 *ni* = *hi*; *gañ-gi tshe ni* = *yadā hi*, the text in the Peking Bstan-ḥgyur, Mdo vol. 95, f. 96a. 1 omits *ni*.

5 *yul-dañ-bcas-pai don yin-la*.

6 *rañ-rig-pa dañ rjes-su mthun-pai don* = *sva-saṃvedana-anurūpa-artha*.

7 *gzuñ-byai cha-šas-kyi mtshan-ñid-can-gyi grub-gyi...*

8 *rnam-par-rig-pa-tsam* = *saṃvedana-mātram*.

9 *šes-pa-las tha-dad-pai dños-po med-pai-phyir* = *jñānāt pṛthag vastu-abhāvāt*.

is felt, we then have a judgment regarding the object desired[1] (and the possible purposive action). In the contrary case we have neither (judgment nor possible action).

§ 7. The subject-object relation from the standpoint of the Idealist.

(37a. 2). But how is it then that our knowledge experiences its own self[2]? Is it not bad logic[3] to assume the immanent existence in one real entity of the relations of object, subject and instrument[4] (or process) of cognition?

(37a. 2). This can be explained in the following way. From the stand-point of Absolute Reality[5] the relations of object (subject and instrument of knowledge) do not exist at all. But there is no contradiction in thus using these[6] (expressions) in common life, although they are (really) identical[7] (as referring to the same reality), just as (we say, «light) illuminates (by its lustre», instead of simply saying «there is light»). (37a. 3). Light, indeed, does not depend on something else, (e. g.) on a lamp,[8] in order to light up (an object). A (separate) action of «lighting up» does not exist in reality. Light, as soon as it appears,[9]

---

1 = *buddhāv eva yadā icchā anubhūyate, tadā artha-icchā niścīyate.*

2 *ci-ltar šes-pa bdag-ñid-kyis bdag-ñid ñams-su myoṅ* = *katham jñānam atmanā ātmānam anubhavati?*

3 *rigs-pa ma-yin-pa* = *na yujyate.*

4 = *tasminn eva karma-kartṛ-kāraṇa-bhāvo na yujyate.* — We usually speak of a cognizing Ego and a cognized object, or of an act of cognition and its content. The Hindus in the first case use the triplet (*tripuṭī*) of agent, object and instrument, corresponding to the grammatical notions of a Nominative, Accusative and Instrumental case (*kartā, karma, karaṇa,* all are *kārakas* in different degrees). In epistemology they correspond to *pramātṛ, prameyam, pramāṇam.* In the second case the Hindus speak of instrument (*pramāṇam* = *pramā-karaṇam* = *pramā-sādhakatama-kāraṇam*=*pramā-prakṛṣṭa-upakārakam*) and result (*pramāṇa-phalam*= *pramā* = *pramāṇasya kriyā*). Thus the Hindus use the expression «instrument» when we would speak of an act, the expression the «instrument's result», or the act when we would speak of a content (*pramiti* = *pramā* = *pramiti-kriyā* = *pramāṇa-phalam*).

5 *don-dam-par* = *paramārthataḥ.*

6 = *tatra tathā vyavahāro na virudhyate.*

7 *dei bdag-ñid-kyi-phyir* = *tādātmyāt.*

8 *rab-tu-gsal-ba sgron-me* = *prakāśa-pradīpa.*

9 *rab-tu-gsal-bai bdag-ñid-du skye-bzhin-pa.*

is nothing but the action of lighting up. It is a mere *facon de parler*[1] when we say that light *does* shed light. (37a. 4). In the same manner we can in common life make use of the expression «knowledge[2] enlightens something», but knowledge as soon as it appears is nothing else but the (fact of) our awareness[3] of something. (There is no difference between the act of being intent upon an object and the corresponding content of that knowledge). (Neither is there in reality any external object different from the content of our knowledge). Even if we take our stand (on Realism and maintain the existence of an) external world, (we must confess) that our knowledge of an (external) object goes only as far as our sensations go.[4] To feel internally the object as it really is (externally), is impossible. This has been already pointed out above. (37a. 5). The intention of the author is here the following one. In the preceding part of his work he has established that self-consciousness, (or introspection), is one of the varieties of direct knowledge, (just as sense-perception is in regard to external objects). It has been also stated that the essence of knowledge consists in the fact that it is self-conscious. If after that the author speaks of a result, we could naturally imagine that the result of this variety of our knowledge alone is meant. Thus the words «something is cognized which is desirable or undesirable accordingly as we internally feel it» — these words could be misunderstood as referring to introspection alone.

(37b. 1). But the result is (our attitude towards the cognized object, the possibility of a corresponding purposive action, and) this refers to all the varieties of direct knowledge, (not to introspection alone). Therefore, in order to repudiate the doubt, the author says, «when the idea with the object included in it is the thing cognized, etc.». The words «thing cognized» refer to the content of our

---

expression *yathārthānubhava* is used by the Realists as a definition of right knowledge, cp. Tarka-sangraha, § 35, just as the above mentioned *blo* = *buddhi* = *jñāna* is their term of predilection for knowledge, cp. *ibid* § 34.

1 = *vastv-ātmikā prakāśana-kriyāpi nāsti, prakāśa-ātmakatvena jāyamānaḥ svayam eva prakāśam karoti iti vacana-mātram*(= *brjod-pa-ḥbaḥ-zhig-go*).

2 *blo* = *buddhi.*

3 *myoṅ-bai-bhag-ñid-du skye-bzhin-pai blo* = *anubhavātmatvena jāyamānā buddhiḥ.*

4 *myoṅ-ba ji-lta-ba-bzhin kho-nar don rtogs kyi, don ji-lta-ba bzhin myoṅ-ba ni ma-yin-no* = *yathānubhavam eva artha-pratītir, na tu yathārthānubhavam.*

knowledge. And the words «with the object included in it» refer to all varieties of direct cognition without exception.

(37b. 2). Thus the meaning is the following one. When our knowledge is visualized as a content produced by an act of cognizing, we then may envisage the result as a cognition which determines our attitude in regard to the thing cognized, (whether it be an external object or its mere idea, does not matter). However this will not represent a special result of introspection, but whatsoever be the content of our cognition, it will also be included in this result.[1] (The content of a cognition in so far it determines our purposive actions may be envisaged by both the Realist and the Idealist as its result, since we only artificially distinguish between the content and the act of cognition).[2]

(37b. 3). When we here, (as Idealists), maintain that the result of knowledge is not the cognition of an external world, but self-consciousness, (in the presentation of an object we feel desirable), we must attribute the function of the means (by which that result is attained) only to the grasping aspect (of that same representation).

---

1 Lit., 37a. 5—37b. 3. „But (read *ḥo-na* with Narthang instead of *kho-na* in Peking ed.) what is the use, without telling just this «a thing is cognized which is either desirable or undesirable in accordance with self-feeling», in (telling) this- «the thing is together with the object at that time»? There is an aim (*dgos-pa* = *prayojana*)! Because self-feeling was previously said to be a source of knowledge and by it just the own form of knowledge is being felt (= *jñana-svarūpam eva vedyate*); thus, after having clearly ascertained that it is a result of just self-feeling, after that also when it is said «a thing is cognized which is either desirable or undesirable in accordance with self-feeling» this result is settled exlusively in regard to self-feeling-direct-perception (= *svasaṃvedana-pratyakṣa*), thus there might be some aim. Thus it is the aim of all (this) source of knowledge. Therefore, in order to repudiate that (aim), it is said «when (*yañ-gi tshe ni*) knowledge together with the object (= *viṣaya*) is the thing (= *artha*)». And this word «thing» expresses «the cognized (thing)». And these (words) «together with the object» are no exception with regard to the totality (of perception). Therefore thus it is said «when cognition is referred to as something cognized from the source of knowledge (= *pramāṇasya prameyam yadā apekṣyate*), at that time a thing is cognized according to self-feeling, thus it is not exclusively the result of self-feeling, but thus «when it is also an object then also»".

2 We must thus distinguish between two kinds of introspection (*sva-saṃvedana*), a fully developed one consisting in a conscious observation of our internal life, and a feeling of the self which, according to Buddhists, is immediate (*nirvikalpaka*), always present, belonging to the nature of our consciousness, because every consciousness is necessarily selfconscious. The Realists denial refers to the latter kind.

§ 8. The result of cognition from the standpoint of the Realist.

The following question then arises. If such can be the result from the standpoint of the Idealist, how can it be the same from the standpoint of the Realist?

This question is answered by the following words of the author, «when the external object alone is cognized, (when the object is not immanent in our knowledge), then this its image becomes (in its totality) the means of cognizing it».

(37b. 5). From the standpoint of the Realist we can nevertheless imagine the fact of self-consciousness as a kind of result. But then we will not ascribe to the «grasping aspect» of the image the function of a «means» of cognition, as the Idealist does. We will assume that the whole mental image of the object takes up the rôle of a means of knowledge,[1] (viz., of asource of our cognition of the external world).

(37b. 6). But does not the Realist likewise admit the existence of a «grasping aspect» of our images, since its existence is revealed by introspection? Why then should he not admit that the rôle of a means accomplishing the act of cognition appertains to this grasping aspect only? In answer to this question we have the following words of the author, —

«then, although self-consciousness exists, (the image of the object represents the means of cognizing it, the fact of self-consciousness is, then neglected»).

---

[1] Lit, f. 37b. 3—6. «Here, if there is no external object, self-consciousness (*rañ-rig-pa* = *sva-saṃvedana*) being established as the result, the grasping form is said to be the instrument of knowledge. And therefore, if the external object does not exist as the thing to be cognized, just as, self-consciousness being established as the resnlt, the grasping aspect is admitted as the means of knowledge, just so, also if the external thing to be cognized exists, the grasping aspect alone is the means of knowledge, — this is questioned. Therefore, in order to repudiate this, it is said «at what time etc.». When the external thing is cognized, although we also establish self-consciousness as the result, but the mental fact (*śes-pa*) of the image (*pratibhāsa*) of the object is wholly (*mātram*) assumed to be the means, and not its grasping form, as it is the case of mere internal knowledge».

That our knowledge is self-conscious both the Realist and the Idealist equally admit,[1] but if the object of cognition is represented by a really existing external world, it would not be logical to represent self-cognition as the means of cognizing it. This aspect of our knowledge is, accordingly, neglected, and our images of the external things are alone considered to be the means of cognizing them, not the simultaneous image of our internal life, since in regard to the external object the latter cannot be logically constructed as a cause producing its cognition.[2]

(38a. 1). Because the feeling of ease[3] (has its own object), it has not an object of something foreign to it. If the «grasping» aspect, (of the idea is turned upon itself), if its object is the idea itself, how can it then constitute our means of cognizing (not this idea, but) the external object? If cognition has for its object one thing, it becomes impossible to declare that it is the means of cognizing another thing!

(38a. 2). (The following words of the author contain the answer to this question). He points to the cause of the distinction.[4] «Because, says he, this (external) object is the cognized part (corresponding to its cognition)». «Cognized» means ascertained[5] (with logical necessity).

§ 9. No real knowledge beyond sensation.

(The author further says): «Whatsoever (be the image reflected in our cognition, whether it be the

---

1 The Naiyāyikas have *anu-vyavasāya* as self-consciousness of knowledge, the Mīmāṃskas *jñātatayā jñāna-anumānam*, cp. above p. 355 n. 1, but this they both distinguish from the perception of pleasure and pain which they consider to be direct (*pratyakṣa*), cp. above p. 391 n. 2.

2 Lit., 37b. 6—8. «But the thesis being «when the external object is the thing cognized», then also do we not necessarily assume a grasping form (= *grāhakākāra*), since we are internally conscious of it (= *sva-saṃviditatvāt*)? Why do we not at that time establish it as the means of cognizing? To this he says «at that time although we are internally conscious of cognition etc....» Cognition is being internally felt (*sva-saṃvedyam* instead of *sva-saṃvedanam*, as in Dignāga's text?), thus are the words to be connected. Although the self-revealed self-form (*rañ-rig-par bya-bai rañ-gi ño-bo = svasaṃvedya-svabhāva*) exists at all times, nevertheless, independently from it, there being an external thing cognized, the reflecting (*snañ-ba-ñid = pratibhāsitvam*) of the object cognized alone is the means, the reflecting of the self (*sva-pratibhāsitvam*) is not, because when there is an external object, it is not logical that this should be the producer (= *tasya sādhanatvam na yujyate*)».

3 Peking ed. *mi-rig-pa ni*, Narthang ed. *yi-rañ-ba ni.*

4 *mtshan-ma-ñid-la rgyu gsuñs-pa.*

5 = *prameyam iti niścetavyam ity arthaḥ.*

image of something white, of something non-white or of any other colour, this image together with the object possessing that colour will have the function to produce the cognition)».

(38a. 2). The meaning (of this passage) is that our knowledge of the external (world) reaches only so far as our images go.[1] (The Realist also cognizes only the image, albeit he speaks of the object). It is here just as in the case (of inference). When we say that we have inferred the presence of fire from the presence of smoke, we, as a matter of fact,[2] do not at all infer it from (smoke itself), but from the image of smoke which is produced by (something corresponding to it).[3] In the same manner, when (the Realist) says that the means of cognizing the external object is its image, we must understand that it is our internal sensation stimulated by the (object).[4]

(38a. 4). (Initially) we have only the feeling of something either pleasant or unpleasant, so far it is only self-feeling, (not object-feeling). Whatsoever be the object, say, a patch of colour, it (initially) appears in the shape of some personal feeling. Then another feeling arises which (we call the sense of sameness) consisting in coordination[5] (between an image and the initial sensation). This our sense of sameness determines the object (and our possible reaction to it). It is not otherwise. In this sense only have we in our images (something like) an instrument of cognizing the external world.[6]

(38a. 6). However, in so saying do we not admit that only an image is cognized as produced from an (initial) sensation[7]? Why then

---

[1] Lit., f. 38a. 2 «Knowledge indeed ascertains the external object by the force of the cognized form».

[2] *dños-su* = *vastutaḥ*.

[3] *rgyu-can-gyi du-bai šes-pas* = *hetumad-dhūma-jñānena*.

[4] *dei-sgrub-par-byed-pa-can rañ-rig-pas* = *tat-sādhakavatā sva-saṃvedanena*.

[5] *ḥdra-bai bdog-ñid-kyi rañ-rig-pa* = *sārūpyātmaka-svasaṃvedana*.

[6] Lit. f. 38a. 4—6. «Thus indeed, howsoever the form of the object is definitely settled in knowledge in the form of pleasant, unpleasant etc., thus thus self-feeling displays itself; howsoever it appears, thus thus the object, the pleasant, unpleasant colour etc., is determined. Because if it is born in this form, then there is self-feeling whose essence is sameness with it, and from it, through its influence, the object is being determined, not otherwise, therefore the reflex of the object is the means of cognizing».

[7] *yul dañ ḥdra-ba-ñid rañ-rig-pai ñor sgrub-par-byed-pa-ñid* = *arthena saha sārūpyam svasaṃvedana-rūpeṇa sādhakam* (*pramāṇam*), cp. N. b. I. 19.

has the author not simply said «an image appears», instead of saiyng «the object is cognized through its image»? The intention of the author was to point to the fact that self-feeling assumes here the function of object-feeling, and this produces the perceptual judgment (in the form «this is a blue patch»). But this does not interfere with the obvious fact that only a substitute for the external object is cognized and this alone is the result of (our knowledge of the external world).[1]

(38a. 8). Thus it is that our representations of an act of knowledge (as intent upon the cognition of an external object) and of its resulting content (are different views taken) of the same fact. (The result is not a knowledge of the external world, since even the Realist must admit) that all our proofs for the existence of an external world are nothing but our sensations.[2]

§ 10. The Ultimate Reality.

(38b. 1). But (if the parts of an act of cognition and of its result can be arbitrarily assigned), why then has it been said (by the author) that the result (of the act of cognizing) is self-consciousness?

This has been said from the standpoint of Ultimate Reality.[3] Self-consciousness represents the result, because (there is nothing beyond it), it is identical[4] with our knowledge (in general). It is not a contradiction, when it is said that the cognition of the object can be regarded as a result because artificially[5] (we can diffe-

---

[1] Lit., f. 38a. 6—8. «However, is it not here admitted that the coordination with the object in the form of a self-feeling is cognized as the producer? Therefore he ought to have said «because this appears through its influence»; why there he has said «through it that object is cognized»? There is an intention! Since that self-feeling, which represents the function of object-feeling, produces the ascertainement of the object, therefore he has thns said, in order to make clear that just the feeling of the substitute of an object (= *upacarita-artha-vedanam eva*) must be considered as the result».

[2] Lit., f. 38b. 8—38b. 1. «Thus instrument and result of knowledge have no different object (or domain *yul* = *viṣaya*), because it has been said that there is a self-feeling of just that what is a proof for whatever is external (= *yasyaiva bāhyasya sādhanam tasyaiva sva-saṃvedanam iti vacanāt*)».

[3] *don-dam-par* = *paramārthataḥ*.

[4] *dei-bdag-ñid-kyi-phyir* = *tādātmyāt*, because of «existential identity» which must be distinguished from «logical identity», cp. NBṬ, transl. p. 69 ff.

[5] *ñe-bar btags-pas* = *upacārāt*, «metaphorically».

rentiate it in a process and a result and then the supposed cognition of the object will be the result). (38b. 2). Here, since there is nothing existent beyond mere sensations (and images)[1] the «grasping» aspect of the image is said to represent the act[2] of cognition and its «grasped» aspect the object[3] of cognition.

(38b. 2). The controverted (point) is here the following one. How is it possible that from the standpoint of a philosopher who denies the existence of an external world, there nevertheless is a differentiation of the «grasping» and the «grasped» aspect in that knowledge, which in itself does not contain any differentiation of a source and (a result) of cognition? Therefore, in order to solve this doubt, it is said «thus it is (that our knowledge appears in different aspects»).

The general meaning of this passage is the following one. From the standpoint of «Thisness»,[4] (i. e., of Absolute Reality) there is no difference at all! But hampered as we are by Transcendental Illusion,[5] (we perceive only a refraction of reality). All that we know is exclusively its indirect[6] appearence as differentiated by the construction of a difference of a subject and an object. (38b. 5). Therefore the differentiation into cognition and its object is made from the empirical[7] point of view, but not from the point of view of Absolute Reality.[8]

(38b. 5). But how is it that a thing which is in itself not differentiated appears as differentiated?

(Through illusion!) Just as, when our faculty (of vision) is damaged by magical interference or other causes, we deem to distinguish separate bodies of elephants and other animals in what are simply clumps of clay, and just as in a desert at a great distance we may perceive *(fata morgana)* and small objects seeming to be large; just so this our consciousness, because we are blinded by a Transcendental Illusion, appears in a form which in reality it does not possess.

---

1 *rnam-par-rig-pa-tsam-ñid-la* = *saṃvedana-mātre eva.*

2 *pramāṇa.*

3 *prameya.*

4 *de-kho-na-ñid* = *tathatā.*

5 *ma-rig-pa* = *avidyā.*

6 *mtshon-pa ḥbah-zhig* ste = *lakṣyate eva.*

7 *yathā-dṛṣṭam.*

8 *yathā-tathatām.*

9 *ma-rig-pa* = *avidyā* = *avidyā-vāsanā.*

§ 11. The structure of empirical knowledge.

(38b. 7). (Objection). We cannot imagine that those (forms of our consciousness) which actually exist are produced by a force (comparable to) magic or (disease), because those whose faculty of vision is normal and who observe the objects at close distance are free from such (illusive) perceptions.

(38b. 8). (This is answered in the following words), «thus the foundation of our multiform cognitive consciousness (is its double aspect as subject and object), (and on this foundation a further) construction is raised in the double shape of the two methods of cognition[1] and their respective two different objects.

The word «thus» points to the two aspects of our consciousness (its subject aspect and its object aspect), which have just been mentioned. «Cognitive consciousness» is consciousness as it is engaged in the action of cognizing. What about it? It is «multiform», i. e., it is differentiated in (two) forms. Those forms are meant which the (above mentioned) Transcendental Illusion exhibits as our distinctly differentiated consciousness,[2] i. e., as its «grasping» aspect and (its grasped aspect).

(39a. 2). When it is said «a further construction is raised in the shape of the two methods of cognition and their respective two different objects»,[3] these words mean that, first of all, we have as (one) subject aspect, pure sensation[4] without any other mental construction[5] and its (respective) object[6] the (absolutely concrete) particular,[7] (the thing in itself), a vivid simple reflex,[8] representing the object-aspect.

---

1 Lit., «And on the substratum (*ñe-bar-blañs-nas* = *upādāya*) of the multiform cognitive consciousness it is being arranged (*ñe-bar-ḥdogs* = *upacaryate*) as the cognizing and cognized parts thus and thus».

2 Thus the «clear and distinct» cognitions which Descartes thought to be a guarantee of truth are here just the reverse of truth; in this idealistic system, only empirically true; and *eo ipso* they are trascendentally an illusion.

3 Lit., «when thus and thus etc. is said».

4 *mñon-sum tshad-ma* = *pratyakṣa-pramāṇa*.

5 *rnam-par-rtog-pa dañ bral-ba* = *nirvikalpaka*.

6 *gzuñ-bai rnam-pa* = *grāhya-ākāra*.

7 *rañ-gi mtshan-ñid* = *svalakṣaṇa*.

8 *gsal-bar snañ-ba* = *sphuṭābha*.

Further we have another subject-aspect [1] in the shape of inference [2] (or judgment) which is produced by a logical connection [3] (and we have its respective) object, the Universal [4] which is a non-vivid (abstract) reflex following upon the specific vividness of the sensation-reflex.[5] It (also) represents an object-aspect.[6]

(39a. 4). The words «this construction is raised» means it exists empirically.[7] These words contain the following suggestion. They are an indication of what the essence of a source of our knowledge and of its (respective) object are from the empirical point of view.[8] (And this indication is made mainly) in order to clear up the deep obscurity of misconceptions.[9] (39a. 5). Only that knowledge which transcends the (boundaries) of the empirical world [10] is free from Transcendental Illusion.[11] It is the cognition of the immaculate,[12] genuine [13] Absolute.[14] Its exclusive domain is the (absolutely) real object,[15] (the real thing in itself).

(39a. 6). (The act of cognition cannot be distinguished from its content, moreover) because a l l e l e m e n t s o f e x i s t e n c e

---

[1] *ḥdzin-pai rnam-pa* = *grāhaka-ākāra.*

[2] *rjes-su-dpag-pa tshad-ma* = *anumāna-pramāṇa;* it is clear that whatsoever is not pure sensation is thrown into the category of indirect cognition or inference. The perceptual judgment «this is blue» or the negative judgment «there is here no jar» are also included in the category of judgments (*adhyavasāya*) and are not sensations, sensation (*nirvikalpaka-pratyakṣa*) is only an element in the perceptual judgment.

[3] *rtags-las skyes-pa* = *lingād utpanna*, *linga* is the *trirūpa-linga* or invariable connection.

[4] *spyii-mtshan-ñid* = *sāmānya-lakṣaṇa*, it is clear that every thing possessing general features is included in the category of general essences or Universals.

[5] *gsal-bai bye-brag-la rjes-su-hgro-ba-lta-bu mi-gsal-bar snañ-ba* = *sputatva-viśeṣam anugacchann iva asputa-pratibhāsaḥ*, i. e., the image and the perceptual judgment which follow the first moment of pure sensation contain already abstraction or «non-vividness».

[6] *gzuñ-byai rnam-pa* = *grāhya-ākāra.*

[7] = *upacaryate iti vyavahriyate.*

[8] = *vyavahārasya pramāṇa-prameya-svarūpam.*

[9] *log-par-rtogs-pa-rnams-kyi kun-tu-rmoñs-pa bsal-bai ched-du* = *vipratipattīnām sam-moha-nirākāraṇārtham.*

[10] *ḥjig-rten-las hdas-pa kho-na* = *atīndriyam eva, lokottaram eva.*

[11] *rnam-par-ḥkhrul-bas spañ-pa* = *vyāghāta-śūnyam.*

[12] *dri-med* = *amala.*

[13] *ñams-par-med-pa-anupahata.*

[14] *don-dam-pa* = *paramārtha.*

[15] *yañ-dag-pa ni gzhal-bya-o* = *samyak-prameyam.*

have no causal efficiency, (they simply appear in mutual coordination without obtruding upon one another).[1] These words suggest that the (supposed) cognizing activity of cognition[2] is an illusion.

(39a. 6). The empirical condition of existence, the essence of which is not to appear in one aspect, (but always in the double aspect of a thing and of its efficiency), this condition does not exist as absolute reality, because (Monism), not Plurality is that aspect of the Universe which is ultimately real.[3] Plurality is nothing but illusion[4] and (we, worldly beings to whom absolute) knowledge non refracted into the (double) form of subject and object is inaccessible, must be regarded as blinded by (the glamour) of Transcendental Illusion![5]

§ 12. Knowledge and Errcr.

(39a. 8). But now, if all the knowledge of those beings to whom absolute knowledge is inaccessible[6] is incomplete, how can it be that we nevertheless determine what is right and what is wrong cognition?[7]

(39a. 8). To this objection we give the following reply. Although the Biotic Force (which propels our sensations independently from an external world) creates illusion (with regard to cognition of absolute reality), it nevertheless contains a (fundamental) difference, (according to which some of our cognitions are right and others are wrong).[8] When, e. g., a perception of water has been produced and it is followed

---

1 This is equivalent to the general formula of *pratītya-samutpāda*.

2 *šes-pai rig-pa-de* = *etaj jñānasya vedanam.*

3 *de-kho-na-ñid-du chos-gañ-la-yañ rnam-pa-gcig-min-pa mthoñ-bai bdag-ñid kyi tha-sñad srid-pa-ma-yin-te, rnam-pa-rnams yoñs-su ma grub-pa-ñid-kyi-phyir ro* = *tathatayā yasminn api dharma aneka-ākāra-dāršana-ātmaka-vyavahāro na sambhavati ākārāṇām aparinispannatvāt*, lit. «In absolute existence (*tathatayā*) the empirical condition (*vyavahāra*), whose essence is to perceive not-one form (i. e., plurality) does not exist with respect to whatsoever an element (*dharma*) because the forms are not the absolute aspect».

4 *de-ni ḥkhrul-ba kho-na-ste* = *te hi* (sc. *ākārāḥ*) *mithyā eva.*

5 *ma-rig-pas loñ-ba-rnams ni gañ rig-par-bya-ba dañ rig-par-byed-pai rnam pa-med-pai šes-pa-la yañ de-ltar bltao* = *avidyayā hı ye andhās tathā vedya-vedaka ākāra-rahita-jñānam api pašyanti.*

6 *de-kho-na-ñid mi šes-pa-rnams-kyi* = *tathatām ajānatām.*

7 *tshad-ma dañ cig-šos rnam-par-bzhag* = *pramāṇetara-vyavasthā.*

8 *ñe-bar-bslad-pai bag-chags-kyis khyad-par yod-par gyur-ba-las te*, lit. «the difference exists owing to a defective Biotic Force».

by the (corresponding) tactile sensations,[1] and then by the sensations[2] of drinking and of satisfied thirst, (these sensations) do not deceive us empirically[3] and on account of that they are right knowledge. Different sensations would not agree with such a (normal) Biotic Force,[4] and on account of that they are wrong cognitions. (From this standpoint right knowledge is knowledge uncontradicted by experience, without any regard to its absolute truth).

(39b. 2). However, (if our knowledge refers only to ideas), how is it that we infer the existence of a cause from the existence of its result?

Why should this be impossible?

Because (in this case, in the case of inference), the idea of smoke, e. g., always comes first and the idea of fire follows, since (in this case) we do not experience any sensation of fire before the sensation of smoke. Therefore we necessarily should conclude that smoke is not produced by fire (but, on the contrary, that smoke produces fire, since the idea of fire arises after the idea of smoke, smoke comes first)?

(39b. 3). This objection is not founded! In the uninterrupted run of conscious moments (which makes up our personality), a special moment arises when the Biotic Force produces a sensation of fire, from this sensation the sensation of some smoke is produced,[5] it is not produced at random by any sensation. Therefore the idea of smoke is suggestive of the (idea of fire), it points to the appearance of an idea having the form of fire which is (also) clearly evoked by the Biotic Force in the cognizing individual.[6]

(39b. 5). Here the fact representing the cause is inferred, just as from a certain taste etc. we can infer the existence of the colours and other (qualities which always go together). Thus there can be no quarrel (regarding this question).

---

1 *reg-pa = sparša.* 2 *rkyen-rnams = pratyayāḥ.*

3 *srid-pa tha-sñad-la mi-slu-ba = bhava-vyavahāra-avisaṃvādin.*

4 *rnam-pa-de-lta-bui bag-chags dañ bral-bai-phyir = tādṛša-ākāra-vāsanā-abhāvāt.*

5 *mei rnam-pa-can-gyi šes-pa-bskyed-pai bag-chags-kyi khyad-par-dañ-ldan-pa-kho-nai sems-kyi rgyud-ni du-bar snañ-bai blo skyed-par-byed-kyi, gañ-ci-yañ-ruñ-bas ni ma yin-no = agny-ākāravaj-jñāna-utpādaka-vāsanā-višeṣasyaiva citta-santāno dhūma-pratibhāsa-buddhim janayati, na tu yena kenacit (janitam).*

6 *de rtogs-par-byed-pai du-bai šes-pa-ni rtogs-pa-poi bag-chags gsal-bar sad-pa-can mei rnam-pa-can-gyi blo ḥbyuñ-bar-ḥgyur-ba go-bar-byed-do = taj-jñāpaka-dhūma-jñānam pratipattṛ-vāsanā-spaṣṭa-udbodhanavantam agny-ākāravantam buddhy-utpādam gamayati.*

APPENDIX V

Vācaspatimiśra on Buddhist Nominalism (apoha-vāda).

Vācaspatimiśra on Buddhist Nominalism (apoha-vāda).

Nyāya-vārtika-tātparya-ṭīkā, Vizian. ed., pp. 338. 11 ff., Benares ed. (1925) pp. 483. 18 ff.

I[t] PART.

§ 1. Preliminary.

Indian philosophers have devoted a great deal of attention to the problem of Error or Illusion, and a series of solutions have been proposed by them. The school example of an illusion is the erroneous perception of a piece of glittering nacre which at a distance is mistaken for a piece of silver. What happens in that case, according to the realistic schools of Nyāya and Vaiśeṣika, is nothing more that what is expressed in language, one thing is mistaken for another, both being real. This doctrine is called *anyathā-khyāti,* or mistaking one thing for another. On the other extremity of philosophic opinion we have the Buddhist school of Mādhyamikas and the brahmanical Vedāntins. For them all our cognitions are relative and, therefore, illusions. All cognitions are just as wrong as the perception of silver in stead of nacre, *sarvam jñānam mithyā.* The only non-relative, i. e., absolute, reality for the Vedāntins is the Cosmical Soul, or Brahma; for the Mādhyamikas — the Cosmical Body of Buddha, or Dharmakāya. The first of these doctrines is termed *anirvacanīya-khyāti,* cognition of the Unutterable, the second *asat-khyāti,* cognition of the Unreal. There is a third solution which is called the Non-Discrimination theory *(akhyāti)* or the theory of Neglected Difference (*bheda-agraha*). This theory is endorsed by the idealistic Buddhist Logicians (*nyāya-vādino Bauddhāḥ*) and by the Prabhākara section of the Mīmāṃsakas. According to Prabhākara error does not exist, *sarvam jñānam pramāṇam.* Knowledge is knowledge, it is not and cannot be error. What happens in the case of nacre and silver is simply the fact that we do not sufficiently discriminate between them, we neglect their difference. The perception of a glittering surface is at the bottom. It is all right, it is not error, it is knowledge. But it is also not the whole of the possible approach to truth, there is a difference between the glittering of silver and the glittering of nacre, a difference which we have failed to perceive. Having failed to perceive the difference (*bheda-agrahāt*) we identify the one with the other. The Brahmanical and the Buddhist Logicians are here opposed to one another in that the first maintain a positive «cognition of non-difference» (*abheda-graha*), the second, on the contrary, maintain a «non-cognition of difference» (*bheda-agraha*). The Realists assnme that the cognition is positive because non-difference or non-existence is for them nevertheless something real, a «meaning» (*padārtha*). According to the Bnddhists we have a «non-cognition» of the difference, an imputation of identity, an imputed similarity of things absolutely dissimilar (*atyanta-vilakṣaṇānām sālakṣaṇyam*, or *sārūpyam*). The silver and the nacre are quite different, but by a common contrast, in as much as both contain the repudiation of the non-glittering, they can be viewed as identical. They are more or less (*kathamcit*) united by a commou contrast (*eka-vyāvṛttyā*); by further contrasts (*vikalpa-antaraiḥ*) they will be discriminated, cp. N. Kaṇikā, p 256. 15 ff., and 262. 2 ff. Thus the terms *anya-vyāvṛtti, apoha*, *sārūpya* and *bheda-agraha* are convertible. Vācaspatimišra has devoted in Tātp., p. 54 ff. a piece of exceedingly subtle dialectics to the repudiation of the *bheda-agraha* theory, this passage being only a summary of a more detailed exposition contained in his, till now unrecovered, work Brahma-tattva-samīkṣā. The same principle is applied by the Buddhists in order to clear up the mystery of the agreement between the mind and the things. The things are non determined by the mind, neither is the mind determined by the things, nor is there between them any pre-established harmony, but although they are absolutely heterogeneous and different, we mistake the one for the other, just as we mistake nacre for silver, by not perceiving their difference. We thus identify our images—which are internal, notional, logical constructions of our Reason, dialectical, positive-negative products of productive imagination — with the absolutely real things in themselves, the point-instants of external efficient reality.

The same principle of Neglected Difference (*bhedāgraha* = *apoha*) is also resorted to in order to solve the problem of the relation between the Universal and the Particular. For the Universal is always an image, a logical construction, a dialectical distinction, the Particular, on the other hand, i. e., the extreme concrete and particular, the point-instant of efficient reality, is not constructed, hence it is the thing as it is in itself. There is between them no similarity at all, but by neglecting all their difference and by a common contrast we can identify them. Just so there is no similarity at all between two cows, they are «other» entities, but by neglecting this there difference and by fixing our attention upon their contrast with, e. g., horses, we may say that they are cows, i. e., in this case, non-horses. If there were no objects with which they could be contrasted they would be quite dissimilar.

The importance of this theory lies in the fact that it radically eliminates every attempt to maintain the reality of Universals, whether as real entities (*sattā*), eternal and ubiquitous, residing in all attaining particulars (*svaviṣaya-sarva-gata*), or as «meanings» (*padārtha*), having whatsoever objective reality. Universals are purely notional, their indirect reality is, so to speak, dynamic, as a guide of onr purposive actions directed towards some point of efficient, external reality.

The theory of *apoha* has been first started by Dignāga in the 5th chapter of his Pramāna-samuccaya. The first chapter of Dharmakīrti's Pramāṇavārtika is partly devoted to it. Dharmottara has written a special work on it (Bstan-hgyur, Mdo, vol. 112). A short tract Apoha-siddhi by Ratnakīrti (written in one night and, probably for this reason, lacking clearness) has been edited among the Six Buddhist Nyāya tracts, Calcutta, 1910 (B. I.). Šāntirakṣita has devoted to it a chapter — Šabdārtha-parīkṣā — of his compendium Tattvasangraha and Kamalašīla has commented upon it. The Tibetan litterature dealing with the problem is very vast. Among the Brahmanical authors besides Vācaspatimišra whose exposition and critique is translated here, we find chapters on it in the Šloka-vārtika, in the Šāstradīpikā (p. 378 ff., Benares 1908), in the Nyāya-vārtika, Nyāya-mañjarī, Nyāya-kandalī etc. etc., scarcely any older Nyāya-work omits to devote some remarks to it. Haribhadra-sūri the Jain (not to be confounded with the Buddhist ācārya Haribhadra, the author of Abhisamaya-alankāra-āloka) discusses the problem in ch. IV of his Anekānta-jaya-patāka.

§ 2. Names are connotative of mental constructions or Universals.

(338.11). The following (theory) is here noteworthy. Names indeed, are (not signs of ultimate reality, but) of mental constructions. The objects named are the same as the objects of these constructions.[1] The latter are the cause of the former, (but) we understand both as containing the same objective reference.[2] However these our mental constructions have (various degrees of unreality, from this point of view) they can be divided in four classes inasmuch as their objects are either 1) real substances, as e. g., a cow, or 2) unreal substances, as e. g., God,[3] 3) real attributes, as e. g., blue and 4) unreal attributes,[4] as e. g., eternal, (i. e., never changing).[5] (338. 15). The proper function[6] of a

1 This is an indirect reference to Dignāga's words, *vikalpa-yonayaḥ šabdāḥ vikalpāḥ šabda-yonayaḥ*, cp. Anekāntaj., p. 318.

2 Lit., p. 338. 12—13. «Words have indeed an origin in constructive thought (*vikalpa-yonayaḥ*). They are directly intent (*abhi-nivišante*) upon just that what is the field of mental constructions (*vikalpānām*), because cause and effect are understood as having co-substrateness (*samānādhikaraṇyam*)». — This *vikalpa* is further explained as synthesis (*anusandhāna*), but it also means differentiation, and it is also, a synonym of *kalpanā* (= *yojanā*) arrangement, construction, mental construction or imagination, «productive imagination», because the fnnction of the mind is conceived as differentiation, comparison and unification, synthesis. As synthesis it is then a characteristic fnnction of all judgments, it thus becomes a synonym of *adhyavasāya* judgment and *niścaya* ascertainement. Its real function is to affirm identity in difference, as here stated, bnt the differentiation, refraction, of an original concrete unity seems to have been its most primitive function, cp. Tātp., p. 89. 11 — *ekam avibhāgam svalakṣaṇam... tathā tathā vikalpyate;* Kamalašīla p. 284. 13. — *bahuṣv aniyata-eka-samudāyi-bheda-avadhāraṇam vikalpaḥ*, and Madhy. vṛtti, p. 350. 12 ff.

3 *īšvara.*

4 Read *sad-asad-dharmi-sad-asad-dharma.*

5 Lit., p. 338. 13—14. «And fourfold is this class of constructions, as referring to existing and non existing substances, existing and non-existing attributes, cow, God, blue, eternal etc.». — Cow and blue, although images and constructions, are here characterized as realities, inasmuch as they refer to real external substrates.

6 Read *sa ca vikalpānām.*

mental construction (or judgment) is to construct[1] (a unity in difference), to represent as a unity what includes a difference of place, time and quality,[2] (or simply to produce judgments of the form) «this is that». Such mental constructions are alone capable of receiving a (connotative) name. The connotation[3] of names is the result of an arbitrary agreement.[4] (They consequently are all Universals). The particulars, (i. e., the ultimate particulars, the things in themselves) are not (synthetical) mental constructions. In all the universe of things they are unique, (shorn of all relations, they are unutterable).[5] The Universals, on the other hand, (although they can be named), are not (external) realities, they are not real objects. And this is just the reason why the absolute particulars do not *possess* them. Since the Universals do not exist (as efficient points of reality), neither does their «possession» by the particulars also really exist.[6]

§ 3. The absurdity of Realism.

(338.19). Further, let us admit (with the Realists) that Universals exist (as external realities and that the particulars «possess» them). They are, however, supposed (by the Realists) to be eternal (never changing) entities which cannot be efficiently acted upon (so as to be modified by causes). They therefore cannot be (really) «supported» by the particulars, because a «support« is always a cause. (To be supported means to be modified by a special cause). Apples etc. which naturally would fall down to the ground are transformed in non-

---

1 Read *vikalpyate*.

2 Lit., p. 338. 15—17. «And that is the field of mental construction (*vikalpānām*) what is put into relations (*vikalpyate*); what through a difference of place, time and condition is afterwards (*anu-*) put together in a unity, «this is just that». And this alone is the field of words, since in respect of them an agreement is possible». — On *vikalpa* = *anusandhāna* cp. above p. 405 n. 2.

3 Proper names (*yadṛcchā-śabdo ḍittha iti*) will also include a certain amount of connotation (*vikalpa*) since they also are designations of unity in difference, cp. Tātp. p. 102. 3.

4 These judgments are again either perceptual, e. g, «this is blue», or inferential, e. g., «there must be a fire on that hill», or negative, e. g., «there is here no jar».

5 Lit., p. 338. 17. «And the own-essences (*svalakṣaṇāni*), being dissimilar from the three worlds, are not such, hence they are not the domain of mental constructions, (of productive imagination)».

6 According to this terminology, an individual cow, e. g., being a synthetic image, will be a Universal.

falling-down objects when they are supported by a basket. But an eternal (never changing) Ens cannot be transformed,[1] and therefore cannot be supported (by a substratum).

(338. 23). (Nor could it be possible for one particular to «support» several Universals). Thus the facts[2] of «being a tree» and of «being an Aśoka-tree» are two separate Universals, each has its own (separate) name. They, consequently, cannot be possessed in common by the same supporting (particular), just as a cow and a horse do not represent (two characteristics) possessed by one (common substratum).

(338. 24). But let us admit (for the sake of argument) that even an eternal (and unchanging) Ens can be influenced and supported by a particular substratum (upon which it resides). The following dilemma[3] then arises. The given[4] particular, (the efficient point instant), does it influence the fact of «being a tree» by just the same its own intrinsic nature by which it also supports the fact of «being an Aśoka-tree» or by another (moment) of its existence? If the latter is the case, (if both these Universals are supported by different moments of efficient reality), then, since there is an existential difference,[5] there will be, two particulars), one particular supporting the Universal «tree» and another particular supporting the Universal «Aśoka». (The result will be) just the same (as before; the two Universals) cannot have in common the same supporting particular, (they will be different entities), as a cow and a horse.

(338. 28). Let us then suppose that the Particular influences all the (attaining) Universals (at once), by the same act of its existence, (what will be the consequence?). There will be no existential difference between all these Universals. If one of them will then be suggested by a name or by a conception,[6] all the remaining ones, since their existence will depend upon the same cause, will also be *eo ipso* suggested and they practically will all become synonyms. Thus the Universals Existence, Substantiality, Solidity, Arboreity and Aśoka-ness,

---

1 *kriyate* = *vikriyate*.

2 *-tva*.

3 *vikalpa* here in its original sense of a dilemma.

4 *tat*.

5 According to the Buddhists the relation is an analytical one (*svabhāva-linga*), which reposes on existential identity (*tādātmya*).

6 *vikalpena*.

(if they be realities produced at once by the same cause), must have the same meaning.[1] (Dharmakīrti) puts it thus,[2]—

«If one supporter (for many Universals) is known and there are no other supporters, then all will be equally known when one is known; those that at that time are not perceived will nevertheless be known (as synonyms)».

(339. 6). Thus (it is wrong to maintain that) our conceptions correspond to individual things possessing general characteristics. Neither do they correspond to (extreme, bare) particulars.[3] Hence it is also wrong to suppose that they correspond to (real) forms of the external objects which are picked up by our thought.

§ 4. The synthetic function of a perceptual judgment.

(339. 7). What is the meaning of (Dharmottara's) words that a perceptual judgment represents as real a subjective image which is (objectively) unreal? The perceptual judgment (of the pattern «this is that») is intent upon a subjective image which has nothing external in it. However it is identified with an external object. This (quasi-) external object is thus nothing but an (objectivized) image.[4]

---

1 Lit., p. 339. 1—4. «And then, since the own-nature will not be different, and when a particular possessing one Universal, among the Universals whose own existence depends upon the support of this (particular), becomes apprehended by one word or by one mental construction, because all the Universals, whose own existence depends upon the one support of it, will be (also) apprehended, there will be a deduction of synonymousness of the words and of the constructions Existence, Substantiality, Solidity, Arboreity, Aśoka-ness». — Cp. the similar argument used by the Vedāntins for establishing Monism by proving the synonymity of all Universals, cp. Śrī-bhāṣya, ad I. 1. 1, (Thibaut's transl. p. 32).

2 Cp. above, p. 89. 28—90. 3, cp. there the literal rendering.

3 Lit., p. 339. 6. «By repudiating the objectivity of single extreme particulars (*svalakṣaṇa-bheda*) the objectivity of mentally cognized forms (*jñāna-grāhya-ākāra*) is also rejected». — According to the Buddhists «objectivity» or intentness upon an object (*viṣayatā*, Husserl's «Intention») is produced by «coordination» (*sārūpya*) between a point of external reality and an image, cp. Tātp. p. 463. 26— *sārūpya-samutpatti api viṣaya-lakṣaṇam*. This view is contrasted with the standpoint of naive realism according to which universals (*ākāra* = *jāti*), particulars (*svalakṣaṇa* = *vyakti*) and their combinations (*sāmānyavad-bheda* = *ākṛti*) are all external real objects cognized by special contacts with the senses.

4 Lit., p. 339. 7—9. «In ascertaining its own non-external form as external, a mental construction (viz., a perceptual judgment «this is that») has an external object in its own form; is that so? according to what has been said, «it operates in ascertaining a real thing in the non-reality which is its own form?». Cp. N. Kaṇikā, p. 259 23, Kamalaśīla, p. 289. 3.

(339. 9). Now, what is the meaning of the term «to identify (in a judgment «this is that»)? Does it mean 1) to «grasp»[1] (the object), or 2) to produce (a change[2] in it), or 3) to subsume[3] it (under a class), or 4) to impose[4] (a mental construction upon an external reality).

(The first and the second of these alternatives must be rejected, because) how could our construction apprehend an unreal image as a real thing or how could it convert (the first into the second)? If something is yellow (by its nature) it cannot be apprehended as blue or converted (in something naturally blue) even by hundreds of skilled men!

(339. 12). Nor is (the third alternative better). (In the perceptual judgment of the pattern «this is that», the element «this» refers to the thing itself, the element «that» to a constructed image). Since

---

[1] *grahaṇam*, the Naiyāyika doctrine of extreme realism according to which the senses travel to the place where the object is situated, come in contact with it, seize its «form» and travel back with that booty. This is followed gradually by a clear and distinct cognition or perceptual judgment (*adhyavasāya*) and a corresponding introspective consciousness (*anu-vyavasāya*).

[2] According to the Mimāṃsakas a change is produced in the object by its cognition, a new quality «cognizedness» (*jñātatā = prakāśa*) is created (*karaṇa = vikṛti*). Thought is pure, imageless (*nirākāra*) and immediate self-consciousness (*svasaṃvedana*) does not exist. Cognition is revealed to the cognizer through an inference from the fact of the change existing in the cognized object, cp N. Kaṇikā, the passage translated above p. 335, and p. 267. 12 —

pūrvam sā (jñātatā = ākāratā) gṛhyate, paścād
jñānam taj-jñātatā-vaśāt.

[3] *yojanā*, «combination» of a point of reality with a Universal, of the element «this» with the element «that», or subsumption of an individual under a class notion. This is the usual interpretation of *vikalpa = adhyavasāya*, cp. Tipp., p. 23. 4 — *«sa evāyam» ity anena vikalpasyāvasthā ucyate*, cp. above Tātp., p. 338. 16. The interpretation is here seemingly rejected in order to characterize the mental operation of an existential judgment more precisely.

[4] *āropa = adhyāsa* «imposition» or «imputation» is a term very much used by Buddhists and Vedāntins to express the relation of a mental construction or image to transcendental reality. It is here also seemingly rejected in order to emphasize its meaning of a wrong imputation. Tattvs., p. 285, mentions that somephilosophers have admitted an imputation of mental images upon external reality without denying the reality of the Categories (*dravyādiṣu pāramārthikeṣv adhyastam buddhyākāram paramārthataḥ śabdārtham icchanti*). For the Buddhists the reality is transcendental and our language is not capable of expressing it at all — *na kiṃcid bhāvato 'bhidhīyate śabdaiḥ* (*ibid*). Although some kind of imputation is admitted on both sides, the difference between these two theories is capital (*mahān viśeṣaḥ*).

the particular thing is (in itself) uncognizable, how could a judgment cause it to coalesce with an image which is a construction. (This would mean that the thing in itself is cognizable in a judgment). However we have just established that it is uncognizable.[1]

(339.14). (The fourth alternative must be also rejected, since the words that our knowledge) imposes its own categories[2] which are (objectively) unreal upon an object which is real, have no (intelligible meaning). It is impossible, first of all, to impose an image before having apprehended it. We must begin by accounting for the perception of the image. (Supposing we have succeeded in explaining this), the question then arises, whether the imputation of the image follows on its apprehension or whether both operations are simultaneous[3]? The first (hypothesis must be rejected), because constructive thought is momentary, it cannot perform the (operations) of perceiving (an image) and translating (it to another object) gradually.

(339.17). On the second hypothesis, (the hypothesis of simultaneity, we are faced by the following incongruity). The constructed image is something internal, whose presence in us we feel by an immediate[4] introspective feeling. If transferred into the external world, it would loose its own natural place.[5] We cannot conceive it as existing in the external world, separated[6] from us. Nor can we conceive it as united with a particular, with (a point) of external (reality), because, (as has been already stated), this external (absolute) particular (is uncognizable in discursive thought).[7]

---

1 Lit., p. 339.12—14. «Nor can a judgment (*vikalpaḥ*) produce coalescence of its own form with the (ultimate) particular which has not been grasped. And it has been established (p. 338.17) that the (ultimate) particular is not the object of a judgment (*vikalpa-gocara*)».

2 *sva-ākāram*.

3 Lit., p 339.14—16. «And it does not impose its own form, the non-object, upon the object. First, the non-grasped own form cannot be imposed, thus its apprehension must be found out; does it then impose after having grasped or does it impose just then when it grasps?».

4 *avikalpa-svasaṃvedana-pratyakṣāt*; it must be noticed that constructive imaginative thought is constructive with respect to the external particular (*bāhyārthapekṣayā savikalpakam*), but for our introspective feeling it is an immediate nonconstructed object (*svāpekṣayā sva-saṃviditam nirvikalpakam*).

5 *svāgocaro*. 6 Read *bhinnaḥ*.

7 Lit., p. 339.16—21. «At first, not the former alternative. Indeed constructive thought (*vikalpa-jñānam*) is momentary, it cannot produce the gradual grasping and superimposing. But on the second alternative, a conception (*vikalpo*) which is

(339.21). Thus we are driven to the conclusion that the object corresponding to our mental construction is neither external nor is it a (real) cognition, nor an image (of reality). It is an illusion. Accordingly it has been said by the venerable Dharmottara,[1]

> «The object[2] cognized by productive imagination[3] as separate from others (particulars) is an idea, it is not objective reality[4]».

(It is an unfounded belief!).

§ 5. How is purposive action guided by Universals possible?

(339.23). (Objection). But then, people striving for conscious aims would not be able to take action directed towards external objects when guided by their thoughts[5]?

(339.24). (Answer). Therefore is it that the objects of our mental images are illusively projected[6] into the external world. (They are internal), their externality consists in overlooking the difference[7] (between external and internal), not in perceiving something (internal) in place of the external.[8] If the external (image) would represent a (real) object of our conceptive faculty,[9] (if conceptions would be as immediate as sensations), illusions[10] would be impossible. (339.26).

---

transferred (*samāropyamāṇo*) from the constructed image (*vikalpākārāt*), whose place is the Ego, and which is immediately felt (*pratyakṣāt*) by a non-constructive immediate self-feeling (*avikalpa-svasaṃvedana-pratyakṣāt*) is not an object, not its own (*nāsvagocaro*, viz. is not non-internal), it cannot be cognized as something else (read *bhinnaḥ*). Nor can it be cognized as united with the external particular, because constructive imagination (*vikalpa-jñānena*) does not reflect the external (absolute) particular».

1 This passage is not found in the NBT, it is probably a quotation from Pramāṇa-viniścaya-ṭīkā.

2 *rūpa*.

3 *buddhyā kalpikayā*.

4 Lit., p. 339.22—23. «That form which is touched (*ullikhyate*) by constructive thought as different from others is our thought, not external».

5 Lit., p. 339.23—24. «And thus from constructed knowledge (*vikalpa-jñānāt*) there would be no action directed to the external by those who wish it».

6 *alīka-bāhyam*.

7 *bheda-agraha*.

8 *abheda-graha*.

9 *vikalpa-gocare bāhye*.

10 *abheda-graha* = *anyathā-khyāti*, the perception of one thing instead of another.

Therefore our conceptions, which follow on our pure sensations, dont seize the difference between the external object of a pure sensation and the internal image of thought-construction. But since our images are indirectly products of external points of reality, they are capable of directing the purposive actions of men towards these points of reality, and thus they are (indirectly right knowledge, since) they do not contradict the immediate human experience.

(339. 28). Now, the mutual difference between the objects of the same mental construction is not included in that construction, nor are there other (special) conceptions (for apprehending the particularity of every object). Therefore, overlooking the difference[2] (of all concrete particulars belonging to the same class), we wrongly think that they are identical. Having thus established the identity (of a Universal), we imagine the identity of a series of repeated perceptions,[3] and from this identity a further identity is (imagined), the identity of their causes, the momentary sensations.[4] The objects corresponding to them, the real particulars[5] (the moments of reality) become then also identical[6] (or similar), as has been stated by (Dharmakīrti),

---

1 Lit., p. 339. 24—28. «Therefore their object is the wrongly external, its externality consists in *not-grasping* the difference from the external, but not in the *grasping of the non-difference* from the external. If the external were the object of constructive imagination (*vikalpa*), the grasping of its non-difference from that would be impossible. Therefore conceptions (*vikalpāḥ*) which arise on the back of pure sensation (*nirvikalpaka*), not grasping the difference of the illusion (*alīkasya*), which they grasp, from the external particular which is introduced by it (*tad-upanīta* = *nirvikalpaka-upanīta*), direct the acting persons towards them (towards the particulars); and because of an indirect connection with them, since there is success (*prāpter*), they do not deceive people». — Abont the theory of *bhedāgraha* cp. preliminary note.

2 *bheda-agraha.* — Tattvas., p. 317, says, that just as there are many remedies against fever, which are quite different, but have the same efficiency (*eka-artha-kāritayā sāmyam*), so there is a repetition (*pratyavamarśa*) of cows without any reality of the genus «cow» (*antareṇāpi vastu-bhūtam sāmānyam*).

3 *avamarṣo* = *pratyavamarṣo*, cp. Tattvas., p. 317. 6.

4 *avikalpa-dhī.* 5 *svalakṣaṇa.*

6 When we have a series of similar perceptions, «a cow», «a cow», «a cow» etc. etc., we according to the European philosophers, concentrate our attention on the similar features, abstract them and thus construct, or perceive, the Universal «cow-ness». This is also the view of early Buddhism when it defines our conceptions (*saṃjñā*) as abstractions (*nimitta-udgrahaṇa*), cp. Abh. Koša, I. 14. The Indian Realists, Naiyāyiks, Vaišeṣikas, Mīmāṃsakas and others, (but not the Sānkhyas) admitted then the existence of real ubiquitous and eternal Universals and their perceptibility through a special contact (*saṃyukta-samavāya-sannikarṣa*) with the

«The sensation of sameness is produced by a repeated series of the same perception and the sameness of particulars is the consequence of the fact that they produce the same sensation [1]».

§ 6. All names denote relations.

(340.5). It is thus established that a quasi-external world [2] constitutes the object of our conceptions and of our speech. And these (quasi-external objects are essentially relative, they always have two

---

senses. They laid down the rule that the *organ* which apprehends a thing through a contact also apprehends the Universal inherent in the thing and its negation, or absence, as well. The Mahāyāna Buddhists and the Sautrāntikas replaced the realistic conceptions (*saṃjñā*) and the real Universals (*sāmānya, jāti*) by names and images (*śabda-vikalpau*). They were consequently Conceptualists and at the same time Nominalists of a special kind. It would perhaps be more adequate to call them Constructionists or Rationalists, because there main point is that the forms of our cognition are due not to experience, but to an innate constructive capacity of the Reason, to *vikalpa-vāsanā*, not to *anubhava-vāsanā* or *saṃskāra*. The formation of concepts they did not explain by a process of abstraction of similar features, because this implied the objective existence of these similar features or Universals, but by a process of «neglecting the difference» (*bhedāgraha=agrahaṇa=akhyāti*). The Realists deny *apoha*, because it must be conceived as a *svarūpa-apoha* not as an *apoha-apoha*, cp. Tātp., p. 344. 18 — *svarūpeṇa eva apoho vācyaḥ, na ca, apoha-apohena.* There is absolutely nothing similar between the abstract idea, say, of water and the efficient moment, say, of drinking water. The first is imagined, relative, unreal, unefficient in itself. The second non-imagined, real and efficient. But there is a coordination (*sārūpya = anya-vyāvṛtti = apoha*) between them, owing to which the abstract idea of water receives an indirect reality as leading to a successful purposive action. We could say that it is not a direct reflex, but a «conditioned», indirect reflex. The efficient particular point is really a particular, i. e., unique (*svalakṣaṇam na deśe na kāle anugacchati*), the «repetition» (*pratyavamarśa*) of the same points is a construction (*mānasa-jñāna*), a kind of illusion explained by the principle of «neglected difference» (*bhedāgraha*).

[1] Lit., p. 339. 28—340. 5. «And the mutual difference of these objects of mental constructions is not grasped neither by these very constructions (*vikalpaiḥ*) nor by other mental constructions. Thus man imputes a non-difference, because he does not seize the difference. And from their non-difference a non-difference of repeated perceptions. And from their non-difference the non-difference of their causes, the non-constructive thoughts (*avikalpa-dhī*). And from their non-difference the non-difference also of the particular essences (*svalakṣaṇa*) which are the objects of the non-constructive thoughts; as has been said, «Because of the causality of the repeated perception of one thing the thought is non-different and there is non-difference of the particulars through being the cause of one thought».

sides, and if we attend to the one) we exclude the other.[1] (That they are not realities in themselves, but only relations), is proved, 1) by the fact that they are subject to both affirmation and negation,[2] 2) by the fact that they create a kind of sameness between things absolutely dissimilar,[3] and 3) by some immediate experience of relativity.[4]

(340. 7). Indeed, (as to the first point we can throw it into the form of the following syllogism).

> (Major premise). If something can be (alternately) affirmed and denied,[5] it necessarily is relative.[6]
>
> (Example). As e. g., the quality of not being an extended body of limited dimensions [7]; this property is equally to be found in consciousness [8] and in the (imagined) horns on the head of a hare.[9]
>
> (Minor premise). And such are the objects corresponding to our images, the subject of this discourse, the jars, cloths etc. (They can be both affirmed and denied).
>
> (Conclusion). (They are relative).

This is an analytical deduction [10] (the relativity being deduced from the possibility of both affirmation and denial).

---

1 *anya-vyāvṛtti-rūpam* = *apoha-rūpam*.

2 *bhāva-abhāva-sādhāraṇam*.

3 *atyanta-vilakṣaṇa*, sc. *svalakṣaṇa* = *ananya-bhāk*=*asādhāraṇa* cp. Kamalaśīla, p. 378. 19.

4 *tādrūpya* = *sārūpya* = *anya-vyāvṛtti*, *ibid.*, p. 560. 18. — According to A. Bain, Logic, I p. 55 it would be more precise to charasterize the Names founded on Relativity as Positive and Negative names with the understanding that «negative» has always a real existence, no less than the «positive». It will be seen that the Buddhists likewise put the negative and positive names on the same level, but relativity for them means just relativity, i. e., want of independent reality in itself, *śūnyatva* = *svabhāva-śūnyatva*. In this sense the Yogācāras and Sautrāntikas are also *śūnya-vādins*. — The three points are somewhat differently formulated in Tātp. p. 12 cp. transl. above.

5 *bhāva-abhāva-sādhāraṇa-grahaṇam*.

6 *anya-vyāvṛtti-rūpam eva* = *apoha-rūpam eva*, merely correlative, nothing in itself.

7 *mūrtatva* impenetrability, materiality (=*sapratighatva* = *audārikatva* = *paricchinna-pariṇāmavattva*), a relative quality.

8 *vijñāne*.

9 i. e., we can imagine things real as well as unreal, such that are connected with a point of reality (*svalakṣaṇa*) and such that are not, non-materiality will be the common property of consciousness and all unreal objects.

10 The judgment «whatsoever can be alternately affirmed and denied is relative» is an analytical one, since the predicate is contained, although not very obviously at the first glance, in the subject.

(340. 10). Indeed the object of our conception «a cow» is equally fit to be affirmed and to be denied (in the existential judgments) «this is a cow», «this is not a cow». If it were always existent [1] as the extreme concrete and particular [2] (thing in itself), which is essentially affirmation,[3] then the predicate «is not» could not be applied, because it would be a contradiction. Neither would there be (any need) to apply the predicate «is», since this would be a useless repetition.

(340. 13). The circumstance that a thing can be (alternately) affirmed and denied (points to contingent existence). It is not without a cause, nor does it depend upon an undefinite cause.[4] If, on the contrary, something is subject to real affirmation only or is essentially nothing but affirmation itself,[5] (it is not contingent, since) it is not possible to find a cause for thus receiving the additional characteristic of an affirmation, (in the form of «existence is»), (this characteristic would be superfluous).[6]

(340. 15). Thus the possibility of affirmation-negation [7] is a mark [8] of contingency,[9] (whatsoever is existence in itself, as the real particular is, cannot be denied). In the contrary cases,[10] (i. e., in the domain of absolute existence, the «thing in itself» there is only existence), no non-existence, no contingency,[11] contingency as a predicate [12] is

---

1 Read *bhāva-sādhāraṇye.*

2 *sva-lakṣaṇa.*

3 Lit., «Being pervasively (*sādhāraṇye*) existence, just as the self-essence (*svalakṣaṇa*) whose essence (*rūpa*) is affirmation (*vidhi*)». — According to the Realists the genus Existence (*sattā*) is inherent in the «cow». The Buddhist evidently wishes to say that if «existence» were inherent in cow, the judgment «the cow in not» or «there is no cow» would be a contradiction.

4 Lit. «another cause».

5 *vidhi-rūpa-viṣaya* is a *tatpuruṣa ṣaṣṭhī-samāsa* compound, and *vidhi-svarūpa-viṣaya* is a *karmadhāraya,* the first implies a difference of *svalakṣaṇa* as object and *nirvikalpaka* as subject, the second their identity *vidhi-svarūpam eva viṣayaḥ,* object and subject coalesce then in *svalakṣaṇa,* cp. my Nirvāṇa, p. 144.

6 Lit., p. 340. 13—14. «Indeed the condition of a cause is impossible there for an object of essential affirmation or for an object which itself is affirmation».

7 *sādhāraṇa-grahaṇa.*

8 *vyāpta.*

9 *nimittavattā,* «being contingent on a cause».

10 *vipakṣāt.*

11 *nimittavattvasya anupalabdhyā.*

12 *vyāpaka.*

absent. Therefore this impossibility [1] (of affirmation-negation in regard of real existence) proves the invariable concomitance [2] of affirmation-negation with relativity, (whatsoever can be alternately affirmed and denied is correlative), its essence [3] being a negation of the counterpart.[4]

(340. 17). Moreover (as regards the second point, we can throw it in the form of the following syllogism),

> (Major premise). Similarity between things absolutely dissimilar can be established (only relatively), only by the (common) exclusion of the counterpart.[1]
>
> (Example). Cows, horses, buffaloes and elephants, although as dissimilar by themselves as possibly may be, possess the common feature of not being lions, (they thus belong to the class of non-lions).
>
> (Minor premise). And such is the sameness of the absolutely real [5] external thing (in itself),[6] the (pure) form of affir-

---

1 *vyāvartamāna.*

2 *pratibandha.*

3 *viṣaya*, lit. «object» of the operation of excluding the counterpart.

4 Lit., p. 340. 15—17. «Therefore the common perception (of existence and non-existence) is subaltern to the fact (-*tayā*) of having a canse. By non-perception of the container (*vyāpaka*), of the fact of having a cause, it is excluded from the dissimilar cases, it is contained in the fact of being the object of an exclusion of the other (*anya-vyāvṛtti*), thus the establishment of the connexion». — The major premise (*anvaya*) will be *yatra yatra bhāvābhāva-sādhāraṇa-grahaṇam, tatra tatra nimittavattvam.* Its contraposition (*vyatireka*) will be, *yatra yatra nimittavattvam nāsti, tatra bhāvābhāva-sādharaṇa-grahaṇam api nāsti.* The *sapakṣa* is *nimittavattvam* or contingent existence, the *vipakṣa* is *animittavattvam* or absolute existence. Since in the absolute there is no possibility of affirmation-negation (*nopalabhyate sādhāraṇa-grahaṇam*), everything we can alternately affirm and deny is excluded (*vyāvartamānam*) from the domain of real (*vipakṣāt*), i. e., absolute, existence. The particular, *svalakṣaṇa*, is existence itself, pure or absolute existence (*bhāva-svarūpa = vidhi-svarūpa*), we cannot say «existence does not exist». The Universal is not existence in itself, it can be affirmed and denied, it is contingent, it is relative or correlative, being a refraction of reality in two mutually exclusive counterparts. According to the Realists Existence is the *summam genus*, according to the Buddhists it is the thing in it self.

5 *paramārtha-sataḥ.*

6 *bāhyasya*, the external point of efficiency, the substratum of the universal image.

mation,[1] the (extreme concrete and) particular,[2] with the absolutely dissimilar,[3] transcendentally unreal[4] (constructed object).

(Conclusion). (This similarity is not real as being produced by the common exclusion of the counterpart).

This (again) is an analytical deduction.[5]

(340. 20). Indeed, (what is the similarity between the external thing in itself) which is pure existence[6] (and the Universal cow which can be affirmed and denied? It is the fact that both are) *not non-cows.* If the constructed object[7] «cow» is nothing beyond its contrast with non-cows, the similarity (with the point of reality expressed in the element «this») becomes possible (and this explains the possibility of the existential judgment «this is a cow»). Not otherwise! (340. 22). Here also similarity is the mark[8] of contingent existence.[9] In contrary cases,[10] (i. e., in absolute existence, in the points of reality which always are unique) there is no[11] (similarity). The impossibility[12] of similarity in absolute existence establishes its invariable concomitance (with contingent existence), its own predicate.[13] Contingent existence is thus relative (as consisting in the negation of the counterpart).[14]

---

1 *vidhi-rūpa.*

2 *svalakṣaṇa.*

3 *atyanta-vilakṣaṇa.*

4 *aparamārtha-sataḥ.*

5 *svabhāva-hetuḥ.* The judgment «similarity is established by a common contrast, or common negation» is an analytical one, since similarity aud common negation are identical.

6 *vidhi-rūpa = sattā-mātra.*

7 *vikalpa-viṣaya.*

8 *vyāpta.*

9 *nimittavattā.*

10 *vipakṣāt.* The *vipakṣa* is *svalakṣaṇa* which is *trailokya-vyāvṛtta.*

11 *anupalabdhyā.*

12 *vyāvartamāna.*

13 *svasādhyena.*

14 Lit., p. 340. 20—23. «Indeed the external, although being in its essence (mere) affirmation, is excluded from non-cow. And the object mentally constructed (*vikalpa-viṣaya*), if it is excluded from non-cow, therefrom comes similarity, not otherwise. And thus similarity is also subordinate to the condition of having a cause. By non-perception of this, being excluded from the contrary cases, it is embraced by its own consequence, thus concomitance is proved».

(340. 23). Moreover[1] (our immediate feeling testifies to the fact) that determined perceptions[2] are directly felt[3] as something *distinct*, something whose essence consists in the negation of other objects.[4] Indeed, if that were not the case, if the objects of determined perception were not reflected directly[5] (as negations of other things), then (the following would happen). Supposing a man has been ordered to tie up a cow. If the cow were not immediately present to his mind as something implying the negation of a horse, the man could proceed to tie up the horse (instead of the cow). But if this negation is at once present to his mind,[6] how is it possible to deny that the negation of «non-cows» is not present in the reflex? Therefore Names as well as Universals[7] are relative as implyng the negation of their courterparts.

(340. 27). This theory is alluded to by the author of the Vārtika[8] when he says, «both these (Names and Universals) operate in the manner of a negation of non-existing things, (their counterparts, and) they refer to one thing (as their substratum)». This means that in a perceptual judgment they determine[9] one particular (point of reality). A perceptual jndgment,[10] as has been stated, consists in the non-differentiation, (or in the mental association), of its object, (the Universal), with the particular (point of reality).[11]

---

1 This is the third argument in favour of the relativity of Names since all names are at the same time positive and negative. In the passage above, p. 12. 27, cp. transl. above p. 305—306, where also a set of three arguments in favour of relativity was brought forward, the third argument is different (*niyata-pratibhāsatvāt* instead of *tādrūpya-anubhavāt*). The argument here seems to be in contradiction with the one put forward in p. 340. 1.

2 *vikalpa-viṣaya*, lit. «object of mental construction», an object of determined perception (*savikalpaka-pratyakṣa*) is meant, an object which is constructed by productive imagination.

3 *anubhūyante* = *pratibhāsante*.

4 (*anya-*) *vyāvṛtti-rūpāḥ*.

5 *tad-apratibhāsena* = *anya-vyāvṛtti-ananubhavena*.

6 *pratibhāse vā*.

7 Lit. «mental constructions» (*vikalpa*).

8 Cp. N. Vart., p. 331. 12.

9 *adhyavasyataḥ* = *adhikurutaḥ*, drop the *cheda* before *ekam*.

10 *adhyavasāya* = *vikalpa* as has been defined above, p. 338. 15.

11 The Buddhist theory of Names and of Universals aims at finding out a link between reality which is but a string of point-instants and our conceptions which are intended for things having stability, cp. Tattvas., kār. 906. The Universals are not external, they are internal mental constrnctions, but their difference from

II[d] PART.

The answer of the Realist.

(341. 1). (The Realist). Our answer (to these arguments) is as follows.

§ 1. The Universals and the Particulars are equally real.

(341. 1). That the Universal[1] is a real entity, has been proved (by us above).[2] Consequently the possessor of the Universal, the (quali-

the external points of reality is overlooked and we through an inveterate habit (*anādi-vāsanā*) deem them to be external. The external world is moreover split in discrete point-instants which are «particulars», i. e., individually distinct, discontinuous. Purposive action of sentient beings is directed towards some point when it is similar to what has been previously experienced by them as pleasant. The Universal, the image, cannot attract our action because it is unreal, unefficient, neither can the particular do it because it is unique and dissimilar. The problem is solved by assuming a «coordination» (*sārūpya*) between the point-instant of reality and the imagined Universal. But this coordination consists in a negative similarity (*anya-vyāvṛtti* = *apoha* = *sārūpya*). Just as the Universal «cow» is nothing but a negation of «non-cow», just so the point of efficient reality is also a negation of «non-cow», thus the unity in difference, the similarity between the absolutely dissimilar, is supposed to be explained and the judgment «this is a cow», the union between the particular «this» and the universal «cow» becomes possible. The Realists objected, cp. Tātp., p. 342. 27, that the unique point instaut is not only a negation of non cows, but also a negation of any other object, thus all objects would coalesce if such common negation were sufficient for establishing a coordinatiou. They coalesce indeed in the Absolute, but empirically every point-instant has its own efficiency, it calls forth a corresponding image. Thus the Universal is explained as a non-difference of the particulars (*jātimattā* = *vyaktīnām abhinnatā*), not as a unity of them, *bhedāgraha*, not *abheda-graha*. Prabhākara draws the consequence that, strictly speaking, error does not exist, *sarvam jñānam pramāṇam*. The Buddhists, on the contrary, think that all knowledge of Universals and the process of life is transcendentally an illusion, a continuous dream. If we could awake to transcendental knowledge, as the Buddhist Saint is supposed to do, we would view plurality as a dream and intuit the essence of the Universe as one undifferentiated motionless whole. But owing to a Force (*vāsanā*), which is variously imagined as the Biotic Force driving the world dream or the Force of Transcendental Illusion (*avidyā-vāsanā*) or an inveterate habit (*abhyāsa*), the Universe appears as a moving plurality. This illusion also consists in the fact of overlooking the difference (*bhedāgraha*) between reality and imagination.

[1] *jāti* = *sāmānya*, it is a «meaning» (*padārtha*), it does not possess the genus *sattā*.

[2] Cp. N. S., II. 2. 58 ff.

fied) Particular, is an ultimate reality[1] as well. The relation between such a Particular and such a Universal is a natural (primary) one.[2] There is no need of a (special) agency[3] (in order to bring their union about).

(341.3). That (such a Particular with its inherent Universals, being) a thing of limited duration,[4] can efficiently (and gradually) be changed[5] (under the influence of special causes and conditions), this will be moreover proved by us in the section devoted to the refutation of the Buddhist theory of a Universal Flux.[6]

(341.4). (As to the Buddhist argument[7] consisting in putting emphasis on the fact that at great distance) we discern only the mere presence (of something indefinite), while all the other Universals (which are supposed to be just as real as the Universal Existence) ought to be equally perceived, since as characteristics of the thing (they are on the same footing with the Universal Existence) — this argument has been already refuted in the section devoted to the examination of the definition of sense perception.[8]

§ 2. No Coordination of images with external point-instants, but images adequate to reality.

(341.5). The problem of a Coordination[9] between the imagined Universal and the absolutely real Particular, has already been touched[10] by the author of the Vārtika[11] when he insisted that an illusion is

---

1 *paramārtha-satī*.

2 *svābhāvika* here refers to *samavāya*, not to a *svabhāva-sambandha*, cp. Pariśuddhi, p. 624.

3 *upakāra* here refers to a *saṃyoga* relation, or to an efficient conjunction in general. Substance and quality are conjoined by inherence as soon as the thing springs into being «from its own causes». However Tarkabhāṣā, p. 28, admits that in the first moment of its existence the substance appears without its qualities.

4 *anityasya*, e. g., *ghaṭasya*, for the Realist it will not be a *kṣaṇa*.

5 *upakāryatā*, lit. «the fact of being efficiently affected».

6 Lit., «And also the fact of being efficiently-affected of the non-eternal will be proved in the break of the moment-break», cp. Tātp., p. 379.25 ff., where it will be proved that causation obtains not only between moments, but also between things possessing duration and stability.

7 Cp. above, text pp. 89.24 ff. and 93.26 ff., transl. pp. 268 ff. and 287 ff.

9 Tātp., text p. 88.1 ff., transl. in Appendix I.

10 Read *sārūpyasya prathā; sārūpyam* is *bhedāgrahaḥ* for the Buddhist, *abheda-grahaḥ* = *anyathā-khyāti* for the Naiyāyik, cp. Tātp., p. 54.1 ff.

11 N. Vārt., p. 25.10 ff.

always founded on some (positive) similarity, because an absolutely non-existing thing can be similar to nothing.[1] We have also commented upon that.[2]

(341. 7). Therefore, the conceptions (of our thought) and the meanings (of our language) are intent on particular things in which the Universals are inherent, i. e., these (particular things) with (the Universals) inherent in them constitute the (positive) form (of the objects, their form) which is distinguished from the objects not possessing the same attributes.

(341. 8). If therefore a man is ordered to bind up a cow (he goes and binds the cow, but) not the horse, because when he has understood the word «cow» (an image is called forth in his imagination, an image which adequately represents the real external object cow), but not alone a negation of horses etc.[3]

§ 3. Refutation of the Buddhist theory that all connotative names are relative, because they are positive and negative.[4]

(341. 9). Nor is it right to maintain that if the Universal were (a reality) expressed in its name, the name could not be positive and negative, (as admitting equally a connection with existence and non-existence).[5]

(341. 10). A Universal, indeed, is by itself an eternal (unchanging) entity, but as residing in an infinite number of particulars scattered about in space and time it can be alternately affirmed and denied. We can sometimes say «it is», and sometimes «it is not». Its existence is nothing but its actual presence in a particular thing, its non-existence is (its absence, i. e.), its residence in a past or in a future space-time. (341. 13). Thus the proposition «whatsoever can be alter-

[1] Lit., p. 341. 5. «And by nobody there is cognition (*prathā*) of the similarity of the absolutely non-existent».

[2] Tātp., p. 53 ff.

[3] According to the Buddhist the image corresponds to a bare point-instant of efficient external reality.

[4] Answer to p. 340. 24 of the text.

[5] E. g., «a cow is», «a cow is not»; we cannot say «something is», «something is not», because something is a thing and «is» by itself, cp. Tātp., p. 338. 1. According to the Naiyāyiks the genus Existence (*sattā*) is inherent in a cow, it must then be inseparable from it. According to the Buddhist Existence or «Something» existent is the transcendental substratum of a cow's reality.

nately affirmed and denied (is unreal)», this proposition cannot be admitted as proved,[1] since its contraposition, (viz., the proposition «whatsoever is real cannot be alternately affirmed and denied») is not proved. It is even wrong,[2] (since we have given an explanation of the fact of an alternate affirmation and negation). Thus the particular with the inherent Universals is an (external) object (adequately) corresponding to our distinct perceptions,[3] it is not a mere conception.[4] There is consequently no need of having recourse to the principle of a resemblance from the negative side,[5] in order to explain the coordination of a Universal[6] with a particular.[7]

§ 4. The theory of a relational and negative Universal criticized.

(341.15). (The Realist). And further, what similarity can there be between a point-instant[8] and a Universal,[9] if the latter differs from the former in every respect? (The first, you maintain), is (the focus of) efficiency, the essence of every affirmation,[10] (the second) an idea.[11] devoid of any kind of causal efficiency.[12]

(The Buddhist). (The Universal is nothing but) the Distinction[13] (of a given point-instant from all) other (point instants).

1 Lit., p. 341.13. «Thus the community of existence and non-existence is not absolute (*anaikāntika*), because of a doubtful contraposition».— *anaikāntikatva* = *saṃdigdha-vyatirekita*, cp. Tātp., p. 143.17.

2 *asiddhārthatā* = *anyathā-siddhārthatā*, cp. Tātp., p. 143.19.

3 *vikalpa* = *savikalpaka-pratyakṣa*.

4 *alīkam* = *avāstavam* = *alīka-bāhyam*.

5 *anya-vyāvṛtti-rūpatā* = *apoha-rūpatā* = *bhedāgrahaḥ* = *sārūpyam*.

6 *alīkasya* = *sāmānya-lakṣaṇasya*.

7 *vastunā* = *paramārthasatā* = *svalakṣaṇena*. — Lit., p., 341.14—15. «For the sake of whose similarity with the real, the idea (*rūpatā*) of the exclusion of the different is assumed».

8 *svalakṣaṇena* = *kṣaṇena*.

9 *alīkasya* = *alīka-bāhyasya* = *jāteḥ*.

10 *vidhi-rūpa* = *asti-rūpa* = *sat* = *dravyam*, cp. Tātp., p. 338.1.

11 *alīkasya* = *na vāstavasya* = *mānasasya* = *kālpanikasya* = *alīka-bāhyasya*,

12 Lit., p. 341.15—16. «Moreover what resemblance is there between the spurious, which is devoid of every efficiency, which is absolutely dissimilar, and the efficient own-essence which has the essence of affirmation».

13 *anya-vyāvṛtti* = *apoha*, a given point-instant is being *distinguished* from all other point-instants, it does not at all *possess* an inherent real universal, e. g., a cow *in abstracto* is the negation of all non-cows.

(The Realist). Now, is this Distinction a real entity, (or is it a mere idea)? If it is real,[1] is it identical with the point-instant, or is it something else[2]? It cannot be identical,[3] since the point-instant is positive, (and distinction is negative), there would be a contradiction.

(341.18). If you deny this contradiction, the affirmation (of the point-instant) and the negation (included in the Universal) will be one and the same thing. Why do you then deny the positive character of the Universal? It becomes quite superflous to establish its negative (relational) character in order to explain its coordination with the positive point-instant of reality, (since it is then identical with the latter).[4]

(341.20). (The Buddhist). This is impossible! The positive particular cannot coalesce[5] with the negative (Universal).[6]

(The Realist). Well, there must be then a negative essence in the particular (point of reality[7]) also, in order that it should resemble to the negative Universal![8] And thus you will be assuming for the same particular (point-instant) a combination of two incompatible natures, the one real, the other unreal! You are wonderfully clever! You are really the beloved of the gods!

(341.24). (The Buddhist). The (principle of) Distinction of all other (point-instants from the given) particular (point-instant) produces a coordination of the universal idea, which also contains the negation of all other (point-instants), with the given particular (point-instant).

(The Realist). No! If that were so, a donkey could produce similarity between a fly and an elephant![9]

---

1 Read *bhāvikī cet.*

2 *anyo vā = dharmo vā*, cp. below p. 341.25.

3 *tat-svabhāva = svalakṣaṇa-svabhāva.*

4 Lit., p. 341.18—20. «And if there is no contradiction, then, because of the unity of affirmation and negation, it is useless to establish the negative (*anya-vyāvṛtti*) nature of the unreal (Universal), for the sake of its similarity with the particular (*svalakṣaṇa*), through a negation of its affirmation-nature».

5 *sārūpyām* is here = *samānādhikaraṇyam.*

6 Lit., p. 341.20—21. «How is the similarity of the inane with the not inane possessor of the affirmation-essence?».

7 *svalakṣaṇasya = kṣaṇasya.*

8 *alīkasya = sāmānya-lakṣaṇasya.*

9 Lit., p. 341.24. «And the negation of (every thing) different from the own-essence, cannot make the non-real which is a negation of (every thing) different similar to the own-essence; if that were so, the ass would make fly and elephant similar».

(341.25). Nor is negation an appartenance of the point-instant.[1] You indeed do not admit that a point-instant of reality could possess an attribute[2] (in the shape of a negation of something).

§ 5. The empirical and the transcendental particular.

(341.26). (The Buddhist). This would be so, (i. e., there would be nothing in common between the efficient point-instant of external reality and the general image which is internally constructed in our mind, if the particular point, as it appears in a perceptual judgment, were the transcendental reality. But it is not so!). The particular (point), as it appears in a perceptual judgment,[3] is not the thing ultimately real,[4] it is also a thought-construction.[5] Therefore, there is nothing contradictory for such a particular to be (alternately) asserted and denied. Contradictory attributes cannot belong to a real entity, but an (imagined), unreal one can possess them.[6] Therefore such a particular is similar to a constructed, unreal Universal; it also can forsake the positive form and assume the negative one. (342. 2). Such is the meaning (of Dignāga's?) words when he says, «(the element «this») which has been cognized directly (in a sensation) and (the element «that») which has been ascertained (in a perceptual judgment), these two (elements, when joined in one cognition), both refer, not to the ultimate reality, but to its relations».[7]

---

1 This is the second part of the dilemma stated p. 341.18 — *anyo vā*, read *na ca dharmo.*

2 The point-instant as the limit of all thought-constructions possesses altogether no attributes.

3 *adhyavasīyamānam.*

4 *na paramārtha-sat.*

5 *kalpitam.*

6 The terms «a thing» (*dravya*) and «assertion» (*vidhi*) are synonyms with existence (*sat*), they contain no negation, they are repulsive to negation, cp. Tātp., p. 338. 2. The term «cow» is relative or negative since it implies a distinction from horses etc. The terms «this cow» or «this something is a cow» contains an illicit synthesis of pure affirmation in the element «this» (*idaṃtā* = *vidhi-svarūpa* = *svalakṣaṇa*) with the negative i. e. relational, «that» (*tattā* = *apoha-svarūpa* = *sāmānya-lakṣaṇa*).

7 Lit., p. 342. 3. «What is grasped and what is judged, these both are two exclusions of the different, (i. e., are relative), not two realities (read *vastunī*). — The same quotation we find, in a slightly modified form, in N. Kaṇikā, p. 148. 1—3, — *yad anumānena* (sic!) *gṛhyate, yac cādhyavasīyate, te dve apy anya-vyāvṛttī, na vastunī, svalakṣaṇa-avagāhitve abhilāpa-saṃsarga-yogya-prati-*

(342. 4). (The Realist). (But then, you are assuming a second, unreal particular!). What will be the result of so assuming a community between an unreal, (imagined) particular and an unreal, (imagined Universal)? No purposive action, (which is the test of reality), could be directed towards it, because an unexisting (object) cannot be the aim of an efficient action.

(342. 5). The real aim[1] (is the underlying point of efficiency but it) has nothing in common with the unreality (of the image). If there were some *trait d'union* between them, it would be superfluous to admit a (second, empirical) imagined particular.

(342. 6). (The Buddhist). We do not resort to a second, imagined particular. (The burning and cooking efficiency is the only test of a real fire), but this burning and cooking we fictitiously connect with the image of a fire as it is contructed (in our mind).[2] The latter is not the (ultimately real) particular, because the real particular is a thing shorn of all extensions,[3] (it is unique in itself), it is unutterable,[4] it is unimaginable,[5] (it is transcendental). (The cooking and burning) which we can name and which we can extend (to every cooking and burning) is not the (real) particular.

(342. 10). Thus it is that the function of our empirical conceptions is to call forth human activity with its various aims, by imputing efficiency to an unefficient (image) with its extensions[6] and distinctions.[7] (And because our empirical conceptions, constructions though they be), are indirectly[8] related to reality, (they are to a certain extent real), they therefore lead to successful action in regard of a causally efficient

---

bhāsatva-anupapatteḥ. Usually the terms *grah* and *adhyavasā* are used in opposition to one another, the first refers to direct perception by the senses, the second to judgment or thought construction, cp. N. Kaṇ., 257. 4 ff. (translated above) and NBṬ, p. 12. 16. But in *savikalpaka-pratyakṣa* both sources of our knowledge coalesce, *anumānātmakatvād vikalpasya;* the Buddhist will not admit that they coalesce really or transcendentally (*vyāpāra-anubandhitayā*), but they coalesce empirically (*pratipatti-anubandhitayā*)

1 Read *pravṛtti-viṣayasya.*

2 i. e., in accordance with the categories of our understanding and with the grammatical categories of language.

3 *sarvato vyāvṛttyā.*

4 *abhilāpa-saṃsarga-ayogya.*

5 *vikalpa-jñāna-pratibhāsa-abhāva.*

6 *sva-anvayino = alīkasya = sāmānyasya.*

7 *anya-vyāvṛtti-rūpasya = vyavacchinna-rūpasya*

8 through pure sensation (*nirvikalpaka-pratyakṣa*).

reality,[1] thus bringing about (the efficacy of thought and) producing consistent human experience.[2] This, in our opinion, is the right view!

§ 6. THE IMAGES ARE SHAPED ACCORDING TO EXPERIENCE.

(342.12). (The Realist). (You maintain) that there is an imputation of causal efficiency no that[4] (image of a fire, which being a thought-construction) does not (really) possess any.[5] (The question arises, whether in so doing) we are influenced by former experience,[6] or we are doing it (*a priori*), on the basis of a primordial Biotic Force[7] (hidden in the depth of human Reason)? (342.14). The (real) particular thing, indeed, is a thing shorn of association, being (merely) the faculty of affecting[8] (our sensitivity), it possesses nothing in common with the image which contains (all kind) of extensions (in space, time and characteristics), and which is absolutely devoid of every kind of causal efficiency. (342.15). (You maintain) that there is a link,[9] a negative one[10] (in as much as the image of a fire contains a distinction from all non-fire, and the corresponding point of efficient reality also contains the negation of all non-fire). (We answer) that this implies[11] a correspondence also on the positive side betweeen (the efficient point

---

1 *samartham vastu prāpayanto.*

2 *na visaṃvādayanti.*

3 Lit., p. 342. 10—12. «Therefore, by imagining the efficacy of the non efficient, of the self-extended, whose essence consists in the exclusion of the different, the common life ideas proceed in propelling (read *pravartayantaḥ*) the acting beings which are desirous of this and that, in making them reach, through an indirect connection, the efficient thing, they do not deceive people, this we regard as being right».

4 *asya* = *alīkasya.*

5 *atad* = *na tasya* i. e., *alīkasya arthakriyā.*

6 *dṛṣṭa-arthakriyā-svalakṣaṇa-sādharmyeṇa* = «through similarity with formerly experienced particular (cases) of causal efficiency». — It must be clear from the the text translated in App. I that only the forms of our ideas, the Categories of our understanding, are admitted by the Buddhist to owe their origin, not to experience, but to a spontaneous capacity of our Reason. Their contents are sensations which are even (if we discount the *grāhya-grāhaka-kalpanā*) the very stuff of reality. But here the Realist, evidently for the sake of the argument, imputes to the Buddhist a wholesale rationalism.

7 *anādi-vāsanā-vaśāt*, on *vāsanā* see notes on pp. 367—8.

8 *samarthena;* it is *ākāra-ādhāyaka.*

9 *sārūpye.*

10 *anya-vyāvṛttyā* (read so).

11 *prasanga.*

and the image). We have already established that there is no difference between the positive and the negative formulations.[1]

(342.16). But if the connection[2] (between a fire-image and the corresponding focus of efficiency) is produced by an innate capacity[3] (of our Reason), then a man arriving from another continent,[4] (who never has seen a fire), must (*a priori*) be cognizant of its faculty to burn and cook, although he sees it for the first time (in his life)!

(342.17). (The Buddhist). We impute to the unreal (imaged fire) that kind (of burning and cooking), (simply) because we neglect its difference from, (and identify it with), the particular (point-instant, the focus of that energy) which is the real producer of burning and cooking. Is it not so?

(342.18). (The Realist). But is the particular (point instant, the thing in itself) cognized, (at that time) or is it not cognized? The first is impossible, because, as you maintain, (the ultimate reality is uncognizable), it is not an imaginable object![5] It produces a momentary sensation[6] which apprehends the thing itself,[7] (but nothing *about* the thing), it cannot introduce this its object, (the bare thing without any attributes), into our conceptual thinking.[8] The one is as different (as possible) from the other, they know nothing abut the existence of one another.

(342.21). Neither can our conceptual thought seize the (absolute) particular, even if we assume (with the Buddhist) an indirect function[9] of the immediately preceding sensation,[10] because, as has been stated, (conceptual thought) apprehends only such objects (as are utterable), whose images are capable of being designated by a (connotative) name.

(342.24). (The Buddhist). (The first moment in the cognition of an external object) is pure sensation. The image follows immediately in its track. The particular (momentary thing) is not the object ade-

---

1 Cp. Apohasiddhi, p. 6 — *apaha-śabdena anya-apoha-viśiṣṭo vidhir ucyate*

2 *āropa.*

3 *anādi-vāsanā.*

4 Lit. «from *Nārikera-dvīpa*».

5 *vikalpa-jñāna-gocaratva-abhāvāt.*

6 *tat-samaya-bhāvi.*

7 *tattvam.*

8 *vikalpe.*

9 *vyāpāra-pāramparye 'pi.*

10 *samanantara-utpanna-nirvikalpaka.*

quate to the image, but it appears as though it were its object, because *indirectly* (the image) is produced from it,[1] (the image is the indirect function of some focus of external efficiency).[2]

(342.25). (The Realist). (Quite right!). This is possible,[3] but only (on the empirical hypothesis, i.e., if you admit that our images are constructed) from traces left in our consciousness by former experience,[4] (and that our images thus correspond exactly to external reality). It becomes, on the contrary, (quite impossible on the hypothesis of rationalism, i.e., if we admit that the forms of our thoughts) have nothing corresponding to them in the external world, that they are created (by our Reason) which is a Force producing the (transcendental) Illusion (of an empirically real world).[5]

(342.26). And even if you admit that (our conceptions are partly) produced by the force of (former) impressions,[6] the illusion that we perceive in them (a genuine reality), this illusion cannot be explained simply by the fact that they are (indirectly) produced from a (sensory stimulus), if reality itself continues to remain uncognizable.[7]

(342.27). (We also cannot admit the principle of Identity) through Neglecting the Difference.[8] If the fire as an ultimate particular remains uncognized and our image of a fire is nevertheless (wrongly) indentified with it, because their difference is neglected, then the whole Universe might also be identified with it, because there is no reason for limitation.[9]

---

[1] Lit., p. 342.24—25. «Since it is produced from sensation (*avikalpāt*) as its immediately preceding homogeneous cause (*sam-anantara-pratyayāt*), through the medium of its function, although not its object, it appears as though it were its object».

[2] But the external objects are nevertheless really moments of a motion, not stable substances having attributes and duration.

[3] *bhaved apīyam gatiḥ.*

[4] *anubhava-vāsanā-prabhaveṣu* (read thus), i.e., *saṃskāreṣu*, cp above notes on *vāsanā*, p. 367—8.

[5] Lit., p. 342.25—26. «But not is it possible (with concepts) merged in transcendental non-existence, originating in the Force of (transcendental) Illusion».

[6] *anubhava-vāsanā.*

[7] Lit., p. 342.26. «Moreover even for (the image) originating from the force of experience, the illusion of the objectivity of it, (i.e. of the particular), while it is not cognized, simply because it is produced by it, (i.e., the image by the particular) cannot arise».

[8] *bheda-agraha* = *akhyāti.*

[9] Lit., p. 342.27. «But if the particular essence of fire is not grasped, if its form is imputed through not apprehending the difference from it, the consequenc

(343. 1). If the fire as a thing in itself[1] is not cognized at the time when (we have its image present to us), the whole Universe is in the same position. If the limitation consists merely in the fact of the origin of the image, (in its origin) from the sensation produced by the real fire, well then, there will be no limit at all, there will be no reason why the ideas of a God, of Matter (as it is imagined in the Sānkhya-system) etc., these ideas which also have their origin in a (congenital) Force of Illusion, (should also not be identified with the point-instant representing the real fire, through neglecting their difference). And we have just mentioned that to explain the correspondence of the image to the point-instant of external reality by the principle of Neglected Difference is inadmissible. Consequently it is idle talk to assume that the object corresponding to our conceptions is (an objetivized mental image) and that its presence in the external world is not true.[2]

§ 7. The Buddhist teory reduced ad absurdum.[3]

(343. 5). (The Realist). And further, (you maintain that our concepts, and the names expressing them, are not intent on external reality, but upon our objectivized images. We answer), neither is the objectivized image the object on which our conceptual thinking is intent. (It fares not better than the uncognizable) thing in itself or the (relational and negative universal) image.[4] It depends, indeed, upon an act of our productive imagination. When this act is produced, it (viz., the concept) *quasi* arises; when the act is over, it *quasi* vanishes. It apparently changes with every change in the activity of our conceptual imagination. (Hence it changes constantly), and can never be conceived[5] as a unity (in the shape one idea having relative stability).

---

will be the imputation of the form of the three worlds, since there is no cause for limitation ».

1 *vahni-svalakṣaṇa;* it must be clear from all this context that the transcendental cause affecting our sensitivity is meant.

2 *alīkasya bāhyatvam.*

3 The Buddhist theory is that reality, being a constant flow of momentary events, cannot be named and grasped by conceptual thought, or by imagination, because images or concepts require stability and duration. Vācaspati now turns the Buddhist argument against itself. He says that imagination also consists of momentary events, hence the images or concepts having no stability cannot be named.

4 *ākāravat = pratibhāsavat = na tu niścayavat.*

5 Read *pratipattum.*

(The Buddhist). By neglecting the difference (a relative stability is produced).

(The Realist). But then its essence, (the unity of this objectivied image) will equally be neglected?

(The Buddhist). O yes! it will!

(The Realist). Then it neither will be imagined, (since the image is a unity).

(The Buddhist). But the discontinuity of the image is not real. (When we talk of an object as a string of momentary events) we mean reality, its discontinuity or continuity, but not (the discontinuity) of the objectivized image.

(343.10). (The Realist). We can concede the point. The discontinuity of the image is not ultimately real. But you must admit that the objectivized image depends upon an act of our imagination. It changes whenever there is a change in the latter, or else it would not depend[1] on it. (343.11). The dependence of the image upon the act of imagination consists just in the fact that it follows every change, or non-change, in the latter. If it did not so depend,[2] it would not be imagined, and it would not be an image erroneously (projected into the external world). (343.13). Therefore let us leave alone the question about the reality of the continuity or of the discontinuity of the image. However, what depends on a changing imagination cannot appear to us as a unity, it must appear as being discontinuous, (as split into discrete moments).

(343.15). Consequently (the following syllogism can be) established,

(Thesis). The objectivized image (being a unity) *is not* the object upon which our conceptual imagination is intent.

(Reason). Because that image (must be) unutterable.

(Example). Just as a momentary feeling of pleasure[3] or (pain is unutterable).

(Major premise). (Whatsoever is unutterable is a moment which is not the object upon which our conceptual imagination is intent).

---

1 Read *tad-anadhīnatva-āpatteḥ.*

2 Read *tad-anadhīnatve.*

3 *sukhādi-svalakṣaṇavat.*

(343.16). It is indeed impossible to give it a name, because it is impossible to agree (upon its connotation), just as it is impossible (to express in speech) what the momentary feeling[1] of pleasure or (pain) is.

(343.17). We can really give a name to something when we can agree on its connotation. (The name) is concomitant with (such an agreement), otherwise we would be landed in the over-absurdity (of every name meaning anything).

(343.18). Since there is no such (possibility of agreement) upon the import of an objectivized image which changes with every (moment of) our imagination, there neither can be any possibility of giving names (to the objectivized images constituting the external empirical world). It is thus proved that whatsoever is conceived is unutterable, (i. e., just the contrary of the Buddhist idea that whatsoever is transcendentally real is unutterable).[2]

§ 8. A final argument against the Buddhist theory.

(343.20). (The Realist). (You maintain that the genus «cow» is an objectivized image and is relative, being merely the negation of all non-cows. We then ask), this negation of all non-cows is it the image itself[3] or only its attribute? If the essence (of the image) is a negation of non-cows, this cannot be understood without assuming the reality of (the positive counter part), the cow. Non-cow is but a negation of cow. Its reality depends upon the reality of the cow. You cannot escape being accused of a hopeless circle, (cow being dependent upon non-cow, and non cow upon cow).

(343.22). But if it is only an attribute (of the image), the genus «cow» must be positive, and its attribution also positive. And thus an end is made of the objectivized image which is (supposed te be) nega-

---

1 Read *svalakṣaṇavat.*

2 Lit., p. 343.18—19. «This (impossibility of agreement) being excluded from the spurious externality (of the image) which is different with every (moment) of imagination, produces also an exclusion of the possibility of coalescing with a name, thus the connection is established». — This is a negative deduction formulated according to the 3^d^ figure of negation (*vyāpaka-anupalabdhi*), cp. NBT, p. 32, text.

3 Cp. Lotze, Logik § 40, according to whom «non-cows» would be «ein widersinniges Erzeugniss des Schulwitzes».

tive in essence. And we have (*eo ipso*) discarded the theory that its attributes are identical with it, (i. e., the theory that there is no substance-attribute relation which would be transcendentally real). That such a Universal can be (alternately) asserted and denied we have already explained.

(343. 24). Wishing to escape redundancy we are afraid to have fallen in still greater verbosity! We must nevertheless have an end with this process of tempering the arrogance of the Nihilists!

APPENDIX VI

Corrections to the texts of the Nyāya-bindu, Nyāya-bindu-ṭīkā and Nyāya-bindu-ṭīkā-Ṭippaṇī printed in the Bibliotheca Buddhica.

Corrections to the text of Nyāya-bindu and ṭīkā.

7.12 before the words *bhrāntam hy anumānam* the following passage must be inserted in accordance with MSS and the Tib. translation: *tathābhrānta-grahaṇen-āpy anumānam nirastam syāt, kalpanāpoḍha-grahaṇam tu vipratipatti-nirā kāraṇārtham.*

11.23 insert *arthasya* after *bhāvyamānasya.*

13.15 insert *eva* before *vastunah.*

15. 2 insert *grāhyād* before *arthād.*

15. 3 drop the *cheda* before *sa eva.*

18. 9 *sātrāpy* instead of *atrāpy.*

19. 2 *jñānotpādāpekṣa* » » *jñānāpekṣa.*

23.16 insert *mātra* before *bhāvini.*

25.15 *tasya* instead of *tasyā-.*

25.17 insert *na* before *sa.*

28.19 » *bhūtale* » *bhāsamāne.*

38.19 *bhavābhāvāsiddheḥ* instead of *bhāvāsiddheḥ.*

38.21 drop the *cheda* after *sidhyati.*

46.4—5 *vyatiriktaviśeṣana-* instead of *vyatiriktam.*

47.13 *kṛtakatvam* » » *katakatvam.*

50. 1 *vaidharmyavataḥ* » » *vaidharmavataḥ.*

50. 1 *upalabdhi-* » » *upalabni-.*

50. 6 drop the *cheda* after *asattva-nivṛttiś ca.*

50.16 » » » » *uktaḥ.*

53.18 *etam eva* instead of *evam eva.*

56.13 *etena* » » *etane.*

56.21 *aho-* » » *ohā-.*

65.18 *tathāparasya* instead of *tathā parasya.*

66.1, 3 (bis), 6 *nityatva* » » *anityatva.*

66. 7 *nityaḥ* » » *anityaḥ.*

67.10 *saṃdeha* » » *sadeha.*

68.14 *avasthādḥāna-yogyo* instead of *avasthāna-yogyo.*
70. 7 *'rtho* » » *'tho.*
70 11 insert *ca* after *evam.*
71. 3 *adṛśyasya* instead of *adṛṣṭasya.*
71.14 *vidhiḥ* » » *vimdhih.*
72.1,2 *vākāraṇasya* instead of *vā kāraṇasya.*
72. 7 *rūpāsiddhi* » » *rūpādisiddhi-.*
72.16—85—86 » » 86.
76. 8 *viyuktam* » » *aviyuktam.*
77.10 *asiddheḥ* » » *asiddhiḥ.*
77.10 drop the words *tābhyam na vyatiricyate* and insert them in 77.18 after *asiddheḥ* (instead of *asiddhiḥ*).
78.20 *nāntarīyakatvāt* instead of *-vatvāt.*
82. 6 *svabhāvasyo-* » » *svabhāvo-*
85.23 insert a *cheda* after *punas tat.*
90.8 *yathāsarvajñaḥ* instead of *yathā sarva-.*
90.16 *ityādi hetuḥ* » » *ityadihetuḥ.*
92.12 insert *na* before *sa.*
95.2 *niścayābhāvo* » » *-abhāvau.*

Corrections to the text of Nyāya-bin-du-ṭīkā Ṭippaṇī.

8.13 read *pradarśakam* and *pravartanādikam.*
11. 7 *-avayavyāder* instead of *avayavāder.*
12. 1 read *svapnajñānena prāptiḥ.prāpti-kāla-bhedena.....*
12.12 *-śāntirakṣitābhyām* instead of*-śāntabhadrā-.*
12.13 *-uttaratrāpi* » » *atrāpi.*
16.16 *trirūpāl* instead of *virūpāl.*
18. 4 read *śikhā-lakṣaṇam.tathā pratyakṣam anūdya.....*
19.4—5 *yogācāra-matena* instead of *yogācāra-mate. na...*
19. 8 *abhrānta-śabdo* » » *bhrānta-.*
19.13 *prasiddha-* » » *siddhi.*
20.13 *tatrāsaty abhrānta-* (fat type) » » *tathā sati.*
20.16 *tathābhrānta-grahaṇenetyādi* fat type.
21.14 *ity avirodhaḥ* instead of *iti nirodhaḥ.*
22.14 read *yathā cakṣur-vijñānam.*
22. 5 *yaḥ* instead of *ya.*
26. 6 *bhrānter* » » *bhrānte.*
27. 5 *na santi* » » *na samprati.*
29.16 *sarvam indriyā-* » » *sarvendriyā-.*
30.15—16 read *yathendriya.... bhinnatvam na tatha....*
37. 5 insert *na* before *bhavati.*
37. 3 *nīla-* instead of *nīlam.*
40.12 *abhinnatvam* » » *bhinnatvam.*
42. 4 *nimitta-bhāvo* » » *nimittābhāvo.*
42.14 *evāṃśāṃśitayā* » » *evāṃśaṃśitayā.*

INDICES.

I. Proper names.

II. Schools.

III. Sanscrit Works.

IV. Sanscrit Words and Expressions.